Test Bank for

Stewart's Calculus
Early Transcendentals

SEVENTH EDITION

Prepared by

William Steven Harmon

BROOKS/COLE
CENGAGE Learning™

Australia • Brazil • Japan • Korea • Mexico • Singapore • Spain • United Kingdom • United States

BROOKS/COLE
CENGAGE Learning

For product information and technology assistance, contact us at **Cengage Learning Customer & Sales Support, 1-800-354-9706**

For permission to use material from this text or product, submit all requests online at **www.cengage.com/permissions**
Further permissions questions can be emailed to **permissionrequest@cengage.com**

ISBN-13: 978-0-8400-5419-7
ISBN-10: 0-8400-5419-X

Brooks/Cole
20 Davis Drive
Belmont, CA 94002-3098
USA

Cengage Learning is a leading provider of customized learning solutions with office locations around the globe, including Singapore, the United Kingdom, Australia, Mexico, Brazil, and Japan. Locate your local office at: **www.cengage.com/global**

Cengage Learning products are represented in Canada by Nelson Education, Ltd.

To learn more about Brooks/Cole, visit **www.cengage.com/brookscole**

Purchase any of our products at your local college store or at our preferred online store **www.cengagebrain.com**

Printed in the United States of America
1 2 3 4 5 6 7 14 13 12 11 10

Table of Contents

10 PARAMETRIC EQUATIONS AND POLAR COORDINATES

Form A - Free Response
Form B - Free Response
Form C - Multiple Choice
Form D - Multiple Choice
Form E - Mixed (Free Response/Multiple Choice)
Form F - Mixed (Free Response/Multiple Choice)
Form G - Mixed (Free Response/Multiple Choice)
Form H - Mixed (Free Response/Multiple Choice)

11 INFINITE SEQUENCES AND SERIES

Form A - Free Response
Form B - Free Response
Form C - Multiple Choice
Form D - Multiple Choice
Form E - Mixed (Free Response/Multiple Choice)
Form F - Mixed (Free Response/Multiple Choice)
Form G - Mixed (Free Response/Multiple Choice)
Form H - Mixed (Free Response/Multiple Choice)

12 VECTORS AND THE GEOMETRY OF SPACE

Form A - Free Response
Form B - Free Response
Form C - Multiple Choice
Form D - Multiple Choice
Form E - Mixed (Free Response/Multiple Choice)
Form F - Mixed (Free Response/Multiple Choice)
Form G - Mixed (Free Response/Multiple Choice)
Form H - Mixed (Free Response/Multiple Choice)

13 VECTOR FUNCTIONS

Form A - Free Response
Form B - Free Response
Form C - Multiple Choice
Form D - Multiple Choice
Form E - Mixed (Free Response/Multiple Choice)
Form F - Mixed (Free Response/Multiple Choice)
Form G - Mixed (Free Response/Multiple Choice)
Form H - Mixed (Free Response/Multiple Choice)

14 PARTIAL DERIVATIVES

Form A - Free Response
Form B - Free Response
Form C - Multiple Choice
Form D - Multiple Choice
Form E - Mixed (Free Response/Multiple Choice)
Form F - Mixed (Free Response/Multiple Choice)

Form G - Mixed (Free Response/Multiple Choice)
Form H - Mixed (Free Response/Multiple Choice)

15 MULTIPLE INTEGRALS

Form A - Free Response
Form B - Free Response
Form C - Multiple Choice
Form D - Multiple Choice
Form E - Mixed (Free Response/Multiple Choice)
Form F - Mixed (Free Response/Multiple Choice)
Form G - Mixed (Free Response/Multiple Choice)
Form H - Mixed (Free Response/Multiple Choice)

16 VECTOR CALCULUS

Form A - Free Response
Form B - Free Response
Form C - Multiple Choice
Form D - Multiple Choice
Form E - Mixed (Free Response/Multiple Choice)
Form F - Mixed (Free Response/Multiple Choice)
Form G - Mixed (Free Response/Multiple Choice)
Form H - Mixed (Free Response/Multiple Choice)

17 SECOND-ORDER DIFFERENTIAL EQUATIONS

Form A - Free Response
Form B - Free Response
Form C - Multiple Choice
Form D - Multiple Choice
Form E - Mixed (Free Response/Multiple Choice)
Form F - Mixed (Free Response/Multiple Choice)
Form G - Mixed (Free Response/Multiple Choice)
Form H - Mixed (Free Response/Multiple Choice)

FE FINAL EXAMS

Form A - Free Response
Form B - Multiple Choice
Form C - Mixed (Free Response/Multiple Choice)

Preface

This test bank was written to accompany *Stewart's Calculus Early Transcendentals 7th edition*. The test bank contains more than 2,800 test items. Each chapter has eight separate testing forms intended to give the instructor optimal flexibility. Each form is composed of 20 test items of medium difficulty, immediately followed by an answer key.

It has been my goal to make this test bank as accurate as possible. To ensure accuracy, this test bank has been reviewed through a quality assurance process. However, with 2,800 test items, it is certainly possible that errors remain. To help us ensure accuracy in following editions, please note any discrepancies you may find and let me know through my e-mail listed below.

I'd like to take this opportunity to give special thanks to my wife Liz and to my children, Taylor and Caitlin who have patiently shared their dad with this project for many months.

Steve Harmon
Steve.Harmon@sbcglobal.net

1. The graphs of $f(x)$ and $g(x)$ are given.

a) For what values of x is $f(x) = g(x)$?

b) Find the values of $f(-4)$ and $g(3)$.

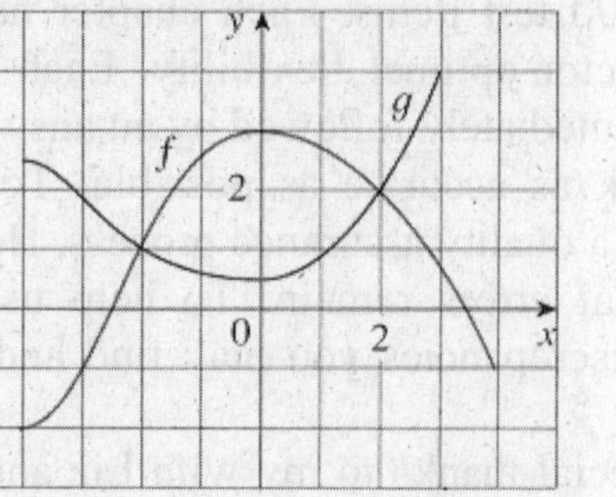

2. If $f(x) = x^2 - x + 2$, evaluate the difference quotient $\dfrac{f(a+h) - f(a)}{h}$.

3. Find the domain of the function.

$$f(x) = \frac{5}{3x-1}$$

4. Find the domain, range, and x-intercept(s) of the function.

$$f(x) = \ln(x-1) - 1$$

5. Find an expression for the function $y = f(x)$ whose graph is the bottom half of the parabola $x + (8-y)^2 = 0$.

6. A spherical balloon with radius r inches has volume $4\pi r^3/3$. Find a function that represents the amount of air required to inflate the balloon from a radius of r inches to a radius of $r + 2$ inches.

7. An open rectangular box with volume 3 m^3 has a square base. Express the surface area of the box as a function $S(x)$ of the length x of a side of the base.

8. Determine whether f is even, odd, or neither.

$$f(x) = \frac{2x^2}{x^4 + 1}$$

9. In the function $f(x) = 3x + d$, what is the value of d, if $f(6) = 1$?

10. If $f(x) = 3x + \ln x$, find $f^{-1}(3)$.

11. Graph the function by hand, not by plotting points, but by starting with the graph of one of the standard functions and then applying the appropriate transformations.

$$y = 2 - 2x - x^2$$

12. If the point (7, 3) is on the graph of an even function, what other point must also be on the graph?

13. Use the table to evaluate the expression $(f \circ g)(3)$.

x	1	2	3	4	5	6
$f(x)$	3	2	1	0	1	2
$g(x)$	6	5	2	3	4	6

14. Use the Law of Exponents to rewrite and simplify the expression.

$$\frac{x^{2n} \cdot x^{3n-1}}{x^{n+2}}$$

15. Many physical quantities are connected by *inverse square laws*, that is, by power functions of the form $f(x) = kx^{-2}$. In particular, the illumination of an object by a light source is inversely proportional to the square of the distance from the source. Suppose that after dark you are in a room with just one lamp and you are trying to read a book. The light is too dim and so you move halfway to the lamp. How much brighter is the light?

16. Express the function in the form of $f \circ g$.

$v(t) = \sec(t^2)\tan(t^2)$

17. The monthly cost of driving a car depends on the number of miles driven. Samantha found that in October it cost her \$312.5 to drive 500 mi and in February it cost her \$375 to drive 1,000 mi. Express the monthly cost C as a function of the distance driven d assuming that a linear relationship gives a suitable model.

18. Find the inverse function $f^{-1}(x)$.

$$f(x) = \frac{x+1}{2x+1}$$

19. Find all solutions of the equation correct to two decimal places.

$\sqrt{x} = x^3 - 1$

20. Solve each equation for x.

(a) $\ln x = 2$ (b) $e^{e^x} = 3$

ANSWER KEY

Stewart - Calculus ET 7e Chapter 1 Form A

1. a) $x = -2,\ 2$
b) $f(-4) = -2,\ \ g(3) = 4$

2. $2a + h - 1$

3. $\{x \mid x \neq 1/3\}$

4. Domain: $(1, \infty)$
Range: $(-\infty, \infty)$
x-intercept: $x = e + 1$

5. $y = 8 - \sqrt{-x}$

6. $\frac{8}{3}\pi(3r^2 + 6r + 4)$

7. $S(x) = x^2 + \frac{12}{x}$

8. even

9. -17

10. $f^{-1}(3) = 1$

11.

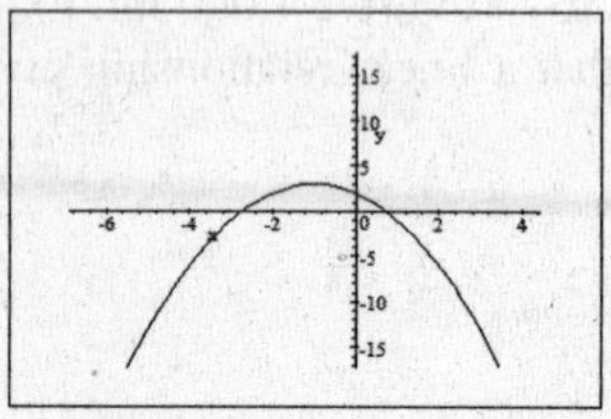

12. $(-7, 3)$

13. 2

14. x^{4n-3}

15. The light is 4 times brighter.

16. $f(t) = \sec(t)\tan(t)$
$g(t) = t^2$

17. $C = 0.125d + 250$

18. $f^{-1}(x) = -\frac{x-1}{2x-1}$

19. 1.29

20. $x = e^2$, $x = \ln(\ln 3)$

1. The graphs of $f(x)$ and $g(x)$ are given.

a) For what values of x is $f(x) = g(x)$?

b) Find the values of $f(0)$ and $g(3)$.

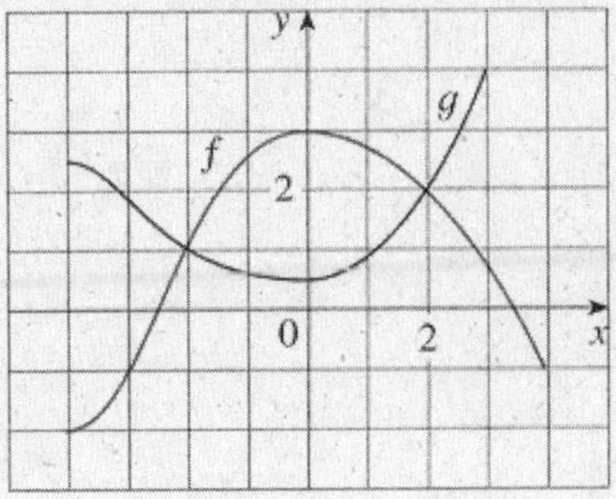

2. If $f(x) = x^2 - x + 4$, evaluate the difference quotient $\dfrac{f(a+h) - f(a)}{h}$.

3. Find the domain of the function.

$f(x) = \sqrt{8 - 2x^2}$

4. Suppose that the graph of $y = \log_2 x$ is drawn on a coordinate grid where the unit of measurement is an inch. How many miles to the right of the origin do we have to move before the height of the curve reaches 3 ft? Round your answer to the nearest mile.

5. In the function $f(x) = 6x + b$, what must be the coefficient b, if $f(5) = 1$?

6. It makes sense that the larger the area of a region, the larger the number of species that inhabit the region. Many ecologists have modeled the species-area relation with a power function and, in particular, the number of species S of bats living in caves in central Mexico has been related to the surface area A measured in m^2 of the caves by the equation $S = 0.7A^{0.3}$.

(a) A particular cave in Mexico has a surface area of $A = 60\,\text{m}^2$. How many species of bats would you expect to find in that cave?

(b) If you discover that four species of bats live in a cave, estimate the area of the cave rounded to two decimal places.

7. If $f(x) = 4x + \ln x$, find $f^{-1}(4)$.

8. Graph the function by hand, not by plotting points, but by starting with the graph of one of the standard functions and then applying the appropriate transformations.

$y = -2 + 2x + x^2$

9. The monthly cost of driving a car depends on the number of miles driven. Ann found that in October it cost her \$285 to drive 100 mi and in May it cost her \$335 to drive 300 mi.

Express the monthly cost C as a function of the distance driven d assuming that a linear relationship gives a suitable model.

10. A box with an open top is to be constructed from a rectangular piece of cardboard with dimensions $b = 13$ in. by $a = 20$ in. by cutting out equal squares of side x at each corner and then folding up the sides as in the figure.

Express the volume V of the box as a function of x.

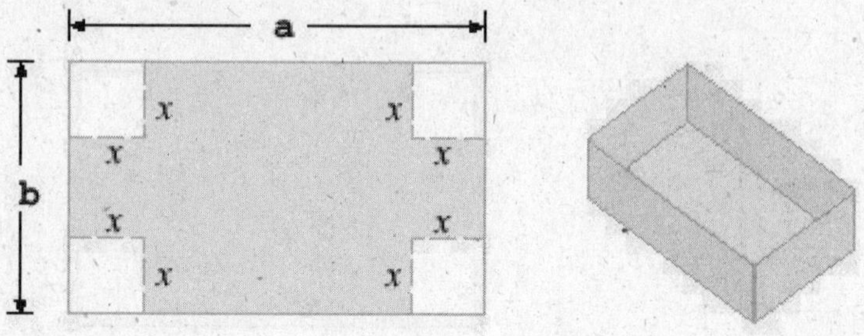

11. If the point (8, 4) is on the graph of an even function, what other point must also be on the graph?

12. Find the domain, range, and x-intercept(s) of the function.

$f(x) = \ln(x-3) - 3$

13. Use the table to evaluate the expression $(f \circ g)(3)$.

x	1	2	3	4	5	6
$f(x)$	0	1	2	3	4	5
$g(x)$	4	5	2	4	1	5

14. Express the function in the form of $f \circ g$.

$v(t) = \csc(t^2)\cot(t^2)$

15. A stone is dropped into a lake, creating a circular ripple that travels outward at a speed of 46 cm/s. Express the radius r of this circle as a function of the time t (in seconds) and find $A \circ r$, if A is the area of this circle as a function of the radius.

16. Use the Law of Exponents to rewrite and simplify the expression.

$$\frac{\sqrt{a\sqrt{b}}}{\sqrt[4]{ab}}$$

17. For what values of x is the inequality $|\sin x - x| < 0.2$ true?

Write your answer correct to two decimal places.

18. Many physical quantities are connected by *inverse square laws*, that is, by power functions of the form $f(x) = kx^{-2}$. In particular, the illumination of an object by a light source is inversely proportional to the square of the distance from the source. Suppose that after dark you are in a room with just one lamp and you are trying to read a book. The light is too dim and so you move three-fourths the distance to the lamp. How much brighter is the light?

19. Find all solutions of the equation correct to two decimal places.

$\tan x = \sqrt{1 - x^2}$

20. If a bacteria population starts with 100 bacteria and doubles every three hours, then the number of bacteria after t hours is $n = f(t) = 100(2^{t/3})$.

When will the population reach 50,000? Round the answer to the nearest tenth.

ANSWER KEY

Stewart - Calculus ET 7e Chapter 1 Form B

1. a) $x = -2, 2$
   b) $f(0) = 3,\ g(3) = 4$

2. $2a + h - 1$

3. $[-2, 2]$

4. 1,084,588

5. –29

6. a) two species
   b) 335.58m^2

7. $f^{-1}(4) = 1$

8. 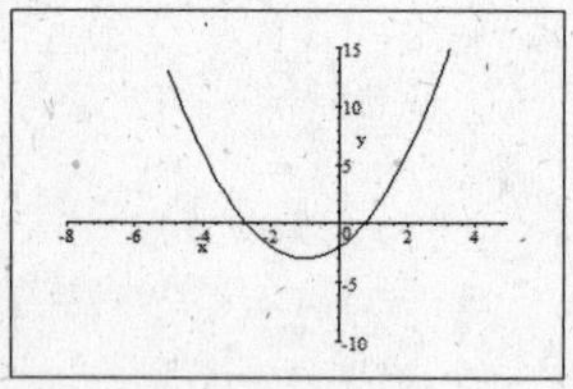

9. $C = 0.25d + 260$

10. $V(x) = x(20 - 2x)(13 - 2x)$

11. (–8,4)

12. Domain: $(3, \infty)$
    Range: $(-\infty, \infty)$
    x-intercept: $x = e^3 + 3$

13. 1

14. $f(t) = \csc(t)\cot(t)$
    $g(t) = t^2$

15. $r(t) = 46t,\ 2116\pi t^2$

16. $a^{1/4}$

17. (–1.08, 1.08)

18. The light is 16 times brighter.

19. 0.65

20. 26.9 h

1. Use the Law of Exponents to rewrite and simplify the expression.

$$\frac{\sqrt{a\sqrt{b}}}{\sqrt[3]{ab}}$$

a. $\frac{a^{1/6}}{b^{1/12}}$ b. $\frac{a^{1/6}}{b^{1/3}}$ c. $\frac{a^{1/6}}{b}$ d. $\frac{a}{b^{1/12}}$ e. none of these

2. Find the range of the function.

$y = 2 + \cos x$

Select the correct answer.

a. $(-\infty, \infty)$ b. $(2, \infty)$ c. $(-1, 3)$ d. $[1, 3]$ e. $[-1, 1]$

3. The graphs of $f(x)$ and $g(x)$ are given. For what values of x is $f(x) = g(x)$?

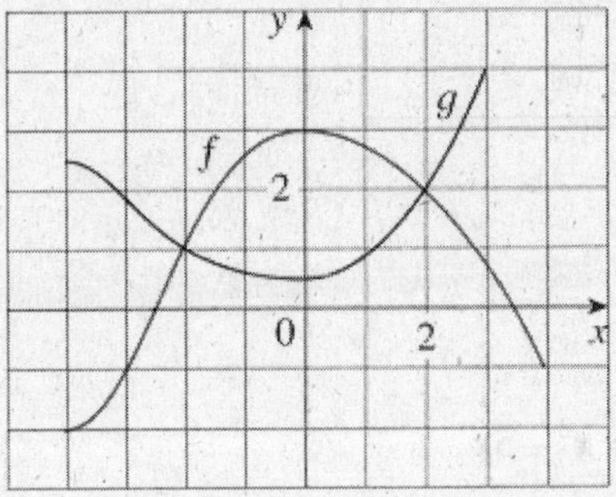

Select the correct answer.

a. 2
b. −2, 2
c. −1, 2
d. 0
e. 1, 2

4. Suppose that the graph of $y = \log_2 x$ is drawn on a coordinate grid where the unit of measurement is an inch. How many miles to the right of the origin do we have to move before the height of the curve reaches 2 ft? Rounded to the nearest mile.

Select the correct answer.

a. 265 mi
b. 269 mi
c. 259 mi
d. 261 mi
e. 271 mi

5. Graph the function by hand, not by plotting points, but by starting with the graph of one of the standard functions and then applying the appropriate transformations.

$y = 2 + 2x - x^2$

Select the correct answer.

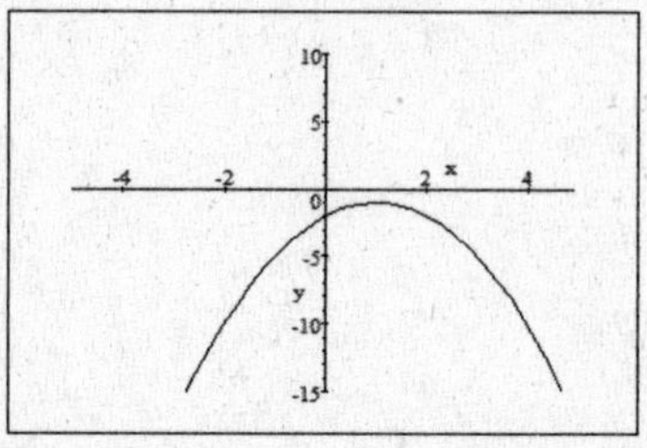

a.

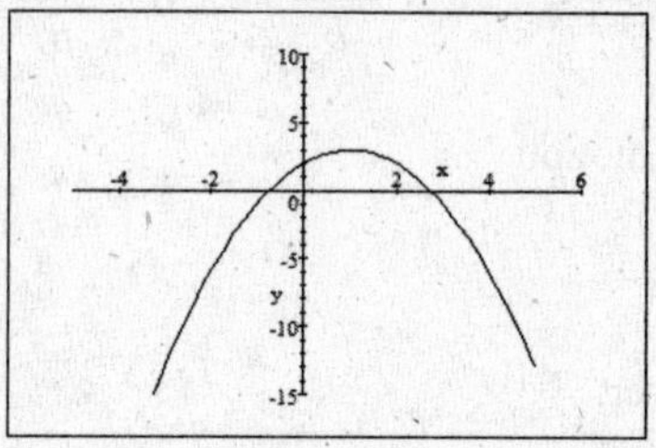

b.

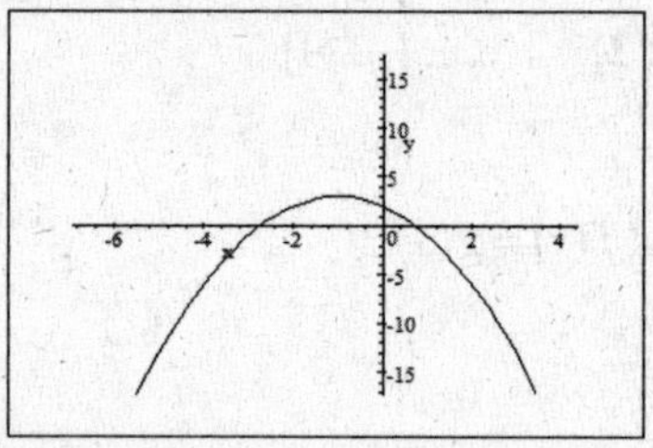

c.

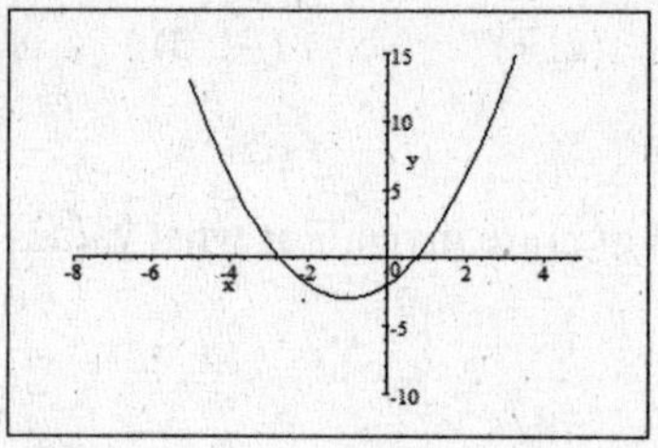

d.

6. Which of the following graphs is neither even nor odd?

Select the correct answer.

a. $f(x) = 6x^3 + 8x^2 + 7$ b. $f(x) = \dfrac{2x^2}{x^4 + 1}$ c. $f(x) = x^3 - 5x$

7. Many physical quantities are connected by *inverse square laws*, that is, by power functions of the form $f(x) = kx^{-2}$. In particular, the illumination of an object by a light source is inversely proportional to the square of the distance from the source. Suppose that after dark you are in a room with just one lamp and you are trying to read a book. The light is too dim and so you move two-thirds the distance to the lamp. How much brighter is the light?

Select the correct answer.

a. 9 times b. 9/4 times c. 4/9 times d. 3/2 times e. 9/2 times

8. If the point (9, 7) is on the graph of an even function, what other point must also be on the graph?

Select the correct answer.

a. (0, 0) b. (9, –7) c. (–9, 7) d. (–9, –7) e. none of these

9. If $f(x) = x^2 - x + 4$, evaluate the difference quotient $\dfrac{f(a+h) - f(a)}{h}$.

Select the correct answer.

a. h b. $2a - 2$ c. $2a - h - 2$ d. $2a + h - 2$ e. none of these

10. A box with an open top is to be constructed from a rectangular piece of cardboard with dimensions $b = 5$ in. by $a = 28$ in. by cutting out equal squares of side x at each corner and then folding up the sides as in the figure. Express the volume V of the box as a function of x.

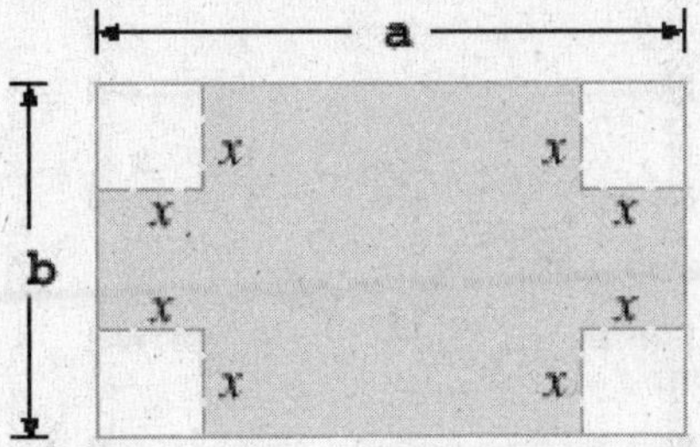

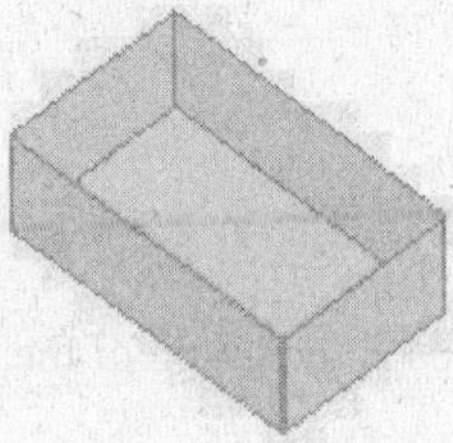

Select the correct answer.

a. $V(x) = 4x^3 - 66x^2 + 140x$

b. $V(x) = x^3 - 33x^2 + 140x$

c. $V(x) = x^3 - 65x^2 + 140x$

d. $V(x) = x^3 - 66x^2 + 140x$

e. $V(x) = x^3 + 66x^2 + 140x$

11. Find an expression for the function $y = f(x)$ whose graph is the bottom half of the parabola $x + (8 - y)^2 = 0$.

Select the correct answer.

a. $y = 8 + \sqrt{x}$ b. $y = 64 - \sqrt{-x}$ c. $y = 8 - \sqrt{-x}$ d. $y = 8 - x^2$ e. $y = 64 - x^2$

12. If $f(x) = x + 5$ and $h(x) = 4x - 5$, find a function g such that $g \circ f = h$.

Select the correct answer.

a. $g(x) = 4x + 25$ b. $g(x) = 4x - 15$ c. $g(x) = 4x - 25$ d. $g(x) = 4x$ e. $g(x) = 5x - 4$

13. Starting with the graph of $y = e^x$, find the equation of the graph that results from reflecting about the line $y = 5$.

Select the correct answer.

a. $y = -e^x$

b. $y = -e^{x+10}$

c. $y = -e^x + 10$

d. $y = e^{-x} + 10$

e. $y = -e^{-5x} + 10$

14. Use the table to evaluate the expression $(f \circ g)(3)$.

x	1	2	3	4	5	6
$f(x)$	3	2	1	0	1	2
$g(x)$	6	5	2	3	4	6

Select the correct answer.

a. 2 b. 3 c. 1 d. 5 e. 6

15. Which of the following graphs is the graph of the function?

$f(x) = \sin|4x|$

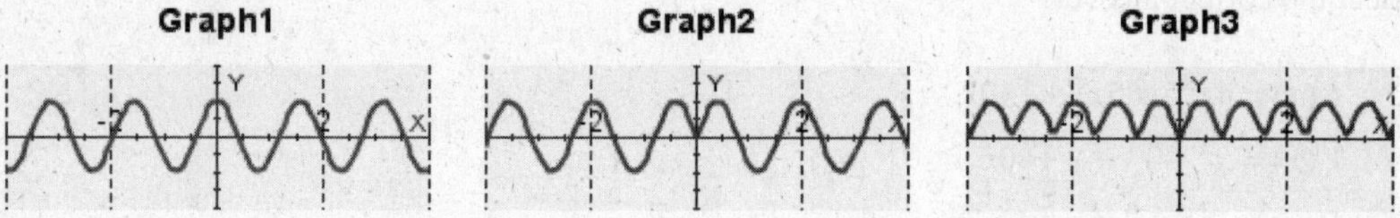

Select the correct answer.

a. Graph 3
b. Graph 1
c. Graph 2

16. If a bacteria population starts with 100 bacteria and doubles every three hours, then the number of bacteria after t hours is $n = f(t) = 100(2^{t/3})$. When will the population reach 50,000?

Select the correct answer.

a. 100 hours
b. 26.9 hours
c. 20.9 hours
d. 10.9 hours
e. 22.5 hours

17. What is $\sqrt[10]{x}$, given that $H = f \circ g \circ h$ and $H(x) = \sqrt[10]{\sqrt{x} - 3}$?

Select the correct answer.

a. $g(x)$
b. $h(x)$
c. $f(x)$

18. A rectangle has perimeter 10 m.

Express the area of the rectangle as a function $A(l)$ of the length l of one of its sides.

Select the correct answer.

a. $A(l)=5l+l^2$
b. $A(l)=10l-l^2$
c. $A(l)=5-l$
d. $A(l)=10l+l^2$
e. $A(l)=5l-l^2$

19. Find the inverse function of $f(x)=\dfrac{x+1}{2x+1}$

Select the correct answer.

a. $f^{-1}(x)=-(x+1)(2x+1)$
b. $f^{-1}(x)=(x+1)(2x+1)$
c. $f^{-1}(x)=-\dfrac{2x-1}{x-1}$
d. $f^{-1}(x)=-\dfrac{x-1}{2x-1}$
e. $f^{-1}(x)=\dfrac{x}{2x-1}$

20. Find all solutions of the equation correct to two decimal places.

$\tan x=\sqrt{4-x^2}$

Select the correct answer.

a. –2.29, 2.21
b. –4.47
c. 4.47
d. 1.04
e. –1.04, 1.04

ANSWER KEY

Stewart - Calculus ET 7e Chapter 1 Form C

1. a
2. d
3. b
4. a
5. b
6. a
7. a
8. c
9. e
10. a
11. c
12. c
13. c
14. a
15. c
16. b
17. c
18. e
19. d
20. d

1. A rectangle has perimeter 18 m. Express the area of the rectangle as a function $A(l)$ of the length l of one of its sides.

Select the correct answer.

a. $A(l) = 9l + l^2$ b. $A(l) = 9l - l^2$ c. $A(l) = 18l + l^2$ d. $A(l) = 18l - l^2$ e. $A(l) = l - 9l^2$

2. The graph of the function f is given. State the value of $f(0)$.

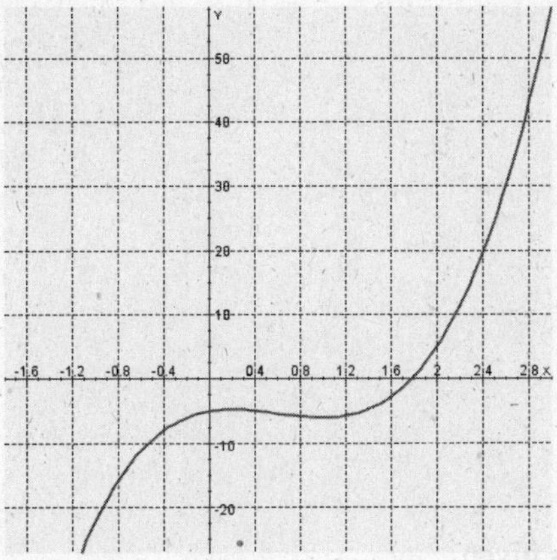

Select the correct answer.

a. $f(0) = -10$ b. $f(0) = 10$ c. $f(0) = 5$ d. $f(0) = 0$ e. $f(0) = -5$

3. Find the domain, range, and x-intercept of the function.

$f(x) = \ln(x-3) - 3$

a. Domain: $(3, \infty)$ Range: $(-\infty, \infty)$ x-intercept: $x = e^3 + 3$

b. Domain: $(-\infty, \infty)$ Range: $(-\infty, \infty)$ x-intercept: $x = e^3$

c. Domain: $(-\infty, \infty)$ Range: $(0, \infty)$ x-intercept: $x = 0$

d. Domain: $(0, \infty)$ Range: $(-\infty, \infty)$ x-intercept: $x = e^3 - 3$

e. Domain: $(-3, \infty)$ Range: $(-\infty, \infty)$ x-intercept: $x = 3$

4. Use the Law of Exponents to rewrite and simplify the expression.

$$\frac{x^{4n} \cdot x^{3n+1}}{x^{n-3}}$$

a. x^{4n-3} b. x^{6n-2} c. x^{6n+4} d. x^{3n+4} e. x^{6n-4}

5. The function $f(x)=\sqrt{1+cx^2}$ is graphed below.

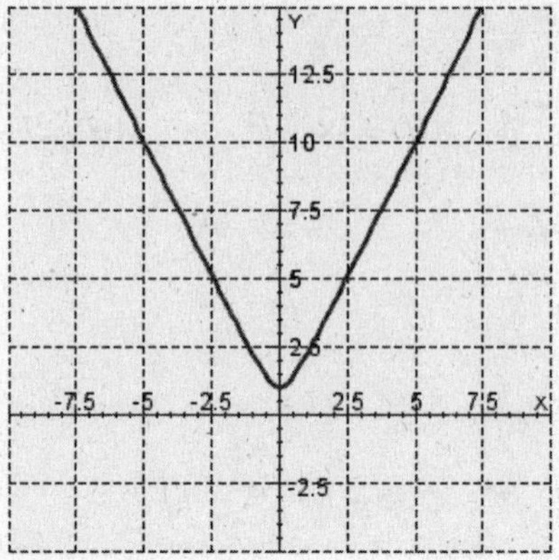

Select the correct answer.

a. $c=0$
b. $c>0$
c. $c<0$

6. Find the exponential function $f(x)=Ca^x$ whose graph is given.

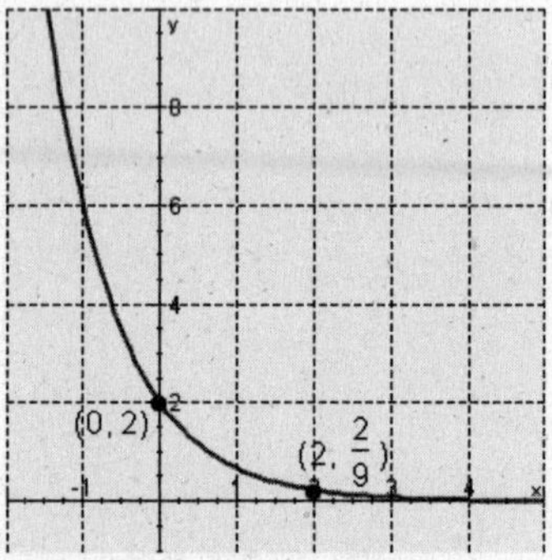

Select the correct answer.

a. $f(x)=\dfrac{1}{3^x}$ b. $f(x)=4\left(\dfrac{1}{3}\right)^x$ c. $f(x)=\left(\dfrac{3}{4}\right)^x$ d. $f(x)=2\left(\dfrac{1}{3}\right)^x$ e. $f(x)=\left(\dfrac{2}{3}\right)^x$

7. If $f(x)=x^2-3x+1$, evaluate the difference quotient $\dfrac{f(a+h)-f(a)}{h}$.

Select the correct answer.

a. h b. $3a-3$ c. $2a-h-3$ d. $2a+h-3$ e. none of these

8. Use the table to evaluate the expression $(f \circ g)(3)$.

x	1	2	3	4	5	6
$f(x)$	3	2	1	0	1	2
$g(x)$	6	5	2	3	4	6

Select the correct answer.

a. 2 b. 3 c. 1 d. 5 e. 6

9. The graph shown gives the weight of a certain person as a function of age. Find the age at which the person started an exercise program.

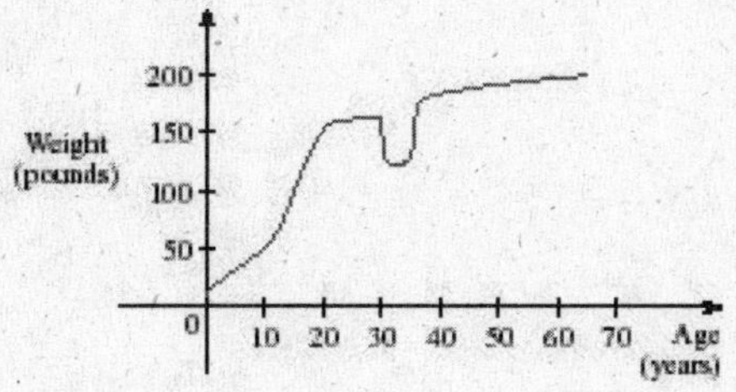

Select the correct answer.

a. 30 b. 38 c. 20 d. 54 e. 35

10. Starting with the graph of $y = e^x$, write the equation of the graph that results from shifting 2 units right.

Select the correct answer.

a. $y = e^x - 2$

b. $y = e^{x+2}$

c. $y = e^x + 2$

d. $y = e^{x-2}$

e. $y = 2e^{x-2}$

11. Determine whether f is even, odd, or neither.

$$f(x) = \frac{2x^2}{x^4 + 1}$$

Select the correct answer.

a. even
b. odd
c. neither

12. Find a formula for the inverse of the function.

$y = \ln(x+8)$

Select the correct answer.

a. $y = e^{x+8}$ b. $y = e^x - 8$ c. $y = e^x + 8$ d. $y = 8e^x$ e. $y = -8e^x$

13. The relationship between the Fahrenheit and Celsius temperature scales is given by the linear function.

$F = \frac{9}{5}C + 32$

What is the F-intercept and what does it represent?

Select the correct answer.

a. $9/5$, Fahrenheit temperature corresponding to $0^\circ C$
b. 32, Fahrenheit temperature corresponding to $0^\circ C$
c. 32, Celsius temperature corresponding to $0^\circ F$
d. 0, Fahrenheit temperature corresponding to $32^\circ C$
e. $9/5$, Celsius temperature corresponding to $32^\circ C$

14. Find the exact value of the expression.

$\log_5 10 + \log_5 40 - 4\log_5 2$

Select the correct answer.

a. 2 b. 5 c. 3 d. 4 e. 1

15. In the function $f(x) = 7x + d$, what must be the value d, if $f(3) = 1$?

Select the correct answer.

a. $d = -20$ b. $d = 20$ c. $d = -22$ d. $d = 22$ e. $d = -1$

16. The table gives the population of the United States, in millions, for the years 1900 - 2000. Use a graphing calculator with exponential regression capability to model the U.S. population since 1900. Use the model to estimate the population in 1955 and to predict the population in the year 2015.

Year	1900	1910	1920	1930	1940	1950	1960	1970	1980	1990	2000
Population (millions)	76	92	106	123	131	150	179	203	227	250	281

Select the correct answer.

a. 113 million, 288 million
b. 163 million, 412 million
c. 163 million, 352 million
d. 113 million, 352 million
e. 163 million, 163 million

17. Which of the following is the equation for the function $g(x)$?

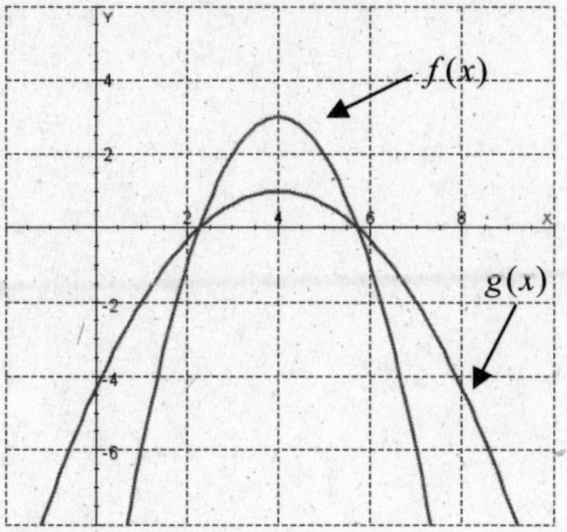

Select the correct answer.

a. $g(x) = 3f(x)$ b. $g(x) = \frac{1}{3}f(x)$ c. $g(x) = -f(x+4)$ d. $g(x) = -f(x)+2$ e. $g(x) = f(x)-2$

18. The monthly cost of driving a car depends on the number of miles driven. Julia found that in October it cost her \$500 to drive 600 mi and in July it cost her \$650 to drive 900 mi. Express the monthly cost C as a function of the distance driven d assuming that a linear relationship gives a suitable model.

Select the correct answer.

a. $C = 0.5d - 200$ b. $C = 200d + 0.5$ c. $C = 200d - 0.5$ d. $C = 0.5d + 200$ e. $C = 2d + 200$

19. Which of the following graphs is the graph of the function?

$f(x) = \sin|2x|$

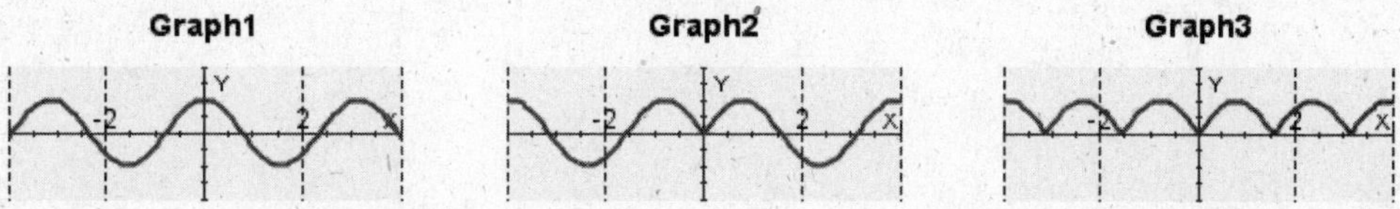

Select the correct answer.

a. Graph 1 b. Graph 3 c. Graph 2

20. Find all solutions of the equation correct to two decimal places.

$x^3 - 9x^2 - 4 = 0$

Select the correct answer.

a. $x = 4.00,\ x = 9.05$
b. $x = -4.00,\ x = 9.05$
c. $x = 0,\ x = 9.05$
d. $x = 9.05$
e. $x = 0,\ x = 4.01,\ x = 9.05$

ANSWER KEY

Stewart - Calculus ET 7e Chapter 1 Form D

1. b
2. e
3. a
4. c
5. b
6. d
7. d
8. a
9. a
10. d
11. a
12. b
13. b
14. a
15. a
16. c
17. b
18. d
19. c
20. d

1. If $f(x) = x^2 - 2x + 1$, evaluate the difference quotient $\dfrac{f(a+h) - f(a)}{h}$.

2. Find the domain, range, and x-intercept(s) of the function.

$f(x) = \ln(x-2) - 2$

3. If the point (5, 3) is on the graph of an even function, what other point must also be on the graph?

4. In the function $f(x) = 5x + d$, what must be the coefficient d, if $f(4) = 1$?

5. If a bacteria population starts with 100 bacteria and doubles every three hours, then the number of bacteria after t hours is $n = f(t) = 100(2^{t/3})$. When will the population reach 50,000?

6. Suppose that the graph of f is given. Describe how the graph of the function $y = f(x-3) - 3$ can be obtained from the graph of f.

Select the correct answer.

a. Shift the graph 3 units to the right and 3 units down.
b. Shift the graph 3 units to the left and 3 units down.
c. Shift the graph 3 units to the right and 3 units up.
d. Shift the graph 3 units to the left and 3 units up.
e. none of these

7. It makes sense that the larger the area of a region, the larger the number of species that inhabit the region. Many ecologists have modeled the species-area relation with a power function and, in particular, the number of species S of bats living in caves in central Mexico has been related to the surface area A measured in m^2 of the caves by the equation $S = 0.7A^{0.3}$.

(a) A particular cave in Mexico has a surface area of $A = 128\,\text{m}^2$. How many species of bats would you expect to find in that cave?
(b) If you discover that five species of bats live in a cave, estimate the area of the cave rounded to two decimal places.

8. Many physical quantities are connected by *inverse square laws*, that is, by power functions of the form $f(x) = kx^{-2}$. In particular, the illumination of an object by a light source is inversely proportional to the square of the distance from the source. Suppose that after dark you are in a room with just one lamp and you are trying to read a book. The light is too dim and so you move one-fourth the distance to the lamp. How much brighter is the light?

Select the correct answer.

a. 4/3 times b. 9 times c. 16 times d. 16/9 times e. 9/16 times

9. If $f(x) = 9x + \ln x$, find $f^{-1}(9)$.

10. Which of the following graphs is the graph of the function $f(x) = \sin|3x|$?

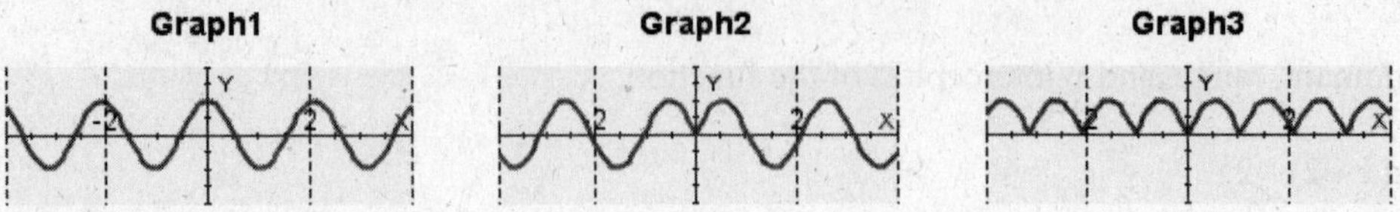

11. Express the function in the form of $f \circ g$.

$v(t) = \sin(t^2)\cos(t^2)$

12. A spherical balloon with radius r inches has volume $\frac{4}{3}\pi r^3$. Find a function that represents the amount of air required to inflate the balloon from a radius of r inches to a radius of $r + 1$ inches.

13. What is $\sqrt[10]{x}$, given that $H = f \circ g \circ h$ and $H(x) = \sqrt[10]{\sqrt{x} - 3}$?

Select the correct answer.

a. $f(x)$ b. $g(x)$ c. $h(x)$

14. Use the table to evaluate the expression $(f \circ g)(6)$.

x	1	2	3	4	5	6
$f(x)$	0	1	2	3	4	5
$g(x)$	4	5	2	4	1	5

15. For what values of x is the inequality true?

$|\sin x - x| < 0.1$

16. Which of the following is the equation for the function $g(x)$?

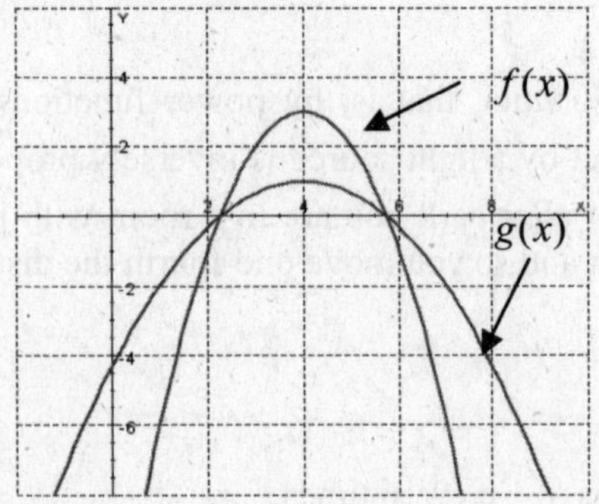

Select the correct answer.

a. $g(x) = 3f(x)$ b. $g(x) = f(x)/3$ c. $g(x) = -f(x+4)$ d. $g(x) = -f(x) + 2$ e. $g(x) = f(x) - 2$

17. The monthly cost of driving a car depends on the number of miles driven. Julia found that in October it cost her $500 to drive 600 mi and in July it cost her $650 to drive 900 mi. Express the monthly cost C as a function of the distance driven d assuming that a linear relationship gives a suitable model.

Select the correct answer.

a. $C = 0.5d - 200$ b. $C = 200d + 0.5$ c. $C = 200d - 0.5$ d. $C = 0.5d + 200$ e. $C = 2d + 200$

18. A box with an open top is to be constructed from a rectangular piece of cardboard with dimensions $b = 13$ in. by $a = 20$ in. by cutting out equal squares of side x at each corner and then folding up the sides as in the figure. Express the volume V of the box as a function of x.

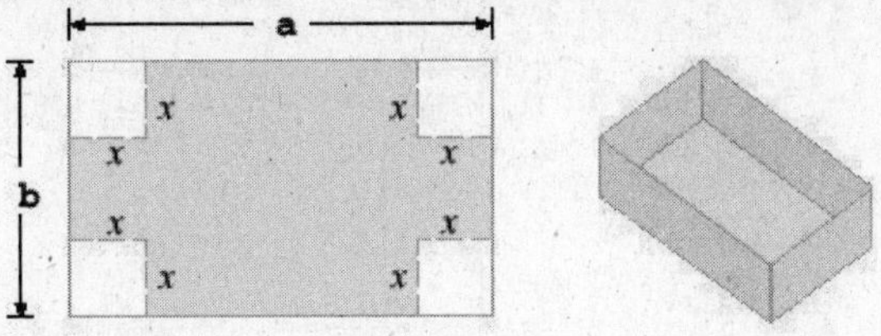

19. Simplify the expression.

$\sin(2\cos^{-1} 4x)$

20. Find all solutions of the equation correct to two decimal places.

$\sqrt{x} = x^3 - 3$

ANSWER KEY

Stewart - Calculus ET 7e Chapter 1 Form E

1. $2a+h-2$

2. Domain: $(2,\infty)$
   Range: $(-\infty,\infty)$
   x-intercept: $x=e^2+2$

3. $(-5, 3)$

4. -19

5. 26.9 h

6. a

7. a) three species
   b) 701.84 m^2

8. d

9. $f^{-1}(9)=1$

10. 2

11. $f(t)=\sin(t)\cos(t)$
    $g(t)=t^2$

12. $\frac{4}{3}\pi(3r^2+3r+1)$

13. a

14. 4

15. $(-0.85, 0.85)$ (to two decimal places)

16. b

17. d

18. $V(x)=x(20-2x)(13-2x)$

19. $8x\sqrt{1-16x^2}$

20. 1.62

1. Find the domain, range, and x-intercept(s) of the function.

$f(x) = \ln(x-2) - 2$

2. Use the Law of Exponents to rewrite and simplify the expression.

$$\frac{\sqrt{a\sqrt{b}}}{\sqrt[4]{ab}}$$

3. Find an expression for the function $y = f(x)$ whose graph is the bottom half of the parabola $x + (3-y)^2 = 0$.

4. A rectangle has perimeter 18 m.

Express the area of the rectangle as a function $A(l)$ of the length l of one of its sides.

5. An open rectangular box with volume 5 m^3 has a square base. Express the surface area of the box as a function $S(x)$ of the length x of a side of the base.

Select the correct answer.

a. $S(x) = x^2 + \dfrac{20}{x^2}$ b. $S(x) = 2x + \dfrac{5}{x}$ c. $S(x) = 2x^2 + \dfrac{5}{x^2}$ d. $S(x) = x^2 + \dfrac{10}{x}$ e. $S(x) = x^2 + \dfrac{20}{x}$

6. A box with an open top is to be constructed from a rectangular piece of cardboard with dimensions $b = 17$ in. by $a = 23$ in. by cutting out equal squares of side x at each corner and then folding up the sides as in the figure.

Express the volume V of the box as a function of x.

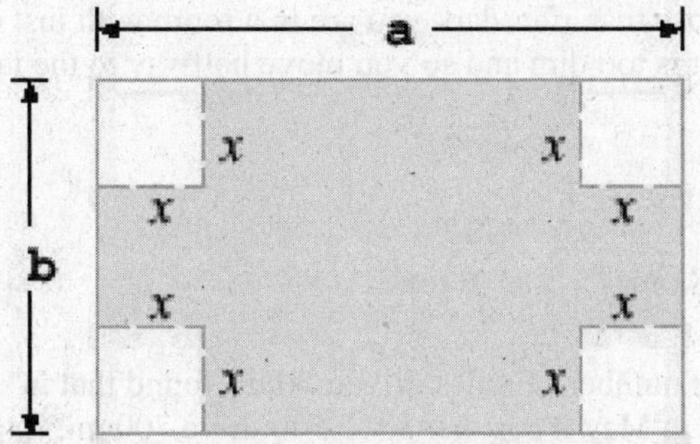

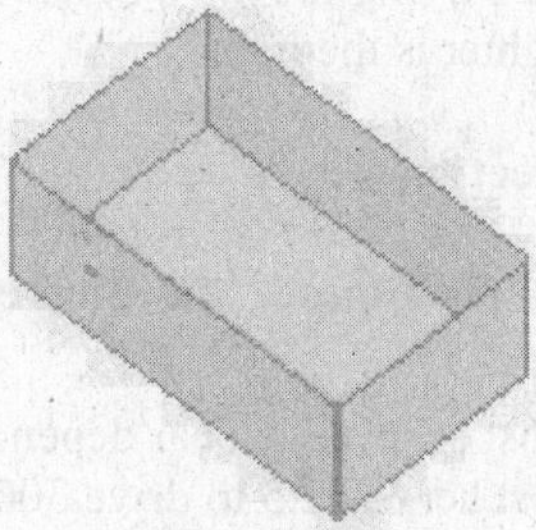

7. What is the equation of this graph?

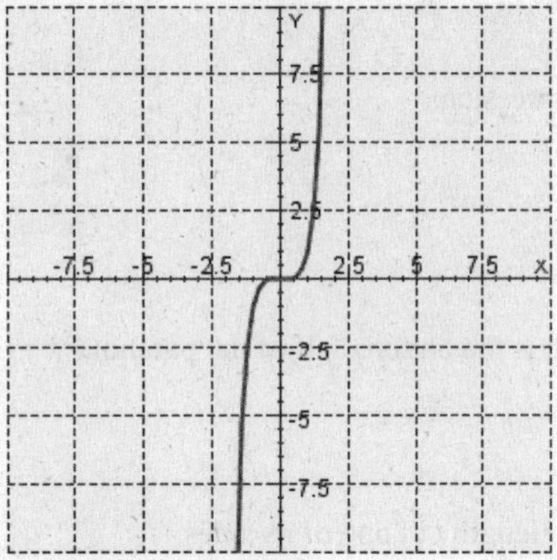

Select the correct answer.

a. $y=x^6$ b. $y=x^2$ c. $y=x^5$ d. $y=x^4$ e. $y=\sqrt[3]{x}$

8. If the point (9, 8) is on the graph of an even function, what other point must also be on the graph?

9. Find the domain of the function.

$$f(x)=\frac{2}{1-e^x}$$

10. In the function $f(x)=4x+c$, what must be the coefficient c, if $f(5)=1$?

11. Many physical quantities are connected by *inverse square laws*, that is, by power functions of the form $f(x)=kx^{-2}$. In particular, the illumination of an object by a light source is inversely proportional to the square of the distance from the source. Suppose that after dark you are in a room with just one lamp and you are trying to read a book. The light is too dim and so you move halfway to the lamp. How much brighter is the light?

Select the correct answer.

a. 2 times b. 4 times c. 3 times d. 8 times e. 6 times

12. The monthly cost of driving a car depends on the number of miles driven. Mary found that in December it cost her \$267.5 to drive 300 mi and in May it cost her \$317.5 to drive 700 mi. Express the monthly cost C as a function of the distance driven d assuming that a linear relationship gives a suitable model.

Select the correct answer.

a. $C=0.125d+230$
b. $C=230d+0.125$
c. $C=0.125d-230$
d. $C=230d-0.125$
e. $C=0.125d+200$

13. A stone is dropped into a lake, creating a circular ripple that travels outward at a speed of 58 cm/s. Express the radius r of this circle as a function of the time t (in seconds) and find $A \circ r$, if A is the area of this circle as a function of the radius.

14. Determine whether f is even, odd, or neither.

$$f(x) = \frac{3x^2}{x^4 + 1}$$

Select the correct answer.

a. even
b. odd
c. neither

15. When a camera flash goes off, the batteries immediately begin to recharge the flash's capacitor, which stores electric charge given by

$$Q(t) = Q_0\left(1 - e^{-t/a}\right)$$

(The maximum charge capacity is Q_0 and t is measured in seconds.) How long does it take to recharge the capacitor to 90% of capacity if $a = 4$?

Select the correct answer.

a. $-4\ln(1)$ seconds

b. $-4\ln\left(\frac{9}{10}\right)$ seconds

c. $-4\ln(10)$ seconds

d. $-4\ln\left(\frac{1}{10}\right)$ seconds

e. $-\ln\left(\frac{4}{9}\right)$ seconds

16. It makes sense that the larger the area of a region, the larger the number of species that inhabit the region. Many ecologists have modeled the species-area relation with a power function and, in particular, the number of species S of bats living in caves in central Mexico has been related to the surface area A measured in m^2 of the caves by the equation $S = 0.7A^{0.3}$.

(a) A particular cave in Mexico has a surface area of $A = 140\,\text{m}^2$. How many species of bats would you expect to find in that cave?
(b) If you discover that two species of bats live in a cave, estimate the area of the cave rounded to two decimal places.

17. Find a formula for the inverse of the function.

$y = \ln(x+2)$

18. Express the function in the form of $f \circ g \circ h$.

$H(x) = 3 - 6^{x^2}$

19. Under ideal conditions a certain bacteria population is known to double every three hours. Suppose that there are initially 25 bacteria. What is the size of the population after 15 hours?

Select the correct answer.

a. 810 bacteria
b. 1,600 bacteria
c. 3,000 bacteria
d. 800 bacteria
e. 950 bacteria

20. Find all solutions of the equation correct to two decimal places.

$x^3 - 9x^2 - 4 = 0$

Select the correct answer.

a. $x = 4.00,\ x = 9.05$
b. $x = -4.00,\ x = 9.05$
c. $x = 0,\ x = 9.05$
d. $x = 9.05$
e. $x = 0,\ x = 4.01,\ x = 9.05$

ANSWER KEY

Stewart - Calculus ET 7e Chapter 1 Form F

1. Domain: $(2,\infty)$
   Range: $(-\infty,\infty)$
   x-intercept: $x = e^2 + 2$

2. $a^{1/4}$

3. $y = 3 - \sqrt{-x}$

4. $A(l) = (9 - l)l$

5. e

6. $V(x) = x(23 - 2x)(17 - 2x)$

7. c

8. (–9, 8)

9. $(-\infty,0)\cup(0,\infty)$

10. –19

11. b

12. a

13. $r(t) = 58t, 3364\pi t^2$

14. a

15. d

16. a) three species
    b) 33.1 m^2

17. $y = e^x - 2$

18. $h(x) = x^2, g(x) = 6^x, f(x) = 3 - x$

19. d

20. d

1. The graphs of $f(x)$ and $g(x)$ are given.
   a) For what values of x is $f(x) = g(x)$?
   b) Find the values of $f(-4)$ and $g(3)$.

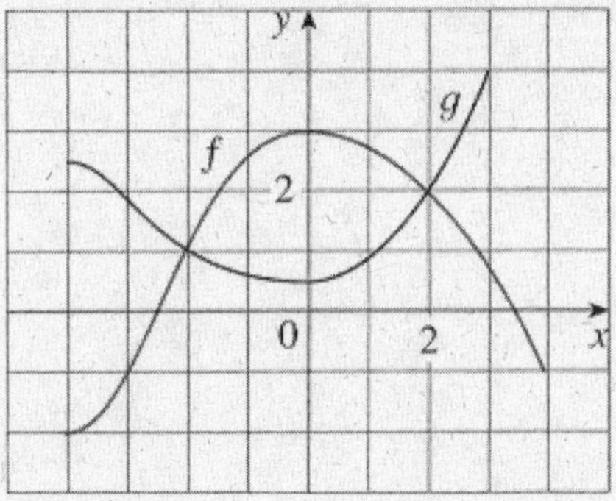

2. Find the domain of the function.

$$f(x) = \frac{2}{1-e^x}$$

3. Find the range of the function.

$$h(x) = \sqrt{16-x^2}$$

4. Starting with the graph of $y = e^x$, write the equation of the graph that results from shifting 2 units left.

Select the correct answer.

a. $y = e^{x-2}$
b. $y = e^{x+2}$
c. $y = e^x - 2$
d. $y = e^x + 2$
e. $y = -2e^x + 2$

5. If $f(x) = x^2 - 2x + 1$, evaluate the difference quotient $\dfrac{f(a+h)-f(a)}{h}$.

6. A rectangle has perimeter 20 m.

Express the area of the rectangle as a function $A(l)$ of the length l of one of its sides.

7. If the point (8, 2) is on the graph of an even function, what other point must also be on the graph?

8. Graph the function by hand, not by plotting points, but by starting with the graph of one of the standard functions and then applying the appropriate transformations.

$y = 2 + 2x - x^2$

Select the correct answer.

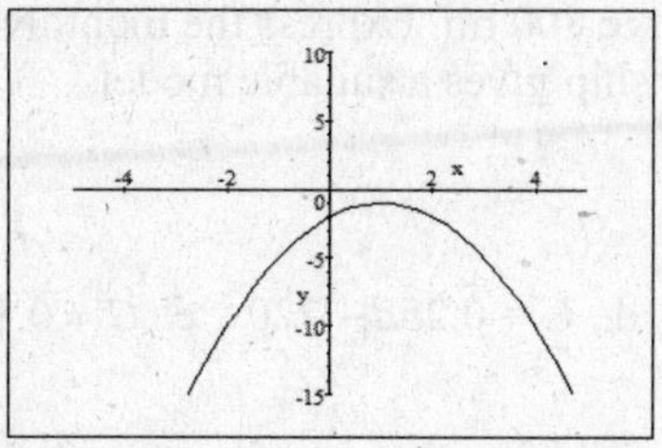
a.

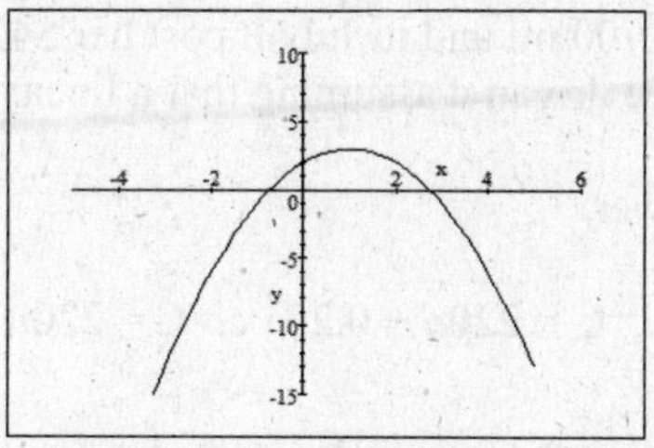
b.

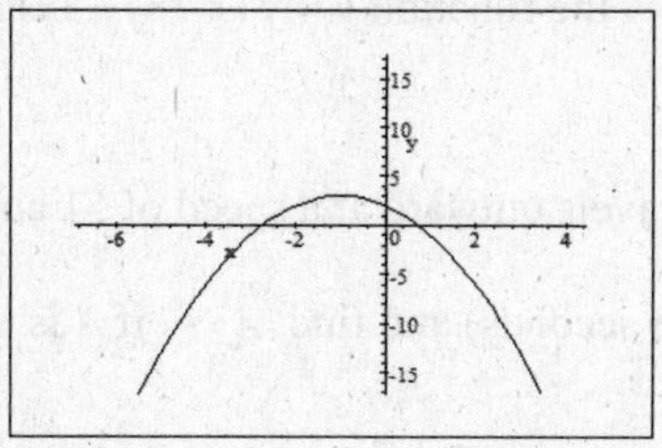
c.

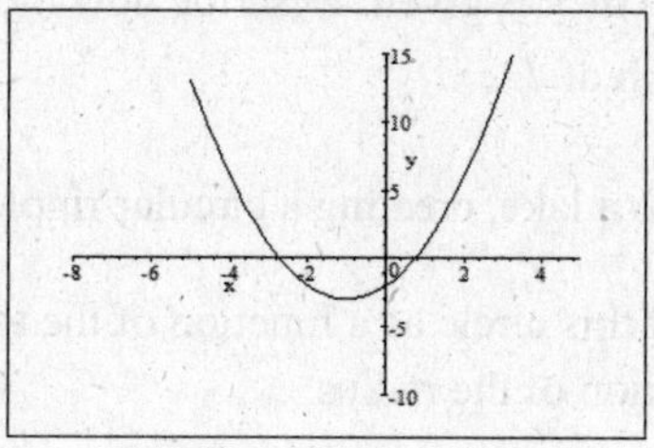
d.

9. Find the exact value of the expression.

$\tan\left(\arcsin\dfrac{1}{2}\right)$

10. A box with an open top is to be constructed from a rectangular piece of cardboard with dimensions $b = 15$ in. by $a = 24$ in. by cutting out equal squares of side x at each corner and then folding up the sides as in the figure. Express the volume V of the box as a function of x.

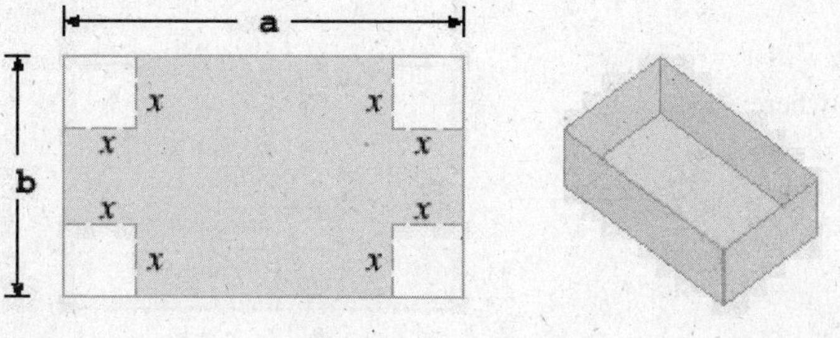

11. The relationship between the Fahrenheit and Celsius temperature scales is given by the linear function.

$F = \dfrac{9}{5}C + 32$

Complete the table and find the slope.

$^\circ C$	$^\circ F$
15	
–25	
slope	

12. Many physical quantities are connected by *inverse square laws*, that is, by power functions of the form $f(x) = kx^{-2}$. In particular, the illumination of an object by a light source is inversely proportional to the square of the distance from the source. Suppose that after dark you are in a room with just one lamp and you are trying to read a book. The light is too dim and so you move three-fourths the distance to the lamp. How much brighter is the light?

13. The monthly cost of driving a car depends on the number of miles driven. Mary found that in January it cost her $395 to drive 700 mi and in July it cost her $420 to drive 800 mi. Express the monthly cost C as a function of the distance driven d assuming that a linear relationship gives a suitable model.

Select the correct answer.

a. $C = 0.25d + 220$ b. $C = 220d + 0.25$ c. $C = 220d - 0.25$ d. $C = 0.25d - 220$ e. $C = 0.125d + 230$

14. Suppose that the graph of f is given. Describe how the graph of the function $y = f(x-3) - 3$ can be obtained from the graph of f.

15. A stone is dropped into a lake, creating a circular ripple that travels outward at a speed of 51 cm/s.

Express the radius r of this circle as a function of the time t (in seconds) and find $A \circ r$, if A is the area of this circle as a function of the radius.

16. If $f(x) = x + 2$ and $h(x) = 3x - 4$, find a function g such that $g \circ f = h$.

Select the correct answer.

a. $g(x) = 3x + 10$ b. $g(x) = 3x - 2$ c. $g(x) = 3x - 10$

17. Find all solutions of the equation correct to two decimal places.

$\sqrt{x} = x^3 - 3$

18. Fill in the blanks.

Let $f(x) = 3 + x^2 + \tan\left(\dfrac{\pi x}{2}\right)$, where $-1 < x < 1$.

$f^{-1}(3) =$ ________ $f(f^{-1}(5)) =$ ________

19. Solve each equation for x.

(a) $\ln x = 2$ (b) $e^{e^x} = 3$

20. Use the table to evaluate the expression $(f \circ g)(3)$.

x	1	2	3	4	5	6
$f(x)$	3	2	1	0	1	2
$g(x)$	6	5	2	3	4	6

Select the correct answer.

a. 2 b. 3 c. 1 d. 5 e. 6

ANSWER KEY

Stewart - Calculus ET 7e Chapter 1 Form G

1. a) $x=-2,\ 2$
   b) $f(-4)=-2,\ \ g(3)=4$

2. $(-\infty,0)\cup(0,\infty)$

3. $0\le h(x)\le 4$

4. b

5. $2a+h-2$

6. $A(l)=(10-l)l$

7. $(-8,\ 2)$

8. b

9. $\sqrt{3}/3$

10. $V(x)=x(24-2x)(15-2x)$

11. (15, 59); (–25, –13); slope = 1.8

12. 16 times brighter

13. a

14. Shift the graph 3 units to the right and 3 units down.

15. $r(t)=51t,\ 2601\pi t^2$

16. c

17. 1.62

18. 0, 5

19. $x=e^2$, $x=\ln(\ln 3)$

20. a

1. Find the exponential function $f(x) = Ca^x$ whose graph is given.

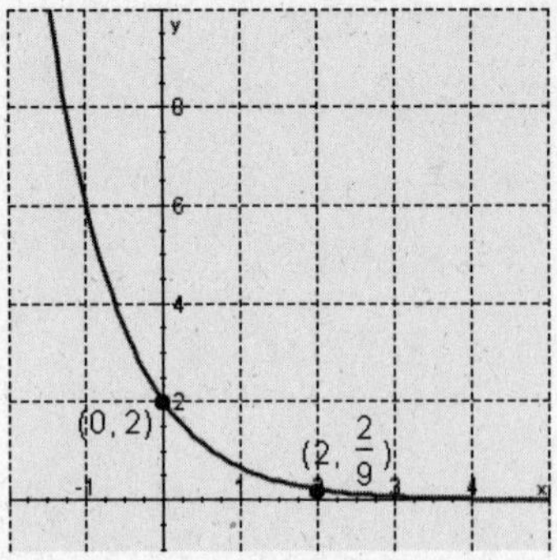

2. The graphs of $f(x)$ and $g(x)$ are given.

a) For what values of x is $f(x) = g(x)$?

b) Find the values of $f(0)$ and $g(3)$.

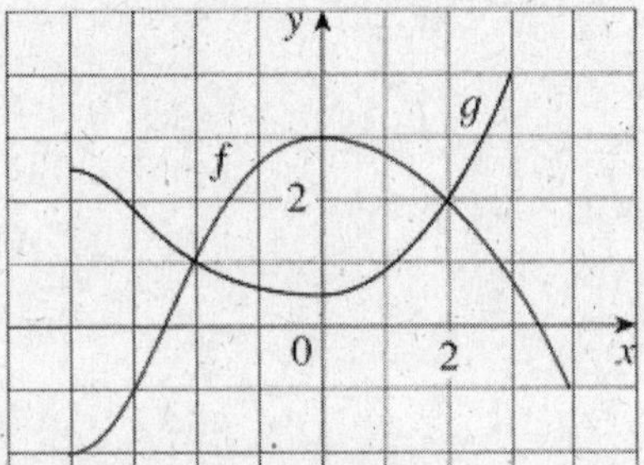

3. Find the domain, range, and x-intercept(s) of the function.

$f(x) = \ln(x-3) - 3$

4. Find an expression for the function $y = f(x)$ whose graph is the bottom half of the parabola $x + (3-y)^2 = 0$.

Select the correct answer.

a. $y = 3 + \sqrt{-x}$ b. $y = 3 - \sqrt{x}$ c. $y = 3 + \sqrt{x}$ d. $y = 3 - \sqrt{-x}$ e. $y = 3 - x^2$

5. A rectangle has perimeter 24 m. Express the area of the rectangle as a function $A(l)$ of the length l of one of its sides.

Select the correct answer.

a. $A(l) = 12l + l^2$
b. $A(l) = 24l - l^2$
c. $A(l) = 24l + l^2$
d. $A(l) = 12 - l$
e. $A(l) = 12l - l^2$

6. It makes sense that the larger the area of a region, the larger the number of species that inhabit the region. Many ecologists have modeled the species-area relation with a power function and, in particular, the number of species S of bats living in caves in central Mexico has been related to the surface area A measured in m^2 of the caves by the equation $S = 0.7A^{0.3}$.

   (a) A particular cave in Mexico has a surface area of $A = 140\,m^2$. How many species of bats would you expect to find in that cave?
   (b) If you discover that two species of bats live in a cave, estimate the area of the cave rounded to two decimal places.

7. A box with an open top is to be constructed from a rectangular piece of cardboard with dimensions $b = 7$ in. by $a = 28$ in. by cutting out equal squares of side x at each corner and then folding up the sides as in the figure.

   Express the volume V of the box as a function of x.

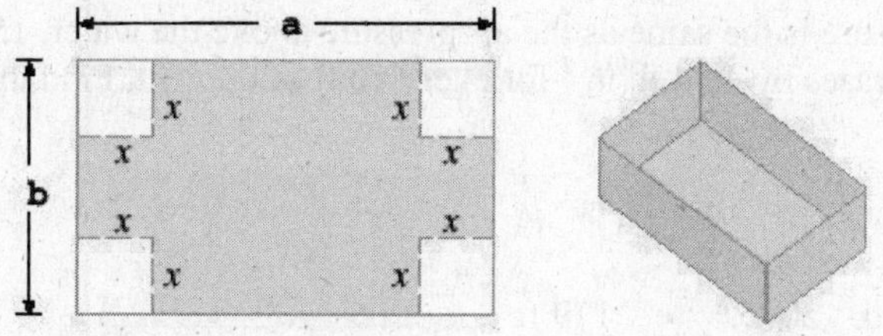

   Select the correct answer.

   a. $V(x) = x^3 - 35x^2 + 196x$
   b. $V(x) = 4x^3 - 70x^2 + 196x$
   c. $V(x) = x^3 - 70x^2 + 196x$
   d. $V(x) = 4x^3 + 35x^2 + 196x$
   e. $V(x) = 4x^3 + 70x^2 + 196x$

8. If the point (8, 3) is on the graph of an even function, what other point must also be on the graph?

9. For what values of x is the inequality true?

   $6\,|\sin x - x| < 0.6$

10. In the function $f(x) = 7x + d$, what must be the coefficient d, if $f(1) = 1$?

   Select the correct answer.

   a. $d = -6$ b. $d = 8$ c. $d = 6$ d. $d = -8$ e. $d = 1$

11. Biologists have noticed that the chirping rate of crickets of certain species is related to temperature, and the relationship appears to be very nearly linear. A cricket produces 113 chirps per minute at 70°F and 173 chirps at 80°F per minute. Find the rate of chirping, if the temperature is 100°F.

   Select the correct answer.

   a. 907 b. −7 c. 293 d. 173 e. 55

12. Many physical quantities are connected by *inverse square laws*, that is, by power functions of the form $f(x) = kx^{-2}$. In particular, the illumination of an object by a light source is inversely proportional to the square of the distance from the source. Suppose that after dark you are in a room with just one lamp and you are trying to read a book. The light is too dim and so you move two-thirds the distance to the lamp. How much brighter is the light?

13. When a camera flash goes off, the batteries immediately begin to recharge the flash's capacitor, which stores electric charge given by $Q(t) = Q_0\left(1-e^{-t/a}\right)$ (The maximum charge capacity is Q_0 and t is measured in seconds.) How long does it take to recharge the capacitor to 70% of capacity if $a = 3$?

Select the correct answer. All choices given in *seconds*.

a. $-3\ln 3$ b. $-3\ln\left(\frac{7}{10}\right)$ c. $-3\ln\left(\frac{3}{10}\right)$ d. $-3\ln 10$ e. $-7\ln 10$

14. At the surface of the ocean, the water pressure is the same as the air pressure above the water, 15 lb/in^2. Below the surface, the water pressure increases by 4.34 lb/in^2 for every 10 ft of descent. Find the depth if the pressure is 80 lb/in^2.

Select the correct answer.

a. 169 ft b. 150 ft c. 129 ft d. 20 ft e. 179 ft

15. Find $f+g$.

$$f(x) = x^3 + 6x^2$$
$$g(x) = 4x^2 - 2$$

Select the correct answer.

a. $(f+g)(x) = x^3 + 10x - 2$
b. $(f+g)(x) = x^3 + 10x^2 - 2$
c. $(f+g)(x) = x^3 + 2x + 2$
d. $(f+g)(x) = x^3 + 10x$
e. $(f+g)(x) = x^3 + x^2 - 1$

16. An isotope of sodium, ^{24}Na, has a half-life of 15 hours. A sample of this isotope has mass 1 g. Find the amount remaining after 60 hours.

Select the correct answer.

a. 0.015625 g
b. 0.0625 g
c. 0.0385 g
d. 0.0001 g
e. 0.0051 g

17. What is $\sqrt[4]{x}$, given that $H = f \circ g \circ h$ and $H(x) = \sqrt[4]{\sqrt{x} - 4}$.

Select the correct answer.

a. $g(x)$
b. $h(x)$
c. $f(x)$

18. A stone is dropped into a lake, creating a circular ripple that travels outward at a speed of 40 cm/s. Express the radius r of this circle as a function of the time t (in seconds) and find $A \circ r$, if A is the area of this circle as a function of the radius.

19. If $f(x) = x + 6$ and $h(x) = 6x - 2$, find a function g such that $g \circ f = h$.

20. Graph the function by hand, not by plotting points, but by starting with the graph of one of the standard functions and then applying the appropriate transformations.

$y = 2 + 2x - x^2$

Select the correct answer.

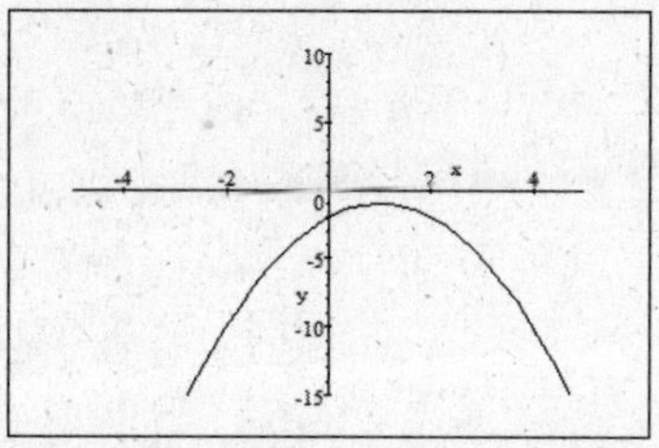

a.

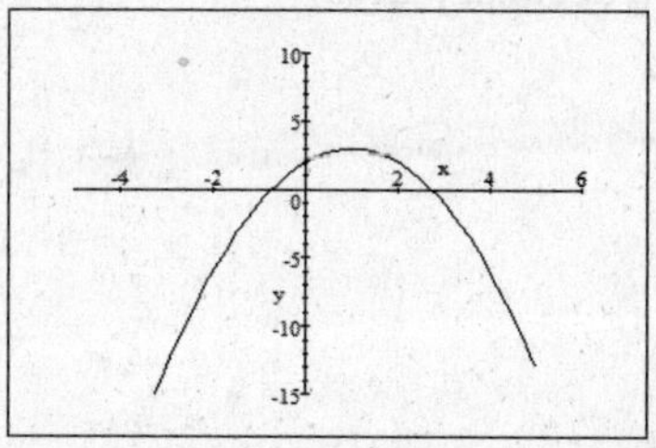

b.

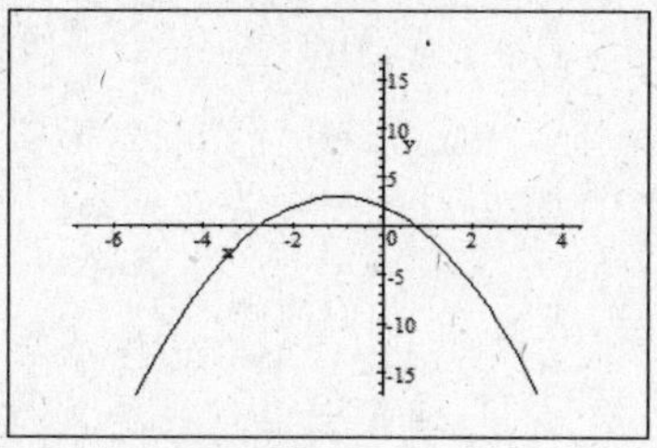

c.

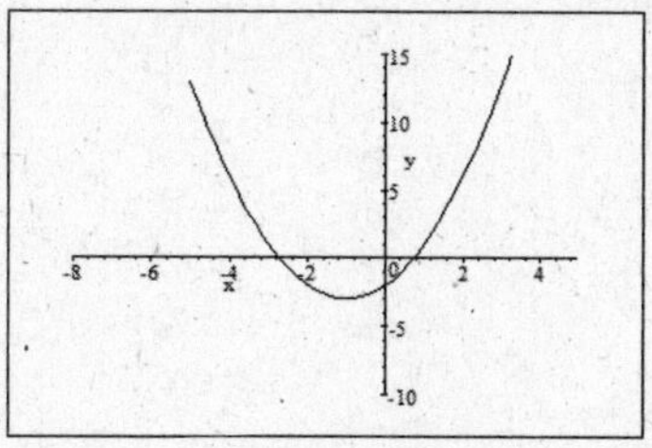

d.

ANSWER KEY

Stewart - Calculus ET 7e Chapter 1 Form H

1. $f(x) = 2(1/3)^x$

2. a) $x = -2,\ 2$
   b) $f(0) = 3,\ g(3) = 4$

3. Domain: $(3, \infty)$
   Range: $(-\infty, \infty)$
   x-intercept: $x = e^3 + 3$

4. d

5. e

6. a) three species
   b) 33.1 m^2

7. b

8. $(-8,3)$

9. $(-0.85, 0.85)$ (to two decimal places)

10. a

11. c

12. 9 times brighter

13. c

14. b

15. b

16. b

17. c

18. $r(t) = 40t,\ 1600\pi t^2$

19. $6x - 38$

20. b

1. The point $P(4,2)$ lies on the curve $y=\sqrt{x}$. If Q is the point $(x,\sqrt{x})$, use your calculator to find the slope of the secant line PQ (correct to six decimal places) for the value $x=3.99$.

2. The position of a car is given by the values in the following table.

t (seconds)	0	1	2	3	4	5
s (feet)	0	19	33	74	114	178

Estimate the instantaneous velocity when $t=2$ by averaging the average velocities for the periods [1, 2] and [2, 3].

3. If a rock is thrown upward on the planet Mars with a velocity of 10 m/s, its height in meters t seconds later is given by $y=10t-1.86t^2$. Find the average velocity over the time interval [1, 2].

4. Find the limit.

$$\lim_{x\to-\infty}\frac{\sqrt{x^2-9}}{2x-6}$$

5. Find an equation of the tangent line to the curve $y=5x^3$ at the point $(-3,-135)$.

6. Use the graph of the function to state the value of $\lim_{x\to0} f(x)$, if it exists.

$$f(x)=\frac{x^2+x}{2\sqrt{x^3+x^2}}$$

7. Find the derivative of the function.

$$f(x)=14-3x+5x^2$$

8. If $1\le f(x)\le x^2+2x+2$, for all x find the limit.

$$\lim_{x\to-1} f(x)$$

9. If an equation of the tangent line to the curve $y=f(x)$ at the point where $a=2$ is $y=4x-5$, find $f(2)$ and $f'(2)$.

10. How close to 2 do we have to take x so that $5x+3$ is within a distance of 0.01 from 13?

11. Find the vertical asymptotes of the function.

$$y=\frac{2x^2+1}{3x-2x^2}$$

12. If $g(x)=\sqrt{3-5x}$, find the domain of $g'(x)$.

13. Estimate the value of

$$\lim_{x \to 0} \frac{2\sin x}{\sin \pi x}$$

by graphing the function $f(x) = (2\sin x)/(\sin \pi x)$. State your answer correct to two decimal places.

14. Evaluate the limit, if it exists.

$$\lim_{h \to 0} \frac{(x-h)^3 - x^3}{h}$$

15. A machinist is required to manufacture a circular metal disk with area 1000 cm^2. If the machinist is allowed an error tolerance of ± 7 cm^2 in the area of the disk, how close to the ideal radius must the machinist control the radius?

16. For $x = 5$, determine whether f is continuous from the right, from the left, or neither.

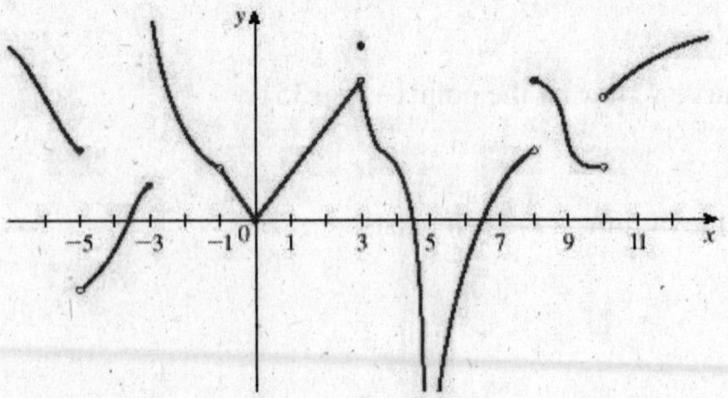

17. Find the point at which the given function is discontinuous.

$$f(x) = \begin{cases} \dfrac{1}{x-4}, & x \neq 4 \\ 4, & x = 4 \end{cases}$$

18. By graphing the function $f(x) = (\cos x - \cos 2x)/x^2$ and zooming in toward the point where the graph crosses the y-axis, estimate the value of $\lim_{x \to 0} f(x)$.

19. Use the definition of the derivative to find $f'(-2)$, where $f(x) = x^3 - 2x$.

20. How would you define $f(3)$ in order to make f continuous at 3?

$$f(x) = \frac{x^2 - 2x - 3}{x - 3}$$

ANSWER KEY

Stewart - Calculus ET 7e Chapter 2 Form A

1. 0.250156

2. 27.5

3. 4.42 m/s

4. $-1/2$

5. $y = 135x + 270$

6. does not exist

7. $10x - 3$

8. 1

9. $f(2) = 3$
$f'(2) = 4$

10. $|x - 2| < 0.002$

11. $x = 0,\ x = 3/2$

12. $(-\infty, 3/5)$

13. 0.64

14. $-3x^2$

15. 0.06234

16. neither

17. 4

18. 1.5

19. 10

20. $f(3) = 4$

1. The point $P(4, 2)$ lies on the curve $y = \sqrt{x}$. If Q is the point $(x, \sqrt{x})$, use your calculator to find the slope of the secant line PQ (correct to six decimal places) for the value of $x = 4.01$.

2. If a cylindrical tank holds 100,000 gallons of water, which can be drained from the bottom of the tank in an hour, then Torricelli's Law gives the volume of water remaining in the tank after t minutes as

$$V(t) = 100{,}000\left(1 - \frac{1}{60}t\right)^2, \quad 0 \le t \le 60$$

Find the rate at which the water is flowing out of the tank (the instantaneous rate of change of V with respect to t) as a function of t.

3. If a rock is thrown upward on the planet Mars with a velocity of 10 m/s, its height in meters t seconds later is given by $y = 10t - 1.86t^2$. Find the average velocity over the time interval [1, 2].

4. How would you define $f(3)$ in order to make f continuous at 3?

$$f(x) = \frac{x^3 - 27}{x^2 - 9}$$

5. Find an equation of the tangent line to the parabola $y = x^2 + 6x$ at the point (3, 27).

6. Evaluate the function $f(x) = 2\dfrac{\sqrt{x} - \sqrt{2}}{x - 2}$ at the given numbers (correct to six decimal places). Use the results to guess the value of the limit $\lim_{x \to 2} f(x)$.

x	$f(x)$
1.6	
1.8	
1.9	
1.99	
1.999	
2.4	
2.2	
2.1	
2.01	
2.001	
Limit	

7. Evaluate the limit.

$$\lim_{x \to \infty} \frac{8x^2 - 9x + 1}{3x^2 + 9x - 3}$$

8. If an equation of the tangent line to the curve $y = f(x)$ at the point where $a = 2$ is $y = 5x - 2$, find $f(2)$ and $f'(2)$.

9. If $1 \le f(x) \le x^2 + 6x + 6$ for all x, find $\lim_{x \to -1} f(x)$.

10. Estimate the value of the limit by graphing the function $f(x) = (3\sin x)/(\sin \pi x)$. State your answer correct to two decimal places.

$$\lim_{x \to 0} \frac{3\sin x}{\sin \pi x}$$

11. Use the graph of the function to state the value of $\lim_{x \to 0} f(x)$, if it exists.

$$f(x) = \frac{1}{1+4^{1/x}}$$

12. Find the limit.

$$\lim_{t \to 2} \frac{t^2 - 4}{t^3 - 8}$$

13. The cost (in dollars) of producing x units of a certain commodity is $C(x) = 4{,}336 + 13x + 0.08x^2$. Find the average rate of change with respect to x when the production level is changed from $x = 101$ to $x = 103$.

14. If $g(x) = \sqrt{3 - 5x}$, find the domain of $g'(x)$.

15. If f and g are continuous functions with $f(3) = 3$ and $\lim_{x \to 3}[3f(x) - g(x)] = 3$, find $g(3)$.

16. Evaluate the limit.

$$\lim_{x \to -9} |x + 9|$$

17. Write an equation that expresses the fact that a function f is continuous at the number 6.

18. By graphing the function $f(x) = (\cos 2x - \cos x)/x^2$ and zooming in toward the point where the graph crosses the y-axis, estimate the value of $\lim_{x \to 0} f(x)$.

19. Evaluate the limit.

$$\lim_{x \to 0} \frac{(9 + x)^{-1} - 9^{-1}}{x}$$

20. For the function f whose graph is shown, state the following.

$$\lim_{x \to -4} f(x)$$

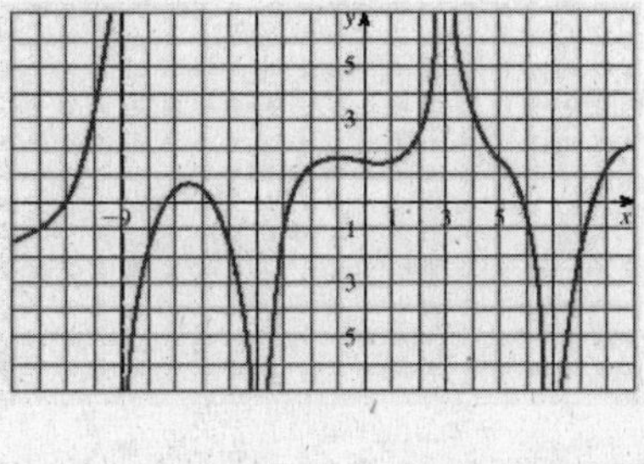

ANSWER KEY

Stewart - Calculus ET 7e Chapter 2 Form B

1. 0.249844

2. $V'(t) = \frac{-10000}{3} + \frac{500t}{9}$

3. 4.42 m/s

4. $f(3) = 9/2$

5. $y = 12x - 9$

6. 0.746512, 0.725728, 0.716174, 0.707993, 0.707195, 0.674899, 0.690261, 0.698482, 0.706225, 0.707018, *Limit* 0.707107

7. 8/3

8. $f(2) = 8$
$f'(2) = 5$

9. 1

10. 0.95

11. does not exist

12. 1/3

13. 29.32

14. $(-\infty, 3/5)$

15. 6

16. 0

17. $\lim_{x \to 6} f(x) = f(6)$

18. –1.5

19. $-\frac{1}{81}$

20. $-\infty$

1. A cardiac monitor is used to measure the heart rate of a patient after surgery. It compiles the number of heartbeats after t minutes. When the data in the table are graphed, the slope of the tangent line represents the heart rate in beats per minute. The monitor estimates this value by calculating the slope of a secant line. Use the data to estimate the patient's heart rate after 42 minutes using the secant line between the points with $t = 38$ and $t = 42$.

t (min)	36	38	40	42	44
Heartbeats	2,570	2,640	2,840	3,000	3,070

Select the correct answer.

a. –89 b. 180 c. 90 d. 100 e. 89 f. 95

2. If an equation of the tangent line to the curve $y = f(x)$ at the point where $a = 2$ is $y = 4x - 11$, find $f(2)$ and $f'(2)$.

Select the correct answer.

a. $f(2) = -4$, $f'(2) = 4$ b. $f(2) = 3$, $f'(2) = 4$ c. $f(2) = -4$, $f'(2) = 3$ d. $f(2) = -3$, $f'(2) = 4$ e. none of these

3. The displacement (in feet) of a certain particle moving in a straight line is given by $s = t^3/8$ where t is measured in seconds. Find the average velocity over the interval [1, 1.8].

Select the correct answer.

a. 0.865 b. 0.654 c. 0.765 d. 0.756 e. 0.745 f. 0.755

4. For the function f whose graph is shown, find the equations of the vertical asymptotes.

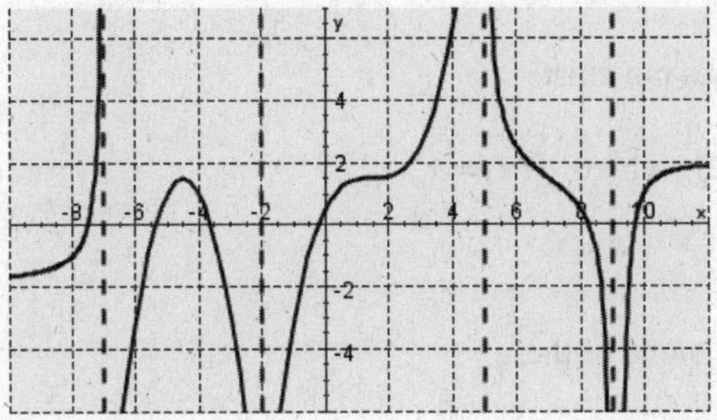

Select all that apply.

a. $x = -7$ b. $x = 9$ c. $x = 5$ d. $x = -3$ e. $x = 10$ f. $x = -2$

5. Estimate the value of the limit by graphing the function $f(x) = (2\sin x)/(\sin \pi x)$. State your answer correct to two decimal places.

$$\lim_{x \to 0} \frac{2\sin x}{\sin \pi x}$$

Select the correct answer.

a. 3.14 b. 2.01 c. 1.0 d. 0 e. 0.64

6. Find the limit.

$$\lim_{x \to -\infty} \frac{\sqrt{x^2 - 9}}{2x - 6}$$

Select the correct answer.

a. –1/2 b. 3 c. –3 d. 0 e. does not exist

7. Evaluate the limit.

$$\lim_{x \to 1} (x+2)^3 (x^2 - 6)$$

Select the correct answer.

a. 27 b. –45 c. –135 d. 29 e. –125

8. If $1 \le f(x) \le x^2 + 8x + 8$ for all x, find $\lim_{x \to -1} f(x)$.

Select the correct answer.

a. 1 b. 8 c. –1/8 d. –1/16 e. does not exist

9. Use the definition of the derivative for find $f'(-2)$, where $f(x) = x^3 - 2x$.

Select the correct answer.

a. 4 b. 10 c. –4 d. –10 e. none of these

10. How would you define $f(3)$ in order to make f continuous at 3?

$$f(x) = \frac{x^2 - x - 6}{x - 3}$$

Select the correct answer.

a. $f(3) = 5$ b. $f(3) = 0$ c. $f(3) = 1$ d. $f(3) = -5$ e. none of these

11. A machinist is required to manufacture a circular metal disk with area 1000 cm^2. If the machinist is allowed an error tolerance of ± 10 cm^2 in the area of the disk, how close to the ideal radius must the machinist control the radius? Round down the answer to the nearest hundred thousandth.

Select the correct answer.

a. $\delta \le 0.08898$ cm b. $\delta \le 0.08908$ cm c. $\delta \le 0.08999$ cm d. $\delta \le 0.08913$ cm e. $\delta \le 0.09913$ cm

12. Use the graph of the function to state the value of $\lim_{x\to 0} f(x)$, if it exists.

$$f(x) = \frac{1}{1+2^{1/x}}$$

Select the correct answer.

a. 1/2 b. 0 c. 1/3 d. ∞ e. does not exist

13. Choose an equation from the following that expresses the fact that a function f is continuous at the number 6.

Select the correct answer.

a. $\lim_{x\to 0} f(x) = 6$ b. $\lim_{x\to 6} f(x) = f(6)$ c. $\lim_{x\to 0} f(x) = f(6)$ d. $\lim_{x\to 6} f(x) = -\infty$ e. $\lim_{x\to 6} f(x) = \infty$

14. Determine where f is discontinuous.

$$f(x) = \begin{cases} \sqrt{-x} & \text{if } x < 0 \\ 3 - x & \text{if } 0 \le x < 3 \\ (3-x)^2 & \text{if } x > 3 \end{cases}$$

Select the correct answer.

a. 0 *and* 3 b. 0 *only* c. 3 *only* d. 0 *and* −3 e. −3 *only*

15. If $g(x) = \sqrt{3-5x}$, find the domain of $g'(x)$.

Select the correct answer.

a. $(-\infty, 0) \cup (0, \infty)$ b. $[-3/5, 3/5]$ c. $[-\infty, 3/5)$ d. $(-\infty, 3/5)$ e. $(0, \infty)$

16. Use the graph of the function to state the value of $\lim_{x \to 0} f(x)$, if it exists.

$$f(x) = \frac{x^2 + x}{3\sqrt{x^3 + x^2}}$$

Select the correct answer.

a. $-1/3$ b. ∞ c. $1/3$ d. $-\infty$ e. does not exist

17. Find the vertical asymptotes of the function.

$$y = \frac{2x^2 + 1}{3x - 2x^2}$$

Select the correct answer.

a. $x = 3$ b. $x = 2/3$ c. $x = 0,\ x = 2/3$ d. $x = -2/3$ e. none of these

18. The cost (in dollars) of producing x units of a certain commodity is $C(x) = 4{,}571 + 19x + 0.01x^2$. Find the instantaneous rate of change with respect to x when $x = 103$. (This is called the *marginal cost.*)

Select the correct answer.

a. 26.06
b. 20.06
c. 21.06
d. 18.06
e. 31.06

19. If the tangent line to $y = f(x)$ at (8, 4) passes through the point (5, –32), find $f'(8)$.

Select the correct answer.

a. $f'(8) = 24$
b. $f'(8) = 20$
c. $f'(8) = -12$
d. $f'(8) = 12$
e. $f'(8) = 32$

20. At what point is the function $f(x) = |6 - x|$ not differentiable.

Select the correct answer.

a. 6
b. –6
c. 1
d. –1
e. 0

ANSWER KEY

Stewart - Calculus ET 7e Chapter 2 Form C

1. c

2. d

3. f

4. a, b, c, f

5. e

6. a

7. c

8. a

9. b

10. a

11. a

12. e

13. b

14. a

15. d

16. e

17. e

18. e

19. d

20. a

1. The position of a car is given by the values in the following table. Find the average velocity for the time period beginning when $t = 2$ and lasting 2 seconds.

t (seconds)	0	1	2	3	4	5
s (feet)	0	18	35	74	110	175

Select the correct answer.

a. 35.5 b. 47.5 c. 39 d. 37.5 e. 33.5

2. If an equation of the tangent line to the curve $y = f(x)$ at the point where $a = 2$ is $y = 4x - 11$, find $f(2)$ and $f'(2)$.

Select the correct answer.

a. $f(2) = -4$, $f'(2) = 4$ b. $f(2) = 3$, $f'(2) = 4$ c. $f(2) = -4$, $f'(2) = 3$ d. $f(2) = -3$, $f'(2) = 4$ e. none of these

3. Use the graph of the function to state the value of $\lim_{x \to 0} f(x)$, if it exists.

$$f(x) = \frac{x^2 + x}{3\sqrt{x^3 + x^2}}$$

Select the correct answer.

a. 0 b. $\frac{1}{3}$ c. $-\frac{1}{3}$ d. ∞ e. does not exist

4. The slope of the tangent line to the graph of the exponential function $y = 8^x$ at the point (0, 1) is $\lim_{x \to 0} \frac{8^x - 1}{x}$.

Estimate the slope to three decimal places.

Select the correct answer.

a. 1.293 b. 2 c. 2.026 d. 1.568 e. 2.079 f. 2.556

5. Find the limit.

$$\lim_{x \to -\infty} \frac{\sqrt{x^2 - 9}}{2x - 6}$$

Select the correct answer.

a. $-1/2$ b. $3/2$ c. $-3/2$ d. 0 e. does not exist

6. Find an equation of the tangent line to the curve $y = x^3 - 2x$ at the point $(2,4)$.

Select the correct answer.

a. $y = 16 - 10x$ b. $y = 10x - 8$ c. $y = x - 16$ d. $y = 10x + 16$ e. none of these

7. Estimate the value of the limit by graphing the function $f(x) = (3\sin x)/(\sin \pi x)$. State your answer correct to two decimal places.

$$\lim_{x \to 0} \frac{3\sin x}{\sin \pi x}$$

Select the correct answer.

a. 3.00 b. 3.14 c. 0.95 d. 0.64 e. –3.14 f. –6.28

8. Let $F(x) = \dfrac{x^2 - 1}{|x - 1|}$. Find the following limits.

$$\lim_{x \to 1^+} F(x), \quad \lim_{x \to 1^-} F(x)$$

Select the correct answer.

a. both 2 b. 2 and 1 c. 2 and –2 d. 2 and –1 e. both 1

9. Use continuity to evaluate the limit.

$$\lim_{x \to 13\pi} \sin(x + 4\sin x)$$

Select the correct answer.

a. 13π b. –1 c. 0 d. ∞ e. 1

10. If $g(x) = \sqrt{3 - 5x}$, use the definition of a derivative to find $g'(x)$.

Select the correct answer.

a. $g'(x) = -\frac{5}{2}(3 - 5x)^{-1/2}$

b. $g'(x) = -\frac{1}{2}(3 - 5x)^{1/2}$

c. $g'(x) = -(3 - 5x)^2$

d. $g'(x) = -\frac{5}{2}(3 - 5x)^{-2}$

e. none of these

11. For what value of the constant c is the function f continuous on $(-\infty, \infty)$?

$$f(x) = \begin{cases} cx + 7 & for \quad x \le 2 \\ cx^2 - 5 & for \quad x > 2 \end{cases}$$

Select the correct answer.

a. $c = 1$ b. $c = 2$ c. $c = 6$ d. $c = -2$ e. $c = 7$

12. How would you define $f(4)$ in order to make f continuous at 4?

$$f(x) = \frac{x^2 - x - 12}{x - 4}$$

Select the correct answer.

a. $f(4) = 0$ b. $f(4) = 1$ c. $f(4) = 7$ d. $f(4) = 4$ e. none of these

13. Use the graph of the function to state the value of $\lim_{x \to 0} f(x)$, if it exists.

$$f(x) = \frac{1}{1 + 4^{1/x}}$$

Select the correct answer.

a. 0
b. 1/5
c. 1
d. ∞
e. does not exist

14. If $2x - 1 \le f(x) \le x^2$ for $0 < x < 3$, find $\lim_{x \to 1} f(x)$.

Select the correct answer.

a. 1 b. –1 c. 0 d. 3 e. 5

15. Find the slope of the tangent line to the curve $y = 3x^2$ at the point (–3, 27).

Select the correct answer.

a. –18 b. 81 c. 27 d. –3 e. 18

16. The cost (in dollars) of producing x units of a certain commodity is $C(x) = 4{,}280 + 13x + 0.03x^2$. Find the average rate of change with respect to x when the production level is changed from $x = 102$ to $x = 118$.

Select the correct answer.

a.	29.6
b.	19.6
c.	18.6
d.	26.6
e.	24.6

17. Find the limit.

$$\lim_{t \to \infty} \frac{t^2 + 3}{t^3 + t^2 - 1}$$

Select the correct answer.

a. ∞ b. 0 c. –3 d. 3 e. 2

18. If a ball is thrown into the air with a velocity of 58 ft/s, its height (in feet) after t seconds is given by

$H = 58t - 16t^2$. Find the velocity when $t = 4$.

Select the correct answer.

a. 58 ft/s b. –70 ft/s c. 70 ft/s d. –58 ft/s e. –56 ft/s

19. Is there a number a such that $\lim\limits_{x \to -3} \dfrac{6x^2 + ax + a + 2}{x^2 + x - 6}$ exists? If so, find the value of a and the value of the limit.

Select the correct answer.

a. a=14, limit equals 1.4
b. a=17, limit equals 1.6
c. a=28, limit equals 1.4
d. a=28, limit equals 1.6
e. a=14, limit equals 1.6

20. Evaluate the limit, if it exists.

$$\lim_{h \to 0} \frac{(x-h)^3 - x^3}{h}$$

Select the correct answer.

a. 1 b. –3 c. $3x^2$ d. $-3x^2$ e. does not exist

ANSWER KEY

Stewart - Calculus ET 7e Chapter 2 Form D

1. d

2. d

3. e

4. e

5. a

6. e

7. c

8. c

9. c

10. a

11. c

12. c

13. e

14. a

15. a

16. b

17. b

18. b

19. d

20. d

1. A tank holds 1000 gallons of water, which drains from the bottom of the tank in half an hour. The values in the table show the volume V of water remaining in the tank (in gallons) after t minutes. If P is the point (15, 263) on the graph of V, fill the table with the slopes of the secant lines PQ where Q is the point on the graph with the corresponding t.

t (min)	5	10	15	20	25	30
V (gal)	686	481	263	171	22	0

Enter your answer to two decimal places.

t	slope
5	
10	
20	
25	
30	

2. For the function f whose graph is shown, find the equations of the vertical asymptotes.

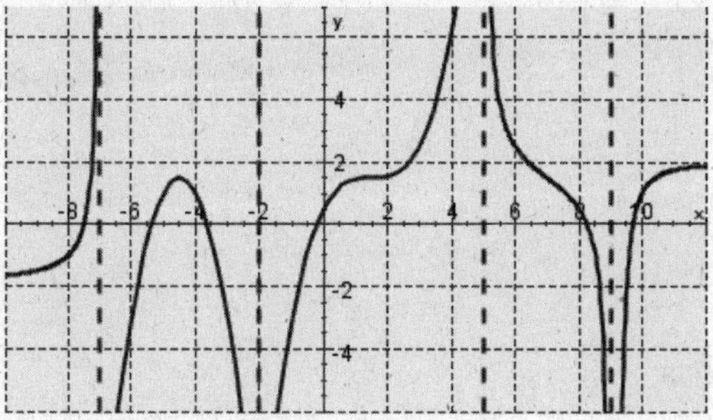

Select all that apply.

a. $x = -7$ b. $x = 9$ c. $x = 5$ d. $x = -3$ e. $x = 10$ f. $x = -2$

3. If a rock is thrown upward on the planet Mars with a velocity of 10 m/s, its height in meters t seconds later is given by $y = 10t - 1.86t^2$. Find the average velocity over the time interval [1, 2].

Select the correct answer.

a. 3.5 m/s b. 2.56 m/s c. 1.86 m/s d. 12.56 m/s e. 4.42 m/s

4. Use the graph of the function to state the value of $\lim_{x \to 0} f(x)$, if it exists.

$$f(x) = \frac{1}{1 + 2^{1/x}}$$

5. The position of a car is given by the values in the following table. Estimate the instantaneous velocity when $t = 2$ by averaging the average velocities for the periods [1, 2] and [2, 3].

t (seconds)	0	1	2	3	4	5
s (feet)	0	19	38	76	128	173

Select the correct answer.

a.	27.5
b.	28.5
c.	28
d.	30
e.	28.51
f.	30.5

6. By graphing the function $f(x) = (\cos x - \cos 2x)/x^2$ and zooming in toward the point where the graph crosses the y-axis, estimate the value of $\lim_{x \to 0} f(x)$.

7. If an equation of the tangent line to the curve $y = f(x)$ at the point where $a = 2$ is $y = 4x - 11$, find $f(2)$ and $f'(2)$.

8. Consider the following function.

$$f(x) = \begin{cases} 3 - x & x < -1 \\ x & -1 \le x < 3 \\ (x-3)^2 & x \ge 3 \end{cases}$$

Determine the values of a for which $\lim_{x \to a} f(x)$ exists.

9. Evaluate the limit.

$$\lim_{x \to 0} \frac{(7+x)^{-1} - 7^{-1}}{x}$$

10. Let $F(x) = \dfrac{x^2 - 1}{|x - 1|}$

Find the following limits.

$$\lim_{x \to 1^+} F(x), \qquad \lim_{x \to 1^-} F(x)$$

11. Evaluate the limit, if it exists.

$$\lim_{h \to 0} \frac{-(x-h)^3 + x^3}{h}$$

12. Is there a number a such that $\lim\limits_{x\to -3} \dfrac{10x^2 + ax + a + 8}{x^2 + x - 6}$ exists? If so, find the value of a and the value of the limit.

Select the correct answer.

a. a =49, limit equals 1.6
b. a =13, limit equals 2.2
c. a =49, limit equals 2.2
d. a =19, limit equals 1.6
e. a =49, limit equals 2.7

13. How close to 2 do we have to take x so that $5x + 3$ is within a distance of 0.025 from 13?

14. Find a function g that agrees with f for $x \neq 25$ and is continuous on $\Re$.

$$f(x) = \frac{5 - \sqrt{x}}{25 - x}$$

15. Find the slope of the tangent line to the curve $y = 3x^2$ at the point (–3, 27).

Select the correct answer.

a. –18 b. 81 c. 27 d. –3 e. 18

16. Use the given graph of $f(x) = x^2$ to find a number δ such that $|x^2 - 1| < 1/2$ whenever $|x - 1| < \delta$.

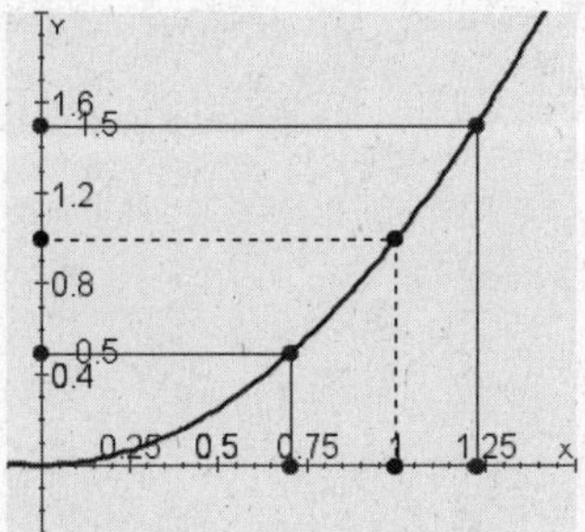

17. How would you define $f(2)$ in order to make f continuous at 2?

$$f(x) = \frac{x^2 - x - 2}{x - 2}$$

18. Find the derivative of the function.

$$f(x) = 14 - 3x + 5x^2$$

19. How close to –9 do we have to take x so that $1/(x+9)^4 > 10000$?

20. Evaluate the limit.

$$\lim_{x\to\infty} \frac{8x^2 - 9x + 1}{3x^2 + 9x - 3}$$

ANSWER KEY

Stewart - Calculus ET 7e Chapter 2 Form E

1. (5, –42.3); (10, –43.6); (20, –18.4); (25, –24.1); (30, –17.53)

2. a, b, c, f

3. e

4. does not exist

5. b

6. 1.5

7. $f(2) = -3$
   $f'(2) = 4$

8. $(-\infty, -1) \cup (-1, 3) \cup (3, \infty)$

9. –1/49

10. 2, –2

11. $3x^2$

12. c

13. $|x - 2| < 0.005$

14. $g(x) = \dfrac{1}{5 + \sqrt{x}}$

15. a

16. $\delta \leq 0.22$ *(to two decimal places)*

17. $f(2) = 3$

18. $10x - 3$

19. $|x + 9| < 0.1$

20. 8/3

1. The displacement (in meters) of an object moving in a straight line is given by $s = 1 + 2t + t^2/4$, where t is measured in seconds. Find the average velocity over the time period [1, 1.5].

2. If a ball is thrown into the air with a velocity of 45 ft/s, its height in feet after t seconds is given by $y = 45t - 16t^2$. Find the instantaneous velocity when $t = 4$.

3. If $\lim_{x\to 3^-} f(x) = 4.5$, then if $\lim_{x\to 3} f(x)$ exists, find the value where it exists.

Select the correct answer.

a. 6.5 b. 4.5 c. 1 d. 2 e. 6

4. For the function f whose graph is shown, find the limit.

$\lim_{x\to -9^+} f(x)$

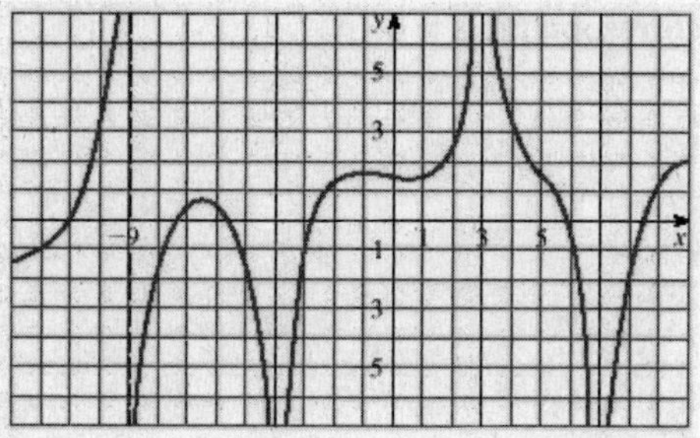

5. If an equation of the tangent line to the curve $y = f(x)$ at the point where $a = 2$ is $y = 5x - 2$, find $f(2)$ and $f'(2)$.

6. Find the limit, if it exists.

$$\lim_{x\to\infty} \frac{8x^2 - 9x + 1}{3x^2 + 9x - 3}$$

7. Use the graph of the function to state the value of $\lim_{x\to 0} f(x)$, if it exists.

$$f(x) = \frac{x^2 + x}{3\sqrt{x^3 + x^2}}$$

8. Find the limit.

$$\lim_{x\to 0^+} \tan^{-1}(1/x)$$

9. Use the graph of the function to state the value of $\lim_{x\to 0} f(x)$, if it exists.

$$f(x) = 1/\left(1 + 4^{1/x}\right)$$

10. Estimate the value of the limit to two decimal places by graphing the function $f(x)=(2\sin x)/(\sin \pi x)$.

$$\lim_{x\to 0}\frac{2\sin x}{\sin \pi x}$$

11. Find the derivative of the function using the definition of derivative.

$$f(x)=19-9x+2x^2$$

12. Use a graph to find a number δ such that $\left|\sin x-\frac{1}{2}\right| < 0.1$ whenever $\left|x-\frac{\pi}{6}\right| < \delta$.

Round down the answer to the nearest thousandth.

13. Use the definition of the limit to find values of δ that correspond to $\varepsilon = 0.75$.

Round down the answer to the nearest thousandth.

$$\lim_{x\to 1}\left(4+x-3x^3\right)=2$$

14. Determine where f is discontinuous.

$$f(x)=\begin{cases}\sqrt{-x} & \text{if } x<0\\ 3-x & \text{if } 0\le x<3\\ (3-x)^2 & \text{if } x>3\end{cases}$$

15. If f and g are continuous functions with $f(2)=2$ and $\lim_{x\to 2}[2f(x)-g(x)]=2$, find $g(2)$.

16. Evaluate the limit, if it exists.

$$\lim_{h\to 0}\frac{-(x+h)^3+x^3}{h}$$

17. How would you define $f(4)$ in order to make f continuous at 4?

$$f(x)=\frac{x^2-x-12}{x-4}$$

18. Find a function g that agrees with f for $x\neq 4$ and is continuous on $\Re$.

$$f(x)=\frac{2-\sqrt{x}}{4-x}$$

19. If $2x-1 \le f(x) \le x^2$ for $0 < x < 3$, find $\lim_{x \to 1} f(x)$.

Select the correct answer.

a. 1 b. −1 c. 0 d. 3 e. 5

20. Find the slope of the tangent line to the parabola $y = x^2 + 3x$ at the point $(4, 28)$.

ANSWER KEY

Stewart - Calculus ET 7e Chapter 2 Form F

1. 2.625 m/s

2. –83 ft/s

3. b

4. $-\infty$

5. $f(2)=8$
$f'(2)=5$

6. 8/3

7. does not exist

8. $\dfrac{\pi}{2}$

9. does not exist

10. 0.64

11. $4x-9$

12. $\delta \leq 0.112$

13. $\delta \leq 0.085$

14. *at* 0 *and* 3

15. 2

16. $-3x^2$

17. $f(4)=7$

18. $g(x)=\dfrac{1}{2+\sqrt{x}}$

19. a

20. 11

1. Find the derivative of the function using the definition of the derivative.

$$f(x) = 10 - x + 6x^2$$

2. Consider the following function.

$$f(x) = \begin{cases} 1-x & x < -1 \\ x & -1 \le x < 1 \\ (x-1)^2 & x \ge 1 \end{cases}$$

Determine the values of a for which $\lim_{x\to a} f(x)$ exists.

3. Use the graph of the function to state the value of $\lim_{x\to 0} f(x)$, if it exists.

$$f(x) = \frac{1}{1+3^{1/x}}$$

Select the correct answer.

a. ∞   b. 0   c. –1/4   d. –∞   e. does not exist

4. Find the vertical asymptotes of the function.

$$y = \frac{2x^2+1}{3x-2x^2}$$

5. Find the value of the limit.

$$\lim_{x\to 0} 3\frac{\tan 5x - 5x}{x^3}$$

Select the correct answer.

a. 121   b. 135   c. 134   d. 130   e. 125

6. If an equation of the tangent line to the curve $y = f(x)$ at the point where $a = 2$ is $y = 4x - 11$, find $f(2)$ and $f'(2)$.

7. Evaluate the limit.

$$\lim_{x\to 1}(x+1)^3(x^2-10)$$

8. Evaluate the limit.

$$\lim_{x\to 3}\left(\frac{x^3-5}{x^2-4}\right)$$

9. Estimate the value of

$$\lim_{x\to 0}\frac{2\sin x}{\sin \pi x}$$

by graphing the function $f(x)=(2\sin x)/(\sin \pi x)$. State your answer correct to two decimal places.

10. Let

$$F(x)=\frac{x^2-81}{|x-9|}$$

Find the following limits.

$$\lim_{x\to 9^+}F(x),\quad \lim_{x\to 9^-}F(x)$$

Select the correct answer.

a.	18 and 9
b.	18 and –18
c.	both 18
d.	18 and –9
e.	81 and 9

11. Evaluate the limit.

$$\lim_{x\to\infty}\frac{8x^2-9x+3}{3x^2+4x-4}$$

12. Use a graph to find a number δ such that $|\sqrt{4x+1}-3|<0.5$ whenever $|x-2|<\delta$.

13. How would you define $f(2)$ in order to make f continuous at 2?

$$f(x)=\frac{x^3-8}{x^2-4}$$

14. Find the slope of the tangent line to the curve $y=5x^3$ at the point (–4, –320).

15. If f and g are continuous functions with $f(5)=2$ and $\lim_{x\to 5}[2f(x)-g(x)]=5$, find $g(5)$.

Select the correct answer.

a. $g(5)=2$ b. $g(5)=-1$ c. $g(5)=9$ d. $g(5)=3$ e. $g(5)=5$

16. Which of the given functions is discontinuous?

a. $f(x) = \begin{cases} \dfrac{1}{x-2}, & x \geq 5 \\ \dfrac{1}{3}\ , & x < 5 \end{cases}$

b. $f(x) = \begin{cases} \dfrac{1}{x-5}, & x \neq 5 \\ 3\ , & x = 5 \end{cases}$

17. Find the limit.

$$\lim_{x \to 3} \frac{x^2 + 3x - 18}{x - 3}$$

Select the correct answer.

a. 6 b. 8 c. 5 d. 9 e. 18

18. Evaluate the limit, if it exists.

$$\lim_{h \to 0} \frac{-(x-h)^3 + x^3}{h}$$

19. By graphing the function $f(x) = 2(\cos x - \cos 2x)/x^2$ and zooming in toward the point where the graph crosses the y-axis, estimate the value of $\lim_{x \to 0} f(x)$.

20. At what point is the function $f(x) = |8 - x|$ not differentiable.

ANSWER KEY

Stewart - Calculus ET 7e Chapter 2 Form G

1. $12x - 1$

2. $(-\infty, -1) \cup (-1, 1) \cup (1, \infty)$

3. e

4. $x = 0,\ x = 3/2$

5. e

6. $f(2) = -3$
$f'(2) = 4$

7. –72

8. 22/5

9. 0.64

10. b

11. 8/3

12. $\delta \le 0.6875$

13. $f(2) = 3$

14. 240

15. b

16. b

17. d

18. $3x^2$

19. 3

20. 8

1. The point $P(4, 2)$ lies on the curve $y = \sqrt{x}$. If Q is the point $(x, \sqrt{x})$, use your calculator to find the slope of the secant line PQ (correct to six decimal places) for the value of $x = 3.99$.

Select the correct answer.

a. 0.250157 b. 0.250156 c. –0.250154 d. –0.250156 e. 0.250154

2. The displacement (in feet) of a certain particle moving in a straight line is given by $s = \frac{t^3}{8}$ where t is measured in seconds. Find the instantaneous velocity when $t = 3$.

3. Given that $\lim_{x\to 8} f(x) = -10$, and $\lim_{x\to 8} g(x) = 8$, evaluate the limit.

$$\lim_{x\to 8}\left(f(x) + g(x)\right)$$

4. If $\lim_{x\to 2^+} f(x) = 7.5$, then if $\lim_{x\to 2} f(x)$ exists, to what value does it converge?

Select the correct answer.

a. 5 b. 8.5 c. 8 d. 11.5 e. 7.5

5. If f and g are continuous functions with $f(2) = 3$ and $\lim_{x\to 2}\left[3f(x) - g(x)\right] = 5$, find $g(2)$.

6. Estimate the value of the limit by graphing the function $f(x) = (3\sin x)/(\sin \pi x)$. State your answer correct to two decimal places.

$$\lim_{x\to 0}\frac{3\sin x}{\sin \pi x}$$

7. Find the limit.

$$\lim_{x\to -\infty}\frac{\sqrt{x^2 - 9}}{2x - 6}$$

8. Evaluate the limit.

$$\lim_{x\to 0}\frac{(5 + x)^{-1} - 5^{-1}}{x}$$

9. How close to 2 do we have to take x so that $5x + 3$ is within a distance of 0.075 from 13?

10. Find the slope of the tangent line to the parabola $y = x^2 + 8x$ at the point (8, 128).

11. How would you define $f(1)$ in order to make f continuous at 1?

$$f(x) = \frac{x^3 - 1}{x^2 - 1}$$

12. If an equation of the tangent line to the curve $y = f(x)$ at the point where $a = 2$ is $y = 4x - 7$, find $f(2)$ and $f'(2)$.

13. Use a graph to find a number δ such that $\left| \sqrt{4x+1} - 3 \right| < 0.4$ whenever $\left| x - 2 \right| < \delta$.

Round down the answer to the nearest hundredth.

14. Evaluate the limit, if it exists.

$$\lim_{h \to 0} \frac{-(x+h)^3 + x^3}{h}$$

15. Write an equation that expresses the fact that a function f is continuous at the number 3.

16. Which of the given functions is discontinuous?

a. $f(x) = \begin{cases} \dfrac{1}{x-2}, & x \geq 5 \\ \dfrac{1}{3}, & x < 5 \end{cases}$ b. $f(x) = \begin{cases} \dfrac{1}{x-5}, & x \neq 5 \\ 3, & x = 5 \end{cases}$

17. If a ball is thrown into the air with a velocity of 62 ft/s, its height (in feet) after t seconds is given by

$H = 62t - 16t^2$.

Find the velocity when $t = 5$.

18. Use continuity to evaluate the limit.

$$\lim_{x \to 8\pi} \sin(x + 6 \sin x)$$

Select the correct answer.

a. ∞ b. -1 c. 1 d. 0 e. 8π

19. Find a function g that agrees with f for $x \neq 16$ and is continuous on $\Re$.

$$f(x) = \frac{4 - \sqrt{x}}{16 - x}$$

20. Find the value of $\lim_{x \to 0^+} f(x)$.

$$f(x) = \frac{1}{1 + 2^{1/x}}.$$

Select the correct answer.

a. –0.8 b. –0.5 c. 0.3 d. 0 e. 0.8

ANSWER KEY

Stewart - Calculus ET 7e Chapter 2 Form H

1. b

2. 3.375 ft/s

3. –2

4. e

5. 4

6. 0.95

7. –1/2

8. –1/25

9. $|x-2|< 0.015$

10. 24

11. $f(1)=\frac{3}{2}$

12. $f(2)=1$
 $f'(2)=4$

13. $\delta \le 0.56$

14. $-3x^2$

15. $\lim_{x\to 3} f(x) = f(3)$

16. b

17. –98 ft/s

18. d

19. $g(x)=\frac{1}{4+\sqrt{x}}$

20. d

1. Find f' in terms of g'.

$f(x) = x^2 g(x)$

2. Find the points on the curve $y = 2x^3 + 3x^2 - 12x + 1$ where the tangent is horizontal.

3. Find the equation of the tangent to the curve at the given point.

$y = \sqrt{1 + 4\sin x}$, $(0,1)$

4. Differentiate.

$g(x) = x^7 \cos x$

5. Differentiate the function.

$$G(u) = \ln\sqrt{\frac{3u+6}{3u-6}}$$

6. The height (in meters) of a projectile shot vertically upward from a point 2 m above ground level with an initial velocity of 24.5 m/s is $h = 2 + 24.5t - 4.9t^2$ after t seconds.

a) When does the projectile reach its maximum height?
b) What is the maximum height?

7. Use implicit differentiation to find an equation of the tangent line to the curve at the given point.

$y \sin 2x = x \cos 2y$, $(\pi/2, \pi/4)$

8. Calculate y'.

$y = \sqrt{x} \cos \sqrt{x}$

9. A spherical balloon is being inflated. Find the rate of increase of the surface area $S = 4\pi r^2$ with respect to the radius r when $r = 1$ ft.

10. Find the derivative of the function.

$y = 2\cos^{-1}\left(\sin^{-1} t\right)$

11. Find an equation of the tangent line to the curve.

$y = \frac{\sqrt{x}}{x+6}$ at $(4, 0.2)$

12. The top of a ladder slides down a vertical wall at a rate of 0.15 m/s. At the moment when the bottom of the ladder is 3 m from the wall, it slides away from the wall at a rate of 0.2 m/s. How long is the ladder?

13. Find the limit if $g(x) = x^5$.

$$\lim_{x\to 2} \frac{g(x) - g(2)}{x - 2}$$

14. A company makes computer chips from square wafers of silicon. It wants to keep the side length of a wafer very close to 16 mm. The area is $A(x)$. Find $A'(16)$.

15. Calculate y'.

$$xy^4 + x^2y = x + 3y$$

16. Find the first and the second derivatives of the function.

$$y = \frac{x}{3 - x}$$

17. Find the given derivative by finding the first few derivatives and observing the pattern that occurs.

$$\frac{d^{75}}{dx^{75}}(\sin x)$$

18. If $y = 2x^3 + 5x$ and $\frac{dx}{dt} = 3$, find $\frac{dy}{dt}$ when $x = 5$.

19. The volume of a cube is increasing at a rate of $10\,cm^3/\min$. How fast is the surface area increasing when the length of an edge is $30\,cm$.

20. If $f(x) = \frac{x}{\ln x}$, find $f'(e^3)$.

ANSWER KEY

Stewart - Calculus ET 7e Chapter 3 Form A

1. $f'(x) = 2xg(x) + x^2 g'(x)$

2. $(1, -6), (-2, 21)$

3. $y = 2x + 1$

4. $g'(x) = 7x^6 \cos(x) - x^7 \sin(x)$

5. $G'(u) = \dfrac{-2}{u^2 - 4}$

6. 2.5 s
32.625 m

7. $y = \dfrac{1}{2}x$

8. $y' = -\dfrac{1}{2}\left(\dfrac{\sqrt{x}\sin\sqrt{x} - \cos\sqrt{x}}{\sqrt{x}}\right)$

9. 8π

10. $y' = -\dfrac{2}{\sqrt{(1-t^2)\left(1-(\sin^{-1}(t))^2\right)}}$

11. $y = \dfrac{1}{200}(x-4) + 0.2$

12. 5 m

13. 80

14. 32

15. $y' = \dfrac{1 - y^4 - 2xy}{4xy^3 + x^2 - 3}$

16. $3(3-x)^{-2},\ 6(3-x)^{-3}$

17. $-\cos x$

18. 465

19. $\dfrac{4}{3}\ \text{cm}^2/\text{min}$

20. 2 / 9

1. Calculate y'.

$$y = \ln\left(x^2 e^x\right)$$

2. Differentiate.

$$K(x) = \left(2x^3 + 1\right)\left(x^4 - 2x\right)$$

3. Find the derivative of the function.

$$y = 3\cos^{-1}\left(\sin^{-1} t\right)$$

4. The position function of a particle is given by

$$s = t^3 - 10.5t^2 - 2t, \quad t \geq 0$$

When does the particle reach a velocity of 52 m/s?

5. Find f' in terms of g'.

$$f(x) = \left[g(x)\right]^2$$

6. Use the table to estimate the value of $h'(10.5)$, where $h(x) = f(g(x))$.

x	10	10.1	10.2	10.3	10.4	10.5	10.6
$f(x)$	4.5	3.5	5.6	4.3	2.5	9.9	7.8
$g(x)$	6.5	5.9	4.7	4.2	5.4	10.1	6.3

7. A spherical balloon is being inflated. Find the rate of increase of the surface area $S = 4\pi r^2$ with respect to the radius r when $r = 1$ ft.

8. If $h(2) = 7$ and $h'(2) = -2$, find $\left.\dfrac{d}{dx}\left(\dfrac{h(x)}{x}\right)\right|_{x=2}$

9. Differentiate.

$$y = \frac{\sin x}{7 + \cos x}$$

10. Differentiate.

$$y = \frac{\tan x - 2}{\sec x}$$

11. Find an equation of the tangent line to the curve $y = 3\tan x$ at the point $(\pi/4, 3)$.

12. Calculate y'.

$xe^y = y - 1$

13. Find the differential of the function.

$y = x^4 + 5x$

14. Find all points at which the tangent line is horizontal on the graph of the function.

$y(x) = 6\sin x + \sin^2 x$

15. Use implicit differentiation to find an equation of the tangent line to the curve at the given point.

$x\sin 2y = y\cos 2x, \quad (\pi/2, \pi/4)$

16. If $f(t) = \sqrt{4t+1}$, find $f''(2)$.

17. Find the equation of the tangent to the curve at the given point.

$y = \sqrt{1 + 4\sin x}, \quad (0,1)$

18. Find y''', if $y = \sqrt{2x+1}$.

19. Find the given derivative by finding the first few derivatives and observing the pattern that occurs.

$$\frac{d^{99}}{dx^{99}}(\sin x)$$

20. The top of a ladder slides down a vertical wall at a rate of 0.075 m/s. At the moment when the bottom of the ladder is 3 m from the wall, it slides away from the wall at a rate of 0.1 m/s. How long is the ladder?

ANSWER KEY

Stewart - Calculus ET 7e Chapter 3 Form B

1. $y' = \frac{2}{x} + 1$

2. $6x^2\left(x^4 - 2x\right) + \left(2x^3 + 1\right)\left(4x^3 - 2\right)$

3. $y' = -\frac{3}{\sqrt{(1-t^2)\left(1-(\sin^{-1}(t))^2\right)}}$

4. 9

5. $f'(x) = 2g(x)g'(x)$

6. 24.75

7. 8π

8. –2.75

9. $\frac{dy}{dx} = \frac{7\cos x + 1}{(7 + \cos x)^2}$

10. $\frac{dy}{dx} = \cos(x) + 2\sin(x)$

11. $y = 6x + 3\left(1 - \frac{\pi}{2}\right)$

12. $y' = -\frac{e^y}{xe^y - 1}$

13. $dy = \left(4x^3 + 5 \right) dx$

14. $\left(\left(\frac{\pi}{2}\right) + 2\pi n, 7\right), \left(\frac{3\pi}{2} + 2\pi n, -5\right)$

15. $y = -x + 3\pi / 4$

16. $f''(2) = -\frac{4}{27}$

17. $y = 2x + 1$

18. $3(2x + 1)^{-5/2}$

19. $-\cos x$

20. 5 m

1. Find f' in terms of g'.

$f(x) = x^2 g(x)$

Select the correct answer.

a. $f'(x) = 2xg(x) + x^2 g'(x)$
b. $f'(x) = 2x + g'(x)$
c. $f'(x) = x^2 g(x) + 2x^2 g'(x)$
d. $f'(x) = 2xg'(x)$
e. $f'(x) = 2xf'(x) + 2xg'(x)$

2. Find the equation of the tangent to the curve at the given point.

$y = \sqrt{1 + 4\sin x}$, $(0,1)$

Select the correct answer.

a. $y = 4x + 4$ b. $y = 2x + 4$ c. $y = 1 - 2x$ d. $y = 4x + 1$ e. $y = 2x + 1$

3. Calculate y'.

$y = \ln\left(x^2 e^x\right)$

Select the correct answer.

a. $y' = \frac{2}{x} + 1$
b. $y' = \frac{2}{x} + 2$
c. $y' = 3x^2$
d. $y' = x \ln 2x + x^2$
e. $y' = \frac{2e^x + x \ln x^2}{x}$

4. Calculate y'.

$y = \frac{e^x}{x^2}$

Select the correct answer.

a. $y' = \frac{e^x}{2x}$ b. $y' = e^x\left(\frac{x-1}{x^4}\right)$ c. $y' = e^x\left(\frac{x-2}{x^3}\right)$ d. $y' = e^x\left(\frac{x+2}{x^3}\right)$ e. $y' = e^x\left(\frac{x-2}{2x}\right)$

5. Find equations of the tangent lines to the curve $y = \dfrac{x-8}{x+8}$ that are parallel to the line $x - y = 8$.

Select all that apply.

a. $x - y = -17$
b. $x - y = -12$
c. $x - y = -15$
d. $x - y = -1$
e. $x - y = -4$

6. The height (in meters) of a projectile shot vertically upward from a point 1.5 m above ground level with an initial velocity of 25.48 m/s is $h = 1.5 + 25.48t - 4.9t^2$ after t seconds.

a) When does the projectile reach its maximum height?
b) What is the maximum height?

Select the correct answer.

a. 2.8 s, 34.428 m
b. 2.6 s, 34.624 m
c. 2 s, 32.86 m
d. 2.4 s, 34.428 m
e. 2.3 s, 34.183 m

7. The mass of the part of a metal rod that lies between its left end and a point x meters to the right is $S = 4x^2$. Find the linear density when x is 1 m.

Select the correct answer.

a. 4 b. 16 c. 8 d. 12 e. 18

8. If f is the focal length of a convex lens and an object is placed at a distance v from the lens, then its image will be at a distance u from the lens, where f, v, and u are related by the *lens equation* $\dfrac{1}{f} = \dfrac{1}{v} + \dfrac{1}{u}$.

Find the rate of change of v with respect to u.

Select the correct answer.

a. $\dfrac{dv}{du} = -\dfrac{f}{(u-f)^2}$

b. $\dfrac{dv}{du} = -\dfrac{f^2}{(u-f)^2}$

c. $\dfrac{dv}{du} = -\dfrac{f^2}{u-f}$

d. $\dfrac{dv}{du} = \dfrac{f^2}{(u-f)^2}$

e. $\dfrac{dv}{du} = \dfrac{2f^2}{(u-f)^2}$

9. Use implicit differentiation to find an equation of the tangent line to the curve at the given point.

$y \sin 2x = x \cos 2y, \quad (\pi/2, \pi/4)$

Select the correct answer.

a. $y = x/4 + \pi/8$ b. $y = x/4$ c. $y = x/2$ d. $y = 2x - 3\pi/4$ e. $y = -x/2 + \pi/2$

10. Evaluate.

$$\lim_{x \to \infty} \frac{\sinh x}{e^x}$$

Select the correct answer.

a. $-\infty$ b. $1/2$ c. ∞ d. 0 e. $-1/2$

11. If $f(x) = \dfrac{x}{\ln x}$, find $f'(e^3)$.

Select the correct answer.

a. 9/2 b. 3/2 c. 2/9 d. $e^3/9$ e. 0.3

12. Suppose that $F(x) = f(g(x))$ and $g(14) = 2,\ g'(14) = 5,\ f'(14) = 15$, and $f'(2) = 12$.

Find $F'(14)$.

Select the correct answer.

a. 60 b. 140 c. 24 d. 17 e. 20

13. Gravel is being dumped from a conveyor belt at a rate of 35 ft^3/min and its coarseness is such that it forms a pile in the shape of a cone whose base diameter and height are always equal. How fast is the height of the pile increasing when the pile is 15 ft high? Round the result to the nearest hundredth.

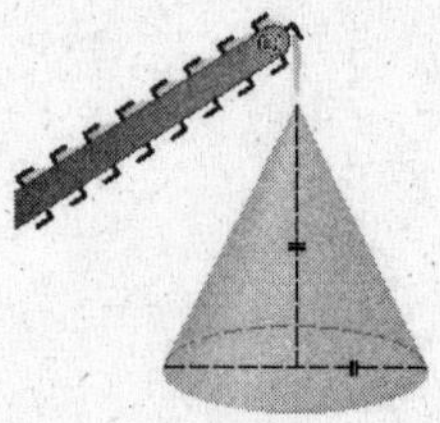

Select the correct answer.

a. 0.27 ft/min b. 1.24 ft/min c. 0.14 ft/min d. 0.2 ft/min e. 0.6 ft/min

14. If $f(t)=\sqrt{4t+1}$, find $f''(2)$.

Select the correct answer.

a. $-\frac{4}{27}$ b. 3 c. $-\frac{2}{3}$ d. $\frac{2}{3}$ e. $\frac{4}{27}$

15. If $y=2x^3+6x$ and $\frac{dx}{dt}=6$, find $\frac{dy}{dt}$ when $x=5$.

Select the correct answer.

a. 948 b. 836 c. 946 d. 928 e. none of these

16. Use differentials to estimate the amount of paint needed to apply a coat of paint 0.18 cm thick to a hemispherical dome with diameter 60 m.

Select the correct answer.

a. 2.52π b. 3.24π c. 3.82π d. 2.28π e. 4.11π

17. Calculate y' .

$xy^4+x^2y=x+3y$

Select the correct answer.

a. $y'=\frac{-y^4-2xy}{4xy^3+x^2}$

b. $y'=\frac{1-y^4-2xy}{4xy^3+x^2-3}$

c. $y'=-\frac{xy^3+2x-3}{x^2y^2(4x-1)}$

d. $y'=-\frac{1-y^4-2x^2}{4xy^3+x^2-3}$

e. none of these

18. The top of a ladder slides down a vertical wall at a rate of 0.15 m/s . At the moment when the bottom of the ladder is 1.5 m from the wall, it slides away from the wall at a rate of 0.2 m/s . How long is the ladder?

Select the correct answer.

a. 2 m b. 2.5 m c. 2.3 m d. 2.8 m e. none of these

19. Let $C(t)$ be the total value of US currency (coins and banknotes) in circulation at time. The table gives values of this function from 1980 to 2000, as of September 30, in billions of dollars. Estimate the value of $C'(1990)$.

t	1980	1985	1990	1995	2000
$C(t)$	129.9	187.3	271.9	409.3	568.6

Select the correct answer. Answers are in billions of dollars per year.

a. 16.92
b. 27.48
c. 44.4
d. 22.2
e. 137.4

20. Find the derivative of the function.

$$y = 2\cos^{-1}\left(\sin^{-1} t\right)$$

Select the correct answer.

a. $y' = -\dfrac{2}{\sqrt{1-(\sin^{-1}(t))^2}}$

b. $y' = -\dfrac{2}{\sqrt{(1-t^2)}}$

c. $y' = -\dfrac{2}{\sqrt{(1+t^2)\left(1+(\sin^{-1}(t))^2\right)}}$

d. $y' = -\dfrac{2}{\sqrt{(1-t^2)\left(1-(\sin^{-1}(t))^2\right)}}$

e. $y' = -\dfrac{2}{\sqrt{(1-t^2)\left(1-\sin^{-1}(t)\right)}}$

ANSWER KEY

Stewart - Calculus ET 7e Chapter 3 Form C

1. a
2. e
3. a
4. c
5. a, d
6. b
7. c
8. b
9. c
10. b
11. c
12. a
13. d
14. a
15. e
16. b
17. b
18. b
19. d
20. d

1. The height (in meters) of a projectile shot vertically upward from a point 1.5 m above ground level with an initial velocity of 25.48 m/s is $h = 1.5 + 25.48t - 4.9t^2$ after t seconds.

a) When does the projectile reach its maximum height?
b) What is the maximum height?

Select the correct answer.

a.	b.	c.	d.	e.
2.8 s 34.428 m	2.6 s 34.624 m	2 s 32.86 m	2.4 s 34.428 m	2.3 s 34.183 m

2. If $f(x) = 4\cos x + \sin^2 x$, find $f'(x)$ and $f''(x)$.

Select all correct answers.

a. $f''(x) = -4\cos(x) + 2\cos(2x)$
b. $f''(x) = -2\cos(2x) + 4\cos(x)$
c. $f'(x) = -4\sin(2x) + \sin(x)$
d. $f'(x) = -4\sin(x) + \sin(2x)$
e. $f''(x) = -4\cos(2x) + 2\cos(x)$

3. Find the derivative of the function.

$y = (3x+1)^3(x^4-6)^5$

Select the correct answer.

a. $y' = (20x+9)(3x+1)^3(x^4-6)^5$
b. $y' = 9(3x+1)^2(x^4-6)^5 + 20x^3(3x+1)^3(x^4-6)^4$
c. $y' = 9(3x+1)^2(x^4-6)^5 + 20x(3x+1)^3(x^4-6)^5$
d. $y' = 9(3x+1)^2(x^4-6)^5 + (3x+1)^3(x^4-6)^5$
e. $y' = (x+1)^2(x^4-6)^5 + 20x(3x+1)^3(x^3-6)^4$

4. The equation of motion is given for a particle, where s is in meters and t is in seconds. Find the acceleration after 4.5 seconds.

$s = \sin 2\pi t$

Select the correct answer.

a. $9\pi \text{ m/}s^2$
b. $-9\pi \text{ m/}s^2$
c. $0 \text{ m/}s^2$
d. $81\pi^2 \text{ m/}s^2$
e. $-81\pi^2 \text{ m/}s^2$

5. Use implicit differentiation to find an equation of the tangent line to the curve at the given point.

$y\sin 2x = x\cos 2y, \quad (\pi/2, \pi/4)$

Select the correct answer.

a. $y = x/4 + \pi/8$
b. $y = x/4$
c. $y = x/2$
d. $y = 2x - 3\pi/4$
e. $y = -x/2 + \pi/2$

6. Find the derivative of the function.

$y = 2\cos^{-1}\left(\sin^{-1} t\right)$

Select the correct answer.

a. $y' = -\dfrac{2}{\sqrt{1-(\sin^{-1}(t))^2}}$

b. $y' = -\dfrac{2}{\sqrt{(1-t^2)}}$

c. $y' = -\dfrac{2}{\sqrt{(1+t^2)\left(1+(\sin^{-1}(t))^2\right)}}$

d. $y' = -\dfrac{2}{\sqrt{(1-t^2)\left(1-(\sin^{-1}(t))^2\right)}}$

e. $y' = -\dfrac{2}{\sqrt{(1-t^2)\left(1-\sin^{-1}(t)\right)}}$

7. Use logarithmic differentiation to find the derivative of the function.

$y = x^{6x}$

Select the correct answer.

a. $y' = 6x^{6x}(6\ln x + 1)$
b. $y' = 6(\ln x + 1)$
c. $y' = 6x^{6x}(\ln x + 1)$
d. $y' = -6x^{6x}(\ln x + 6)$
e. $y' = x^{x}(\ln 6x + 1)$

8. Use the linear approximation of the function $f(x) = \sqrt{9-x}$ at $a = 0$ to approximate the number $\sqrt{9.09}$.

Select the correct answer.

a. 3.02 b. 0.15 c. 7.44 d. 7.4 e. 2.25

9. Determine the values of x for which the given linear approximation is accurate to within 0.07 at $a = 0$.

$\tan x \approx x$

Select the correct answer.

a. $-0.71 < x < 0.48$
b. $0.06 < x < 0.68$
c. $-1.04 < x < 1.55$
d. $-0.57 < x < 0.57$
e. $-0.19 < x < 0.28$

10. A turkey is removed from the oven when its temperature reaches $175\,^{\circ}F$ and is placed on a table in a room where the temperature is $70\,^{\circ}F$. After 10 minutes the temperature of the turkey is $160\,^{\circ}F$ and after 20 minutes it is $150\,^{\circ}F$. Use a linear approximation to predict the temperature of the turkey after half an hour.

Select the correct answer.

a. 36 b. 130 c. 134 d. 140 e. 160

11. Two cars start moving from the same point. One travels south at 28 mi/h and the other travels west at 70 mi/h. At what rate is the distance between the cars increasing 5 hours later? Round the result to the nearest hundredth.

Select the correct answer.

a. 75.42 mi/h b. 75.49 mi/h c. 76.4 mi/h d. 75.39 mi/h e. 75.38 mi/h

12. The top of a ladder slides down a vertical wall at a rate of 0.15 m/s. At the moment when the bottom of the ladder is 1.5 m from the wall, it slides away from the wall at a rate of 0.2 m/s. How long is the ladder?

Select the correct answer.

a. 2 m
b. 2.5 m
c. 2.3 m
d. 2.8 m
e. none of these

13. Use logarithmic differentiation to find the derivative of the function.

$$y = \sqrt[5]{\frac{x^2+1}{x^2-1}}$$

Select the correct answer.

a. $y' = -\dfrac{4x}{5(x^4-1)}\sqrt[5]{\dfrac{x^2+1}{x^2-1}}$

b. $y' = -\dfrac{5x}{(x^4-1)}\sqrt[5]{\dfrac{x^2+1}{x^2-1}}$

c. $y' = -\dfrac{20x}{x^4-1}$

d. $y' = -\dfrac{20x}{x^4-1}\sqrt[5]{\dfrac{x^2+1}{x^2-1}}$

e. $y' = \dfrac{5x}{4x^4-1}\sqrt[5]{\dfrac{x^2+1}{x^2-1}}$

14. A plane flying horizontally at an altitude of 2 mi and a speed of 490 mi/h passes directly over a radar station. Find the rate at which the distance from the plane to the station is increasing when it is 10 mi away from the station.

Select the correct answer.

a. ≈ 495 mi/h b. ≈ 480 mi/h c. ≈ 455 mi/h d. ≈ 970 mi/h e. ≈ 870 mi/h

15. Two sides of a triangle are 2 m and 3 m in length and the angle between them is increasing at a rate of 0.03 rad/s. Find the rate at which the area of the triangle is increasing when the angle between the sides of fixed length is $\pi/3$.

Select the correct answer.

a. 5.045 m^2/s b. –0.955 m^2/s c. 0.045 m^2/s d. –1.955 m^2/s e. 1.145 m^2/s

16. If two resistors with resistances R_1 and R_2 are connected in parallel, as in the figure, then the total resistance R measured in ohms (Ω), is given by $\dfrac{1}{R} = \dfrac{1}{R_1} + \dfrac{1}{R_2}$. If R_1 and R_2 are increasing at rates of 0.1 Ω/s and 0.4 Ω/s respectively, how fast is R changing when $R_1 = 75$ and $R_2 = 100$? Round the result to the nearest thousandth.

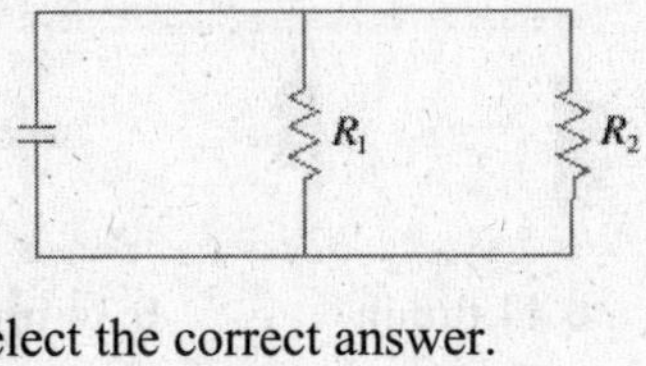

Select the correct answer.

a. 0.159 Ω/s b. 0.145 Ω/s c. 1.196 Ω/s d. 0.106 Ω/s e. 0.168 Ω/s

17. Find the average rate of change of the area of a circle with respect to its radius r as r changes from 5 to 6.

Select the correct answer.

a. 11π b. 6π c. 36π d. 12π e. 8π

18. Find the given derivative by finding the first few derivatives and observing the pattern that occurs.

$$\frac{d^{89}}{dx^{89}}(\sin x)$$

Select the correct answer.

a. $\cos x$ b. $-\cos x$ c. $\sin x$ d. $-\sin x$ e. none of these

19. Find $\frac{d^4}{dx^4}(x^3 \ln x)$.

Select the correct answer.

a. $\frac{d^4}{dx^4}(x^3 \ln x) = \frac{6}{x^4}$

b. $\frac{d^4}{dx^4}(x^3 \ln x) = \frac{3}{x^4}$

c. $\frac{d^4}{dx^4}(x^3 \ln x) = \frac{3}{x}$

d. $\frac{d^4}{dx^4}(x^3 \ln x) = \frac{6}{x}$

e. $\frac{d^4}{dx^4}(x^3 \ln x) = \frac{6}{x^2}$

20. Gravel is being dumped from a conveyor belt at a rate of 30 ft^3/min and its coarseness is such that it forms a pile in the shape of a cone whose base diameter and height are always equal. How fast is the height of the pile increasing when the pile is 12 ft high? Round the result to the nearest hundredth.

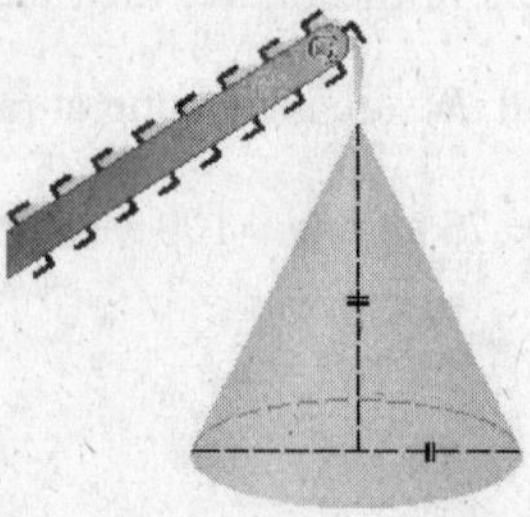

Select the correct answer.

a. 0.21 ft/min b. 1.31 ft/min c. 0.27 ft/min d. 0.44 ft/min e. 0.34 ft/min

ANSWER KEY

Stewart - Calculus ET 7e Chapter 3 Form D

1. b

2. a, d

3. b

4. c

5. c

6. d

7. c

8. a

9. d

10. d

11. d

12. b

13. a

14. b

15. c

16. d

17. a

18. a

19. d

20 c

1. Find f' in terms of g'.

$f(x) = [g(x)]^2$

Select the correct answer.

a. $f'(x) = 2[g'(x)]^3$
b. $f'(x) = 2g(x)g'(x)$
c. $f'(x) = 2[gx][xg' + g]$
d. $f'(x) = 2g(x)$
e. $f'(x) = 2g'(x)$

2. The height (in meters) of a projectile shot vertically upward from a point 1.5 m above ground level with an initial velocity of 25.48 m/s is $h = 1.5 + 25.48t - 4.9t^2$ after t seconds.

a) When does the projectile reach its maximum height?
b) What is the maximum height?

3. If $f(0) = 4, f'(0) = 2, g(0) = 3$ and $g'(0) = -5$, find $(f + g)'(0)$.

Select the correct answer.

a. –11 b. –12 c. 2 d. –3 e. –4 f. –1

4. Find y' by implicit differentiation.

$8 \cos x \sin y = 7$

5. Find the derivative of the function.

$y = \cos^{-1}\left(\sin^{-1} t\right)$

6. Calculate y'.

$xe^y = y - 1$

7. Use implicit differentiation to find an equation of the tangent line to the curve at the given point.

$y \sin 2x = x \cos 2y, \quad (\pi/2, \pi/4)$

8. Let $C(t)$ be the total value of US currency (coins and banknotes) in circulation at time. The table gives values of this function from 1980 to 2000, as of September 30, in billions of dollars. Estimate the value of $C'(1990)$.

t	1980	1985	1990	1995	2000
$C(t)$	129.9	187.3	271.9	409.3	568.6

Select the correct answer.

a. 16.92 b. 27.48 c. 44.4 d. 22.2 e. 137.4

9. The mass of part of a wire is $x(1+\sqrt{x})$ kilograms, where x is measured in meters from one end of the wire. Find the linear density of the wire when $x = 16\,m$.

Select the correct answer.

a. 6 kg / m
b. 4 kg / m
c. 7 kg / m
d. 1.5 kg / m
e. none of these

10. Find an equation of the tangent line to the curve $4x^2 + 3y^2 = 7$ at the point (1, 1).

11. If a tank holds 5000 gallons of water, and that water can drain from the tank in 40 minutes, then Torricelli's Law gives the volume V of water remaining in the tank after t minutes as $V = 5000\left(1-\frac{t}{40}\right)^2$. Find the rate at which water is draining from the tank after 6 minutes.

12. The quantity Q of charge in coulombs C that has passed through a point in a wire up to time t (measured in seconds), is given by $Q(t) = t^3 - 4t^2 + 4t + 10$.

Find the current when $t = 2\,\text{s}$.

13. The volume of a cube is increasing at a rate of $10\,cm^3/\text{min}$. How fast is the surface area increasing when the length of an edge is $30\,cm$.

14. Find the derivative of $f(x)$.

$f(x) = x\cosh x$

15. Newton's Law of Gravitation says that the magnitude F of the force exerted by a body of mass m on a body of mass M is $F = \frac{GmM}{r^2}$.

Find $\frac{dF}{dr}(5)$.

16. Differentiate.

$g(x) = 5\sec x + \tan x$

17. Evaluate

$$\lim_{x\to\infty} \frac{\sinh x}{e^x}$$

18. The displacement of a particle on a vibrating string is given by the equation $s(t) = 8 + \frac{1}{7}\sin(4\pi t)$ where s is measured in centimeter and t in seconds. Find the velocity of the particle after t seconds.

19. Find the given derivative by finding the first few derivatives and observing the pattern that occurs.

$$\frac{d^{25}}{dx^{25}}(\sin x)$$

20. A baseball diamond is a square with side 90 ft. A batter hits the ball and runs toward first base with a speed of 30 ft/s. At what rate is his distance from second base decreasing when he is halfway to first base? Round the result to the nearest hundredth.

ANSWER KEY

Stewart - Calculus ET 7e Chapter 3 Form E

1. b

2. 2.6 s
34.624 m

3. d

4. $\tan(x)\tan(y)$

5. $y' = -\dfrac{1}{\sqrt{(1-t^2)\left(1-(\sin^{-1}(t))^2\right)}}$

6. $y' = -\dfrac{e^y}{xe^y - 1}$

7. $y = \dfrac{1}{2}x$

8. d

9. c

10. $y = -\dfrac{4}{3}x + \dfrac{7}{3}$

11. –212.5

12. 0

13. $\dfrac{4}{3}cm^2$ / min

14. $\cosh(x) + x\sinh(x)$

15. $\dfrac{-2GmM}{125}$

16. $g'(x) = 5\sec(x)\tan(x) + \sec^2 x$

17. $\dfrac{1}{2}$

18. $\dfrac{4\pi}{7}\cos(4\pi t)$

19. $\cos x$

20. 13.42 ft/s

1. If f is a differentiable function, find an expression for the derivative of $y = x^7 f(x)$.

Select the correct answer.

a. $\frac{d}{dx}\left(x^7 f(x)\right) = 7x^6 f(x) + x^7 f'(x)$

b. $\frac{d}{dx}\left(x^7 f(x)\right) = 7x^7 f(x) + x^6 f'(x)$

c. $\frac{d}{dx}\left(x^7 f(x)\right) = 7x^6 f(x) - x^7 f'(x)$

d. $\frac{d}{dx}\left(x^7 f(x)\right) = 7x^7 f(x) - x^6 f'(x)$

e. $\frac{d}{dx}\left(x^7 f(x)\right) = 6x^6 f(x) - x^7 f'(x)$

2. Find the given derivative by finding the first few derivatives and observing the pattern that occurs.

$$\frac{d^{99}}{dx^{99}}(\sin x)$$

3. Calculate y'.

$$y = \ln\left(x^2 e^x\right)$$

Select the correct answer.

a. $y' = \dfrac{2e^{2x} + e^x(\ln x^2)}{x}$ b. $y' = \dfrac{2}{x} + 1$ c. $y' = \dfrac{2e^x}{x} + 1$ d. $y = \dfrac{e^x \ln x^2}{2}$ e. none of these

4. Find the tangent line to the ellipse $\dfrac{x^2}{16} + \dfrac{y^2}{4} = 1$ at the point $\left(2, -\sqrt{3}\right)$.

Select the correct answer.

a. $y = \sqrt{3}x - 4$ b. $y = -\sqrt{6}x - 3$ c. $y = \dfrac{\sqrt{3}}{3}x - 4$ d. $y = \dfrac{\sqrt{3}}{6}x - \dfrac{4\sqrt{3}}{3}$ e. none of these

5. If $f(x) = \dfrac{x}{\ln x}$, find $f'(e^3)$.

6. Find the derivative of the function.

$$y = 3\cos^{-1}\left(\sin^{-1} t\right)$$

7. Suppose that $F(x) = f(g(x))$ and $g(17) = 13$, $g'(17) = 15$, $f'(17) = 2$, and $f'(13) = 6$.

Find $F'(17)$.

8. Calculate y'.

$$xy^4 + x^2y = x + 3y$$

Select the correct answer.

a. $y' = \dfrac{-y^4 - 2xy}{4xy^3 + x^2}$

b. $y' = \dfrac{1 - y^4 - 2xy}{4xy^3 + x^2 - 3}$

c. $y' = -\dfrac{xy^3 + 2x - 3}{x^2y^2(4x - 1)}$

d. $y' = -\dfrac{1 - y^4 - 2x^2}{4xy^3 + x^2 - 3}$

e. none of these

9. The table lists the amount of U.S. cash per capita in circulation as of June 30 in the given year. Use a linear approximation to estimate the amount of cash per capita in circulation in the year 2000.

t	1960	1970	1980	1990
$C(t)$	\$172	\$254	\$571	\$1,068

10. Use the linear approximation of the function $f(x) = \sqrt{7 - x}$ at $a = 0$ to approximate the number $\sqrt{7.1}$.

11. Find an equation of the tangent line to the curve.

$$y = \frac{\sqrt{x}}{x + 6} \quad \text{at } (4, 0.2)$$

12. The height (in meters) of a projectile shot vertically upward from a point 2 m above ground level with an initial velocity of 24.5 m/s is $h = 2 + 24.5t - 4.9t^2$ after t seconds.

a) When does the projectile reach its maximum height?
b) What is the maximum height?

13. A company makes computer chips from square wafers of silicon. It wants to keep the side length of a wafer very close to 19 mm. The area is $A(x)$. Find $A'(19)$.

14. The volume of a cube is increasing at a rate of 10 cm^3/min. How fast is the surface area increasing when the length of an edge is 30 cm.

15. If $f(t)=\sqrt{4t+1}$, find $f''(2)$.

Select the correct answer.

a. $-\frac{4}{27}$ b. 3 c. $-\frac{2}{3}$ d. $\frac{2}{3}$ e. $\frac{4}{27}$

16. The quantity Q of charge in coulombs C that has passed through a point in a wire up to time t (measured in seconds) is given by $Q(t)=t^3-3t^2+4t+3$. Find the current when $t=2$ s.

Select the correct answer.

a. 13 b. 4 c. 2 d. 3 e. 1

17. Newton's Law of Gravitation says that the magnitude F of the force exerted by a body of mass m on a body of mass M is $F=\dfrac{GmM}{r^2}$.

Find $\dfrac{dF}{dr}(6)$.

18. Use implicit differentiation to find an equation of the tangent line to the curve at the given point.

$x\sin 2y = y\cos 2x, \quad (\pi/2, \pi/4)$

19. Use differentials to estimate the amount of paint needed to apply a coat of paint 0.18 cm thick to a hemispherical dome with diameter 60 m.

Select the correct answer.

a. 2.52π b. 3.24π c. 3.82π d. 2.28π e. 4.11π

20. Two carts, A and B, are connected by a rope 40 ft long that passes over a pulley (see the figure below). The point Q is on the floor 10 ft directly beneath and between the carts. Cart A is being pulled away from Q at a speed of 5 ft/s. How fast is cart B moving toward Q at the instant when cart A is 8 ft from Q?

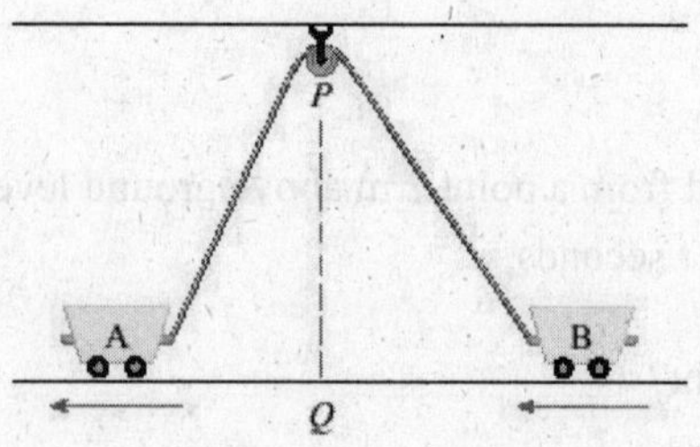

ANSWER KEY

Stewart - Calculus ET 7e Chapter 3 Form F

1. a

2. $-\cos x$

3. b

4. d

5. 2/9

6. $y' = -\dfrac{3}{\sqrt{(1-t^2)\left(1-(\sin^{-1}(t))^2\right)}}$

7. 90

8. b

9. 1565

10. 2.66

11. $y = \frac{1}{200}(x-4)+0.2$

12. 2.5 s
32.625 m

13. 38

14. $\frac{4}{3}\ \text{cm}^2/\text{min}$

15. a

16. b

17. $\dfrac{-2GmM}{216}$

18. $y = -x + 3\pi/4$

19. b

20. 3.36 ft/s

1. Find $f'(a)$.

$f(x) = 10 + x - 5x^2$

2. Differentiate the function.

$B(y) = cy^{-6}$

Select the correct answer.

a. $B'(y) = \dfrac{7c}{y^6}$ b. $B'(y) = -\dfrac{c}{6y^7}$ c. $B'(y) = -\dfrac{6c^7}{y}$ d. $B'(y) = -\dfrac{6c}{y^7}$ e. $B'(y) = -\dfrac{7c}{y^6}$

3. Find the equation of the tangent line to the given curve at the specified point.

$y = 4xe^x$, $(0,0)$

a. $y = 4x$
b. $y = 4x + e^4$
c. $y = 0$
d. $y = 4e^x + 4$
e. $y = x + 4$

4. Find the given derivative by finding the first few derivatives and observing the pattern that occurs.

$$\frac{d^{30}}{dx^{30}}(\sin x)$$

5. Differentiate.

$Y(u) = (u^{-2} + u^{-3})(2u^5 - u^3)$

6. Differentiate the function.

$$G(u) = \ln\sqrt{\frac{3u+6}{3u-6}}$$

7. The position function of a particle is given by $s = t^3 - 3t^2 - 5t,\ t \geq 0$.

When does the particle reach a velocity of 139 m/s?

8. The height (in meters) of a projectile shot vertically upward from a point 2 m above ground level with an initial velocity of 24.5 m/s is $h = 2 + 24.5t - 4.9t^2$ after t seconds.

a) When does the projectile reach its maximum height?
b) What is the maximum height?

9. The mass of part of a wire is $x(1+\sqrt{x})$ kilograms, where x is measured in meters from one end of the wire. Find the linear density of one the wire when $x = 4\text{ m}$.

10. A mass on a spring vibrates horizontally on a smooth level surface (see the figure). Its equation of motion is $x(t) = 3\sin t$, where t is in seconds and x in centimeters.

Find the velocity at time t.

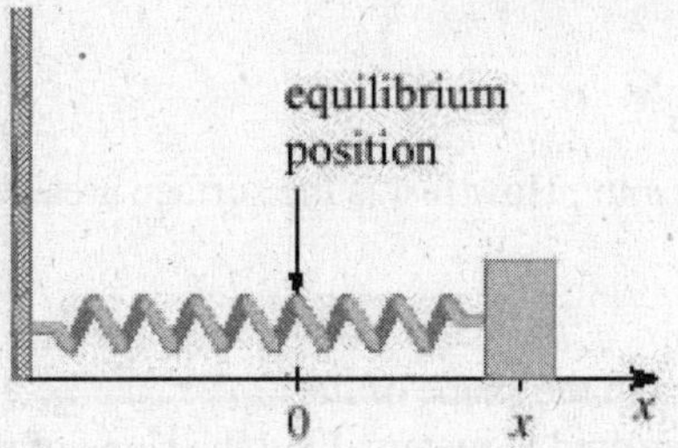

Select the correct answer.

a. $v(t) = \cos 3t$
b. $v(t) = \sin 3t$
c. $v(t) = 3\sin 3t$
d. $v(t) = 3\cos t$
e. $v(t) = 2\cos 3t$

11. Find the equation of the tangent to the curve at the given point.

$y = \sqrt{1+4\sin x}$, $(0,1)$

12. If a snowball melts so that its surface area decreases at a rate of 4 cm^2/min, find the rate at which the diameter decreases when the diameter is 39 cm.

13. Two cars start moving from the same point. One travels south at 27 mi/h and the other travels west at 50 mi/h. At what rate is the distance between the cars increasing 3 hours later? Round the result to the nearest hundredth.

14. The top of a ladder slides down a vertical wall at a rate of 0.15 m/s. At the moment when the bottom of the ladder is 3 m from the wall, it slides away from the wall at a rate of 0.2 m/s. How long is the ladder?

15. The altitude of a triangle is increasing at a rate of 3 cm/min while the area of the triangle is increasing at a rate of 4 cm^2/min. At what rate is the base of the triangle changing when the altitude is 10 cm and the area is 90 cm^2.

16. A water trough is 20 m long and a cross–section has the shape of an isosceles trapezoid that is 20 cm wide at the bottom, 60 cm wide at the top, and has height 50 cm. If the trough is being filled with water at the rate of 0.7 m^3/min, how fast is the water level rising when the water is 45 cm deep? Round the result to the nearest hundredth.

17. A boat is pulled into a dock by a rope attached to the bow of the boat and passing through a pulley on the dock that is 1 m higher than the bow of the boat. If the rope is pulled in at a rate of 2 m/s how fast is the boat approaching the dock when it is 3 m from the dock? Round the result to the nearest hundredth if necessary.

18. The volume of a cube is increasing at a rate of $10\,cm^3\,/\,\text{min}$. How fast is the surface area increasing when the length of an edge is $30\,cm$.

19. A telephone line hangs between two poles at 12 m apart in the shape of the catenary $y = 30\cosh(x/30) - 25$, where x and y are measured in meters. Find the slope of this curve where it meets the right pole.

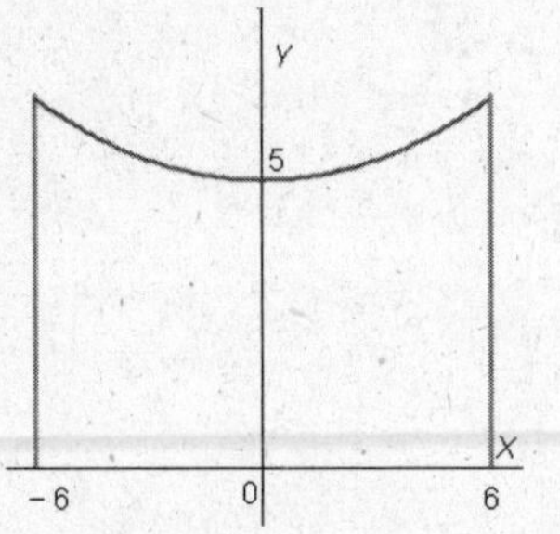

Select the correct answer.

a. $\sinh\left(\frac{5}{6}\right)$ b. $\sinh 6$ c. $\frac{\sinh 5}{6}$ d. $\sinh\left(\frac{1}{5}\right)$ e. $\sinh\left(\frac{1}{6}\right)$

20. The circumference of a sphere was measured to be 90 cm with a possible error of 0.5 cm. Use differentials to estimate the maximum error in the calculated volume.

ANSWER KEY

Stewart - Calculus ET 7e Chapter 3 Form G

1. $1-10a$

2. d

3. a

4. $-\sin x$

5. $Y'(u)=6u^2+4u-1$

6. $G'(u)=-\dfrac{2}{u^2-4}$

7. 8

8. 2.5 s
32.625 m

9. 4 kg / m

10. d

11. $y=2x+1$

12. $\dfrac{2}{39\pi}$

13. 56.82

14. 5 m

15. –4.6

16. 6.25 cm/min

17. 2.11

18. $\dfrac{4}{3}$ cm^2 / min

19. d

20. 205

1. Find the limit if $g(x) = x^5$.

$$\lim_{x \to 2} \frac{g(x) - g(2)}{x - 2}$$

2. Differentiate the function.

$$f(t) = \frac{1}{3}t^6 - 2t^4 + t$$

3. Find an equation of the tangent line to the curve $15(x^2 + y^2)^2 = 289(x^2 - y^2)$ at the point (4, 1).

Select the correct answer.

a. $y = -1.11x + 17$
b. $y = -1.11x + 3.43$
c. $y = -1.11x + 5.43$
d. $y = 1.11x + 5.43$
e. none of these

4. In this exercise we estimate the rate at which the total personal income is rising in the Richmond-Petersburg, Virginia, metropolitan area. In 1999, the population of this area was 961,600, and the population was increasing at roughly 9,400 people per year. The average annual income was $30,591 per capita, and this average was increasing at about $1,300 per year (a little above the national average of about $1,225 yearly). Use the Product Rule and these figures to estimate the rate at which total personal income was rising in the Richmond-Petersburg area in 1999.

5. The mass of the part of a metal rod that lies between its left end and a point x meters to the right is $S = 3x^2$.

Find the linear density when x is 1 m.

Select the correct answer.

a. 9 b. 3 c. 6 d. 2 e. 1

6. Use implicit differentiation to find an equation of the tangent line to the curve at the given point.

$x \sin 2y = y \cos 2x, \quad (\pi/2, \pi/4)$

7. Refer to the law of laminar flow. Consider a blood vessel with radius 0.01 cm, length 3 cm, pressure difference 3,500 dynes/ cm^2 and viscosity $\eta = 0.028$.

Find the velocity of the blood at radius $r = 0.004$.

8. Differentiate.

$g(x) = 8 \sec x + \tan x$

9. Find an equation of the tangent line to the curve $y = \sec x - 9 \cos x$ at the point $(\pi/3, -2.5)$.

10. Find the limit.

$$\lim_{\theta \to 0} \frac{\sin(\sin \theta)}{\sec \theta}$$

11. Use logarithmic differentiation to find the derivative of the function.

$$y = \sqrt[3]{\frac{x^2+1}{x^2-1}}$$

12. Find the given derivative by finding the first few derivatives and observing the pattern that occurs.

$$\frac{d^{89}}{dx^{89}}(\sin x)$$

13. Find y'.

$$y = \ln\left(x^2 e^x\right)$$

14. The height (in meters) of a projectile shot vertically upward from a point 2 m above ground level with an initial velocity of 24.5 m/s is $h = 2 + 24.5t - 4.9t^2$ after t seconds.

a) When does the projectile reach its maximum height?
b) What is the maximum height?

15. If $f(t) = \sqrt{4t+1}$, find $f''(2)$.

Select the correct answer.

a. $-4/27$ b. 3 c. $-2/3$ d. $2/3$ e. $4/27$

16. Find the first and the second derivatives of the function.

$$G(r) = \sqrt{r} + \sqrt[5]{r}$$

17. Find the equation of the tangent line to the given curve at the specified point.

$$y = 4xe^x,\ (0,0)$$

18. Find a third-degree polynomial Q such that $Q(1) = 2$, $Q'(1) = 7$, $Q''(1) = 14$, and $Q'''(1) = 18$.

19. Calculate y'.

$$\cos(xy) = x^2 - y$$

20. If $f(x) = \dfrac{x}{\ln x}$, find $f'(e^3)$.

ANSWER KEY

Stewart - Calculus ET 7e Chapter 3 Form H

1. 80

2. $f'(t) = 2t^5 - 8t^3 + 1$

3. c

4. $1,537,635,400

5. c

6. $y = -x + 3\pi / 4$

7. 0.88

8. $g'(x) = 8\sec(x)\tan(x) + \sec^2 x$

9. $y = 6.5\sqrt{3}(x - \pi / 3) - 2.5$

10. 0

11. $y' = \dfrac{-4x}{3(x^4 - 1)} \sqrt[3]{\dfrac{x^2 + 1}{x^2 - 1}}$

12. $\cos x$

13. $y' = \dfrac{2}{x} + 1$

14. 2.5 s
 32.625 m

15. a

16. $\dfrac{1}{2}r^{-1/2} + \dfrac{1}{5}r^{-4/5}, \dfrac{-1}{4}r^{-3/2} - \dfrac{4}{25}r^{-9/5}$

17. $y = 4x$

18. $Q = 3x^3 - 2x^2 + 2x - 1$

19. $y' = \dfrac{2x + y(\sin(xy))}{1 - x(\sin(xy))}$

20. $2/9$

1. Find the absolute maximum value of $y=\sqrt{81-x^2}$ on the interval [–9, 9].

2. Find the local and absolute extreme values of the function on the given interval.

$$f(x)=x^3-6x^2+9x+1,\quad [2,4]$$

3. Estimate the absolute minimum value of the function $y=x^3-6x+3$ to two decimal places on the interval $[0, 10]$

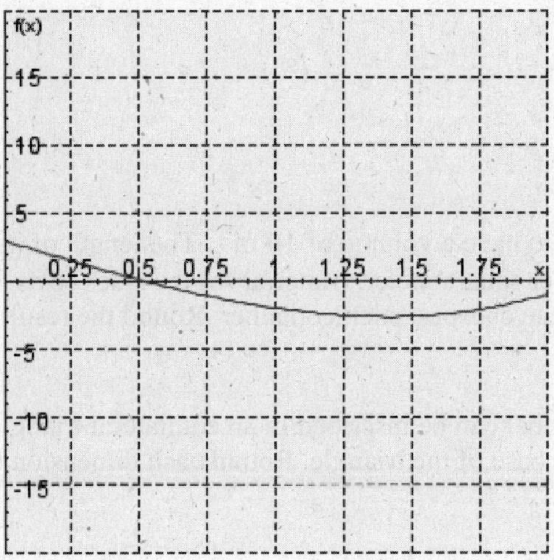

4. Find the critical numbers of the function.

$$y=\frac{x}{x^2+25}$$

5. Find the inflection points for the function.

$$f(x)=8x+3-2\sin x,\quad 0<x<3\pi$$

6. Find the value of the limit.

$$\lim_{x\to\infty}\frac{x^7}{7^x}$$

7. Sketch the curve. Find the equation of the slant asymptote.

$$y=\frac{x^2}{x+1}$$

8. The sum of two positive numbers is 16. What is the smallest possible value of the sum of their squares?

9. The graph of the derivative $f'(x)$ of a continuous function f is shown. On what intervals is f decreasing?

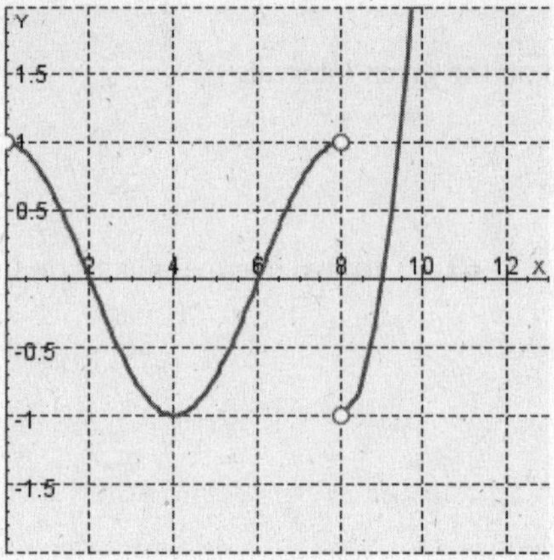

10. A rectangular storage container with an open top is to have a volume of $10\ \text{m}^3$. The length of its base is twice the width. Material for the base costs \$13 per square meter. Material for the sides costs \$10 per square meter. Find the cost of the materials for the cheapest such container. Round the result to the nearest cent.

11. Find the dimensions of the rectangle of largest area that can be inscribed in an equilateral triangle of side $L = 6$ cm if one side of the rectangle lies on the base of the triangle. Round each dimension to the nearest tenth.

12. Estimate the extreme values of the function. Round the answers to the nearest hundredth.

$$y(x) = \frac{1}{3}x^3 - 7x^2 + 40x + 7$$

13. The average cost of producing x units of a commodity is given by the equation $c(x) = 20.4 - 0.0007x$.

Find the marginal cost at a production level of 1,255 units.

14. Find the most general antiderivative of the function.

$$f(x) = 3\cos x - 6\sin x$$

15. For what values of a and b is $(2, 2.5)$ is an inflection point of the curve $x^2y + ax + by = 0$? What additional inflection points does the curve have?

16. What is the minimum vertical distance between the parabolas $y = x^2 + 1$ and $y = x - x^2$?

17. Find the number c that satisfies the conclusion of the Mean Value Theorem on the given interval.

$$f(x) = 2\sqrt{x}, \quad [0, 4]$$

18. Find f.

$$f''(x) = x^3 + \sinh x, \quad f(0) = 1, \quad f(2) = 13/5$$

19. Use Newton's method with the specified initial approximation x_1 to find x_3, the third approximation to the root of the given equation. (Give your answer to four decimal places.)

$x^4 - 12 = 0\,,\ \ x_1 = 8$

20. A rectangular beam will be cut from a cylindrical log of radius 10 inches. Suppose that the strength of a rectangular beam is proportional to the product of its width and the square of its depth. Find the dimensions of the strongest beam that can be cut from the cylindrical log.

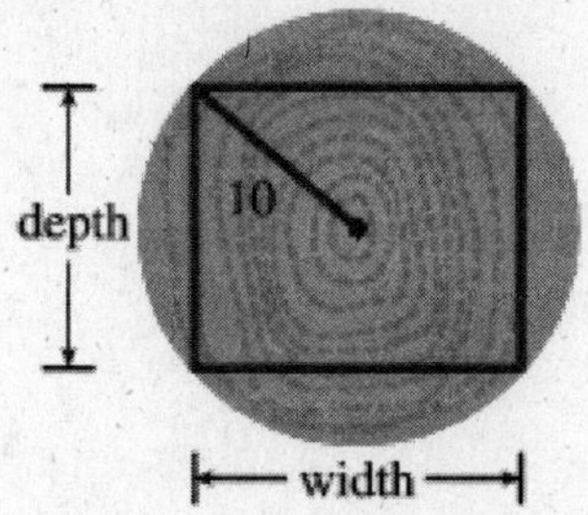

ANSWER KEY

Stewart - Calculus ET 7e Chapter 4 Form A

1. 9

2. Max $(4,5)$, Min $(3,1)$

3. −2.66

4. 5, −5

5. $(\pi,\ 8\pi+3)$, $(2\pi,\ 16\pi+3)$

6. 0

7. 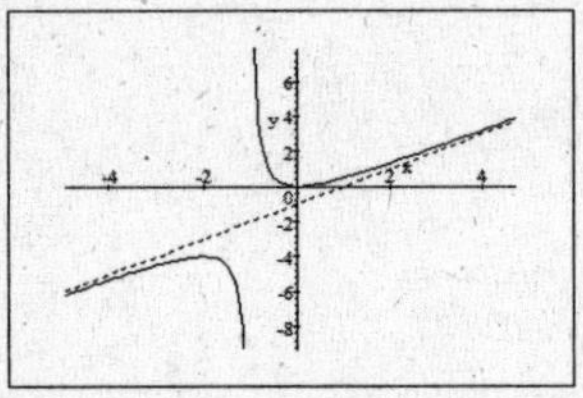 $y = x - 1$

8. 128

9. $(2,6) \cup (8,9)$

10. 250.9

11. 3, 2.6

12. 40.33, 76.33

13. 18.64

14. $3\sin(x) + 6\cos(x) + C$

15.
$a = -20/3$
$b = 4/3$
$(0,0), (-2, -5/2)$

16. $7/8$

17. c=1

18. $f(x) = \frac{1}{20}x^5 + \sinh x - \left(\frac{1}{2}\sinh 2\right)x + 1$

19. 4.5182

20. $20\sqrt{3}/3$ in, $20\sqrt{6}/3$ in

1. Find all the critical numbers of the function.

$g(\theta) = 2\cos\theta + \sin^2\theta$

2. Find the absolute maximum of the function.

$f(x) = \sin(6x) + \cos(6x)$ on the interval $[0, \pi/18]$

3. Find an equation of the line through the point (8, 16) that cuts off the least area from the first quadrant.

4. Find the number *c* that satisfies the conclusion of the Mean Value Theorem on the given interval.

$f(x) = 2\sqrt{x}, \quad [4,9]$

5. Estimate the absolute maximum value of the function $y = x\sqrt{3x - x^2}$ to two decimal places on the interval [0, 3].

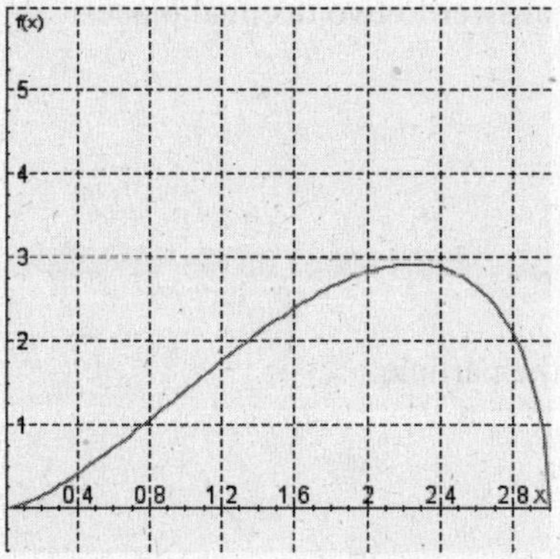

6. At 4:00 P.M. a car's speedometer reads 29 mi/ *h*. At 4:15 it reads 71 mi/h. At some time between 4:00 and 4:15 the acceleration is exactly *x* mi/ h^2. Find *x*.

7. Find *f*.

$f''(x) = x^3 + 4\sinh x, \; f(0) = 1, \; f(2) = 13/5$

8. Find a cubic function $f(x) = ax^3 - bx^2 + cx - d$ that has a local maximum value of 112 at 1 and a local minimum value of –1,184 at 7.

9. Find the inflection points for the function.

$f(x) = 8x + 3 - 2\sin x, \; 0 < x < 3\pi$

10. Evaluate the limit.

$$\lim_{x \to 1^+} \left(\frac{x}{x-1} - \frac{1}{\ln x} \right)$$

11. The sum of two positive numbers is 36. What is the smallest possible value of the sum of their squares?

12. What is the shortest possible length of the line segment that is cut off by the first quadrant and is tangent to the curve $y = 4/x$ at some point?

13. For the cost function (given in dollars), find the average cost of 1,105 units.

$$C(x) = 46{,}410 + 180x + x^2$$

14. A farmer with 800 ft of fencing wants to enclose a rectangular area and then divide it into four pens with fencing parallel to one side of the rectangle. What is the largest possible total area of the four pens?

15. Find the most general antiderivative of the function.

$$f(x) = 8x^{1/7} - 10x^{1/9}$$

16. A painting in an art gallery has height $h = 60$ cm and is hung so that its lower edge is a distance $d = 17$ cm above the eye of an observer (as seen in the figure below). How far from the wall should the observer stand to get the best view? In other words, where should the observer stand so as to maximize the angle θ subtended at his eye by the painting? Round your answer to two decimal places.

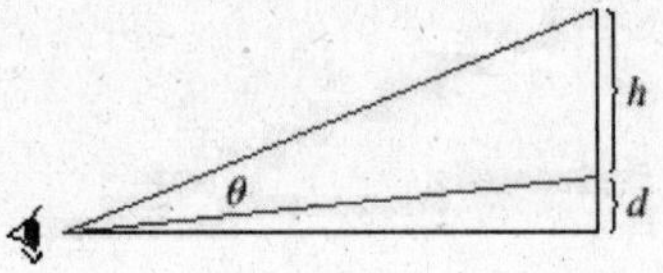

17. A particle is moving with the given data. Find the position of the particle.

$$v(t) = \sin t - \cos t, \quad s(0) = 0$$

18. A rectangular beam will be cut from a cylindrical log of radius 10 inches. Suppose that the strength of a rectangular beam is proportional to the product of its width and the square of its depth. Find the dimensions of the strongest beam that can be cut from the cylindrical log.

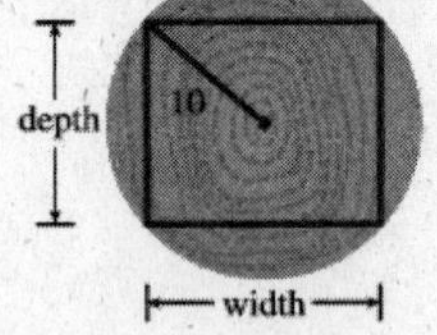

19. For what values of a and b is (2,2.5) is an inflection point of the curve $x^2y + ax + by = 0$? What additional inflection points does the curve have?

20. A steel pipe is being carried down a hallway 15 ft wide. At the end of the hall there is a right-angled turn into a narrower hallway 9 ft wide. What is the length of the longest pipe that can be carried horizontally around the corner?

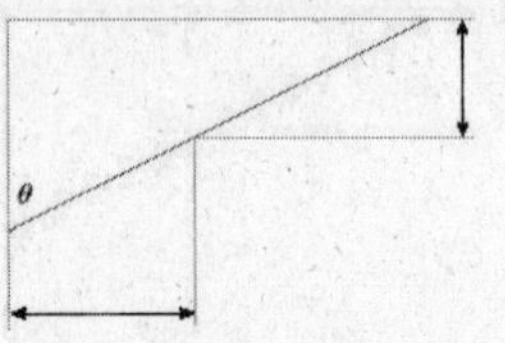

ANSWER KEY

Stewart - Calculus ET 7e Chapter 4 Form B

1. $n\pi$, $n \in$ integers

2. $f\left(\frac{\pi}{24}\right) = \sqrt{2}$

3. $y = -2x + 32$

4. $c = 25/4$

5. 2.25

6. $x = 168$

7. $f(x) = \frac{1}{20}x^5 + 4\sinh x - (2\sinh 2)x + 1$

8. $12x^3 - 144x^2 + 252x - 8$

9. $(\pi,\ 8\pi + 3)$, $(2\pi,\ 16\pi + 3)$

10. $\lim_{x \to 1^+}\left(\frac{x}{x-1} - \frac{1}{\ln x}\right) = \frac{1}{2}$

11. 648

12. $4\sqrt{2}$

13. 1327

14. 16000

15. $7x^{8/7} - 9x^{10/9} + C$

16. 36.18 cm

17. $s(t) = 1 - \cos t - \sin t$

18. $20\sqrt{3}/3$ in, $20\sqrt{6}/3$ in

19. $a = -20/3$
$b = 4/3$
$(0,0), (-2, -5/2)$

20. 33.58 ft

1. Find the number c that satisfies the conclusion of the Mean Value Theorem on the given interval.

$f(x)=2\sqrt{x}, \quad [0,9]$

Select the correct answer.

a. $c=9/4$
b. $c=0$
c. $c=1/4$
d. $c=5$
e. none of these

2. Find the absolute maximum value of $y=7\sin\left(\dfrac{\pi}{10}\right)$.

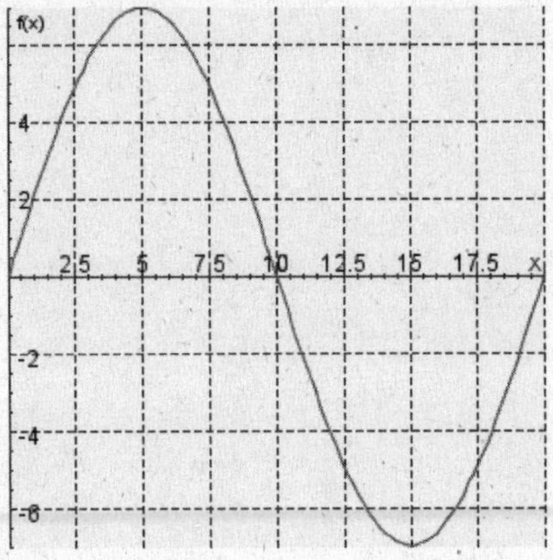

Select the correct answer.

a. 7
b. 15
c. 0
d. 5
e. –6

3. Evaluate the limit.

$$\lim_{x\to 1^+}\left(\frac{x}{x-1}-\frac{1}{\ln x}\right)$$

Select the correct answer.

a. $1/2$
b. 2
c. 0
d. ∞
e. -2

4. Estimate the extreme values of the function.

$$y(x) = \frac{1}{3}x^3 - 9x^2 + 72x + 2$$

Select the correct answer.

a. 146, 182
b. 1,226, –223
c. 383.18, 200.95
d. 150, –223
e. 1,226, 182

5. Find all the critical numbers of the function.

$$g(x) = 4x + \sin(4x)$$

Select the correct answer.

a. $\frac{\pi}{4}$
b. $\frac{\pi(2n+1)}{8}$
c. $\frac{\pi n}{2}$
d. $\frac{\pi(2n+1)}{4}$
e. none of these

6. Find f.

$$f'(t) = 2t - 3\sin t, \quad f(0) = 5$$

Select the correct answer.

a. $f(t) = t^2 + 3\cos t + 2$
b. $f(t) = t^2 + 3\cos t$
c. $f(t) = 2t - 3\sin t + 5$
d. $f(t) = t^2 - 3\cos t - 5$
e. none of these

7. How many points of inflection are on the graph of the function?

$$f(x) = 18x^3 + 5x^2 - 12x - 17$$

Select the correct answer.

a. 1 b. 2 c. 4 d. 3 e. 5

8. What is the shortest possible length of the line segment that is cut off by the first quadrant and is tangent to the curve $y = 5/x$ at some point?

Select the correct answer.

a. $2\sqrt{2}$
b. $5\sqrt{2}$
c. $2\sqrt{10}$
d. $1/5$
e. none of these

9. Sketch the curve.

$y = 3x^3 + 3x$

Select the correct answer.

a.
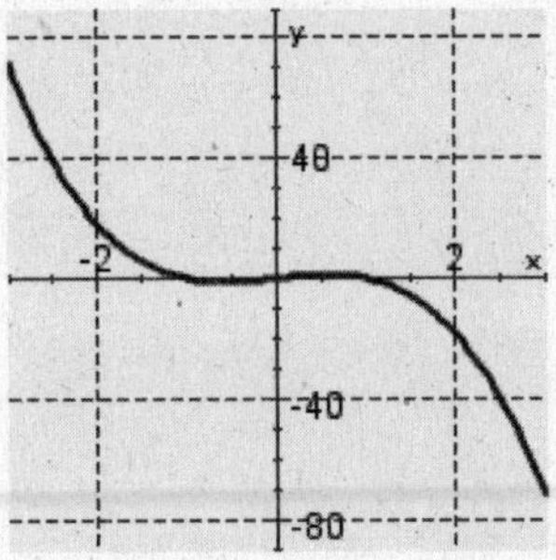

b.
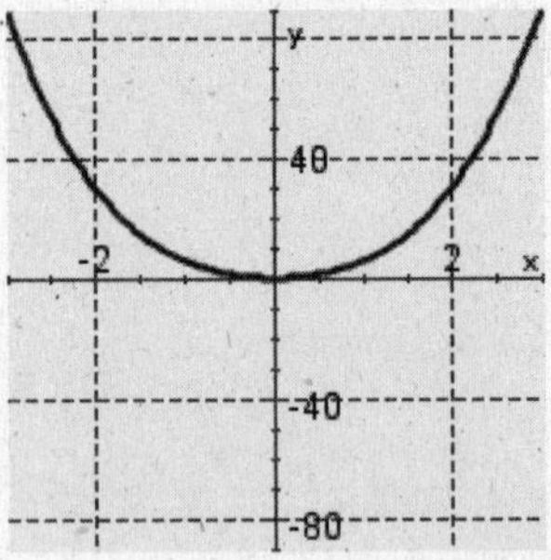

c.
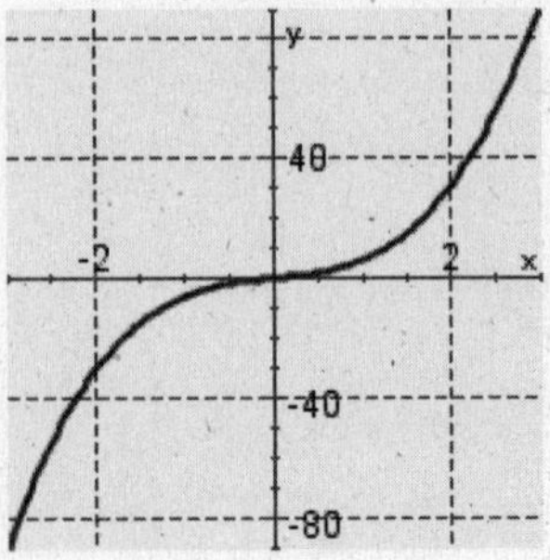

10. Sketch the curve.

$$y = \sqrt{\frac{x}{x-1}}$$

Select the correct answer.

a. 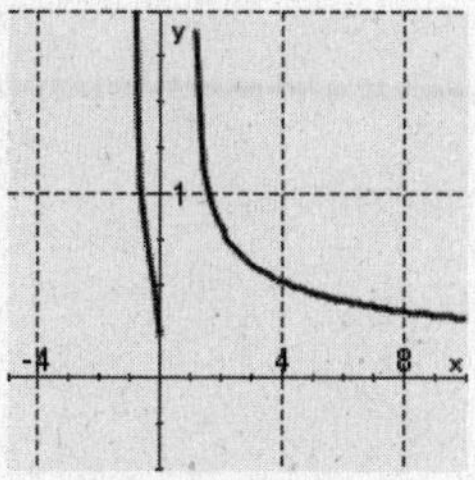

b. 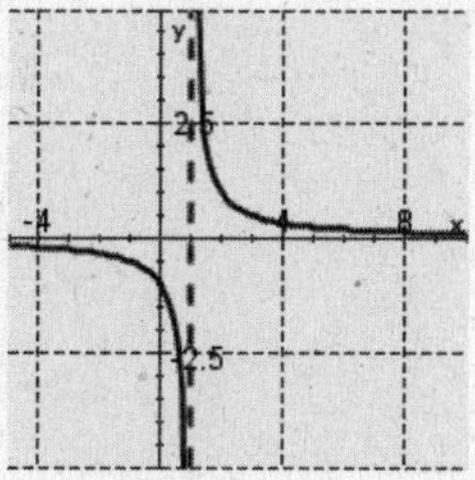

c. 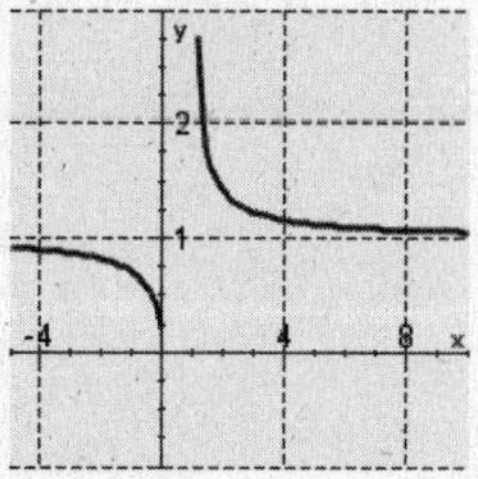

11. What is the function of the graph?

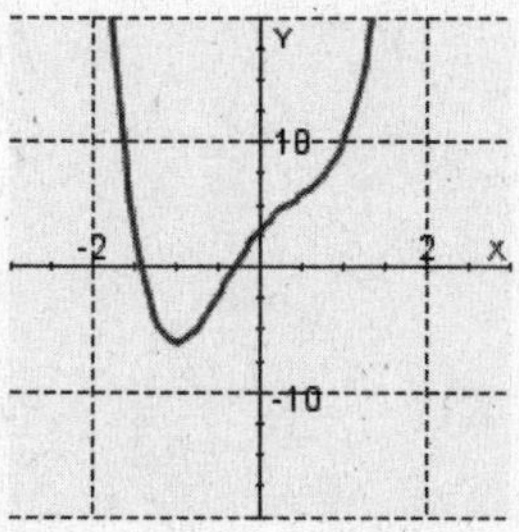

Select the correct answer.

a. $y = 5x^4 - 6x^2 + 8x + 3$
b. $y = 6x^3 - 8x^2 + 5$
c. $y = 6x^4 - 8x^3 + 5x$
d. $y = x^7 - 8x^3 + 5x$
e. $y = x^6 - 8x^2 + 5x$

12. Sketch the curve.

$$y = x \tan 2x\,, \quad -\frac{\pi}{2} < x < \frac{\pi}{2}$$

Select the correct answer.

a.

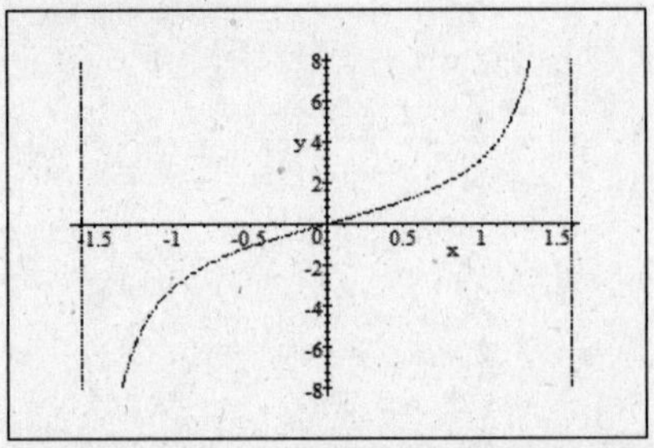

b.

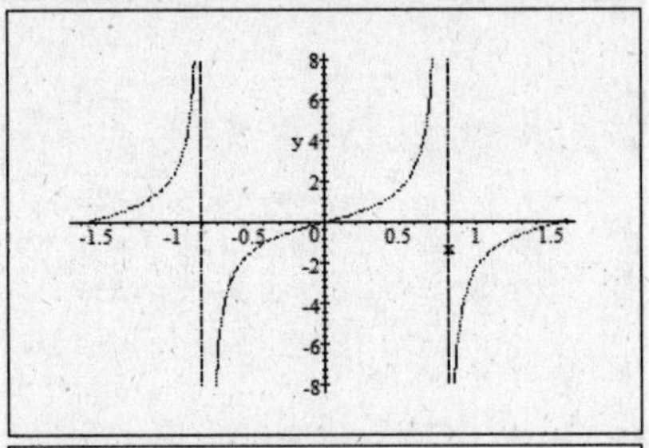

c.

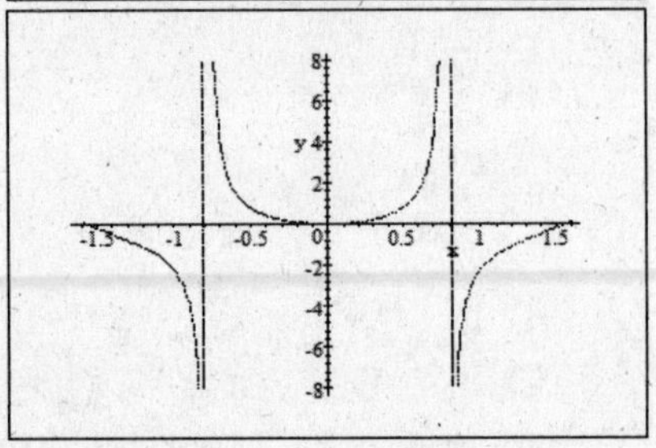

13. Find the inflection points for the function given.

$f(x) = 8x + 2 - \sin x, \quad 0 < x < 3\pi$

Select the correct answer.

a. $(\pi,\ 8\pi),\ (2\pi,\ 16\pi + 2)$

b. $(\pi,\ 2),\ (2\pi,\ 16\pi + 2)$

c. $(\pi,\ 8\pi),\ (2\pi,\ 16\pi)$

d. $(\pi,\ 8\pi + 2),\ (2\pi,\ 16\pi + 2)$

e. $(\pi,\ 8\pi + 2),\ (2\pi\ ,16\pi)$

14. Given that the graph of f passes through the point (4, 69) and that the slope of its tangent line at $(x, f(x))$ is $10x - 4$, find $f(1)$.

Select the correct answer.

a. 1 b. 12 c. 11 d. 6 e. 0

15. Find two positive numbers whose product is 144 and whose sum is a minimum.

Select the correct answer.

a. 4, 36
b. 2, 72
c. 12, 12
d. 3, 48
e. 6, 24

16. A rectangular storage container with an open top is to have a volume of 10 m^3. The length of its base is twice the width. Material for the base costs \$12 per square meter. Material for the sides costs \$5 per square meter. Find the cost of materials for the cheapest such container.

Select the correct answer.

a. \$153.92
b. \$158.1
c. \$152.9
d. \$151.6
e. \$153.9
f. \$152.4

17. Find the dimensions of the rectangle of largest area that can be inscribed in an equilateral triangle of side $L = 9$ cm if one side of the rectangle lies on the base of the triangle. Round the result to the nearest tenth.

Select the correct answer.

a. 9.5 cm , 3.9 cm
b. 7.5 cm , 2.9 cm
c. 4.5 cm , 4 cm
d. 4.5 cm , 3.9 cm
e. 4 cm , 3.91 cm
f. 5.5 cm , 4.4 cm

18. A woman at a point A on the shore of a circular lake with radius 2 mi wants to arrive at the point C diametrically opposite on the other side of the lake in the shortest possible time. She can walk at the rate of 6 mi/h and row a boat at 2 mi/h. How should she proceed? (Find θ). Round the result, if necessary, to the nearest hundredth.

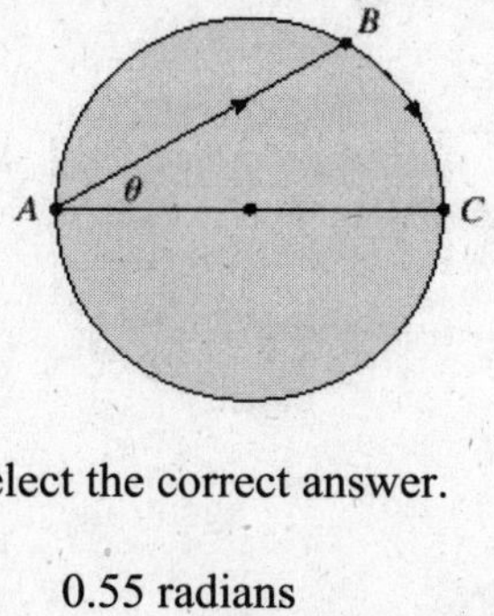

Select the correct answer.

a. 0.55 radians
b. She should walk around the lake from point A to point C.
c. She should row from point A to point C radians
d. 0.34 radians
e. 0.98 radians

19. Find the most general antiderivative of the function.

$f(x) = 18x^2 - 14x + 9$

Select the correct answer.

a. $F(x) = 30x^5 - 28x^4 + 9x + C$

b. $F(x) = 6x^3 - 7x^2 + 9x + C$

c. $F(x) = 18x^3 - 14x^2 + 9x + C$

d. $F(x) = 36x - 14 + C$

e. $F(x) = 6x^2 - 14x + C$

20. The graph of the derivative $f'(x)$ of a continuous function f is shown. On what intervals is f decreasing?

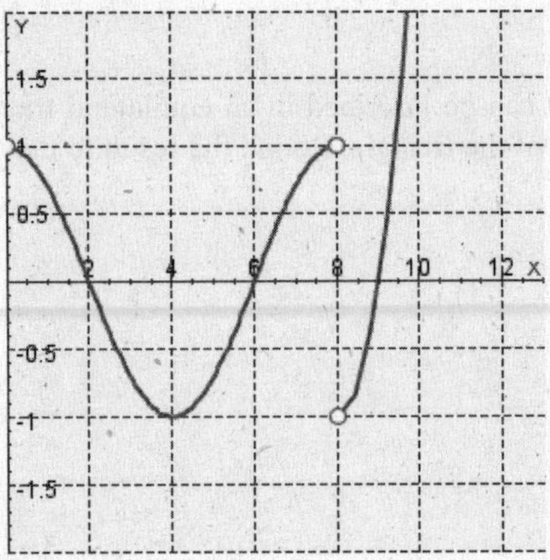

Select the correct answer.

a. $(2,6) \cup (8, 9)$
b. $(-1, 1)$
c. $(8, 9)$
d. $(2,6)$
e. none of these

ANSWER KEY

Stewart - Calculus ET 7e Chapter 4 Form C

1. a
2. a
3. a
4. a
5. d
6. a
7. a
8. c
9. c
10. c
11. a
12. c
13. d
14. d
15. c
16. e
17. d
18. b
19. b
20. a

1. Find the critical numbers of $f(x)=x^4(x-3)^3$.

Select the correct answer.

a. $0,\ 2,\ \frac{12}{7}$ b. $0,\ 3,\ \frac{12}{11}$ c. $0,\ 3,\ \frac{12}{7}$ d. $0,\ 2,\ \frac{12}{11}$ e. $0,\ 2,\ \frac{7}{12}$

2. Find the absolute maximum value of $y=\sqrt{36-x^2}$ on the interval [–6, 6].

Select the correct answer.

a. 5
b. 6
c. 7
d. 0
e. 1

3. How many real roots does the equation $x^5-7x+c=0$ have in the interval [–1, 1]?

Select the correct answer.

a. at most two real roots
b. no real roots
c. at most three real roots
d. at most one real root
e. at most five real roots

4. Find the limit.

$$\lim_{t\to 0}\frac{3^t-2^t}{t}$$

Select the correct answer.

a. ∞
b. 0
c. $\ln 2-\ln 3$
d. $\ln 3-\ln 2$
e. 1

5. Find any absolute or local maximum and minimum values of $f(x)=8-2x$ if $x\geq 6$.

Select the correct answer.

a. –4 is an absolute maximum
b. 6 is an absolute minimum
c. 6 is an absolute maximum
d. 6 is a local minimum
e. –4 is a local maximum
f. –4 is an absolute minimum

6. Evaluate $f(x) = \sin(x^2)$, and tell whether its antiderivative F is increasing or decreasing at the point $x = -4$ radians.

Select the correct answer (to the nearest thousandth).

a. 0.757, decreasing
b. 0.757, increasing
c. –0.288, increasing
d. –0.288, decreasing
e. 0.277, decreasing

7. Find the number c that satisfies the conclusion of the Mean Value Theorem on the given interval.

$f(x) = 2\sqrt{x}, \quad [0,9]$

Select the correct answer.

a. $c = 9/4$
b. $c = 0$
c. $c = 1/4$
d. $c = 5$
e. none of these

8. How many points of inflection are on the graph of the function?

$f(x) = 12x^3 + 14x^2 - 7x - 9$

Select the correct answer.

a. 3
b. 1
c. 4
d. 2
e. 5

9. What is the shortest possible length of the line segment that is cut off by the first quadrant and is tangent to the curve $y = 5/x$ at some point?

Select the correct answer.

a. $2\sqrt{2}$
b. $5\sqrt{2}$
c. $2\sqrt{10}$
d. $1/5$
e. none of these

10. Sketch the curve.

$y = x + 2x^{2/3}$

Select the correct answer.

a.

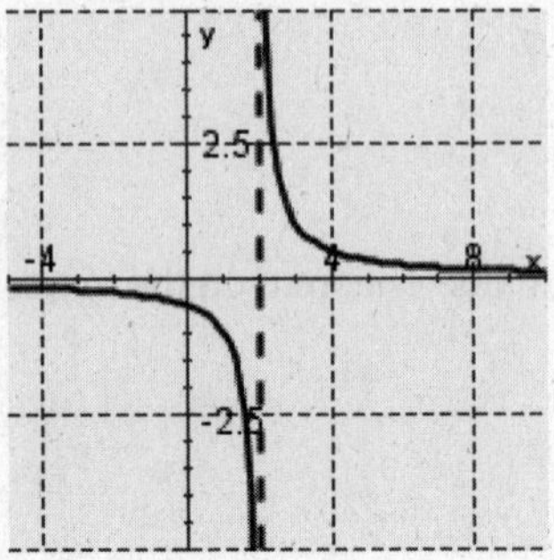

b.

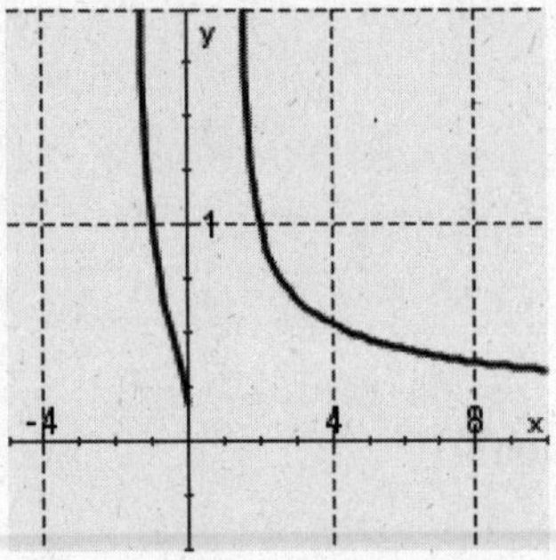

c.

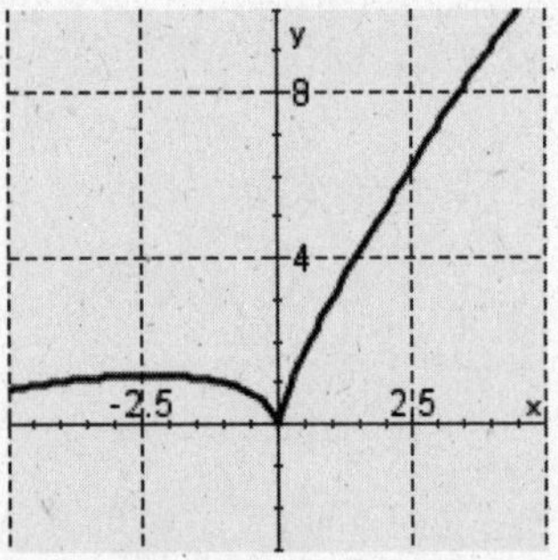

11. Find the slant asymptote of the function $f(x) = \dfrac{x^2 + 7}{x}$.

Select the correct answer.

a. $y = x^3$
b. $y = x^2$
c. $y = 1$
d. $y = x$
e. $y = x^7$

12. Find the maximum or minimum point(s) of the function.

$F(x) = (1 - x^2)^2 + 6x^2$

Select the correct answer.

a. (0, 1)
b. (–8.6, 6)
c. (–8, 2)
d. (8, 0)
e. (16, 1)

13. For what values of c does the curve have maximum and minimum points?

$F(x) = 5x^3 + cx^2 + 10x$

Select the correct answer.

a. $|c| > 15$

b. $|c| > \sqrt{150}$

c. $|c| > 1{,}500$

d. $|c| > \sqrt{30}$

e. $|c| > \sqrt{750}$

14. Find the point on the line $y = 4x + 8$ that is closest to the origin.

Select the correct answer.

a. $\left(-\frac{32}{17}, \frac{10}{17}\right)$

b. $\left(-\frac{34}{17}, \frac{9}{17}\right)$

c. $\left(-\frac{32}{17}, \frac{8}{17}\right)$

d. $\left(-2, \frac{8}{17}\right)$

e. $\left(-\frac{31}{17}, \frac{8}{17}\right)$

15. A piece of wire 10 m long is cut into two pieces. One piece is bent into a square and the other is bent into an equilateral triangle. How should the wire be cut for the square so that the total area enclosed is a minimum? Round the result to the nearest hundredth.

Select the correct answer.

a. 5.35 m
b. 4.4 m
c. 4.35 m
d. 0 m
e. 3.25 m

16. Let $P(x)$ and $Q(x)$ be polynomials.

Find $\lim_{x\to\infty} \dfrac{P(x)}{Q(x)}$ if the degree of $P(x)$ is 5 and the degree of $Q(x)$ is 9.

Select the correct answer.

a. –4
b. 9
c. 4
d. 0
e. 5

17. A rectangular beam will be cut from a cylindrical log of radius 10 inches. Suppose that the strength of a rectangular beam is proportional to the product of its width and the square of its depth. Find the dimensions of the strongest beam that can be cut from the cylindrical log.

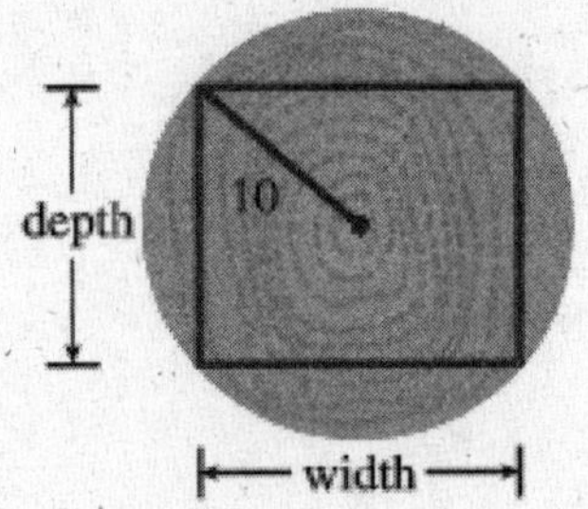

Select the correct answer.

a. $20/\sqrt{3}$ in, $20\sqrt{2/3}$ in
b. 20 in, $\sqrt{2/3}$ in
c. $\sqrt{3}$ in, 20 in
d. $20/\sqrt{3}$ in, $20/\sqrt{3}$ in
e. $20\sqrt{2/3}$ in, $20\sqrt{2/3}$ in

18. Find f.

$f''(x) = 12x + 24x^2$

Select the correct answer.

a. $f(x) = 6x^3 + 4x^4 + Cx + D$
b. $f(x) = 2x^3 + 2x^4 + Cx + D$
c. $f(x) = 4x^3 + 8x^4 + Cx + D$
d. $f(x) = 2x^3 + x^4 + Cx + D$
e. $f(x) = x^3 + 4x^4 + Cx + D$

19. A right circular cylinder is inscribed in a sphere of radius $r = 4$ cm. Find the largest possible surface area of such a cylinder. Round the result to the nearest hundredth.

Select the correct answer.

a. 162.66 cm^2
b. 163.16 cm^2
c. 162.68 cm^2
d. 161.55 cm^2
e. 168.55 cm^2

20. Find the smallest possible area of an isosceles triangle that is circumscribed about a circle of radius r.

Select the correct answer.

a. $3\sqrt{3}r^2$
b. $3\pi\sqrt{3}r^2$
c. $\sqrt{6}r^2$
d. $2\sqrt{3}r^2$
e. $\sqrt{3}r^2$

ANSWER KEY

1. c
2. b
3. d
4. d
5. a
6. d
7. a
8. b
9. c
10. c
11. d
12. a
13. b
14. c
15. c
16. d
17. a
18. b
19. a
20. a

1. Find the number c that satisfies the conclusion of the Mean Value Theorem on the given interval.

$f(x) = 2\sqrt{x}, \quad [4,9]$

Select the correct answer.

a. $c = 25/4$
b. $c = 13/2$
c. $c = 4/9$
d. $c = 5$
e. none of these

2. The graph of the first derivative $f'(x)$ of a function f is shown below. At what values of x does f have a local maximum or minimum?

y=f'(x)

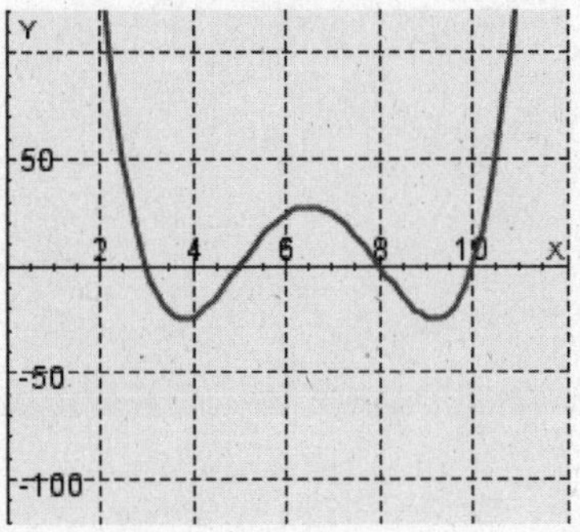

3. Find the absolute minimum value(s) of $y = 2x^2 - 20x + 9$ on the interval [0, 6].

4. Find the limit.

$$\lim_{x\to\infty} \frac{x^7 - 3}{x^6 + 6}$$

Select the correct answer.

a. ∞
b. $-\infty$
c. 0
d. $7/6$
e. $-1/2$

5. Find the critical numbers of the function.

$g(x) = 6x + \sin(6x)$

6. Find an equation of the line through the point (9, 36) that cuts off the least area from the first quadrant.

7. The graph of the derivative $f'(x)$ of a continuous function f is shown. At what values of x does f have a local maximum or minimum?

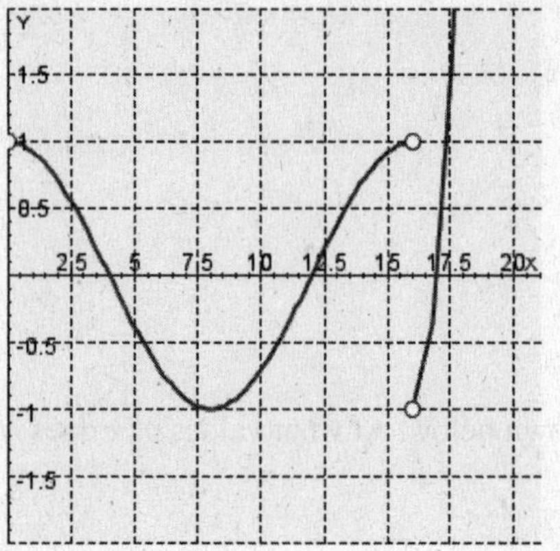

8. Evaluate the limit.

$$\lim_{x \to 0} \frac{1 - \cos x}{x^2 + x}$$

Select the correct answer.

a. –5
b. 0
c. π
d. 1
e. ∞

9. Find the minimum points of the function.

$$F(x) = x^4 - 500x$$

10. If 1,100 cm^2 of material is available to make a box with a square base and an open top, find the largest possible volume of the box.

11. A particle is moving with the given data. Find the position of the particle.

$$v(t) = \sin t - \cos t, \quad s(0) = 0$$

12. Find all the maximum and minimum values of the function.

$$F(x) = \frac{x - 5}{(x - 4)^2}$$

13. Sketch the curve. Find the equation of the slant asymptote.

$$y = \frac{x^2}{x - 2}$$

14. What is the shortest possible length of the line segment that is cut off by the first quadrant and is tangent to the curve $y = 5/x$ at some point?

Select the correct answer.

a. $2\sqrt{2}$
b. $5\sqrt{2}$
c. $2\sqrt{10}$
d. $1/5$
e. none of these

15. Find the smallest possible area of an isosceles triangle that is circumscribed about a circle of radius r.

16. Find the point on the line $y = 4x + 8$ that is closest to the origin.

Select the correct answer.

a. $\left(-\frac{32}{17}, \frac{10}{17}\right)$

b. $\left(-\frac{34}{17}, \frac{9}{17}\right)$

c. $\left(-\frac{32}{17}, \frac{8}{17}\right)$

d. $\left(-2, \frac{8}{17}\right)$

e. $\left(-\frac{31}{17}, \frac{8}{17}\right)$

17. Find *f*.

$f''(x) = x^3 + 2\sinh x,\ f(0) = 1,\ f(2) = 13/5$

18. Use Newton's method to approximate the indicated root of $x^4 + x - 9 = 0$ in the interval [1, 2], correct to six decimal places.

Use $x_1 = 1.5$ as the initial approximation.

19. Find the maximum area of a rectangle that can be circumscribed about a given rectangle with length $L = 8$ and width $W = 3$.

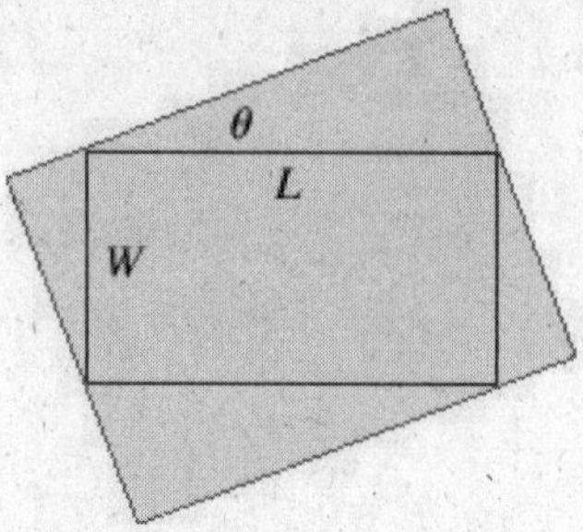

20. Sketch the curve.

$y = x + 3x^{2/3}$

Select the correct answer.

a.

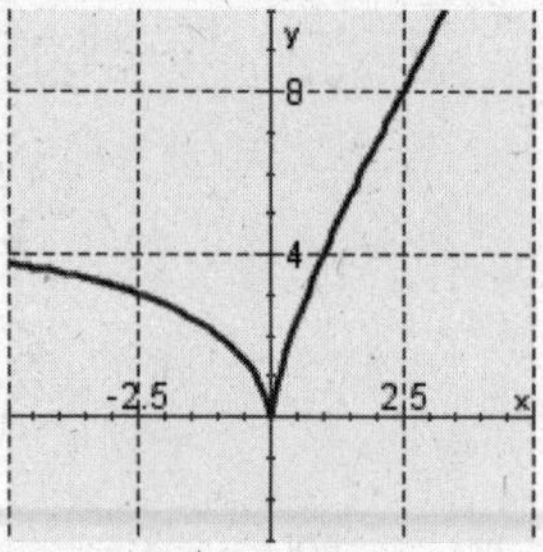

b.

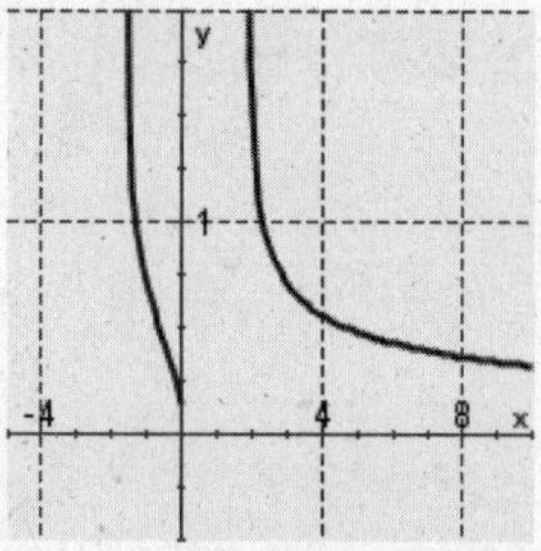

c.

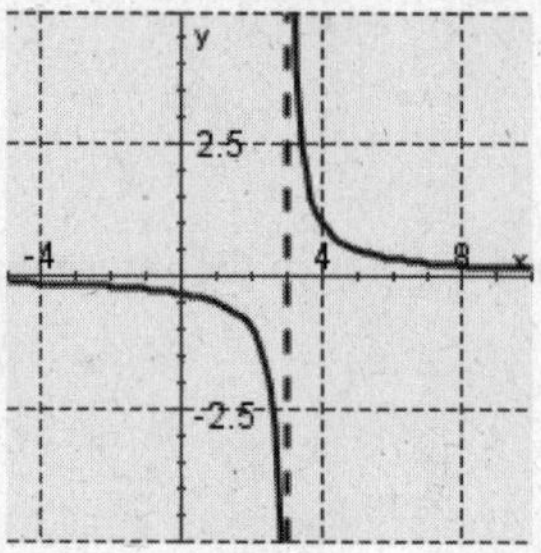

ANSWER KEY

Stewart - Calculus ET 7e Chapter 4 Form E

1. a

2. 3, 5, 8, 10

3. –41

4. a

5. $\dfrac{\pi(2n+1)}{6}$

6. $y=-4x+72$

7. 4, 12, 17

8. b

9. 5

10. 3511

11. $s(t)=1-\cos t-\sin t$

12. $1/4$, maximum at $x=6$

13. 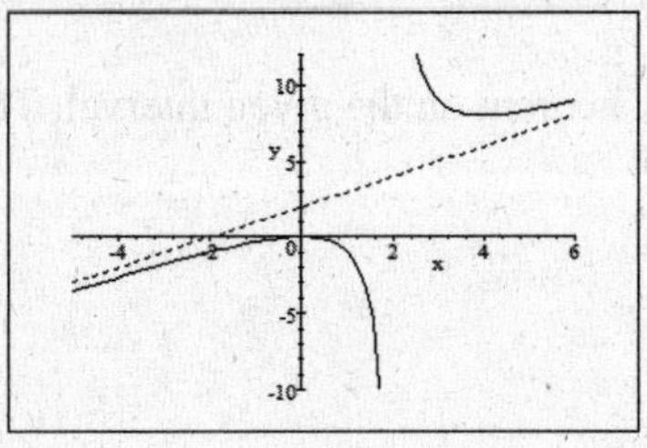

$y=x+2$

14. c

15. $3\sqrt{3}r^2$

16. c

17. $f(x)=\dfrac{1}{20}x^5+2\sinh x-(\sinh 2)x+1$

18. 1.646722

19. 60.5

20. a

1. Find the absolute maximum value of $y = \sqrt{81 - x^2}$ on the interval [–9, 9].

2. Find all the critical numbers of the function.

$g(x) = 4x + \sin(4x)$

Select the correct answer.

a. $\frac{\pi}{4}$

b. $\frac{\pi(2n+1)}{8}$

c. $\frac{\pi n}{2}$

d. $\frac{\pi(2n+1)}{4}$

e. none

3. Find the limit.

$\lim_{y \to -\infty} \left(y + \sqrt{y^2 + 2y} \right)$

4. Verify that the function satisfies the three hypotheses of Rolle's Theorem on the given interval. Then find all numbers c that satisfy the conclusion of Rolle's Theorem.

$f(x) = \sin 5\pi x, \quad \left[-\frac{2}{5}, \frac{2}{5} \right]$

Select the correct answer.

a. $c_1 = \pm\frac{1}{10}, \quad c_2 = \frac{3}{10}$

b. $c_1 = -\frac{1}{10}, \quad c_2 = \pm\frac{1}{10}$

c. $c_1 = \frac{1}{10}, \quad c_2 = \pm\frac{3}{10}$

d. $c_1 = \pm\frac{1}{10}, \quad c_2 = \pm\frac{3}{10}$

e. none

5. For what values of a and b is $(2, 2.5)$ an inflection point of the curve $x^2y + ax + by = 0$? What additional inflection points does the curve have?

6. The graph of the second derivative $f''(x)$ of a function f is shown. State the x-coordinates of the inflection points of f.

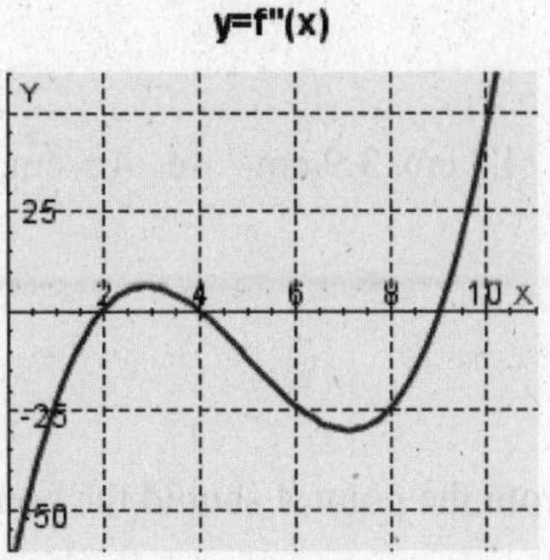

7. The graph of the derivative $f'(x)$ of a continuous function f is shown. On what intervals is f decreasing?

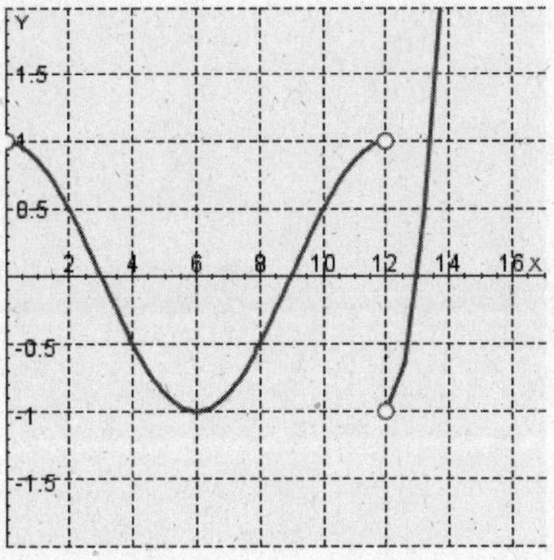

8. For what values of c does the curve have maximum and minimum points?

$$F(x) = 4x^3 + cx^2 + 4x$$

9. Suppose the line $y = 5x - 1$ is tangent to the curve $y = f(x)$ when $x = -8$. If Newton's method is used to locate a root of the equation $f(x) = 0$ and the initial approximation is $x_1 = -8$, find the second approximation x_2.

10. Find the limit.

$$\lim_{x \to 0} \frac{x}{\tan^{-1}(7x)}$$

11. Consider the following problem: A farmer with 890 ft of fencing wants to enclose a rectangular area and then divide it into four pens with fencing parallel to one side of the rectangle. What is the largest possible total area of the four pens?

Select the correct answer.

a. 19,825.5 ft^2 b. 19,802.5 ft^2 c. 19,801.5 ft^2 d. 19,902.5 ft^2 e. 19,791.5 ft^2

12. Find the dimensions of the rectangle of largest area that can be inscribed in an equilateral triangle of side $L = 9$ cm if one side of the rectangle lies on the base of the triangle. Round the result to the nearest tenth.

Select the correct answer.

a. 5.5 cm, 4.4 cm   b. 4 cm, 3.91 cm   c. 7.5 cm, 2.9 cm   d. 4.5 cm, 3.9 cm   e. 4.5 cm, 4 cm

13. Find the most general antiderivative of the function.

$f(x) = 9x^2 - 10x + 3$

14. Consider the figure below, where $a = 7$, $b = 1$ and $l = 6$. How far from the point A should the point P be chosen on the line segment AB so as to maximize the angle θ?

Round the result to the nearest hundredth.

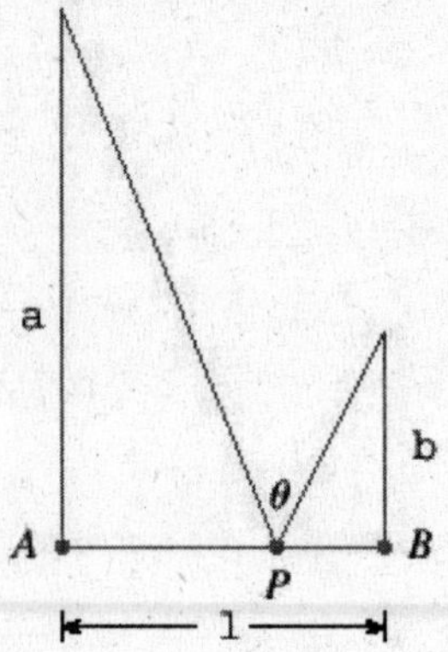

15. Find f.

$f''(x) = x^3 + \sinh x,\ f(0) = 1,\ f(2) = 13/5$

16. Sketch the curve. Find the equation of the slant asymptote.

$y = \dfrac{x^2}{x-1}$

17. What is the shortest possible length of the line segment that is cut off by the first quadrant and is tangent to the curve $y = 5/x$ at some point?

Select the correct answer.

a. $2\sqrt{2}$
b. $5\sqrt{2}$
c. $2\sqrt{10}$
d. $1/5$
e. none of these

18. The sum of two positive numbers is 36. What is the smallest possible value of the sum of their squares?

19. Use Newton's method with the specified initial approximation x_1 to find x_3, the third approximation to the root of the given equation. (Give your answer to four decimal places.)

$x^4 - 13 = 0, \quad x_1 = 2$

20. An aircraft manufacturer wants to determine the best selling price for a new airplane. The company estimates that the initial cost of designing the airplane and setting up the factories in which to build it will be 900 million dollars. The additional cost of manufacturing each plane can be modeled by the function $m(x) = 1{,}600x + 10x^{4/5} + 0.17x^2$ where x is the number of aircraft produced and m is the manufacturing cost, in millions of dollars. The company estimates that if it charges a price p (in millions of dollars) for each plane, it will be able to sell $x(p) = 390 - 5.8p$.

Find the cost function.

ANSWER KEY

Stewart - Calculus ET 7e Chapter 4 Form F

1. 9

2. d

3. –1

4. d

5. $a = -20/3$
$b = 4/3$
$(0,0), (-2, -5/2)$

6. 2, 4, 9

7. (3, 9) ∪ (12, 13)

8. $|c| > \sqrt{48}$

9. 1/5

10. 1/7

11. b

12. d

13. $3x^3 - 5x^2 + 3x + C$

14. 3.26

15. $f(x) = \frac{1}{20}x^5 + \sinh x - \left(\frac{1}{2}\sinh 2\right)x + 1$

16. 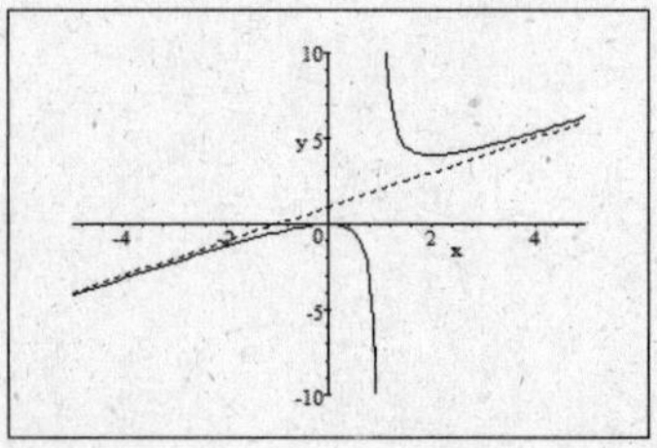

$y = x + 1$

17. c

18. 648

19. 1.8989

20. $C(x) = 900 + 1600x + 10x^{4/5} + 0.17x^2$

1. Find the local and absolute extreme values of the function on the given interval.

$f(x) = x^3 - 6x^2 + 9x + 1, \quad [2,4]$

2. Find the critical numbers of the function.

$g(x) = 8x + \sin 8x$

3. Find the critical numbers of the function.

$y = \dfrac{x}{x^2 + 49}$

4. Verify that the function satisfies the three hypotheses of Rolle's Theorem on the given interval. Then find all numbers c that satisfy the conclusion of Rolle's Theorem.

$f(x) = x^3 - 6x^2 + 8x + 4, \quad [0, 4]$

Select the correct answer.

a. $c = 2 + \dfrac{2\sqrt{3}}{3}$

b. $c = 2 - \dfrac{2\sqrt{3}}{3}$

c. $c_1 = 12 + \dfrac{\sqrt{2}}{3}, \quad c_2 = 12 - \dfrac{\sqrt{2}}{3}$

d. $c_1 = 2 + \dfrac{2\sqrt{3}}{3}, \quad c_2 = 2 - \dfrac{2\sqrt{3}}{3}$

e. $c_1 = 2 + \dfrac{2\sqrt{3}}{3}, \quad c_2 = \dfrac{2\sqrt{3}}{3}$

5. Find the limit.

$\lim\limits_{y \to \infty} \dfrac{2 - 3y^2}{5y^2 + 4y}$

6. Find the most general antiderivative of the function.

$f(x) = x^{1/5} - 4x^{1/3}$

7. Find the point on the line $y = 5x + 9$ that is closest to the origin.

8. Find any absolute, local maximum and minimum values of $f(x) = 2 - 5x, x \geq 1$.

Select the correct answer.

a. 1 is a local minimum
b. –3 is an absolute minimum
c. 1 is an absolute minimum
d. 1 is an absolute maximum
e. –3 is an absolute maximum

9. Find the number c that satisfies the conclusion of the Mean Value Theorem on the given interval.

$f(x) = 2\sqrt{x}, \; [4,9]$

Select the correct answer.

a. $c = 25/4$ b. $c = 13/2$ c. $c = 4/9$ d. $c = 5$ e. none of these

10. A farmer with 710 ft of fencing wants to enclose a rectangular area and then divide it into four pens with fencing parallel to one side of the rectangle. What is the largest possible total area of the four pens?

11. The graph of the first derivative $f'(x)$ of a function f is shown below. At what values of x does f have a local maximum or minimum?

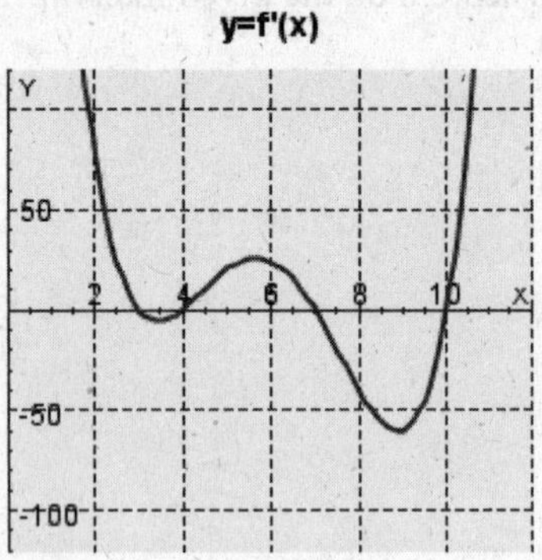

Select the correct answers.

a. 8 b. 9 c. 4 d. 7 e. 10 f. 3

12. Find the inflection points for the function.

$f(x) = 6 - 5x - 2\sin x, \; 0 < x < 3\pi$

Select the correct answer.

a. $(\pi, -5\pi + 6), (2\pi, -10\pi)$
b. $(\pi, -5\pi), (2\pi, -10\pi + 6)$
c. $(\pi, -5\pi + 6), (2\pi, -10\pi + 6)$
d. $(\pi, -5\pi), (2\pi, -10\pi)$
e. $(\pi, 6), (2\pi, -10\pi + 6)$

13. What is the shortest possible length of the line segment that is cut off by the first quadrant and is tangent to the curve $y = 5/x$ at some point?

Select the correct answer.

a. $2\sqrt{2}$ b. $5\sqrt{2}$ c. $2\sqrt{10}$ d. $1/5$ e. none of these

14. For the function f whose graph is given, find the limit.

$$\lim_{x \to -1^-} f(x)$$

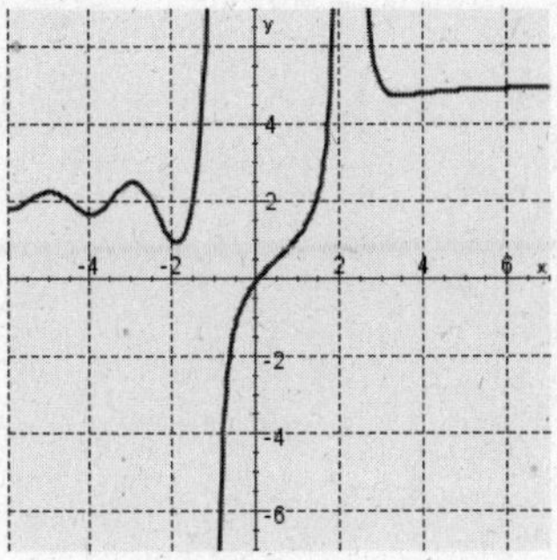

15. Use l'Hospital's Rule to calculate the exact value of the limit $\dfrac{f(x)}{g(x)}$ as $x \to 0$.

$f(x) = e^x - 1$ and $g(x) = x^5 + 4x$

16. A Norman window has the shape of a rectangle surmounted by a semicircle. (Thus the diameter of the semicircle is equal to the width of the rectangle.) If the perimeter of the window is 22 ft, find the dimensions of the window so that the greatest possible amount of light is admitted.

17. What is the minimum vertical distance between the parabolas $y = x^2 + 2$ and $y = x - x^2$?

18. Find the maximum and minimum points of the function.

$$F(x) = \frac{6x}{1 + 36x^2}$$

19. Find f.

$f'(t) = 2t - 3\sin t, \quad f(0) = 5$

20. A particle is moving with the given data. Find the position of the particle.

$v(t) = \sin t - \cos t, \quad s(0) = 0$

Select the correct answer.

a. $s(t) = \cos t - \sin t$

b. $s(t) = 1 - t - \sin t$

c. $s(t) = 1 - \cos^2 t$

d. $s(t) = 1 - \cos t + \sin t$

e. $s(t) = 1 - \cos t - \sin t$

ANSWER KEY

Stewart - Calculus ET 7e Chapter 4 Form G

1. Max $(4,5)$, Min $(3,1)$

2. $\dfrac{\pi(2n+1)}{8}$

3. 7, –7

4. d

5. –3/5

6. $\dfrac{5}{6}x^{6/5} - 3x^{4/3} + C$

7. $\left(-\dfrac{45}{26}, \dfrac{9}{26}\right)$

8. e

9. a

10. 12602.5

11. c, d, e, f

12. c

13. c

14. ∞

15. 1/4

16. 6.16, 3.08

17. 15/8

18. $\dfrac{1}{6}, -\dfrac{1}{6}$

19. $f(t) = t^2 + 3\cos t + 2$

20. e

1. Find the critical numbers of $f(x) = x^4(x-3)^3$.

Select the correct answer.

a. $0,\ 2,\ \dfrac{12}{7}$ b. $0,\ 3,\ \dfrac{12}{11}$ c. $0,\ 3,\ \dfrac{12}{7}$ d. $0,\ 2,\ \dfrac{12}{11}$ e. $0,\ 2,\ \dfrac{7}{12}$

2. Find the absolute maximum of the function $f(x) = \sin(2x) + \cos(2x)$ on the interval $\left[0,\ \dfrac{\pi}{6}\right]$.

3. Evaluate the limit.

$$\lim_{x \to 0} \frac{1-\cos x}{x^2 + x}$$

4. Find the number c that satisfies the conclusion of the Mean Value Theorem on the given interval.

$f(x) = 2\sqrt{x},\quad [4,9]$

Select the correct answer.

a. $c = 25/4$ b. $c = 13/2$ c. $c = 4/9$ d. $c = 5$ e. none of these

5. Find a cubic function $f(x) = ax^3 - bx^2 + cx - d$ that has a local maximum value of 60 at 1 and a local minimum value of -4 at 3.

6. Find the maximum and minimum points of the function.

$F(x) = (1-x^2)^2 + 6x^2$

7. For what values of c does the curve have maximum and minimum points?

$F(x) = 2x^3 + cx^2 + 10x$

Select the correct answer.

a. $|c| > 600$

b. $|c| > 6$

c. $|c| > \sqrt{120}$

d. $|c| > \sqrt{60}$

e. $|c| > \sqrt{30}$

8. Find the maximum area of a rectangle that can be circumscribed about a given rectangle with length $L = 7$ and width $W = 4$.

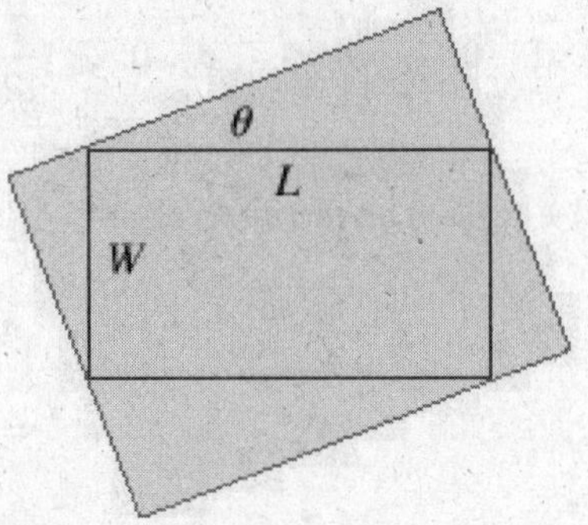

9. Evaluate $f(x) = \sin(x^2)$, and tell whether its antiderivative F is increasing or decreasing at the point $x = -4$ radians.

Select the correct answer (to the nearest thousandth).

a. 0.757, decreasing
b. 0.757, increasing
c. –0.288, increasing
d. –0.288, decreasing
e. 0.277, decreasing

10. A baseball team plays in a stadium that holds 56,000 spectators. With ticket prices at $9, the average attendance had been 32,000. When ticket prices were lowered to $8, the average attendance rose to 36,000. How should ticket prices be set to maximize revenue? Assume the demand function is linear.

11. A manufacturer has been selling 1,200 television sets a week at $400 each. A market survey indicates that for each $30 rebate offered to the buyer, the number of sets sold will increase by 60 per week. Find the demand function.

Select the correct answer.

a. $p(x) = 0.5\,x + 1{,}000$
b. $p(x) = -0.5\,x + 1{,}000$
c. $p(x) = -0.5\,x + 400.5$
d. $p(x) = -0.5\,x + 600$
e. $p(x) = 0.5\,x$

12. The manager of a 138-unit apartment complex knows from experience that all units will be occupied if the rent is $860 per month. A market survey suggests that, on the average, one additional unit will remain vacant for each $10 increase in rent. What rent should the manager charge to maximize revenue?

13. Use Newton's method to approximate the indicated root of $x^4 + x - 9 = 0$ in the interval [1, 2], correct to six decimal places.

Use $x_1 = 1.5$ as the initial approximation.

14. Find f.

$f''(x) = x^3 + 4\sinh x,\ \ f(0) = 1,\ \ f(2) = 13/5$

15. A car braked with a constant deceleration of 40 $ft/\sec^2$, producing skid marks measuring 55 ft before coming to a stop. How fast was the car traveling when the brakes were first applied?

16. Evaluate and determine whether the function's antiderivative is increasing or decreasing at the point $x = -2$ radians.

$f(x) = \sin\left(x^2\right)$

Select the correct answer (to the nearest thousandth).

a. –0.909, decreasing
b. –0.909, increasing
c. –0.757, decreasing
d. –0.757, increasing
e. none of these

17. A particle moves along a straight line with velocity function $v(t) = 2\sin(t) - 4\cos t$ and its initial displacement is $s(0) = 4$. Find its position function.

18. A company estimates that the marginal cost (in dollars per item) of producing items is $2.07 - 0.002x$. If the cost of producing one item is \$561 find the cost of producing 100 items.

19. What constant acceleration is required to increase the speed of a car from 20 ft/s to 45 ft/s in 5 s?

20. What is the shortest possible length of the line segment that is cut off by the first quadrant and is tangent to the curve $y = 1/x$ at some point?

ANSWER KEY

Stewart - Calculus ET 7e Chapter 4 Form H

1. c

2. $f\left(\frac{\pi}{8}\right)=\sqrt{2}$

3. 0

4. a

5. $16x^3-96x^2+144x-4$

6 0

7 d

8 60.5

9. d

10. p=8.5

11. b

12. 1120

13. 1.646722

14. $f(x)=\frac{1}{20}x^5+4\sinh x-(2\sinh 2)x+1$

15. 66.33

16. c

17. $s(t)=6-2\cos(t)-4\sin(t)$

18. $755.93

19. 5

20. $2\sqrt{2}$

1. Use the given graph of f to find the Riemann sum with six subintervals. Take the sample points to be left endpoints.

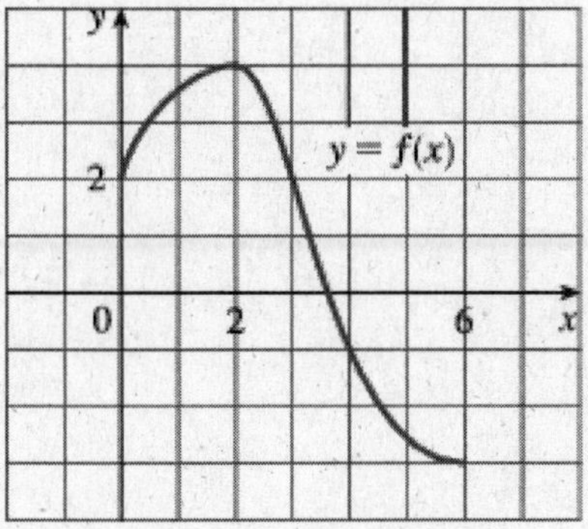

2. The speed of a runner increased steadily during the first three seconds of a race. Her speed at half-second intervals is given in the table. Find a lower estimate for the distance that she traveled during these three seconds.

t (s)	0	0.5	1.0	1.5	2.0	2.5	3.0
(ft/s)	0	3.7	8.3	13.2	15.1	15.7	16.2

3. Find an expression for the area under the graph of f as a limit. Do not evaluate the limit.

$f(x)=x^2+\sqrt{1+2x},\quad 4\le x\le 7$

4. Evaluate the Riemann sum for $f(y)=9-y^2,\ 0\le y\le 2$ with four subintervals, taking the sample points to be right endpoints.

5. If $f(x)=\sqrt{x}-2,\ 1\le x\le 6$, find the Riemann sum with $n=5$ correct to 3 decimal places, taking the sample points to be midpoints.

6. Evaluate the definite integral.

$\int_{-1}^{1}\frac{\sin x}{1+x^2}dx$

7. The velocity function (in meters per second) is given for a particle moving along a line. Find the distance traveled by the particle during the given time interval.

$v(t)=4t-3,\ 0\le t\le 6$

8. If $\int_0^6 f(x)dx=10$ and $\int_0^4 f(x)dx=7$, find $\int_4^6 f(x)dx$.

9. Find the area of the region that lies under the given curve.

$y=\sqrt{5x+2},\quad 0\le x\le 1$

Round the result to the nearest thousandth.

10. Evaluate the integral.

$$\int_0^{1/2} \frac{2dr}{\sqrt{1-r^2}}$$

11. Evaluate the indefinite integral.

$$\int \frac{4+6x}{\sqrt{6+4x+3x^2}}\,dx$$

12. Evaluate

$$\int_0^3 \left(x+\sqrt{9-x^2}\right)dx$$

by interpreting it in terms of areas.

13. Express the sum as a single integral in the form

$$\int_a^b f(z)\ dz$$

$$\int_2^8 f(z)\ dz + \int_8^{11} f(z)\ dz$$

14. Use Part 1 of the Fundamental Theorem of Calculus to find the derivative of the function.

$$h(x) = \int_1^{e^x} 2\ln t\,dt$$

15. Evaluate the integral.

$$\int_0^3 2\left|x^2-4\right|dx$$

16. Evaluate the integral.

$$\int_{\pi/6}^{\pi/4} \sin(t)dt$$

17. Evaluate the integral if it exists.

$$\int \frac{\cos(\ln x)}{x}\,dx$$

18. Alabama Instruments Company has set up a production line to manufacture a new calculator. The rate of production of these calculators after t weeks is $\frac{dx}{dt} = 4{,}500\left(1 - \frac{130}{(t+9)^2}\right)$ calculators per week.

Production approaches 4,500 per week as time goes on, but the initial production is lower because of the workers' unfamiliarity with the new techniques. Find the number of calculators produced from the beginning of the third week to the end of the fourth week.

Round the answer to the nearest integer.

19. The marginal cost of manufacturing x yards of a certain fabric is $C'(x) = 3 - 0.01x + 0.000006x^2$ (in dollars per yard). Find the increase in cost if the production level is raised from 500 yards to 3,000 yards.

20. Evaluate the indefinite integral. Check that your answer is reasonable by graphing both the function and its antiderivative (take C=0).

$$\int e^{\cos x} \sin x \, dx$$

ANSWER KEY

Stewart – Calculus ET 7e Chapter 5 Form A

1. 8

2. 28

3. $\lim_{n\to\infty}\sum_{i=1}^{n}\left[\left(4+\frac{3i}{n}\right)^2+\sqrt{1+2\left(4+\frac{3i}{n}\right)}\right]\cdot\frac{3}{n}$

4. 14.25

5. –0.857

6. 0

7. 54

8. 3

9. 2.092

10. $\pi/3$

11. $2\sqrt{6+4x+3x^2}+C$

12. $\int_0^3\left(x+\sqrt{9-x^2}\right)dx=\int_0^3 x\,dx+\int_0^3\sqrt{9-x^2}\,dx=I_1+I_2$

$I_1 = \textit{Area of a triangle},\ I_2 = \textit{Area of a quarter circle}$

$I_1+I_2=\frac{1}{2}(3)(3)+\frac{1}{4}(\pi)(3)^2=9/2+9\pi/4$

13. $\int_2^{11} f(z)\,dz$

14. $2xe^x$

15. $46/3$

16. $\frac{\sqrt{3}-\sqrt{2}}{2}$

17. $\sin(\ln x)+C$

18. 818

19. 17500

20. $-e^{\cos x}+C$

1. Use the given graph of f to estimate the Riemann sum with six subintervals. Take the sample points to be midpoints.

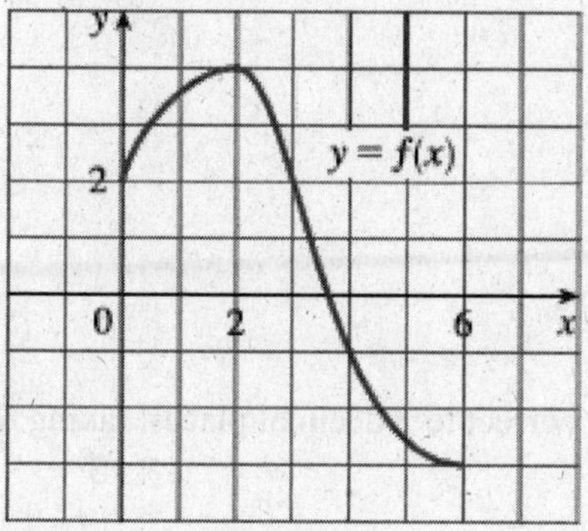

2. If $\int_0^6 f(x)dx = 10$ and $\int_0^4 f(x)dx = 7$, find $\int_4^6 f(x)dx$.

3. Find an expression for the area under the graph of f as a limit. Do not evaluate the limit.

$f(x) = x^2 + \sqrt{1+x}, \quad 5 \le x \le 7$

4. Estimate the area from 0 to 5 under the graph of $f(x) = 81 - x^2$ using five approximating rectangles and right endpoints.

5. A table of values of an increasing function $f(x)$ is shown. Use the table to find an upper estimate of

$$\int_0^{25} f(x)\ dx$$

x	$f(x)$
0	–43
5	–32
10	–22
15	–7
0	6
25	35

6. Evaluate

$$\int_0^2 \left(x + \sqrt{4 - x^2}\right) dx$$

by interpreting it in terms of areas.

7. Given that $\int_4^6 f(x)\,dx = \frac{6}{57}$, find $\int_6^4 f(x)\,dx$.

8. Use Part 1 of the Fundamental Theorem of Calculus to find the derivative of the function.

$$h(x) = \int_1^{\sqrt{x}} \frac{2z^2}{z^4+1}\,dz$$

9. Evaluate the integral.

$$\int_0^{\sqrt{3}/2} \frac{dr}{\sqrt{1-r^2}}$$

10. If $f(r)=\sqrt{r}-2,\ 1 \le r \le 6$, find the Riemann sum with $n=5$ correct to 3 decimal places, taking the sample points to be midpoints.

11. Evaluate the integral.

$$\int_0^9 (10+6y-y^2)\,dy$$

12. Evaluate the integral.

$$\int_0^1 \frac{e^x}{1+e^{2x}}\,dx$$

13. Evaluate the indefinite integral.

$$\int \cos^4 x \sin x\,dx$$

14. The velocity function (in meters per second) is given for a particle moving along a line. Find the distance traveled by the particle during the given time interval.

$$v(t)=4t-3,\quad 0 \le t \le 6$$

15. Evaluate the integral.

$$\int_0^{\pi/6} \frac{2+\cos^2\theta}{\cos^2\theta}\,d\theta$$

16. Evaluate the integral by making the given substitution.

$$\int x^2\sqrt{x^3+1}\,dx,\quad u=x^3+1$$

17. Evaluate the indefinite integral.

$$\int \sqrt{4x}\,\sin(1+x^{3/2})\,dx$$

18. Find the derivative of the function.

$$g(x) = \int_4^{x^2} 5\sqrt{1+t^2}\, dt$$

19. Evaluate the indefinite integral. Check that your answer is reasonable by graphing both the function and its antiderivative (take C=0).

$$\int e^{\sin x} \cos x\, dx$$

20. Evaluate the integral.

$$\int_0^{\pi/4} 4(1+\tan t)^3 \sec^2 t\, dt$$

ANSWER KEY

Stewart - Calculus ET 7e Chapter 5 Form B

1. 5.7

2. 3

3. $\lim_{n\to\infty} \sum_{i=1}^{n}\left[\left(5+\frac{2i}{n}\right)^2+\sqrt{1+\left(5+\frac{2i}{n}\right)}\right]\cdot\frac{2}{n}$

4. 350

5. –100

6. $\int_0^2\left(x+\sqrt{4-x^2}\right)dx=\int_0^2 x\,dx+\int_0^2\sqrt{4-x^2}\,dx=I_1+I_2$

$I_1 = \textit{Area of a triangle},\ I_2 = \textit{Area of a quarter circle}$

$I_1+I_2=\frac{1}{2}(2)(2)+\frac{1}{4}(\pi)(2)^2=2+\pi$

7. –6/57

8. $\frac{\sqrt{x}}{x^2+1}$

9. $\pi/3$

10. –0.857

11. 90

12. $\arctan(e)-\frac{\pi}{4}$

13. $-\frac{1}{5}\cos^5 x+C$

14. 54

15. $\frac{2\sqrt{3}}{3}+\frac{\pi}{6}$

16. $\frac{2}{9}(x^3+1)^{3/2}+C$

17. $-\frac{4}{3}\cos(1+(\sqrt{x})^3)$

18. $10x\sqrt{1+x^4}$

19. $e^{\sin x}+C$

20. 15

1. Estimate to the hundredth the area from 1 to 5 under the graph of $f(x) = \dfrac{4}{x}$ using four approximating rectangles and right endpoints.

Select the correct answer.

a. 5.13
b. 6.65
c. 5.83
d. 3.65
e. 4.23
f. 4.55

2. Evaluate the Riemann sum for $f(r) = 2 - r^2,\ 0 \le r \le 2$, with four subintervals, taking the sample points to be right endpoints.

Select the correct answer.

a. 0.25
b. 1.5
c. 2.5
d. 0.36
e. 0.2

3. Use the given graph of f to find the Riemann sum with six subintervals. Take the sample points to be left endpoints.

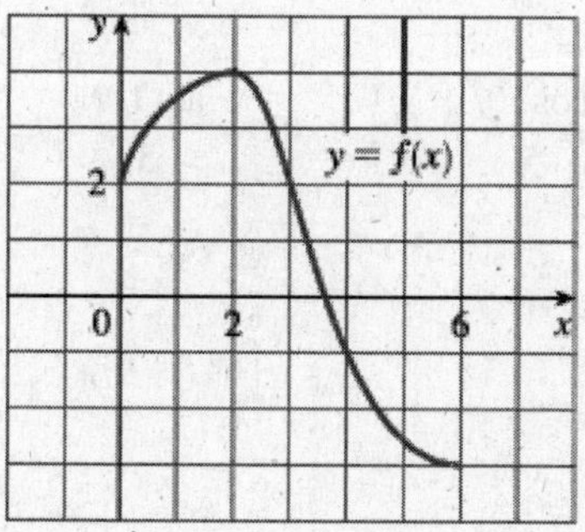

Select the correct answer.

a. 8 b. 6 c. 4 d. 3.5 e. 4.5

4. If $\int_0^6 f(x)\,dx = 10$ and $\int_0^4 f(x)\,dx = 7$, find $\int_4^6 f(x)\,dx$.

Select the correct answer.

a. –10 b. 17 c. 3 d. –3 e. 2

5. Evaluate

$$\frac{d}{dx}\int_0^x (e^{\arctan t})dt$$

Select the correct answer.

a. $e^{\arctan t - \frac{\pi}{4}}$ b. $e^x - \arctan x$ c. $e^{\arctan t}$ d. x e. $e^{\arctan x}$

6. Find the area of the region that lies beneath the given curve.

$$y = \sin x,\ 0 \le x \le \frac{\pi}{3}$$

Select the correct answer.

a. 1.500 b. –1.500 c. 0.500 d. –0.500 e. 1.450

7. Find the general indefinite integral.

$$\int \frac{\sin 20t}{\sin 10t}\,dt$$

Select the correct answer.

a. $\frac{\sin 10t}{5}+C$ b. $\frac{\cos 10t}{5}+C$ c. $\frac{\sin 10t}{10}+C$ d. $-\frac{\cos 10t}{5}+C$ e. $-\frac{\sin 10t}{5}+C$

8. Evaluate the integral.

$$\int_0^{1/2} \frac{dr}{\sqrt{1-r^2}}$$

Select the correct answer.

a. $\pi/3$ b. $\pi/2$ c. $1/6$ d. $1/3$ e. $\pi/6$

9. An animal population is increasing at a rate of $13+51t$ per year (where t is measured in years). By how much does the animal population increase between the fourth and tenth years?

Select the correct answer.

a. 2,220
b. 4,362
c. 2,155
d. 2,064
e. 2,100

10. Evaluate the integral.

$$\int_0^3 \left(6+6y-y^2\right)\,dy$$

Select the correct answer.

a. –18 b. 45 c. 54 d. 36 e. –12

11. The marginal cost of manufacturing x yards of a certain fabric is $C'(x) = 3 - 0.01x + 0.000006x^2$ (in dollars per yard). Find the increase in cost if the production level is raised from 1,000 yards to 4,500 yards.

Select the correct answer.

a. $94,500.00
b. $97,500.00
c. $95,500.00
d. $92,500.00
e. $94,600.00

12. Estimate the area from 0 to 5 under the graph of $f(x) = 81 - x^2$ using five approximating rectangles and right endpoints.

Select the correct answer.

a. 350 b. 1500 c. 500 d. 250 e. 175

13. Alabama Instruments Company has set up a production line to manufacture a new calculator. The rate of production of these calculators after t weeks is $\dfrac{dx}{dt} = 5{,}700\left(1 - \dfrac{130}{(t+18)^2}\right)$ calculators per week.

Production approaches 5,700 per week as time goes on, but the initial production is lower because of the workers' unfamiliarity with the new techniques. Find the number of calculators produced from the beginning of the third week to the end of the fourth week.

Select the correct answer. The choices are rounded to the nearest integer.

a. 8,031
b. 8,027
c. 8,034
d. 8,042
e. 8,142
f. 8,032

14. Evaluate the integral.

$$\int_{-2}^{5} \left|4x - x^2\right|\,dx$$

Select the correct answer. The choices are rounded to the nearest hundredth.

a. 109.00 b. 123.67 c. 102.33 d. 209.00 e. 23.67

15. Use Part 1 of the Fundamental Theorem of Calculus to find the derivative of the function.

$$h(x) = \int_1^{\sqrt{x}} \frac{z^2}{z^4+1}\,dz$$

Select the correct answer.

a. $\dfrac{\sqrt{x}}{x^2+1}$ b. $\dfrac{\sqrt{x^2+1}}{2}$ c. $\dfrac{\sqrt{x+1}}{x^2+2}$ d. $\dfrac{\sqrt{x}}{2(x^2+1)}$ e. none of these

16. Evaluate the indefinite integral.

$$\int \cos^7 x \sin x \, dx$$

Select the correct answer.

a. $\frac{1}{8}\cos^8 x + C$

b. $-\frac{1}{8}\sin^8 x + C$

c. $-\frac{1}{8}\cos^7 x + C$

d. $\frac{1}{8}\sin^8 x + C$

e. $-\frac{1}{8}\cos^8 x + C$

17. Evaluate the integral if it exists.

$$\int \left(\frac{1-x}{x}\right)^2 dx$$

Select the correct answer.

a. $x - \dfrac{1}{2\ln x} + C$

b. $x - 2\ln x - \dfrac{1}{x} + C$

c. $1 - 2\ln x + C$

d. $\ln x - x + C$

e. none of these

18. If h' is a child's rate of growth in pounds per year, which of the following expressions represents the increase in the child's weight (in pounds) between the years 2 and 5?

Select the correct answer.

a. $\int_2^5 h'(t)\,dt$ b. $h'(5) - h'(2)$ c. $\int_5^2 h(t)\,dt$

19. The acceleration function (in m / s ^{2}) and the initial velocity are given for a particle moving along a line. Find the velocity at time t and the distance traveled during the given time interval.

$a(t) = t + 4,\ \ v(0) = 3,\ \ 0 \le t \le 10$

Select the correct answer.

a. $v(t) = \dfrac{t^2}{2} + 4t + 3$ m/s, $396\dfrac{2}{3}$ m

b. $v(t) = \dfrac{t^2}{2} + 4t + 3$ m/s, $391\dfrac{2}{3}$ m

c. $v(t) = \dfrac{t^2}{2} + 3$ m/s, $411\dfrac{2}{3}$ m

d. $v(t) = \dfrac{t^2}{2} + 4t$ m/s, $406\dfrac{2}{3}$ m

e. $v(t) = \dfrac{t^2}{2} + 4t$ m/s, $415\dfrac{2}{3}$ m

20. Evaluate the indefinite integral.

$\int e^{\cos x} \sin x\,dx$

Select the correct answer.

a. $e^{\cos x} \sin x + C$

b. $-e^{\cos x} \sin x + C$

c. $-\sin(e^{\cos x}) + C$

d. $e^{\sin(x)} + C$

e. $-e^{\cos x} + C$

ANSWER KEY

Stewart - Calculus ET 7e Chapter 5 Form C

1. a

2. a

3. a

4. c

5. e

6. c

7. a

8. e

9. a

10. d

11. a

12. a

13. f

14. e

15. d

16. e

17. b

18. a

19. a

20. e

1. Estimate to the hundredth the area from 1 to 5 under the graph of $f(x)=\dfrac{4}{x}$ using four approximating rectangles and right endpoints.

Select the correct answer. The choices are rounded to the nearest hundredth.

a. 6.87 b. 5.85 c. 4.77 d. 5.13 e. 4.59

2. Approximate the area under the curve $y = \sin x$ from 0 to $\pi/2$ using ten approximating rectangles of equal widths and right endpoints.

Select the correct answer. The choices are rounded to the nearest hundredth.

a. 0.72 b. 0.98 c. 0.02 d. 1.08 e. 0.36

3. Use the given graph of f to find the Riemann sum with six subintervals. Take the sample points to be midpoints.

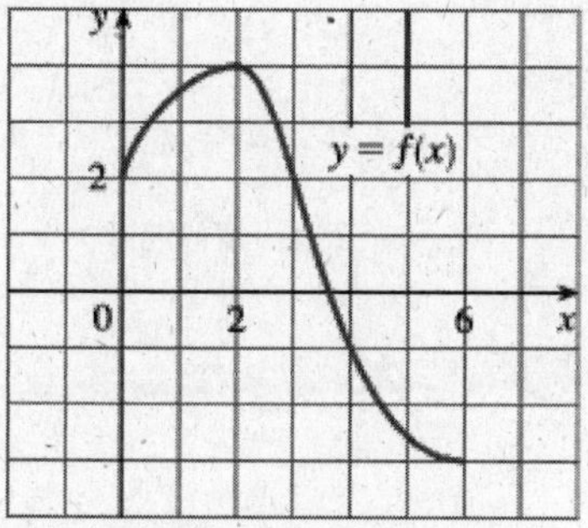

Select the correct answer.

a. 5.7 b. 8 c. 3.7 d. 2.5 e. 4.5

4. If $\int_0^6 f(x)dx = 10$ and $\int_0^4 f(x)dx = 7$, find $\int_4^6 f(x)dx$.

Select the correct answer.

a. –10 b. 17 c. 3 d. –3 e. 2

5. Evaluate the integral.

$$\int_{\pi/4}^{\pi/2} \sin t \, dt$$

Select the correct answer.

a. 1.414
b. –0.707
c. 0.354
d. 0.707
e. –1.414

6. Evaluate.

$$\frac{d}{dx}\int_0^x (e^{\arctan t})dt$$

Select the correct answer.

a. $e^{\arctan t - \frac{\pi}{4}}$ b. $e^x - \arctan x$ c. $e^{\arctan t}$ d. x e. $e^{\arctan x}$

7. The area of the region that lies to the right of the y-axis and to the left of the parabola $x = 5y - y^2$ (the shaded region in the figure) is given by the integral $\int_0^5 (5y - y^2)\ dy$.

Find the area.

Select the correct answer.

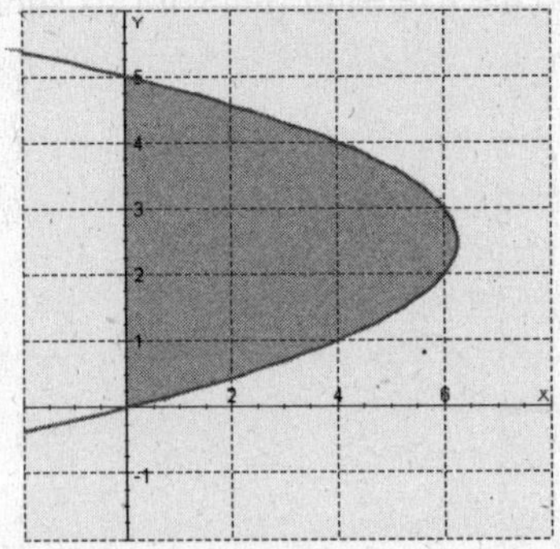

a. 125

b. $\frac{25}{6}$

c. 6.25

d. $\frac{125}{6}$

e. 45.6

8. Estimate the area from 0 to 5 under the graph of $f(x) = 81 - x^2$ using five approximating rectangles and right endpoints.

Select the correct answer.

a. 350 b. 250 c. 175 d. 325 e. none of these

9. Evaluate the integral.

$$\int_0^{1/2} \frac{dr}{\sqrt{1-r^2}}$$

Select the correct answer.

a. $\pi/3$ b. $\pi/2$ c. $1/6$ d. $1/3$ e. $\pi/6$

10. Evaluate the integral.

$$\int_1^4 \frac{x^2+6}{\sqrt{x}}\ dx$$

Select the correct answer.

a. 24.4 b. 37 c. 74 d. 49.2 e. 21.4

11. Evaluate the integral by making the given substitution.

$$\int x^2\sqrt{x^3+2}\,dx,\quad u=x^3+2$$

Select the correct answer.

a. $-\frac{2}{9}(x^3+2)^{3/2}+C$

b. $\frac{1}{9}(x^3+2)^{1/2}+C$

c. $\frac{2}{9}(x^3+2)^{1/2}+C$

d. $\frac{2}{9}(x^3+3)^{3/2}$

e. $\frac{2}{9}(x^3+2)^{3/2}+C$

12. The velocity function (in meters per second) is given for a particle moving along a line. Find the distance traveled by the particle during the given time interval.

$v(t)=6t-6,\ 0\le t\le 5$

Select the correct answer.

a. 105 m b. –15 m c. 51 m d. 148.8 m e. 115 m

13. An animal population is increasing at a rate of $29+37t$ per year (where t is measured in years). By how much does the animal population increase between the fourth and tenth years?

Select the correct answer.

a. 1,728 b. 1,583 c. 1,380 d. 3,282 e. 1,528

14. The velocity of a car was read from its speedometer at ten-second intervals and recorded in the table. Use the Midpoint Rule to estimate the distance traveled by the car.

t (s)	v (mi/h)	t (s)	v (mi/h)
0	0	60	63
10	39	70	60
20	57	80	70
30	54	90	49
40	69	100	43
50	65		

Select the correct answer.

a. 1.7 miles
b. 1.2 miles
c. 1.5 miles
d. 1.6 miles
e. 1.9 miles

15. Evaluate the integral if it exists.

$$\int_0^1 3x^2 \cos(x^3)dx$$

Select the correct answer.

a. $\sin(3)$ b. 0 c. $3\sin(1)$ d. $\cos(1)$ e. none of these

16. Evaluate the definite integral.

$$\int_0^{\pi/8} \sin 8t \, dt$$

Select the correct answer.

a. 0.25 b. 3.25 c. 0.35 d. 1.25 e. –0.25

17. Find the area of the region that lies under the given curve. Round the answer to three decimal places.

$$y = \sqrt{2x+2}, \ 0 \le x \le 1$$

Select the correct answer.

a. 1.834 b. 1.727 c. 1.704 d. 1.724 e. 1.824

18. Use Part 1 of the Fundamental Theorem of Calculus to find the derivative of the function.

$$h(x) = \int_1^{\sqrt{x}} \frac{z^2}{z^4+1} dz$$

Select the correct answer.

a. $\sqrt{x}/(x^2+1)$ b. $\sqrt{x^2+1/2}$ c. $\sqrt{x+1}/(x^2+2)$ d. $\sqrt{x}/(2x^2+2)$ e. none

19. If $F(x) = \int_1^x f(t)\,dt$ where $f(t) = \int_1^{t^2} \frac{\sqrt{2+u^2}}{u} du$ find $F''(2)$.

Select the correct answer.

a. $3\sqrt{2}/2$ b. $3\sqrt{2}$ c. $6\sqrt{2}$ d. $6\sqrt{3}$ e. $3\sqrt{3}$

20. Evaluate the indefinite integral.

$$\int e^{\sin x} \cos x \, dx$$

Select the correct answer.

a. $e^{\cos x} \sin x + C$ b. $-e^{\cos x} \sin x + C$ c. $-\sin(e^{\cos x}) + C$ d. $e^{\sin x} + C$ e. $-e^{\cos x} + C$

ANSWER KEY

1. d
2. d
3. a
4. c
5. d
6. e
7. d
8. a
9. e
10. a
11. e
12. c
13. a
14. c
15. e
16. a
17. d
18. d
19. b
20. d

1. By reading values from the given graph of f, use five rectangles to find a lower estimate, to the nearest whole number, for the area from 0 to 10 under the given graph of f.

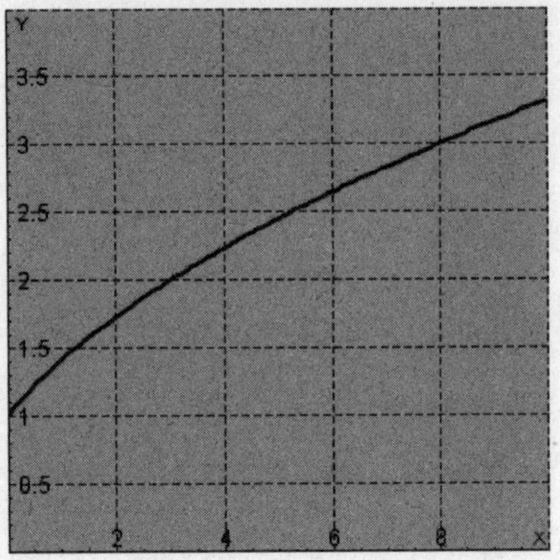

2. Approximate the area under the curve $y = 4/x^2$ from 1 to 2 using ten approximating rectangles of equal widths and right endpoints. Round the answer to the nearest hundredth.

3. Find an expression for the area under the graph of f as a limit. Do not evaluate the limit.

$$f(x) = \sqrt{\sin x}, \quad 0 \le x \le \pi$$

4. The speed of a runner increased steadily during the first three seconds of a race. Her speed at half-second intervals is given in the table. Find a lower estimate for the distance that she traveled during these three seconds.

t (s)	0	0.5	1.0	1.5	2.0	2.5	3.0
v (ft/s)	0	4.9	9.2	13.7	15.5	16.1	16.6

5. Evaluate the Riemann sum for $f(z) = 9 - z^2$, $0 \le z \le 2$, with four subintervals, taking the sample points to be right endpoints.

6. If $f(r) = \sqrt{r} - 2$, $1 \le r \le 6$, find the Riemann sum with $n = 5$ correct to 3 decimal places, taking the sample points to be midpoints.

7. Use Part 1 of the Fundamental Theorem of Calculus to find the derivative of the function.

$$h(x) = \int_1^{\sqrt{x}} \frac{z^2}{z^4 + 1}\, dz$$

Select the correct answer.

a. $\dfrac{\sqrt{x}}{x^2 + 1}$ b. $\dfrac{\sqrt{x^2 + 1}}{2}$ c. $\dfrac{\sqrt{x + 1}}{x^2 + 2}$ d. $\dfrac{\sqrt{x}}{2\left(x^2 + 1\right)}$ e. none of these

8. Find the derivative of the function.

$$F(x) = \int_{x}^{x^2} e^{t^2}\, dt$$

9. Use the Midpoint Rule with $n = 5$ to approximate the integral.

$$\int_{0}^{10} 2\sin\sqrt{q}\, dq$$

Select the correct answer. The choices are rounded to 3 decimal places.

a. 8.998 b. 4.781 c. 12.929 d. 9.998 e. 5.781

10. The velocity graph of a braking car is shown. Use it to estimate to the nearest foot the distance traveled by the car while the brakes are applied.

Use a left sum with $n = 7$.

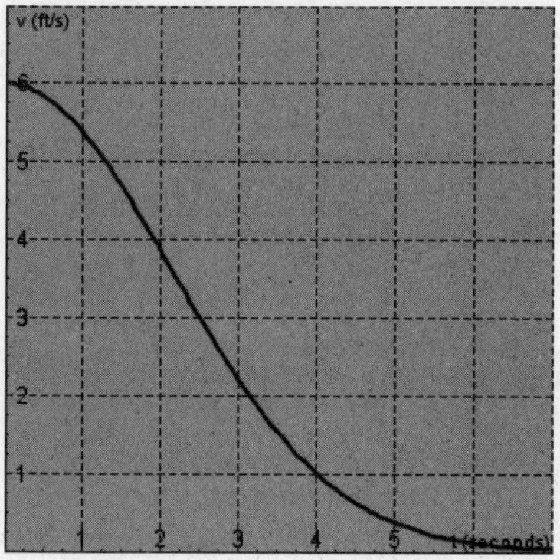

11. Evaluate the integral.

$$\int_{0}^{9} \left(6 + 6y - y^2\right) dy$$

12. Evaluate the integral.

$$\int_{0}^{1/2} \frac{dr}{\sqrt{1-r^2}}$$

13. Evaluate the integral.

$$\int_{6\pi}^{8\pi} \cos\theta\, d\theta$$

14. The marginal cost of manufacturing x yards of a certain fabric is $C'(x) = 3 - 0.01x + 0.000006x^2$ (in dollars per yard). Find the increase in cost if the production level is raised from 1,500 yards to 4,500 yards.

15. Find the general indefinite integral.

$$\int \frac{\sin 14t}{\sin 7t} dt$$

16. Evaluate the integral.

$$\int_{-4}^{3} \left| 2x - x^2 \right| dx$$

17. An animal population is increasing at a rate of $29 + 36t$ per year (where t is measured in years). By how much does the animal population increase between the fourth and tenth years?

Select the correct answer.

a. 1686 b. 1668 c. 1488 d. 686 e. 1268

18. Evaluate the indefinite integral.

$$\int \frac{4 + 10x}{\sqrt{1 + 4x + 5x^2}} dx$$

19. Find the area of the region that lies to the right of the y-axis and to the left of the parabola $x = 5y - y^2$.

20. Evaluate the indefinite integral.

$$\int \frac{e^x}{e^x + 1} dx$$

Select the correct answer.

a. $-\frac{1}{2}\ln\left(e^x + 1\right) + C$

b. $\frac{1}{2}\ln\left(e^x + 1\right) + C$

c. $\ln\left(e^x - 1\right) + C$

d. $\ln\left(e^x + 1\right) + C$

e. $-\ln\left(e^x + 1\right) + C$

ANSWER KEY

Stewart - Calculus ET 7e Chapter 5 Form E

1. 21

2. 1.86

3. $\lim_{n\to\infty} \sum_{i=1}^{n} \left[\sqrt{\sin\left(\frac{\pi i}{n}\right)} \right] \cdot \frac{\pi}{n}$

4. 29.7

5. 14.25

6. –0.857

7. d

8. $F'(x) = 2xe^{x^4} - e^{x^2}$

9. c

10. 19

11. 54

12. $\pi/6$

13. 0

14. 94500

15. $\frac{2\sin 7t}{7} + C$

16. 40

17. a

18. $2\sqrt{1+4x+5x^2} + C$

19. $125/6$

20. d

1. Find an expression for the area under the graph of f as a limit. Do not evaluate the limit.

$f(x)=\sqrt{\sin x},\quad 0\le x\le \pi/4$

2. Estimate to the hundredth the area from 1 to 5 under the graph of $f(x)=4/x$ using four approximating rectangles and right endpoints.

Select the correct answer.

a. 6.87 b. 5.85 c. 4.77 d. 5.13 e. 4.59

3. Evaluate the integral.

$$\int_{2\pi}^{4\pi}\cos x\,dx$$

4. Find the area of the region that lies beneath the given curve.

$y=\sin x,\ 0\le x\le \pi/2$

5. Evaluate the Riemann sum for $f(y)=9-y^2,\ 0\le y\le 2$ with four subintervals, taking the sample points to be right endpoints.

6. Use Part 1 of the Fundamental Theorem of Calculus to find the derivative of the function.

$$h(x)=\int_1^{e^x} 2\ln t\,dt$$

7. Evaluate.

$$\frac{d}{dx}\int_0^x (e^{\arctan t})dt$$

Select the correct answer.

a. $e^{\arctan t-\frac{\pi}{4}}$ b. $e^x-\arctan x$ c. $e^{\arctan t}$ d. x e. $e^{\arctan x}$

8. Evaluate the indefinite integral.

$$\int \sec^2 x\tan x\ dx$$

9. Find a function $f(x)$ such that $5+\int_a^x \frac{f(t)}{t^2}dt=8\sqrt{x}$ for $x>0$ and some number a.

10. Evaluate the integral.

$$\int_0^{1/2}\frac{2dr}{\sqrt{1-r^2}}$$

Evaluate the indefinite integral.

11.

$$\int \cos^3 \sin x \, dx$$

12. Evaluate the integral.

$$\int_{-1}^{3} \left| 2x - x^2 \right| dx$$

Select the correct answer. The choices are rounded to the nearest hundredth.

a. 19.33 b. 22.00 c. 14.67 d. 4.00 e. 32.67

13. The velocity of a car was read from its speedometer at ten-second intervals and recorded in the table. Use the Midpoint Rule to estimate the distance traveled by the car.

Round your answer to the nearest tenth.

t (s)	v (mi / h)	t (s)	v (mi / h)
0	0	60	65
10	37	70	57
20	55	80	60
30	67	90	47
40	69	100	44
50	53		

14. Evaluate

$$\int_0^3 \left(x + \sqrt{9 - x^2} \right) dx$$

by interpreting it in terms of areas.

15. Evaluate the integral.

$$\int_0^1 3x^2 \cos(x^3) dx$$

16. Evaluate the integral by making the given substitution.

$$\int x^2 \sqrt{x^3 + 9} \, dx, \quad u = x^3 + 9$$

Select the correct answer.

a. $\dfrac{\left(x^3+9\right)^{1/2}}{9} + C$ b. $\dfrac{2\left(x^3+9\right)^{3/2}}{9} + C$ c. $\dfrac{2\left(x^3-9\right)^{3/2}}{9} + C$ d. $\dfrac{-2\left(x^3+9\right)^{3/2}}{9} + C$ e. none

17. Evaluate the indefinite integral.

$$\int 4x\left(x^2+3\right)^4\,dx$$

18. Evaluate the indefinite integral.

$$\int \frac{4+10x}{\sqrt{7+4x+5x^2}}\,dx$$

Select the correct answer.

a. $2\sqrt{7+4x+5x^2}+C$

b. $\sqrt{7+4x+5x^2}+C$

c. $-2\sqrt{7+4x+5x^2}$

d. $-2\sqrt{7+4x+5x^2}+C$

e. $3\sqrt{7+4x+5x^2}+C$

19. Evaluate the definite integral.

$$\int_0^1 x^2\left(3+2x^3\right)^2\,dx$$

20. Evaluate the indefinite integral. Check that your answer is reasonable by graphing both the function and its antiderivative (take $C=0$).

$$\int e^{\sin x}\cos x\,dx$$

ANSWER KEY

Stewart - Calculus ET 7e Chapter 5 Form F

1. $\lim_{n\to\infty} \sum_{i=1}^{n} \left[\sqrt{\sin\left(\frac{\pi i}{4n}\right)}\right] \cdot \frac{\pi}{4n}$

2. d

3. 0

4. 1

5. 14.25

6. $2xe^x$

7. e

8. $\frac{1}{2}\sec^2 x + C$

9. $f(x) = 4x^{3/2}$; *for* $a = \frac{25}{64}$

10. $\pi/3$

11. $-\frac{1}{4}\cos^4 x + C$

12. d

13. 1.5

14. $\int_0^3 \left(x + \sqrt{9 - x^2}\right) dx = \int_0^3 x\,dx + \int_0^3 \sqrt{9 - x^2}\,dx = I_1 + I_2$

$I_1 = \textit{Area of a triangle},\ I_2 = \textit{Area of a quarter circle}$

$I_1 + I_2 = \frac{1}{2}(3)(3) + \frac{1}{4}(\pi)(3)^2 = 9/2 + 9\pi/4$

15. sin(1)

16. b

17. $\frac{2}{5}\left(x^2 + 3\right)^5 + C$

18. a

19. $\frac{49}{9}$

20. $e^{\sin x} + C$

1. Estimate to the hundredth the area from 1 to 5 under the graph of $f(x)=\frac{4}{x}$ using four approximating rectangles and right endpoints.

2. Estimate the area from 0 to 5 under the graph of $f(x)=81-x^2$ using five approximating rectangles and right endpoints.

3. Find an expression for the area under the graph of f as a limit. Do not evaluate the limit.

$$f(x)=x^2+\sqrt{1+2x},\quad 4\le x\le 7$$

4. If $\int_0^6 f(x)\,dx=10$ and $\int_0^4 f(x)\,dx=7$, find $\int_4^6 f(x)\,dx$.

Select the correct answer.

a. -10 b. 17 c. 3 d. -3 e. 2

5. The speed of a runner increased steadily during the first three seconds of a race. Her speed at half-second intervals is given in the table. Find a lower estimate for the distance that she traveled during these three seconds.

t (s)	0	0.5	1.0	1.5	2.0	2.5	3.0
v (ft/s)	0	3	7.6	11.7	13	13.7	14.6

6. Evaluate the integral if it exists.

$$\int\left(\frac{1-x}{x}\right)^2 dx$$

Select the correct answer.

a. $x-2\ln x-\frac{1}{x}+C$
b. $2-\ln x+C$
c. $\ln x-x+C$
d. $x-\frac{1}{2\ln x}+C$
e. does not exist

7. Use Part 1 of the Fundamental Theorem of Calculus to find the derivative of the function.

$$h(x)=\int_1^{\sqrt{x}}\frac{z^2}{z^4+1}\,dz$$

8. The area of the region that lies to the right of the y-axis and to the left of the parabola $x = 5y - y^2$ (the shaded region in the figure) is given by the integral $\int_0^5 \left(5y - y^2\right) dy$. Find the area.

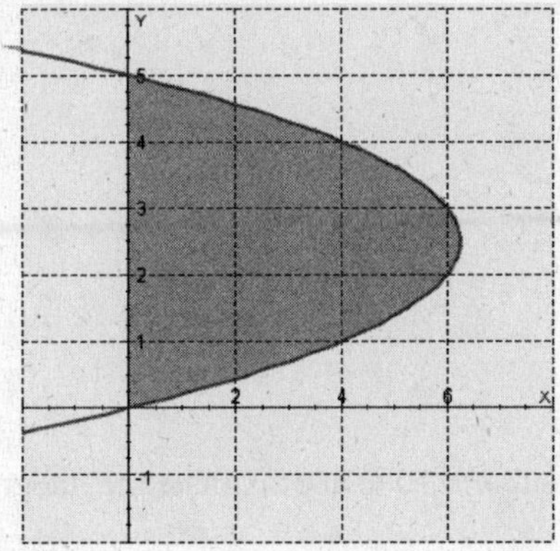

Select the correct answer.

a. 125

b. $\dfrac{25}{6}$

c. 6.25

d. $\dfrac{125}{6}$

e. 45.6

9. The velocity graph of a car accelerating from rest to a speed of 7 km/h over a period of 10 seconds is shown. Estimate to the nearest integer the distance traveled during this period. Use a right sum with $n = 10$.

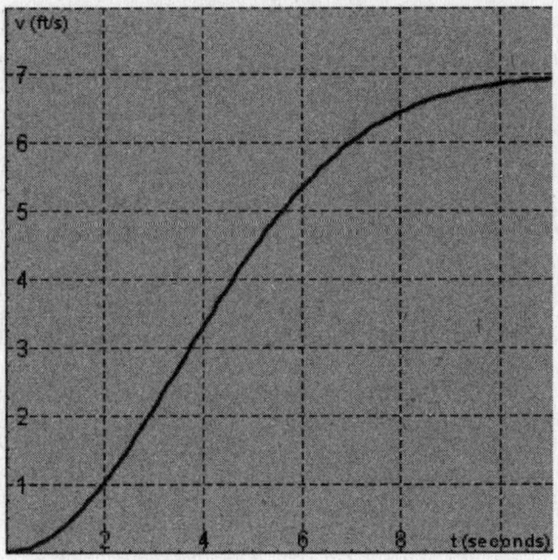

10. Determine a region whose area is equal to $\lim_{n\to\infty} \sum_{i=1}^{n} \dfrac{\pi}{3n} \tan \dfrac{i\pi}{3n}$.

Select the correct answer.

a. $y = \tan x,\ 0 \le x \le \dfrac{\pi}{13}$

b. $y = \tan x,\ 0 \le x \le \dfrac{\pi}{10}$

c. $y = \tan x,\ 0 \le x \le \dfrac{\pi}{3}$

d. $y = \tan x,\ 0 \le x \le \dfrac{\pi}{5}$

e. $y = \tan x,\ 0 \le x \le \dfrac{\pi}{8}$

11. Evaluate the integral.

$$\int_{\pi/4}^{\pi/2} \sin t \, dt$$

Select the correct answer.

a. 1.414
b. –0.707
c. 0.354
d. 0.707
e. –1.414

12. Use the Midpoint Rule with $n = 10$ to approximate the integral.

$$\int_{1}^{2} \sqrt{4+t^2}\, dt$$

Select the correct answer.

a. 2.510608
b. 1.731856
c. 10.042434
d. 2.810608
e. 3.510608

13. Use the Midpoint Rule with $n = 5$ to approximate the integral. Round the answer to 3 decimal places.

$$\int_0^{10} 2\sin\sqrt{t}\, dt$$

14. Express the limit as a definite integral on the given interval.

$$\lim_{n\to\infty} \sum_{i=1}^{n} (4r_i \sin r_i)\Delta r, \quad [4, 9]$$

15. Evaluate the integral if it exists.

$$\int \frac{\cos(\ln x)}{x}\, dx$$

16. Evaluate

$$\int_0^2 \left(x+\sqrt{4-x^2}\right) dx$$

by interpreting it in terms of areas.

17. Evaluate the integral by interpreting it in terms of areas.

$$\int_{-4}^{4} \sqrt{16-x^2}\ dx$$

18. Evaluate the integral by interpreting it in terms of areas.

$$\int_{-1}^{3} (3-x)\ dx$$

19. Given that $\int_{4}^{8} f(x)\ dx = \frac{2}{67}$, find $\int_{8}^{4} f(x)\ dx$.

20. Evaluate the indefinite integral. Check that your answer is reasonable by graphing both the function and its antiderivative (take C=0).

$$\int e^{\cos x} \sin x\, dx$$

ANSWER KEY

Stewart - Calculus ET 7e Chapter 5 Form G

1. 5.13

2. 350

3. $\lim_{n\to\infty} \sum_{i=1}^{n} \left[\left(4+\frac{3i}{n}\right)^2 + \sqrt{1+2\left(4+\frac{3i}{n}\right)} \right] \cdot \frac{3}{n}$

4. c

5. 24.5

6. a

7. $\frac{\sqrt{x}}{2\left(x^2+1\right)}$

8. d

9. 37

10. c

11. d

12. a

13. 12.929

14. $\int_4^9 4r \sin r \, dr$

15. $\sin(\ln x)+C$

16. $\int_0^2 \left(x+\sqrt{4-x^2}\right)dx = \int_0^2 x\,dx + \int_0^2 \sqrt{4-x^2}\,dx = I_1 + I_2$

    $I_1 = \textit{Area of a triangle}, I_2 = \textit{Area of a quarter circle}$

    $I_1 + I_2 = \frac{1}{2}(2)(2) + \frac{1}{4}(\pi)(2)^2 = 2+\pi$

17. 8π

18. 8

19. –2/67

20. $-e^{\cos x} + C$

1. The speed of a runner increased steadily during the first three seconds of a race. Her speed at half-second intervals is given in the table. Find a lower estimate for the distance that she traveled during these three seconds.

t (s)	0	0.5	1.0	1.5	2.0	2.5	3.0
v (ft/s)	0	4.5	8.4	12.1	13.2	13.3	13.8

2. Estimate to the hundredth the area from 1 to 5 under the graph of $f(x) = \dfrac{4}{x}$ using four approximating rectangles and right endpoints.

Select the correct answer.

a. 5.13
b. 6.65
c. 5.83
d. 3.65
e. 4.23
f. 4.55

3. If $\int_0^6 f(x)dx = 10$ and $\int_0^4 f(x)dx = 7$, find $\int_4^6 f(x)dx$.

Select the correct answer.

a. −10 b. 17 c. 3 d. −3 e. 2

4. The velocity graph of a braking car is shown. Use it to estimate to the nearest foot the distance traveled by the car while the brakes are applied. Use a left sum with $n = 7$.

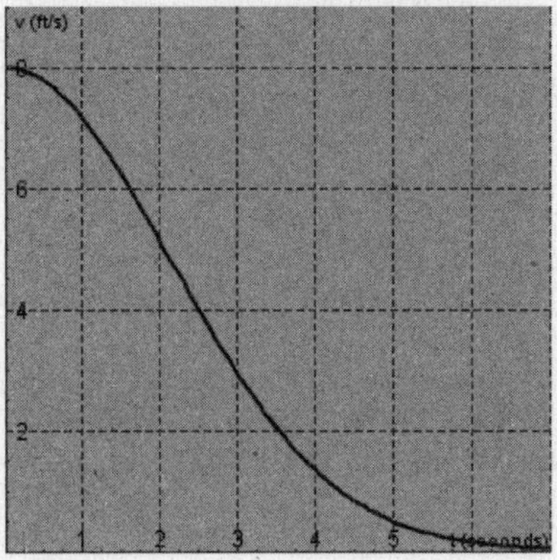

5. Evaluate the Riemann sum for $f(z) = 6 - z^2$, $0 \le z \le 2$ with four subintervals, taking the sample points to be right endpoints.

6. Evaluate the indefinite integral.

$$\int \sec^6 x \tan x \, dx$$

7. Find an expression for the area under the graph of f as a limit. Do not evaluate the limit.

$f(x) = \sqrt{\sin x}, \quad 0 \le x \le \pi$

8. Express the integral as a limit of sums. Then evaluate the limit.

$$\int_0^{\pi} \sin 9x \, dx$$

9. Evaluate the definite integral.

$$\int_{e^9}^{e^{64}} \frac{dx}{x\sqrt{\ln x}}$$

10. Evaluate

$$\int_0^2 \left(x + \sqrt{4 - x^2}\right) dx$$

by interpreting it in terms of areas.

11. Evaluate the integral.

$$\int_0^{\sqrt{3}/2} \frac{dr}{\sqrt{1 - r^2}}$$

12. Use Part 1 of the Fundamental Theorem of Calculus to find the derivative of the function.

$$h(x) = \int_1^{e^x} 2 \ln t \, dt$$

13. Find the general indefinite integral.

$$\int \frac{\sin 20t}{\sin 10t} dt$$

14. The area of the region that lies to the right of the y-axis and to the left of the parabola $x = 3y - y^2$ is given by the integral $\int_0^3 \left(3y - y^2\right) dy$. Find the area of the region.

Select the correct answer.

a. 3/2
b. 9/2
c. 2.25
d. 27
e. 7/2

15. An animal population is increasing at a rate of $29 + 36t$ per year (where t is measured in years). By how much does the animal population increase between the fourth and tenth years?

16. The velocity function (in meters per second) is given for a particle moving along a line. Find the distance traveled by the particle during the given time interval.

$v(t) = 6t - 6, \quad 0 \le t \le 5$

Select the correct answer.

a. 105 m b. –15 m c. 51 m d. 148.8 m e. 115 m

17. If h' is a child's rate of growth in pounds per year, which of the following expressions represent the increase in the child's weight (in pounds) between the years 2 and 5?

Select the correct answer.

a. $\int_2^5 h'(t)\, dt$ b. $h'(5) - h'(2)$ c. $\int_5^2 h(t)\, dt$

18. Find the area of the region to three decimal places that lies under the given curve.

$y = \sqrt{2x+2}, \quad 0 \le x \le 1$

Select the correct answer.

a. 1.834 b. 1.727 c. 1.704 d. 1.724 e. 1.824

19. Evaluate the integral by making the given substitution.

$\int \cos 4x \, dx, \quad u = 4x$

20. Evaluate the indefinite integral. Check that your answer is reasonable by graphing both the function and its antiderivative (take C=0).

$\int e^{\sin x} \cos x \, dx$

ANSWER KEY

Stewart - Calculus ET 7e Chapter 5 Form H

1. 25.75

2. a

3. c

4. 25

5. 8.25

6. $\frac{1}{6}\sec^6 x + C$

7. $\lim_{n\to\infty} \sum_{i=1}^{n} \left[\sqrt{\sin\left(\frac{\pi i}{n}\right)} \right] \cdot \frac{\pi}{n}$

8. 2/9

9. 10

10. $\int_0^2 \left(x + \sqrt{4-x^2}\right) dx = \int_0^2 x\,dx + \int_0^2 \sqrt{4-x^2}\,dx = I_1 + I_2$

$I_1 = Area\ of\ a\ triangle,\ I_2 = Area\ of\ a\ quarter\ circle$

$I_1 + I_2 = \frac{1}{2}(2)(2) + \frac{1}{4}(\pi)(2)^2 = 2 + \pi$

11. $\pi / 3$

12. $2xe^x$

13. $\frac{\sin 10t}{5} + C$

14. b

15. 1686

16. c

17. a

18. d

19. $\frac{1}{4}\sin 4x + C$

20. $e^{\sin x} + C$

1. Sketch the region enclosed by $x = 4 - y^2$ and $x = y^2 - 2$. Find the area of the region.

2. Graph the region between the curves and use your calculator to compute the area correct to five decimal places.

   $y = 2e^{1-x^2}, \quad y = 2x^4$

3. Find the area of the region bounded by the given curves.

   $y = \sin(\pi x/2), \quad y = x^2 - 2x$

4. Find the volume of the solid obtained by rotating the region bounded by $y = \sqrt[3]{x}$ and $y = x$ about the line $y = 1$.

5. Find the volume of the solid obtained by rotating the region bounded by the given curves about the specified axis.

   $y = x^2 + 4, \quad y = 12 - x^2; \quad$ about $y = -1$

6. Find the number b such that the line $y = b$ divides the region bounded by the curves $y = x^2$ and $y = 4$ into two regions with equal area.

7. Find the volume of the frustum of a pyramid with square base of side $b = 19$, square top of side $a = 5$, and height $h = 15$.

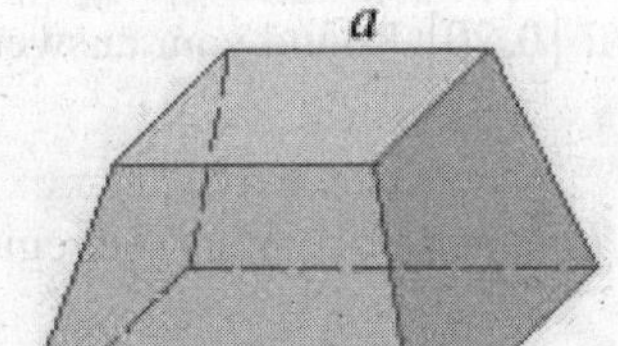

8. The base of S is a circular region with boundary curve $16x^2 + 16y^2 = 4$. Cross-sections perpendicular to the x axis are isosceles right triangles with hypotenuse in the base.

   Find the volume of S.

9. Find the volume of the solid obtained by rotating the region bounded by the given curves about the specified line.

   $y = \ln x, \quad y = 1, \quad y = 3, \quad x = 0;\quad$ about the y-axis

10. A force of 30 N is required to maintain a spring stretched from its natural length of 12 cm to a length of 15 cm. How much work is done in stretching the spring from 12 cm to 25 cm?

11. Find the volume common to two spheres, each with radius $r = 6$ if the center of each sphere lies on the surface of the other sphere.

12. The linear density of a 15 m long rod is $22.5/\sqrt{x+1}$ kg/m, where x is measured in meters from one end of the rod. Find the average density of the rod.

13. Use the method of cylindrical shells to find the volume of solid obtained by rotating the region bounded by the given curves about the x-axis.

    $y^2 - 3y + x = 0, \quad x = 0$

14. Find the work done in pushing a car a distance of 12 m while exerting a constant force of 300 N.

15. The height of a monument is 20 m. A horizontal cross-section at a distance x meters from the top is an equilateral triangle with side $x/4$ meters. Find the volume of the monument.

16. An aquarium 3 m long, 6 m wide, and 1 m deep is full of water. Find the work (in J) needed to pump half of the water out of the aquarium. (Use the facts that the density of water is $1000\ \text{kg/m}^3$ and $g \approx 9.8\,\text{m/s}^2$)

17. In a steam engine the pressure and volume of steam satisfy the equation $PV^{1.4} = k$, where k is a constant. (This is true for adiabatic expansion, that is, expansion in which there is no heat transfer between the cylinder and its surroundings.) Calculate the work done by the engine (in ft-lb) during a cycle when the steam starts at a pressure of $100\ \text{lb/in}^2$ and a volume of $400\ \text{in}^3$ and expands to a volume of $1{,}100\ \text{in}^3$. Use the fact that the work done by the gas when the volume expands from volume V_1 to volume V_2 is $W = \int_{V_1}^{V_2} P\,dV$.

18. Find the average value of the function $f(t) = t\sin(t^2)$ on the interval $[0, 20]$. Round your answer to 3 decimal places.

19. Use a computer algebra system to find the exact volume of the solid obtained by rotating the region bounded by the given curves about the specified line.

    $y = x, \quad y = xe^{1-x/2}$, about $y = 4$

20. Find the values of c such that the area of the region bounded by the parabolas $y = x^2 - c^2$ and $y = c^2 - x^2$ is 576.

ANSWER KEY

Stewart - Calculus ET 7e Chapter 6 Form A

1. $8\sqrt{3}$

2. 7.32031

3. $\frac{4}{3}+\frac{4}{\pi}$

4. $\frac{7\pi}{30}$

5. 384π

6. $4^{2/3}$

7. 2405

8. $\frac{1}{6}$

9. $\frac{\pi}{2}\left(e^6-e^2\right)$

10. 8.45 J

11. 90π

12. 9 kg/m

13. 13.5π

14. 3600

15. $\frac{125\sqrt{3}}{3}\text{m}^3$

16. 22050

17. 2773

18. 0.038

19. $\pi\left(-2e^2+32e-\frac{202}{3}\right)$

20. ± 6

1. Find the area of the region bounded by the curves.

$x = 2y^2, \ x = 4 + y^2$

2. Graph the region between the curves and use your calculator to compute the area correct to five decimal places.

$y = 3e^{1-x^2}, \quad y = 3x^4$

3. The base of S is the parabolic region $\{(x, y) \mid x^2 \le y \le 2\}$. Cross-sections perpendicular to the y axis are squares.

Find the volume of S.

4. Find the volume of a cap of a sphere with radius $r = 50$ and height $h = 3$.

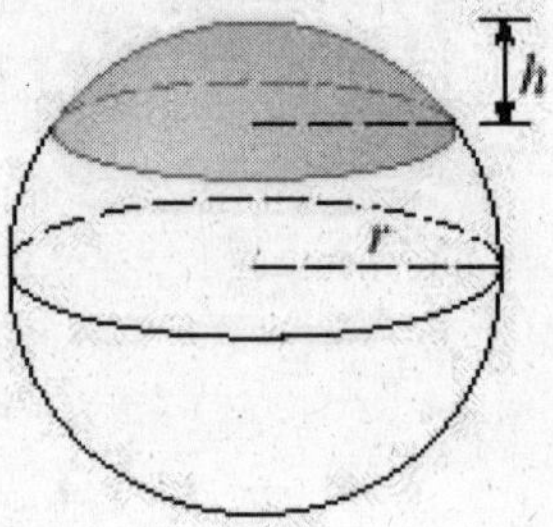

5. The linear density of an 8 m long rod is $12/\sqrt{x+1}$ kg/m, where x is measured in meters from one end of the rod.

Find the average density of the rod.

6. The temperature of a metal rod, 6 m long, is $5x$ (C°) at a distance x meters from one end of the rod.

What is the average temperature of the rod?

7. Find the area of the region bounded by the given curves.

$y = \sin(\pi x), \quad y = x^2 - x$

8. Find the area of the region bounded by the parabola $y = x^2$, the tangent line to this parabola at (1, 1), and the x axis.

9. Find the volume of the solid obtained by rotating the region bounded by the given curves about the specified axis.

$y = x^2 + 2, \quad y = 10 - x^2$; about $y = -1$

10. The region bounded by the given curves is rotated about the specified axis. Find the volume of the resulting solid by any method.

$x^2 + (y-1)^2 = 1$ about the y-axis

11. Find the volume of the solid obtained by rotating the region bounded by the given curves about the specified line.

$y = \ln x, \quad y = 2, \quad y = 3, \quad x = 0;$ about the y-axis

12. A force of 30 N is required to maintain a spring stretched from its natural length of 12 cm to a length of 15 cm. How much work is done in stretching the spring from 12 cm to 24 cm?

13. If 432 J of work are needed to stretch a spring from 8 cm to 14 cm and another 580 J are needed to stretch it from 14 cm to 19 cm, what is the natural length of the spring?

14. Use a computer algebra system to find the exact volume of the solid obtained by rotating the region bounded by the given curves about the specified line.

$y = x, \quad y = xe^{1-x/2},$ about $y = 4$

15. The tank shown is full of water. Given that water weighs 62.5 lb/ft and R = 5, find the work (in lb-ft) required to pump the water out of the tank.

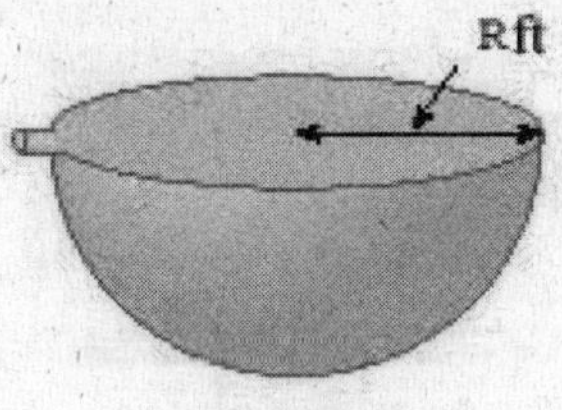

hemisphere

16. Find the average value of the function on the given interval.

$g(x) = 5xe^{-x^2}, \quad [0,5]$

17. The height of a monument is 20 m. A horizontal cross-section at a distance x meters from the top is an equilateral triangle with side $x/4$ meters. Find the volume of the monument.

18. The base of a solid is a circular disk with radius 3. Find the volume of the solid if parallel cross-sections perpendicular to the base are isosceles right triangles with hypotenuse lying along the base.

19. Find the number(s) a such that the average value of the function $f(t) = 25 - 20t + 3t^2$ on the interval $[0, a]$ is equal to 4.

20. Use the Midpoint Rule with $n = 4$ to approximate the area of the region bounded by the given curves.

$y = \sin^2(\pi x/4), \ y = \cos^2(\pi x/4), \ 0 \le x \le 1$

ANSWER KEY

Stewart - Calculus ET 7e Chapter 6 Form B

1. $\frac{32}{3}$

2. 10.98047

3. 8

4. 441π

5. 6 kg/m

6. 15

7. $\frac{1}{6}+\frac{2}{\pi}$

8. $1/12$

9. $896\pi/3$

10. $\frac{4\pi}{3}$

11. $\frac{\pi}{2}\left(e^6-e^4\right)$

12. 7.2 J

13. 2

14. $\pi\left(-2e^2+32e-\frac{202}{3}\right)$

15. 981,748 ft-lb

16. $\frac{1}{2}\left(1-e^{-25}\right)$

17. $\frac{125\sqrt{3}}{3}\text{ m}^3$

18. 36

19. $a=3$ or $a=7$

20. 0.6407

1. Find the area of the region bounded by the curves.

$y = x^2 - 2x, \; y = x + 4$

Select the correct answer.

a. $\frac{125}{3}$ b. $\frac{25}{3}$ c. 5 d. 20 e. $\frac{125}{6}$

2. Sketch the region enclosed by the curves $y = x + 2$, $y = 16 - x^2$, $x = -2$, and $x = 2$. Find the area of the region correct to two decimal places.

Select the correct answer.

a. 50.67
b. 51.67
c. 8.44
d. 16.89
e. 101.33
f. 152.01

3. Find the area of the region bounded by the curves.

$y = \cos x, \; y = \sin 2x, \; x = 0, \; x = \pi/2$

Select the correct answer.

a. $\frac{1}{4}$ b. $\frac{1}{2}$ c. $\frac{1}{3}$ d. 2 e. 4

4. Graph the region between the curves and use your calculator to compute the area correct to five decimal places.

$y = 2e^{1-x^2}, \quad y = 2x^4$

Select the correct answer.

a. 5.43656 b. 10.98047 c. 7.32031 d. 3.141257 e. 3.66016

5. Find the area of the region bounded by the given curves.

$y = \sin(\pi x/4), \quad y = x^2 - 4x$

Select the correct answer.

a. $16 + \frac{2}{\pi}$ b. $32 + \frac{\pi}{4}$ c. $\frac{32}{3} - \frac{\pi}{8}$ d. $\frac{32}{3} + \frac{8}{\pi}$ e. none of these

6. Find the volume of the solid obtained by rotating the region bounded by $y = x^3$ and $x = y^3$ about the x-axis.

Select the correct answer.

a. $\frac{16}{35}\pi$ b. $\frac{16}{7}\pi$ c. $\frac{18}{35}$ d. $\frac{7}{2}$ e. 16π

7. Find the volume of the solid obtained by rotating the region bounded by the given curves about the specified line.

$y = \ln x, \quad y = 1, \quad y = 2, \quad x = 0;$ about the y-axis

Select the correct answer.

a. $\frac{\pi}{2}\left(e^4 - e^2\right)$ b. $\frac{\pi}{2}\left(e^2 + e\right)$ c. $\frac{e^4}{2}$ d. $\frac{e^2 - e^4}{2}$ e. none

8. Find the number b such that the line $y = b$ divides the region bounded by the curves $y = x^2$ and $y = 4$ into two regions with equal area.

Select the correct answer.

a. $4^{2/3}$ b. $4^{1/3}$ c. $1/3$ d. $2^{1/2}$ e. $2/3$

9. Find the number(s) a such that the average value of the function $f(x) = 80 - 34x + 3x^2$ on the interval $[0, a]$ is equal to 10.

Select all that apply.

a. $a = 8$ b. $a = 10$ c. $a = 7$ d. $a = -7$ e. $a = -10$

10. Find the volume of the solid obtained by rotating the region bounded by the given curves about the specified axis.

$y = x^2 + 4, \quad y = 12 - x^2;$ about $y = -1$

Select the correct answer.

a. 384π b. 128π c. 128 d. 96π e. none of these

11. Use the method of cylindrical shells to find the volume generated by rotating the region bounded by the given curves about the specified axis.

$y = x^2, \quad y = 0, \quad x = 1, \quad x = 8;$ about $x = 1$

Select the correct answer.

a. $\frac{20{,}482\pi}{3}$ b. $10{,}246\pi$ c. $10{,}239\pi$ d. $\frac{10{,}241\pi}{6}$ e. 3413π

12. The region bounded by the given curves is rotated about the specified axis. Find the volume of the resulting solid by any method. Round your answer to 3 decimal places.

$y = x^2 + 3x - 10$; about the x-axis and $y = 0$.

Select the correct answer.

a. 1760.025
b. 1752.016
c. 1763.213
d. 880.012
e. none of these

13. The height of a monument is 20 m. A horizontal cross-section at a distance x meters from the top is an equilateral triangle with side $x/4$ meters. Find the volume of the monument.

Select the correct answer.

a. $\frac{25\sqrt{2}}{2}\ \text{m}^3$ b. $25\sqrt{3}\ \text{m}^3$ c. $\frac{125\sqrt{3}}{3}\ \text{m}^3$ d. $\frac{\sqrt{3}}{3}\ \text{m}^3$ e. $\frac{5\sqrt{2}}{3}\ \text{m}^3$

14. The region bounded by the given curves is rotated about the specified axis. Find the volume of the resulting solid by any method.

$x^2 + (y-1)^2 = 1$; about the y axis

Select the correct answer.

a. $V = \frac{5}{3}\pi$ b. $V = \frac{2}{3}\pi$ c. $V = \frac{1}{3}\pi$ d. $V = \frac{4}{3}\pi$ e. $V = \frac{7}{3}\pi$

15. A force of 30 N is required to maintain a spring stretched from its natural length of 12 cm to a length of 15 cm. How much work is done in stretching the spring from 12 cm to 25 cm?

Select the correct answer.

a. 7.2 J b. 8.45 J c. 7.45 J d. 6.25 J e. 3.45 J

16. A heavy rope, 40 ft long, weighs 0.8 lb/ft and hangs over the edge of a building 110 ft high. How much work is done in pulling the rope to the top of the building?

Select the correct answer.

a. 640 ft-lb
b. 590 ft-lb
c. 641 ft-lb
d. 489 ft-lb
e. 740 ft-lb

17. A tank is full of water. Find the work required to pump the water out of the outlet. Round the answer to the nearest thousand.

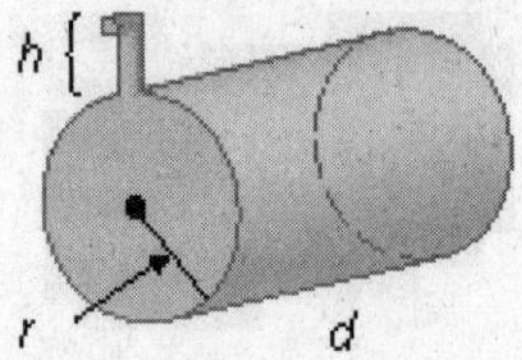

$h = 2$ m , $r = 2$ m , $d = 5$ m

Select the correct answer.

a. $W = 2{,}013{,}000$ J
b. $W = 2{,}184{,}000$ J
c. $W = 2{,}463{,}000$ J
d. $W = 2{,}585{,}000$ J
e. none of these

18. The base of a solid is a circular disk with radius 3. Find the volume of the solid if parallel cross-sections perpendicular to the base are isosceles right triangles with hypotenuse lying along the base.

Select the correct answer.

a. 16 b. 7 c. 49 d. 6 e. none of these

19. Find the average value of the function $f(t) = t\sin(t^2)$ on the interval $[0, 20]$. Round your answer to 3 decimal places.

Select the correct answer.

a. 0.381 b. 0.008 c. 0.028 d. 0.038 e. none of these

20. The temperature of a metal rod, 4 m long, is $3x$ (in degrees Celsius) at a distance x meters from one end of the rod. What is the average temperature of the rod?

Select the correct answer.

a. $T_{ave} = 6^\circ C$ b. $T_{ave} = 22^\circ C$ c. $T_{ave} = 34^\circ C$ d. $T_{ave} = 24^\circ C$ e. $T_{ave} = 46^\circ C$

ANSWER KEY

Stewart - Calculus ET 7e Chapter 6 Form C

1. e

2. a

3. b

4. c

5. d

6. a

7. a

8. a

9. b, c

10. a

11. d

12. a

13. c

14. d

15. b

16. a

17. c

18. e

19. d

20. a

1. Find the area of the region bounded by the given curves.

$y = \sin(\pi x / 2), \quad y = x^2 - 2x$

Select the correct answer.

a. $\frac{32}{3} + \frac{8}{\pi}$ b. $\frac{4}{3} + \frac{4}{\pi}$ c. $4 + \frac{4}{\pi}$ d. $\frac{4}{3} + \frac{\pi}{4}$ e. $16 + \frac{\pi}{8}$

2. Use cylindrical shells to find the volume of the solid.

A sphere of radius r.

Select the correct answer.

a. $V = \frac{2}{3}\pi r^3$ b. $V = \frac{4}{3}\pi r^3$ c. $V = \frac{1}{3}\pi r^3$ d. $V = \frac{5}{3}\pi r^3$ e. $V = \frac{7}{3}\pi r^3$

3. Suppose you make napkin rings by drilling holes with different diameters through two wooden balls (which also have different diameters). You discover that both napkin rings have the same height h as shown in the figure. Use cylindrical shells to compute the volume of a napkin ring created by drilling a hole with radius d through the center of a sphere of radius D and express the answer in terms of h.

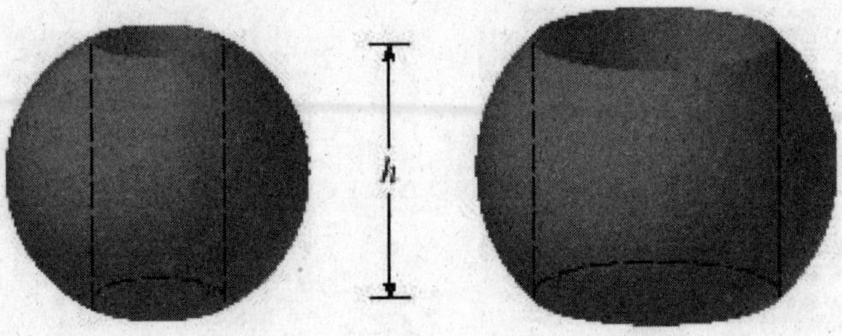

Select the correct answer.

a. $V = \frac{1}{6}\pi h^2$ b. $V = \frac{1}{6}\pi h^3$ c. $V = \frac{1}{4}\pi h^3$ d. $V = \frac{1}{3}\pi h^2$ e. $V = \frac{1}{3}\pi h^3$

4. Sketch a graph to estimate the x-coordinates of the points of intersection of the given curves. Then use this information to estimate the volume of the solid obtained by rotating about the y axis the region enclosed by these curves.

Rounded to the nearest hundredth.

$y = 0, \quad y = -x^4 + 6x^3 - x^2 + 6x$

Select the correct answer.

a. $V = 3{,}346.96\pi$ b. $V = 3{,}331.63\pi$ c. $V = 3{,}323.88\pi$ d. $V = 3{,}326.40\pi$ e. $V = 3{,}745.96\pi$

5. Find the number(s) a such that the average value of the function $z(v) = 51 - 26v + 3v^2$ on the interval $[0, a]$ is equal to 9.

Select the correct answer(s).

a. 6 b. –6 c. 3 d. 7 e. –7

6. A spring has a natural length of 22 cm. If a force of 15 N is required to keep it stretched to a length of 32 cm, how much work is required to stretch it from 22 cm to 40 cm?

Select the correct answer.

a. 3.43 J b. 1.93 J c. 2.93 J d. 3.93 J e. 2.43 J

7. If 90 J of work are needed to stretch a spring from 8 cm to 13 cm and another 294 J are needed to stretch it from 13 cm to 20 cm, what is the natural length of the spring?

Select the correct answer.

a. 5 cm b. 6 cm c. 7 cm d. 4 cm e. 2 cm

8. Use the Midpoint Rule with $n = 4$ to estimate the volume obtained by rotating about the region under the y-axis the region under the curve.

$y = \tan x, \quad 0 \le x \le \dfrac{\pi}{4}$

Select the correct answer. The choices are rounded to the nearest hundredth.

a. $V = 1.142$ b. $V = 1.851$ c. $V = 0.825$ d. $V = 0.491$ e. $V = 0.156$

9. Find the volume of the solid obtained by rotating the region bounded by the given curves about the specified line.

$y = \ln x, \quad y = 1, \quad y = 2, \quad x = 0;$ about the y-axis

Select the correct answer.

a. $\left(e^4 - e^2\right)/2$ b. $2\left(e^4 - e^2\right)$ c. $\dfrac{\pi}{2}\left(e^2 - e\right)$ d. $\dfrac{\pi}{2}\left(e^4 - e^2\right)$ e. none of these

10. A bucket weighs 5 lb and a rope of negligible weight are used to draw water from a well that is 70 ft deep. The bucket starts with 50 lb of water and is pulled up at a rate of 10 ft/s, but water leaks out of a hole in the bucket at a rate of 0.5 lb/s. Find the work done in pulling the bucket to the top of the well.

Select the correct answer.

a. 3,728.5 ft-lb
b. 3,837.5 ft-lb
c. 3,677.5 ft-lb
d. 3,727.5 ft-lb
e. 3,745.5 ft-lb

11. A tank is full of water. Find the work required to pump the water out of the outlet. Round the answer to the nearest thousand.

$h = 1\text{ m}, r = 1\text{ m}, d = 5\text{ m}$

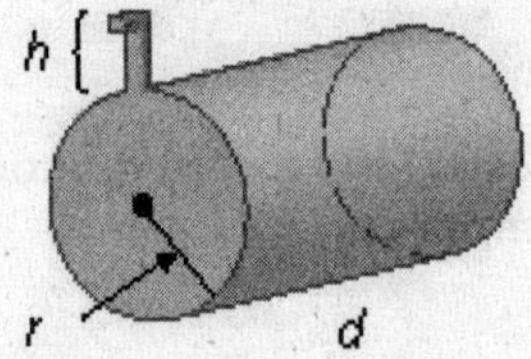

Select the correct answer.

a. $W = 30{,}000$ J b. $W = 308{,}000$ J c. $W = 757{,}000$ J d. $W = 431{,}000$ J e. $W = 305{,}000$ J

12. Newton's Law of Gravitation states that two bodies with masses m_1 and m_2 attract each other with a force $F = G\dfrac{m_1 m_2}{r^2}$ where r is the distance between the bodies and G is the gravitation constant. If one of bodies is fixed, find the work needed to move the other from $r = a$ to $r = d$.

Select the correct answer.

a. $W = Gm_1m_2\left(\dfrac{1}{a^2} - \dfrac{1}{d^2}\right)$

b. $W = Gm_1m_2\left(\dfrac{1}{a} - \dfrac{1}{d}\right)$

c. $W = Gm_1m_2\left(\dfrac{1}{d} - \dfrac{1}{a}\right)$

d. $W = Gm_1m_2\left(\dfrac{1}{d^2} - \dfrac{1}{a^2}\right)$

e. $W = Gm_1m_2\left(\dfrac{1}{a^2} + \dfrac{1}{d^2}\right)$

13. Find the average value of the function $f(t) = t\sin(t^2)$ on the interval $[10, 20]$. Round your answer to 3 decimal places.

Select the correct answer.

a. 0.72 b. 0.69 c. 0.069 d. 0.761 e. 0.076

14. The linear density of a 48 m long rod is $72/\sqrt{x+1}$ kg/m, where x is measured in meters from one end of the rod. Find the average density of the rod.

Select the correct answer.

a. $\rho_{ave} = 19$ kg/m b. $\rho_{ave} = 8$ kg/m c. $\rho_{ave} = 14$ kg/m d. $\rho_{ave} = 18$ kg/m e. $\rho_{ave} = 22$ kg/m

15. An aquarium 7 m long, 1 m wide, and 1 m deep is full of water. Find the work needed to pump half of the water out of the aquarium. (Use the facts that the density of water is 1000 kg/m^3 and $g \approx 9.8$.)

Select the correct answer.

a. 8,575 J
b. 7,575 J
c. 8,425 J
d. 8,586 J
e. 8,585 J

16. In a certain city the temperature (in $^\circ$F) t hours after 7 A.M. was modeled by the function

$$T(t) = 48 + 30\sin\frac{\pi t}{12}$$

Find the average temperature to three decimal places during the period from 7 A.M. to 7 P.M.

Select the correct answer.

a. 67.099 $^\circ$F

b. 52.208 $^\circ$F

c. 43.203 $^\circ$F

d. 72.125 $^\circ$F

e. 69.029 $^\circ$F

17. Find the average value of the function on the given interval.

$h(x) = 3e^{\sin x}\cos x, \quad [0, \pi/2]$

Select the correct answer.

a. $2(e-1)$ b. $\frac{6}{\pi}(e-1)$ c. $\frac{4}{\pi}(e-1)$ d. $\pi\left(e^3-1\right)$ e. e^3-1

18. The temperature of a metal rod, 7 m long, is $6x$ (in degrees Celsius) at a distance x meters from one end of the rod. What is the average temperature of the rod?

Select the correct answer.

a. $T_{ave} = 21^\circ C$

b. $T_{ave} = 38^\circ C$

c. $T_{ave} = 42^\circ C$

d. $T_{ave} = 23^\circ C$

e. $T_{ave} = 32^\circ C$

19. The tank shown is full of water. Given that water weighs 62.5 lb/ft and $R = 7$, find the work required to pump the water out of the tank.

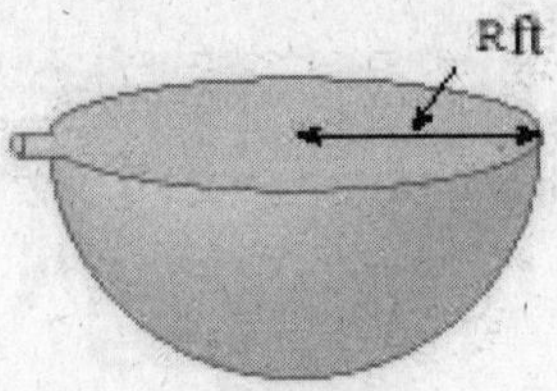

hemisphere

Select the correct answer.

a. 3,771,481 ft-lb
b. 316,858 ft-lb
c. 377,859 ft-lb
d. 117,879 ft-lb
e. 117,749 ft-lb

20. A force of 30 N is required to maintain a spring stretched from its natural length of 12 cm to a length of 15 cm. How much work is done in stretching the spring from 12 cm to 20 cm?

Select the correct answer.

a. 3.5 J b. 3.125 J c. 4.2 J d. 3.2 J e. none of these

ANSWER KEY

Stewart - Calculus ET 7e Chapter 6 Form D

1. b
2. b
3. b
4. d
5. a, d
6. e
7. b
8. a
9. d
10. d
11. b
12. b
13. c
14. d
15. a
16. a
17. b
18. a
19. a
20. d

1. Find the area of the region bounded by the given curves.

$y = \sin(\pi x/4), \quad y = x^2 - 4x$

Select the correct answer.

a. $\frac{32}{3}+\frac{8}{\pi}$ b. $\frac{4}{3}+\frac{4}{\pi}$ c. $4+\frac{4}{\pi}$ d. $\frac{4}{3}+\frac{\pi}{4}$ e. $16+\frac{\pi}{8}$

2. Sketch the region enclosed by $y = 1+\sqrt{x}$ and $y = \frac{8+x}{8}$. Find the area of the region.

Select the correct answer.

a. $\frac{256}{3}$ b. $\frac{32\sqrt{2}}{3}-4$ c. $\frac{8\sqrt{2}}{3}-4$ d. $8\sqrt{2}$ e. $8\sqrt{3}$

3. Graph the region between the curves and use your calculator to compute the area correct to five decimal places.

$y = e^{1-x^2}, \quad y = x^4$

4. Find the average value of the function $z(t) = 6\cos(t)$ on the interval $[0, \pi/2]$.

5. Racing cars driven by Chris and Kelly are side by side at the start of a race. The table shows the velocities of each car (in miles per hour) during the first ten seconds of the race. Use the Midpoint Rule to estimate how much farther Kelly travels than Chris does during the first ten seconds.

t	V_C	V_K	t	V_C	V_K
0	0	0	6	72	83
1	25	27	7	75	86
2	33	38	8	85	97
3	42	48	9	89	101
4	53	60	10	90	102
5	62	71			

6. Find the area of the region bounded by the parabola $y = x^2$, the tangent line to this parabola at (1, 1), and the x axis.

7. Find the number b such that the line $y = b$ divides the region bounded by the curves $y = x^2$ and $y = 4$ into two regions with equal area.

Select the correct answer.

a. $4^{2/3}$ b. $4^{1/3}$ c. $1/3$ d. $2^{1/2}$ e. $2/3$

8. Find the volume of a pyramid with height 4 and base an equilateral triangle with side $a = 13$.

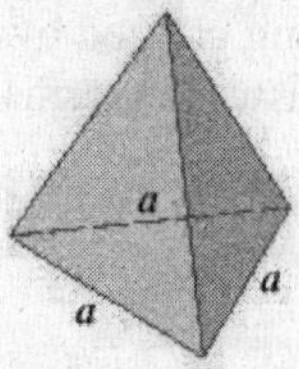

9. The base of S is an elliptical region with boundary curve $16x^2 + 4y^2 = 16$. Cross-sections perpendicular to the x axis are isosceles right triangles with hypotenuse in the base. Find the volume of S.

10. True or False?

The volume of a solid torus (the donut-shaped solid shown in the figure) with $r = 3$ and $R = 19$ is $342\pi^2$.

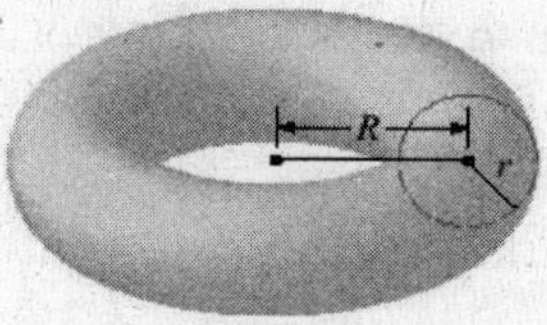

11. Use the method of cylindrical shells to find the volume generated by rotating the region bounded by the given curves about the specified axis.

$y = x^4$, $y = 0$, $y = 1$; about the line $x = 2$

12. Find the average value of the function on the given interval.

$g(x) = 2xe^{-x^2}$, $[0,5]$

13. Find the volume of the solid obtained by rotating the region bounded by the given curves about the specified line.

$y = \ln x$, $y = 2$, $y = 3$, $x = 0$; about the y-axis

Select the correct answer.

a. $\frac{\pi}{2}\left(e^4 - e^2\right)$ b. $\frac{\pi}{2}\left(e^2 + e\right)$ c. $\frac{e^4}{2}$ d. $\frac{\pi}{2}\left(e^6 - e^4\right)$ e. none of these

14. The height of a monument is 20 m. A horizontal cross-section at a distance x meters from the top is an equilateral triangle with side $x/4$ meters. Find the volume of the monument.

Select the correct answer.

a. $\frac{25\sqrt{2}}{2}\ \text{m}^3$ b. $25\sqrt{3}\ \text{m}^3$ c. $\frac{125\sqrt{3}}{3}\ \text{m}^3$ d. $\frac{\sqrt{3}}{3}\ \text{m}^3$ e. $\frac{5\sqrt{2}}{3}\ \text{m}^3$

15. Suppose you make napkin rings by drilling holes with different diameters through two wooden balls (which also have different diameters). You discover that both napkin rings have the same height h as shown in the figure. Use cylindrical shells to compute the volume of a napkin ring created by drilling a hole with radius b through the center of a sphere of radius B and express the answer in terms of h.

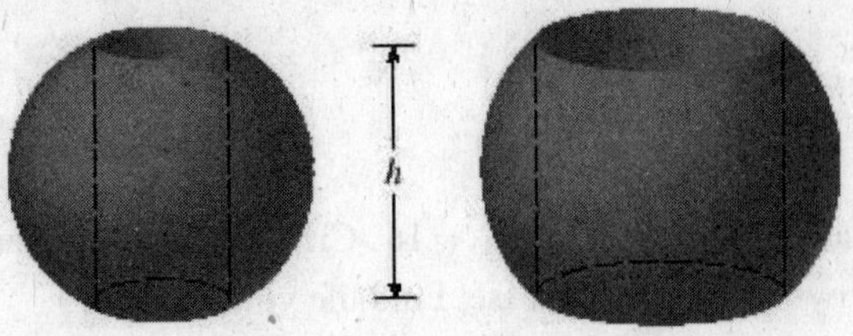

16. Find the work done in pushing a car a distance of 9 m while exerting a constant force of 200 N.

17. A force of 30 N is required to maintain a spring stretched from its natural length of 12 cm to a length of 15 cm. How much work is done in stretching the spring from 12 cm to 18 cm?

18. A tank is full of water. Find the work required to pump the water out of the outlet.

Round the answer to the nearest thousand.

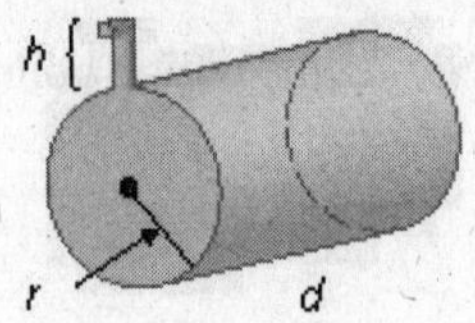

$h = 1\text{ m}, r = 2\text{ m}, d = 7\text{ m}$

19. The tank shown is full of water. Given that water weighs 62.5 lb/ft and R = 9, find the work required to pump the water out of the tank.

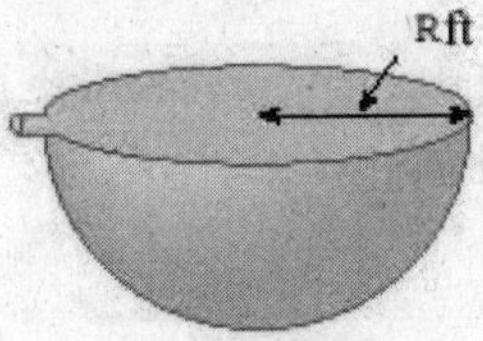

hemisphere

Select the correct answer.

a. 600,061 ft-lb b. 10,306,000 ft-lb c. 1,306,000 ft-lb d. 321,952 ft-lb e. 321,062 ft-lb

20. Use a computer algebra system to find the exact volume of the solid obtained by rotating the region bounded by the given curves about the specified line.

$y = x, \quad y = xe^{1-x/2}$, about $y = 4$

ANSWER KEY

Stewart - Calculus ET 7e Chapter 6 Form E

1. a

2. a

3. 3.66016

4. $\dfrac{12}{\pi}$

5. $\dfrac{352}{3}$ ft

6. $\dfrac{1}{12}$

7. a

8. $\dfrac{169\sqrt{3}}{3}$

9. $\dfrac{16}{3}$

10. T

11. $\dfrac{7\pi}{15}$

12. $\dfrac{1}{5}\left(1-e^{-25}\right)$

13. d

14. c

15. $\dfrac{1}{6}\pi h^3$

16. 1800

17. 1.8 J

18. 2586000

19. b

20. $\pi\left(-2e^2+32e-\dfrac{202}{3}\right)$

1. Find the area of the region bounded by the curves.

   $x = 2y^2, \ x = 4 + y^2$

2. Find the area of the region bounded by the given curves.

   $y = \sin(\pi x), \quad y = x^2 - x$

3. Find the area of the region bounded by the parabola $y = x^2$, the tangent line to this parabola at (5, 25), and the x-axis.

   Select the correct answer.

   a. $44\frac{2}{3}$ b. $42\frac{2}{3}$ c. $41\frac{1}{3}$ d. $47\frac{2}{3}$ e. none of these

4. Find the number b such that the line $y = b$ divides the region bounded by the curves $y = 5x^2$ and $y = 7$ into two regions with equal area.

5. Find the volume of the solid obtained by rotating the region bounded by $y = \sqrt[3]{x}$ and $y = x$ about the line $y = 1$.

6. Find the area of the region bounded by the curves.

   $y = \cos x, \ y = \sin 2x, \ x = 0, \ x = \pi/2$

7. Find the volume of the solid obtained by rotating the region bounded by the given curves about the specified line.

   $y = \ln x, \quad y = 1, \quad y = 3, \quad x = 0;$ about the y-axis

8. Find the volume of the frustum of a pyramid with square base of side $b = 12$, square top of side $a = 2$, and height $h = 3$.

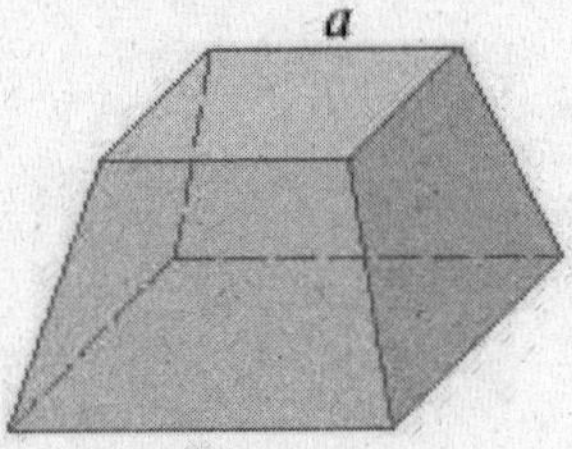

9. A force of 30 N is required to maintain a spring stretched from its natural length of 12 cm to a length of 15 cm. How much work is done in stretching the spring from 12 cm to 20 cm?

10. The base of S is the parabolic region $\{(x, y) \mid x^2 \le y \le 11\}$. Cross-sections perpendicular to the y-axis are equilateral triangles. Find the volume of S.

11. True or False?

The volume of a solid torus (the donut-shaped solid shown in the figure) with $r = 4$ and $R = 14$ is $448\pi^2$.

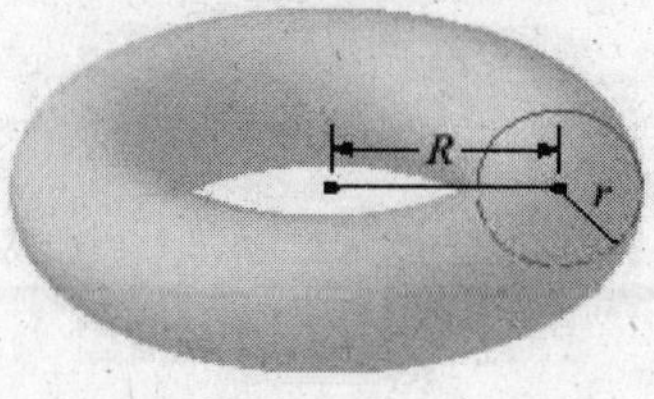

12. Find the values of c such that the area of the region bounded by the parabolas $y = x^2 - c^2$ and $y = c^2 - x^2$ is 576.

13. Find the volume common to two spheres, each with radius $r = 1$ if the center of each sphere lies on the surface of the other sphere.

14. Use the method of cylindrical shells to find the volume generated by rotating the region bounded by the given curves about the specified axis.

$y = x^2,\ y = 0,\ x = 1,\ x = 6;$ about $x = 1$

15. Set up, but do not evaluate, an integral for the volume of the solid obtained by rotating the region bounded by the given curves about the specified axis.

$y = \sin x,\ y = 0,\ x = 2\pi,\ x = 3\pi;$ about the $y-$axis

16. Find the work done in pushing a car a distance of 12 m while exerting a constant force of 300 N.

17. The temperature of a metal rod, 8 m long, is $7x$ (in $^\circ$C) at a distance x meters from one end of the rod. What is the average temperature of the rod?

18. The base of S is an elliptical region with boundary curve $9x^2 + 4y^2 = 36$. Cross-sections perpendicular to the x axis are isosceles right triangles with hypotenuse in the base.

Find the volume of S.

19. Find the average value of the function on the given interval.

$h(x) = \pi e^{\sin x} \cos x, \quad [0, \pi/2]$

20. Find the number(s) b such that the average value of the function $z(v) = 23 - 18v + 3v^2$ on the interval $[0, b]$ is equal to 5.

Select all that apply.

a. 6 b. 3 c. 9 d. –6 e. –7

ANSWER KEY

Stewart - Calculus ET 7e Chapter 6 Form F

1. $\dfrac{32}{3}$

2. $\dfrac{1}{6}+\dfrac{2}{\pi}$

3. e

4. $7\cdot 2^{-2/3}$

5. $\dfrac{7\pi}{30}$

6. $\dfrac{1}{2}$

7. $\dfrac{\pi}{2}\left(e^6-e^2\right)$

8. 172

9. 3.2 J

10. $\dfrac{121\sqrt{3}}{2}$

11. T

12. ± 6

13. $\dfrac{5\pi}{12}$

14. $\dfrac{3025\pi}{6}$

15. $\int_{2\pi}^{3\pi} 2\pi x \sin x \, dx$

16. 3600

17. 28

18. 24

19. $2(e-1)$

20. a, b

1. Graph the region between the curves and use your calculator to compute the area correct to five decimal places.

   $y = 3e^{1-x^2}, \quad y = 3x^4$

2. Find the area of the region bounded by the parabola $y = x^2$, the tangent line to this parabola at $(10,100)$, and the x-axis.

3. Find the area of the region bounded by the given curves.

   $y = \sin(\pi x / 4), \quad y = x^2 - 4x$

4. True or False?

   If a force of 6 lbs is required to hold a spring stretched 5 inches beyond its natural length, then 38.4 lb-in. of work is done in stretching it from its natural length to 8 in. beyond its natural length.

5. The linear density of an 8 m long rod is $12/\sqrt{x+1}$ kg/m, where x is measured in meters from one end of the rod. Find the average density of the rod.

6. Find the volume of the solid obtained by rotating about the x-axis the region under the curve $y = 1/x$ from $x = 6$ to $x = 7$.

7. Find the volume of the solid obtained by rotating the region bounded by $y = x^2$ and $x = y^2$ about the x-axis.

   Select the correct answer.

   a. $6\pi/5$ b. $3\pi/10$ c. $2/5$ d. $\pi/5$ e. $2\pi/5$

8. Find the volume of the solid obtained by rotating the region bounded by $y = x^3$ and $x = y^3$ about the line $x = -1$.

9. Use the method of cylindrical shells to find the volume of solid obtained by rotating the region bounded by the given curves about the x-axis.

   $y^2 - 3y + x = 0, \quad x = 0$

10. The base of a solid is a circular disk with radius 3. Find the volume of the solid if parallel cross-sections perpendicular to the base are isosceles right triangles with hypotenuse lying along the base.

11. Find the volume of the solid obtained by rotating the region bounded by the given curves about the specified line.

    $y = \ln x, \quad y = 1, \quad y = 3, \quad x = 0;$ about the y-axis

12. Find the average value of the function on the given interval.

    $h(x) = 2e^{\sin x} \cos x, \quad [0, \pi/2]$

13. In a certain city the temperature (in $^\circ$F) t hours after 7 A.M. was modeled by the function

$T(t) = 48 + 30\sin(\pi t/12)$

Find the average temperature to three decimal places during the period from 7 A.M. to 7 P.M.

Select the correct answer.

a. 67.099 $^\circ$F b. 52.208 $^\circ$F c. 43.203 $^\circ$F d. 72.125 $^\circ$F e. 69.029 $^\circ$F

14. True or False?

The volume of the frustum of a pyramid with square base of side $b = 17$, square top of side $a = 5$, and height $h = 8$ is 3,192 .

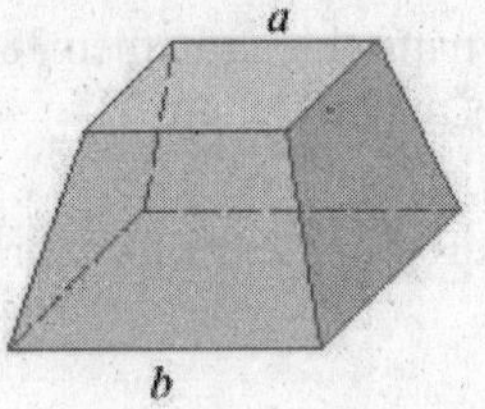

15. The height of a monument is 20 m. A horizontal cross-section at a distance x meters from the top is an equilateral triangle with side $x/4$ meters. Find the volume of the monument.

16. True or False?

The volume of a solid torus (the donut-shaped solid shown in the figure) with $r = 2$ and $R = 12$ is $96\pi^2$.

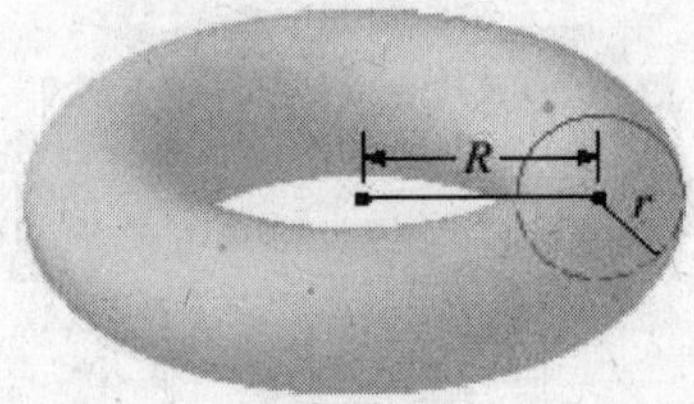

17. Find the volume common to two spheres, each with radius $r = 5$ if the center of each sphere lies on the surface of the other sphere.

18. Find the positive value of c such that the area of the region bounded by the parabolas $y = x^2 - c^2$ and $y = c^2 - x^2$ is 576.

19. Use a computer algebra system to find the exact volume of the solid obtained by rotating the region bounded by the given curves about the specified line.

$y = x, \quad y = xe^{1-x/2}$, about $y = 3$

20. Use the Midpoint Rule with $n = 4$ to approximate the area of the region bounded by the given curves.

$y = \sin^2(\pi x/4), \; y = \cos^2(\pi x/4), \; 0 \le x \le 1$

ANSWER KEY

Stewart - Calculus ET 7e Chapter 6 Form G

1. 10.98047

2. $\dfrac{250}{3}$

3. $\dfrac{32}{3}+\dfrac{8}{\pi}$

4. T

5. 6 kg/m

6. $\dfrac{\pi}{42}$

7. b

8. $\dfrac{51\pi}{35}$

9. 13.5π

10. 36

11. $\dfrac{\pi}{2}\left(e^6-e^2\right)$

12. $\dfrac{4}{\pi}(e-1)$

13. a

14. F

15. $\dfrac{125\sqrt{3}}{3}\ \text{m}^3$

16. T

17. $\dfrac{625\pi}{12}$

18. 6

19. $\pi\left(-2e^2+24e-\dfrac{142}{3}\right)$

20. 0.6407

1. Find the area of the region bounded by the given curves.

$y = \sin(\pi x), \quad y = x^2 - x$

2. Find the volume of the solid obtained by rotating the region bounded by the given curves about the specified axis.

$y = 2x,\ y = x^2$; about the x – axis

3. The linear density of a 24 m long rod is $36/\sqrt{x+1}$ kg/m, where x is measured in meters from one end of the rod. Find the average density of the rod.

4. Find the area of the region bounded by the parabola $y = x^2$, the tangent line to this parabola at (2, 4), and the x-axis.

5. Graph the region between the curves and use your calculator to compute the area correct to five decimal places.

$y = e^{1-x^2}, \quad y = x^4$

6. Find the positive value of c such that the area of the region bounded by the parabolas $y = x^2 - c^2$ and $y = c^2 - x^2$ is 576.

7. Find the volume of the solid obtained by rotating the region bounded by the given curves about the specified line.

$y = \ln x, \quad y = 2, \quad y = 3, \quad x = 0;$ about the y-axis

8. Find the volume of the solid obtained by rotating the region bounded by $x = y^2$ and $x = 5y$ about the y-axis.

9. True or False?

The Mean Value Theorem for Integrals says that if $f(t)$ is continuous on $[a, b]$, then there exists a number m in $[a, b]$ such that $f(m) = f_{ave} = \dfrac{1}{a-b}\displaystyle\int_a^b f(t)\ dt$.

10. Find the volume of the solid obtained by rotating the region bounded by $y = \sqrt[4]{x}$ and $y = x$ about the line $y = 1$.

Select the correct answer.

a. $4\pi/9$ b. $4\pi/15$ c. $1/3$ d. $4/9$ e. $\pi/9$

11. Find the volume of the solid obtained by rotating the region bounded by the given curves about the specified axis.

$y = x^2 + 4, \quad y = 12 - x^2;$ about $y = -1$

12. A force of 30 N is required to maintain a spring stretched from its natural length of 12 cm to a length of 15 cm. How much work is done in stretching the spring from 12 cm to 25 cm?

13. The velocity v of blood that flows in a blood vessel with radius R and length l at a distance r from the central axis is $v(r) = \frac{P}{4ql}\left(R^2 - r^2\right)$ where P is the pressure difference between the ends of the vessel and q is the viscosity of the blood. Find the average velocity (with respect to r) over the interval $0 \le r \le R$.

14. Find the area of the region bounded by the curves.

$y = \cos x,\ \ y = \sin 2x,\ \ x = 0,\ \ x = \pi/2$

15. The base of S is an elliptical region with boundary curve $9x^2 + 4y^2 = 36$. Cross-sections perpendicular to the x axis are isosceles right triangles with hypotenuse in the base.

Find the volume of S.

16. Find the volume of a pyramid with height 5 and base an equilateral triangle with side $a = 4$.

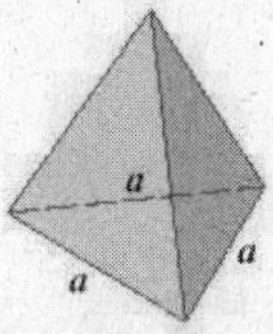

Select the correct answer.

a. $3\sqrt{3}/2$ b. $\sqrt{3}/10$ c. $20\sqrt{3}/3$ d. $4\sqrt{3}/5$ e. $12\sqrt{3}$

17. True or False?

If the center of each of two spheres, each having radius $r = 7$, lies on the surface of the other sphere, then the volume common to both spheres is $1715\pi/12$.

18. Find the average value of the function $f(t) = 5t\sin t^2$ on the interval $\left[0, \sqrt{\pi}\right]$.

Select the correct answer.

a. $10/\sqrt{\pi}$ b. $5/\sqrt{\pi}$ c. $10/\pi$ d. $5/\pi$ e. $1/\pi$

19. In a certain city the temperature (in $^\circ$F) t hours after 4 A.M. was modeled by the function $T(t) = 11 + 30\sin(\pi t/19)$.

Find the average temperature during the period from 4 A.M. to 4 P.M.

20. Use a computer algebra system to find the exact volume of the solid obtained by rotating the region bounded by the given curves about the specified line.

$y = x,\ \ y = xe^{1-x/2}$, about $y = 4$

ANSWER KEY

Stewart - Calculus ET 7e Chapter 6 Form H

1. $\frac{1}{6}+\frac{2}{\pi}$
2. $\frac{64\pi}{15}$
3. 12 kg/m
4. 2/3
5. 3.66016
6. 6
7. $\frac{\pi}{2}\left(e^6-e^4\right)$
8. $\frac{1250\pi}{3}$
9. F
10. b
11. 384π
12. 8.45 J
13. $\frac{PR^2}{6ql}$
14. $\frac{1}{2}$
15. 24
16. c
17. T
18. b
19. 32.2
20. $\pi\left(-2e^2+32e-\frac{202}{3}\right)$

1. Evaluate the integral.

$$\int_0^1 \frac{5}{x^{0.2}}\,dx$$

2. Evaluate the integral.

$$\int \frac{\cos(\ln t)}{t}\,dt$$

3. Find the average value of the function $f(x)$ in the interval $[-\pi, \pi]$.

$$f(x) = \sin^3 x \cos^3 x$$

4. Evaluate the integral.

$$\int_0^{\pi/2} \sin^3\theta \cos^2\theta \, d\theta$$

5. Evaluate the integral using the indicated trigonometric substitution.

$$\int \frac{dx}{x^2\sqrt{x^2-16}}; \quad x = 4\sec\theta$$

6. Evaluate the integral.

$$\int \frac{dx}{\left(x^2+2x+2\right)^2}$$

7. Find the area bounded by the given curves.

$$y = x^2 \ln x, \quad y = 9\ln x$$

8. Evaluate the integral or show that it is divergent.

$$\int_1^{\infty} \frac{\ln x}{x^4}\,dx$$

9. Find the volume of the resulting solid if the region under the curve $y = 1/\left(x^2+3x+2\right)$ from $x = 0$ to $x = 1$ is rotated about the x-axis. Round your answer to four decimal places.

10. Evaluate the integral.

$$\int \frac{\cos x}{4+\sin^2 x}\,dx$$

11. Household electricity is supplied in the form of alternating current that varies from 170 V to –170 V with a frequency of 60 cycles per second (Hz). The voltage is thus given by the function $E(t)$, where t is the time in seconds. Voltmeters read the RMS (root-mean-square) voltage, which is the square root of the average value of $[E(t)]^2$ over one cycle. Calculate the RMS voltage of household current. Round your answer to the nearest integer.

$$E(t) = 170\sin(120\pi t)$$

12. Evaluate the integral.

$$\int \frac{1}{\sqrt{x+1}+\sqrt{x}}\,dx$$

13. Evaluate the integral.

$$\int_0^4 te^{-t}\,dt$$

14. Estimate the area of the shaded region by using the Trapezoidal Rule with $n = 4$. Round the answer to the nearest tenth.

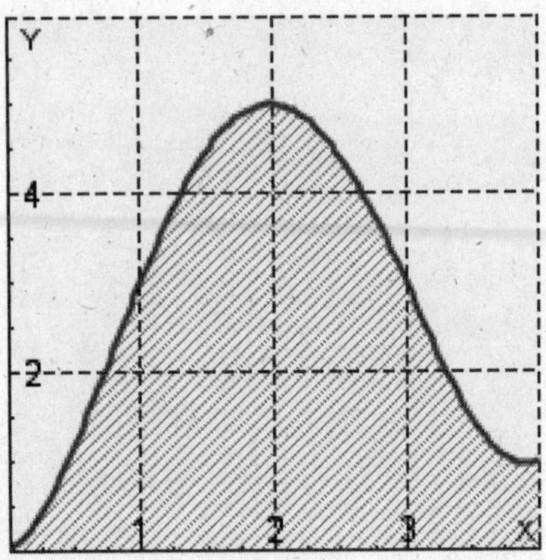

15. For what values of K is the following integral improper?

$$\int_0^K \frac{x}{x^2-19x+90}\,dx$$

16. Evaluate the integral.

$$\int_2^{\infty} \frac{4dy}{y^2+2y-3}$$

17. Evaluate the integral if it is convergent.

$$\int_0^{\infty} e^{-6x}\,dx$$

18. Evaluate the integral.

$$\int_0^{\pi/2} 2\sqrt{1-\cos 4\theta}\, d\theta$$

19. Evaluate the integral.

$$\int te^{\sqrt{t}}\, dt$$

20. Find the area bounded by the curves $y = \cos x$ and $y = \cos^2 x$ between $x = 0$ and $x = \pi / 2$.

ANSWER KEY

Stewart - Calculus ET 7e Chapter 7 Form A

1. 6.25

2. $\sin(\ln t) + C$

3. 0

4. $2/15$

5. $\dfrac{\sqrt{x^2-16}}{16x} + c$

6. $\dfrac{1}{2}\arctan(x+1) + \dfrac{1}{2}\left(\dfrac{x+1}{x^2+2x+2}\right) + C$

7. $18\ln 3 - \dfrac{136}{9}$

8. $1/9$

9. 0.286835

10. $\dfrac{1}{2}\arctan\left(\dfrac{1}{2}\sin x\right) + C$

11. 120

12. $\dfrac{2}{3}\left((x+1)^{3/2} - x^{3/2}\right) + C$

13. $1 - 5e^{-4}$

14. 11.5

15. $K \geq 9$

16. $\ln 5$

17. $\dfrac{1}{6}$

18. $2\sqrt{2}$

19. $2\left(\sqrt{t}\right)^3 e^{\sqrt{t}} - 6te^{\sqrt{t}} + 12\sqrt{t}e^{\sqrt{t}} - 12e^{\sqrt{t}} + C$

20. $1 - \dfrac{\pi}{4}$

1. Evaluate the integral.

$$\int y^3 e^y \, dy$$

2. Evaluate the integral.

$$\int \frac{x-1}{x^2+2x} dx$$

3. Evaluate the integral.

$$\int_0^4 \frac{x}{x+9} dx$$

4. Evaluate the integral.

$$\int_0^1 \left(x^2+1 \right) e^{-x} \, dx$$

5. Evaluate the integral.

$$\int_0^{100} \sqrt{t} \ln t \, dt$$

6. Evaluate the integral to two decimal places.

$$\int_4^7 e^{\sqrt{t}} \, dt$$

7. Evaluate the integral.

$$\int_0^{1/2} 2x \cos \pi x \, dx$$

8. Evaluate the integral.

$$\int_0^{\pi/2} \sin^3 \theta \cos^2 \theta d\theta$$

9. Find the volume obtained by rotating the region bounded by the given curves about $y = -1$.

$$y = \sin x, \ x = 0, \ x = \pi, \ y = 0$$

10. Find the average value of the function $f(x)$ in the interval $[-\pi, \pi]$.

$$f(x) = \sin^4 x \cos^3 x$$

11. Evaluate the integral.

$$\int \frac{\tan^2 x - 1}{\sec^2 x}\, dx$$

12. Evaluate the integral.

$$\int \frac{x^2}{\left(36 - x^2\right)^{3/2}}\, dx$$

13. Evaluate the integral.

$$\int x \sin x \cos x dx$$

14. Evaluate the integral.

$$\int \frac{dx}{\left(x^2 + 8x + 17\right)^2}$$

15. Evaluate the integral.

$$\int e^t \sqrt{49 - e^{2t}}\, dt$$

16. Evaluate the integral.

$$\int_0^{\pi/4} \sqrt{1 - \cos 4\theta}\, d\theta$$

17. A water storage tank has the shape of a cylinder with diameter 10 ft. It is mounted so that the circular cross-sections are vertical. If the depth of the water is 8 ft, what percentage of the total capacity is being used? Round the answer to the nearest tenth.

18. Evaluate the integral.

$$\int_1^{\infty} \frac{dx}{x \ln x}$$

19. Evaluate the integral.

$$\int_{-1/\sqrt{3}}^{1/\sqrt{3}} \frac{e^{\arctan y}}{1 + y^2}\, dy$$

20. Evaluate the integral.

$$\int_2^{\infty} \frac{2dy}{y^2 + 2y - 3}$$

ANSWER KEY

Stewart - Calculus ET 7e Chapter 7 Form B

1. $e^y(y^3-3y^2+6y-6)+C$

2. $\frac{3}{2}\ln(x+2)-\frac{1}{2}\ln x+C$

3. $4-9\ln 13+18\ln 3$

4. $-6e^{-1}+3$

5. $\frac{4000}{3}\ln 2+\frac{4000}{3}\ln 5-\frac{4000}{9}$

6. 31.61

7. $\frac{\pi-2}{\pi^2}$

8. $2/15$

9. $\frac{\pi^2}{2}+4\pi$

10. 0

11. $-\frac{1}{2}\sin(2x)+C$

12. $\frac{x}{\sqrt{36-x^2}}-\arcsin\left(\frac{x}{6}\right)+C$

13. $-\frac{1}{2}x\cos^2 x+\frac{1}{4}\cos x\sin x+\frac{1}{4}x+C$

14. $\frac{1}{2}\left(\arctan(x+4)+\frac{x+4}{x^2+8x+17}\right)+C$

15. $\frac{7^2}{2}\arcsin\left(\frac{e^t}{7}\right)+\frac{1}{2}e^t\sqrt{49-e^{2t}}+C$

16. $\sqrt{2}/2$

17. 85.76%

18. divergent

19. $e^{\pi/6}-e^{-\pi/6}$

20. $\frac{\ln 5}{2}$

1. Evaluate the integral.

$$\int_0^4 \frac{x}{x+9}\,dx$$

Select the correct answer.

a. $4-9\ln 13+18\ln 3$ b. $13-9\ln 4+\ln 3$ c. $\frac{1}{9\ln 13}-\ln 3$ d. $4-13\ln 9+3\ln 18$ e. none

2. Evaluate the integral.

$$\int \frac{x-1}{x^2+2x}\,dx$$

Select the correct answer.

a. $-\frac{\sqrt{2}}{2}\arctan x+C$
b. $\frac{1}{3}x-\frac{1}{3}\ln x+C$
c. $-\ln x-x+C$
d. $\frac{3}{2}\ln(x+2)-\frac{1}{2}\ln x+C$
e. none of these

3. A particle moves on a straight line with velocity function $v(t)=\sin \omega t\cos^3 \omega t$. Find its position function $s=f(t)$ if $f(0)=0$.

Select the correct answer.

a. $\frac{\sin^5 \omega t-1}{5\omega}$ b. $\frac{\cos^3 \omega t+1}{3\omega}$ c. $\frac{1-\cos^4 \omega t+1}{3\omega}$ d. $\frac{1-\cos^4 \omega t}{4\omega}$ e. $\frac{\sin^4 \omega t+1}{4\omega}$

4. Evaluate the integral.

$$\int \frac{dt}{t\csc(\ln t)}$$

Select the correct answer.

a. $-\sin(\ln t)+C$
b. $-\cos(\ln t)+C$
c. $\ln(\sin t)+C$
d. $-\ln t\cos t+C$
e. none of these

5. Use the Table of Integrals to evaluate the integral.

$$\int \frac{\sqrt{25x^2-1}}{x^2}\,dx$$

Select the correct answer.

a. $\frac{\sqrt{25x^2-1}}{x} + \ln\left|5x+\sqrt{25x^2}\right| + C$

b. $5\ln\left|5x+\sqrt{25x^2-1}\right| + C$

c. $\frac{\sqrt{25x^2-1}}{x} + 5\ln\left|5x+\sqrt{25x^2-1}\right|$

d. $-\frac{\sqrt{25x^2-1}}{x} + 5\ln\left|5x+\sqrt{25x^2-1}\right| + C$

e. $\frac{\sqrt{5x^2-1}}{x} + \ln\left|x+\sqrt{5x^2-1}\right| + C$

6. Use long division to evaluate the integral.

$$\int \frac{x^2}{x+2}\,dx$$

Select the correct answer.

a. $\frac{x^2}{2} - 2x + 4\ln(x+2) + C$

b. $\frac{x^2}{2} + 2x + 4\ln(x-2) + C$

c. $\frac{x^2}{2} + 2x + 4\ln|x+2| + C$

d. $\frac{x^2}{2} - 2x + 4\ln|x+2| + C$

e. $\frac{x^2}{2} - 2x + 2\ln|x+2| + C$

7. Evaluate the integral.

$$\int x \sin x \cos x dx$$

Select the correct answer.

a. $-\frac{1}{2}x\cos^2 x+\frac{1}{4}\cos x\sin x+\frac{1}{4}x+C$

b. $-\frac{1}{2}x\cos^2 x+\cos x+\frac{1}{4}x+C$

c. $-\frac{1}{4}\cos x\sin x+\frac{1}{4}x+C$

d. $-\frac{1}{2}x\sin^2 x+\frac{1}{4}\cos x+C$

e. none of these

8. Find the average value of the function $f(x)$ in the interval $[-\pi,\pi]$.

$$f(x)=\sin^2 x\cos^3 x$$

Select the correct answer.

a. π b. 0 c. $\pi/5$ d. $\pi/6$ e. $\pi/12$

9. Evaluate the integral using the indicated trigonometric substitution.

$$\int \frac{x^3}{\sqrt{x^2+25}}\,dx; \quad x=5\tan\theta$$

Select the correct answer.

a. $-\frac{2}{3}\left(x^2+25\right)^{3/2}+x^2\sqrt{x^2+25}+C$

b. $\left(x^2+25\right)^{3/2}-5\sqrt{x^2+25}+C$

c. $\frac{1}{3}\left(x^2+25\right)^{3/2}-\sqrt{x^2+25}+C$

d. $\left(x^2+25\right)^{3/2}-\sqrt{x^2+25}+C$

e. $\frac{3}{2}(x+25)^{3/2}-25\sqrt{x+25}+C$

10. Evaluate the integral.

$$\int \frac{1+5e^x}{1-e^x}\,dx$$

Select the correct answer.

a. $6x-5\ln\left(e^x-1\right)+C$

b. $x+8\ln\left(e^x-1\right)+C$

c. $8x+6\ln|e^x-1|+C$

d. $x-6\ln|e^x-1|+C$

e. $6x-5\ln\left(e^x+1\right)+C$

11. Evaluate the integral.

$$\int_1^{\infty} \frac{dx}{x\ln x}$$

Select the correct answer.

a. $1/2$ b. 0 c. $-1/4$ d. $1/4$ e. divergent

12. Evaluate the integral.

$$\int_2^{\infty} \frac{dy}{y^2+2y-3}$$

Select the correct answer.

a. $\frac{5}{2}$ b. $\frac{1}{\ln 4}$ c. $\frac{5}{4}$ d. $\frac{\ln 5}{4}$ e. divergent

13. Evaluate the integral $\int_0^1 \frac{1}{x^p}\,dx$ for different values of p. Which of the following integrals is equal to 1.25?

Select the correct answer.

a. $\int_0^1 \frac{1}{x^{0.2}}\,dx$ b. $\int_0^1 \frac{1}{x^{0.5}}\,dx$ c. $\int_0^1 \frac{1}{x^{0.7}}\,dx$ d. $\int_0^1 \frac{1}{x^{2}}\,dx$ e. $\int_0^1 \frac{1}{x^{2.5}}\,dx$

14. Evaluate the integral or show that it is divergent.

$$\int_{-\infty}^{\infty} \frac{dx}{4x^2+4x+5}$$

Select the correct answer.

a. $\frac{\pi}{2}$

b. $\frac{\pi}{4}$

c. $\frac{\pi}{8}$

d. $-\frac{\pi}{4}$

e. divergent

15. Evaluate the integral.

$$\int_0^4 \left(x^2+1\right) e^{-x}\, dx$$

Select the correct answer.

a. $-27e^4+3$ b. $-27e^{-4}-1$ c. $27e^{-4}+3$ d. $-27e^{-4}+3$ e. none of these

16. Evaluate the indefinite integral.

$$\int x\cos 7x\, dx$$

Select the correct answer.

a. $\frac{1}{49}\sin 7x+\frac{x}{7}\cos 7x+C$

b. $\frac{1}{7}\cos 7x+\frac{x}{7}\sin 7x+C$

c. $\frac{x}{49}\cos 7x+\frac{x}{7}\sin 7x+C$

d. $\frac{1}{49}\cos 7x+\frac{x}{7}\sin 7x+C$

e. none of these

17. Evaluate the integral.

$$\int \frac{dx}{\left(x^2+2x+2\right)^2}$$

Select the correct answer.

a. $\frac{1}{2}\left(\tan^{-1}(x+1)+\frac{x+1}{x^2+2x+2}\right)+C$

b. $\frac{1}{2}\left(\tan(x+1)+\frac{1}{x^2+2x+2}\right)+C$

c. $\frac{1}{2}\left(\tan(x+1)+\frac{x+1}{x^2+2x+2}\right)+C$

d. $\frac{1}{2}\left(\tan^{-1}(x+1)+\frac{1}{x^2+2x+2}\right)+C$

e. $\frac{1}{2}\left(\tan^{-1}(x+2)+\frac{1}{x^2+2}\right)+C$

18. Evaluate the integral.

$$\int e^t\sqrt{25-e^{2t}}\ dt$$

Select the correct answer.

a. $\frac{25}{2}\arcsin\left(\frac{e^t}{5}\right)+\frac{1}{2}e^t\sqrt{25-e^{2t}}+C$

b. $\arcsin\left(\frac{e^t}{5}\right)+\frac{1}{2}\sqrt{25-e^{2t}}+C$

c. $\frac{25}{2}\arcsin\left(\frac{e^t}{5}\right)+\frac{1}{2}\sqrt{25-e^{2t}}+C$

d. $\arcsin\left(\frac{e^t}{5}\right)+\frac{1}{2}e^t\sqrt{25-e^{2t}}+C$

e. $\frac{25}{2}\arcsin\left(\frac{e^{2t}}{5}\right)+\frac{1}{2}\sqrt{5-e^t}+C$

19. Find the area bounded by the curves $y = \cos x$ and $y = \cos^2 x$ between $x = 0$ and $x = \pi / 2$.

Select the correct answer.

a. $1/2$
b. $1/4$
c. 4
d. $\dfrac{\sqrt{2}}{2}$
e. none of these

20. The region under the curve $y = 4\cos^2 x$, $0 \le x \le \pi / 2$ is rotated about the *x*-axis. Find the volume of the resulting solid.

Select the correct answer.

a. $3\pi^2 / 4$
b. $\pi^2 / 8$
c. $3\pi / 8$
d. $3 / 8\pi$
e. $3\pi^2$

ANSWER KEY

Stewart - Calculus ET 7e Chapter 7 Form C

1. a
2. d
3. d
4. b
5. d
6. d
7. a
8. b
9. a
10. d
11. e
12. d
13. a
14. b
15. d
16. d
17. a
18. a
19. e
20. e

1. Evaluate the integral.

$$\int \frac{x-1}{x^2+2x}dx$$

Select the correct answer.

a. $\frac{1}{2}\ln(x^2+2)-\frac{\sqrt{2}}{2}\arctan x+c$

b. $\frac{1}{3}x-\frac{1}{3}\ln x+c$

c. $-\ln x-x+c$

d. $\frac{3}{2}\ln(x+2)-\frac{1}{2}\ln x+c$

e. none of these

2. Evaluate the integral.

$$\int x\ln(1+x)\ dx$$

Select the correct answer.

a. $\frac{1}{4}x^2-\frac{3}{2}\ln(1+x)+\frac{x^2}{2}(\ln(1+x))+C$

b. $\frac{3}{4}+\frac{1}{2}x-\frac{1}{4}x^2-\frac{1}{2}\ln(1+x)+\frac{x^2}{2}(\ln(1+x))+C$

c. $-\frac{1}{3}x+\frac{1}{6}x^2-\frac{1}{9}x^3+\frac{x^3}{3}\ln(1+x)+\frac{1}{3}\ln(1+x)+C$

d. $\frac{1}{4}x^2-\frac{1}{2}\ln(1+x)+\frac{x^2}{2}(\ln(1+x))+C$

e. $-\frac{1}{3}x+\frac{1}{6}x^2-\frac{1}{9}x^4+\frac{1}{3}\ln(1+x)+C$

3. Evaluate the integral.

$$\int \frac{\cos(\ln t)}{t}dt$$

a. $\sin(\ln t)+C$ b. $-\ln t\sin t+C$ c. $-\frac{\sin t}{t}+C$ d. $\sec(\ln t)+C$ e. $\cos(\ln t)+C$

4. Evaluate the integral.

$$\int_{\pi/6}^{\pi/3} \frac{\ln(\tan x)}{\sin x \cos x}\, dx$$

Select the correct answer.

a. 0 b. $-\frac{1}{8}(\ln 3)^2$ c. $\frac{1}{8}(\ln 3)^2$ d. $-\frac{1}{6}(\ln 3)^2$ e. $\frac{1}{6}(\ln 3)^2$

5. Use the Table of Integrals to evaluate the integral.

$$\int \frac{\sqrt{25x^2-1}}{x^2}\, dx$$

Select the correct answer.

a. $\frac{\sqrt{25x^2-1}}{x} + \ln\left|5x+\sqrt{25x^2}\right| + C$

b. $5\ln\left|5x+\sqrt{25x^2-1}\right| + C$

c. $\frac{\sqrt{25x^2-1}}{x} + 5\ln\left|5x+\sqrt{25x^2-1}\right|$

d. $-\frac{\sqrt{25x^2-1}}{x} + 5\ln\left|5x+\sqrt{25x^2-1}\right| + C$

e. $\frac{\sqrt{5x^2-1}}{x} + \ln\left|x+\sqrt{5x^2-1}\right| + C$

6. Use the Comparison Theorem to determine which of the following integrals is convergent.

Select the correct answer.

a. $\int_1^{\infty} \frac{5\sqrt{1+\sqrt{3x}}}{\sqrt{3x}}\, dx$

b. $\int_1^{\infty} \frac{6\sin^2 5x}{9+x^2}\, dx$

7. Evaluate the integral.

$$\int_0^1 2x \sin \pi x \, dx$$

Select the correct answer.

a. $\dfrac{\pi - 2}{\pi^2}$

b. $\dfrac{\pi}{4}$

c. $\dfrac{\pi}{2}$

d. $\dfrac{2}{\pi}$

e. none of these

8. Evaluate the integral.

$$\int x \sin x \cos x dx$$

Select the correct answer.

a. $-\dfrac{1}{2} x \cos^2 x + \dfrac{1}{4} \cos x \sin x + \dfrac{1}{4} x + c$

b. $-\dfrac{1}{2} x \cos^2 x + \cos x + \dfrac{1}{4} x + c$

c. $-\dfrac{1}{4} \cos x \sin x + \dfrac{1}{4} x + c$

d. $-\dfrac{1}{2} x \sin^2 x + \dfrac{1}{4} \cos x + c$

e. none of these

9. Use the Midpoint Rule to approximate the given integral with the specified value of n. Compare your result to the actual value. Find the error in the approximation.

$$\int_2^3 e^{-\sqrt{x}} \, dx, \quad n = 6$$

Select the correct answer.

a. 0.00014
b. 0.00004
c. 0.10004
d. –0.00016
e. –0.00096

10. Use the Trapezoidal Rule to approximate $\int_2^3 e^{3/x}\,dx$ for $n = 4$ to four decimal places.

Select the correct answer.

a. 3.4215 b. 3.4437 c. 3.4227 d. 3.5227 e. 3.4232

11. Evaluate the integral.

$$\int_0^{\pi/2} \sqrt{1-\cos 4\theta}\,d\theta$$

Select the correct answer.

a. $\sqrt{2}$ b. $\sqrt{2}/2$ c. $2\sqrt{2}$ d. $3\sqrt{2}$ e. $2\sqrt{3}$

12. Evaluate the following integral if it is convergent.

$$I = \int_0^{\infty} e^{-2x}\,dx$$

Select the correct answer.

a. $I = \frac{1}{2}$ b. $I = 2$ c. $I = -2$ d. $I = -\frac{1}{2}$ e. divergent

13. A manufacturer of light bulbs wants to produce bulbs that last about 600 hours but, of course, some bulbs burn out faster than others. Let $F(t)$ be the fraction of the company's bulbs that burn out before t hours. $F(t)$ lies between 0 and 1.

Let $r(t) = F'(t)$. What is the value of $\int_0^{\infty} r(t)dt$?

Select the correct answer.

a. $\int_0^{\infty} r(t)dt = 600$

b. $\int_0^{\infty} r(t)dt = 1$

c. $\int_0^{\infty} r(t)dt = 0$

d. $\int_0^{\infty} r(t)dt = 2$

e. divergent

14. The region $\left\{ (x,\ y) \mid x \geq -5,\ 0 \leq y \leq e^{-x/3} \right\}$ is represented below.

Find the area of this region to two decimal places.

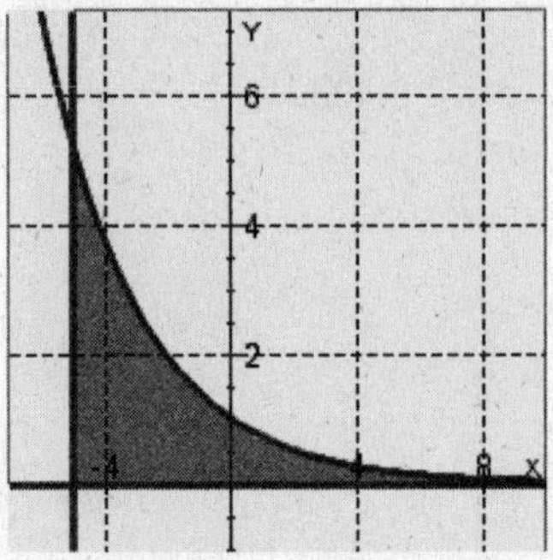

Select the correct answer.

a. 15.89 b. 15.88 c. 16.08 d. 15.87 e. 17.89

15. Let a and b be real numbers. What integral must appear in place of the question mark "?" to make the following statement true?

$$\int_{-\infty}^{a} \frac{8}{x^2+5}\,dx + \int_{a}^{\infty} \frac{8}{x^2+5}\,dx = ? + \int_{b}^{\infty} \frac{8}{x^2+5}\,dx$$

Select the correct answer.

a. $\int_{b}^{-\infty} \frac{8}{x^2+5}\,dx$ b. $\int_{-\infty}^{a} \frac{5}{x^2+8}\,dx$ c. $\int_{-\infty}^{b} \frac{8}{x^2+5}\,dx$ d. $\int_{b}^{-\infty} \frac{8}{x^2-5}\,dx$ e. none of these

16. Evaluate the integral.

$$\int_{2}^{\infty} \frac{4dy}{y^2+2y-3}$$

Select the correct answer.

a. $\frac{1}{\ln 5}$ b. $\frac{5}{2}$ c. $\ln 5$ d. $\frac{\ln 5}{2}$ e. divergent

17. Find the area bounded by the curves $y = \cos x$ and $y = \cos^2 x$ between $x = 0$ and $x = \pi$.

Select the correct answer.

a. $1/2$ b. $1/4$ c. 4 d. $\frac{\sqrt{2}}{2}$ e. none of these

18. Use the Table of Integrals to evaluate the integral.

$$\int e^{4x}\sin 2x\,dx$$

Select the correct answer.

a. $-\frac{1}{5}e^{4x}\sin 2x-\frac{1}{10}e^{4x}\cos 2x$

b. $\frac{1}{5}e^{4x}\sin 2x-\frac{1}{10}e^{4x}\cos 2x+C$

c. $\frac{1}{5}e^{4x}\sin 2x-2e^{4x}\cos 2x+C$

d. $e^{4x}\sin 2x-\frac{1}{8}e^{4x}\cos 2x+C$

e. $\frac{1}{5}e^{x}\sin x-\frac{1}{10}e^{x}\cos x+C$

19. Evaluate the integral.

$$\int \frac{1}{-e^{-x}+e^{x}}\,dx$$

Select the correct answer.

a. $\ln\left(\frac{|e^x-1|}{e^x+1}\right)+C$

b. $\frac{1}{2}\ln\left(\frac{|e^x-1|}{e^x+1}\right)+C$

c. $-\frac{1}{2}\ln\left(\frac{|e^x-1|}{e^x+1}\right)+C$

d. $-\ln\left(\frac{|e^x-1|}{e^x+1}\right)+C$

e. $-\ln\left(\frac{|e^x-1|}{e^x}\right)+C$

20. The region under the curve $y=4\cos^2 x,\ 0\le x\le \pi/2$ is rotated about the x-axis. Find the volume of the resulting solid.

Select the correct answer.

a. $3\pi^2$ b. $3\pi^2/8$ c. $\pi^2/4$ d. $3\pi/4$ e. $\pi/4$

ANSWER KEY

Stewart - Calculus ET 7e Chapter 7 Form D

1. d

2. b

3. a

4. a

5. d

6. b

7. d

8. a

9. b

10. c

11. a

12. a

13. b

14. b

15. c

16. c

17. e

18. b

19. b

20. a

1. Evaluate the integral using integration by parts with the indicated choices of u and dv.

$$\int 9\theta \cos\theta \, d\theta,\ u = 9\theta,\ dv = \cos\theta \, d\theta$$

Select the correct answer.

a. $9\theta \sin\theta + 9\cos\theta + C$
b. $9\sin\theta + 9\cos\theta + C$
c. $9\theta \cos\theta + 9\sin\theta + C$
d. $9\theta \sin\theta - 9\cos\theta + C$
e. none of these

2. Evaluate the integral to six decimal places.

$$\int_0^1 \frac{x^3}{\sqrt{36 - x^2}} \, dx$$

3. Find the area of the region bounded by the hyperbola $9x^2 - 4y^2 = 36$ and the line $x = 4$.

4. A torus is generated by rotating the circle $x^2 + (y-8)^2 = 25$ about the x-axis. Find the volume enclosed by the torus. Round the answer to the nearest hundredth.

5. Evaluate the integral using the indicated trigonometric substitution.

$$\int \frac{x^3}{\sqrt{x^2 + 36}} \, dx;\ x = 6\tan\theta$$

6. Evaluate the integral.

$$\int \frac{\sin 2x}{1 + \cos^4 x} \, dx$$

Select the correct answer.

a. $1 - \cos^2 x + C$

b. $-\arctan\left(\cos^2 x\right) + C$

c. $-\arcsin(\tan x) + C$

d. $-\cos^2 2x + C$

e. none of these

7. Evaluate the integral.

$$\int \frac{dt}{t\csc(\ln t)}$$

8. Evaluate the integral.

$$\int x\sin x\cos x\,dx$$

Select the correct answer.

a. $-\frac{1}{2}x\cos^2 x+\frac{1}{4}\cos x\sin x+\frac{1}{4}x+C$

b. $-\frac{1}{2}x\cos^2 x+\cos x+\frac{1}{4}x+C$

c. $-\frac{1}{4}\cos x\sin x+\frac{1}{4}x+C$

d. $-\frac{1}{2}x\sin^2 x+\frac{1}{4}\cos x+C$

e. none of these

9. Use long division to evaluate the integral.

$$\int \frac{y}{y+3}\,dy$$

10. Use long division to evaluate the integral.

$$\int_0^8 \frac{x^3+4x^2-12x+1}{x^2+4x-12}\,dx$$

Select the correct answer. The choices are rounded to 3 decimal places.

a. 31.757
b. 31.969
c. 8.0310
d. 32.031
e. 34.032

11. Use the Table of Integrals to evaluate the integral to three decimal places.

$$\int_3^5 \frac{1}{x^2\sqrt{4x^2-1}}\,dx$$

12. If f is a quadratic function such that $f(0)=1$ and $\int \frac{f(x)}{x^2(x+1)^3}dx$ is a rational function, find the value of $f'(0)$.

Select the correct answer.

a. $f'(0)=1$ b. $f'(0)=2$ c. $f'(0)=3$ d. $f'(0)=0$ e. $f'(0)=5$

13. Evaluate the integral.

$$\int \frac{\cos x}{9+\sin^2 x}dx$$

14. Evaluate the integral.

$$\int_1^{\infty} \frac{dx}{x\ln x}$$

Select the correct answer.

a. $1/2$ b. 0 c. $-1/4$ d. $1/4$ e. *divergent*

15. Evaluate the integral.

$$\int \frac{1}{\sqrt{x+1}+\sqrt{x}}dx$$

16. Use the Table of Integrals to evaluate the integral.

$$\int \frac{x^2}{\sqrt{x^6-4}}dx$$

17. Use Simpson's Rule to approximate the given integral to six places with the specified value of n.

$$\int_0^{1/2} \sin\left(e^{t/2}\right)dt,\ n=8$$

Select the correct answer.

a. 0.463076 b. 0.707476 c. –0.548035 d. 0.551976 e. 0.481335 f. 0.451976

18. Use the Midpoint Rule to approximate $\int_0^4 \sqrt{x}\sin x\,dx$ for $n=8$. Round the result to four decimal places.

19. Evaluate the integral.

$$\int_0^{\pi/2} 2\sqrt{1-\cos 4\theta}\, d\theta$$

Select the correct answer.

a. $2\sqrt{2}$ b. $3\sqrt{2}$ c. 4 d. $\frac{\sqrt{2}}{2}$ e. none of these

20. A radar gun was used to record the speed of a runner during the first 5 seconds of a race (see the table). Use Simpson's Rule to estimate the distance the runner covered during those 5 seconds. Round the result to the nearest thousandth.

t (s)	v(m/s)
0	0
0.5	4.22
1.0	7.29
1.5	8.78
2.0	9.38
2.5	10.26
3.0	10.53
3.5	10.66
4.0	10.73
4.5	10.82
5.0	10.97

Select the correct answer.

a.	44.288 m
b.	44.798 m
c.	44.309 m
d.	42.287 m
e.	44.298 m

ANSWER KEY

Stewart - Calculus ET 7e Chapter 7 Form E

1. a

2. 0.042059

3. $6\left(2\sqrt{3}-\ln\left(2+\sqrt{3}\right)\right)$

4. 3947.84

5. $216\left(\dfrac{\frac{1}{3}\left(x^2+36\right)^{1.5}}{6^3}-\dfrac{\sqrt{x^2+36}}{6}\right)+C$

6. b

7. $-\cos(\ln t)+C$

8. a

9. $y-3\ln(|y+3|)+C$

10. d

11. 0.018

12. c

13. $\frac{1}{3}\arctan\left(\frac{1}{3}\sin(x)\right)+C$

14. e

15. $\left(\frac{2}{3}\right)\left((x+1)^{3/2}-x^{3/2}\right)+C$

16. $\frac{1}{3}\ln|x^3+\sqrt{x^6-4}|+C$

17. f

18. 1.7874

19. a

20. e

1. Evaluate the integral.

$$\int_{1}^{6} e^{\sqrt{t}}\, dt$$

Round your answer to the nearest hundredth.

2. Evaluate the integral.

$$\int_{0}^{5} \frac{x}{x+10}\, dx$$

3. Evaluate the integral.

$$\int x \sin x \cos x\, dx$$

4. Find the average value of the function $f(x)$ in the interval $[-\pi, \pi]$.

$$f(x) = \sin^3 x \cos^3 x$$

5. Evaluate the integral.

$$\int_{0}^{1/2} 2x \cos \pi x\, dx$$

6. Evaluate the integral to six decimal places.

$$\int_{0}^{0.5} \frac{x^3}{\sqrt{16-x^2}}\, dx$$

7. Evaluate the integral.

$$\int_{0}^{\pi/2} \sin^3 \theta \cos^2 \theta\, d\theta$$

8. Evaluate the integral.

$$\int \frac{x^2}{\left(36-x^2\right)^{3/2}}\, dx$$

9. Evaluate the integral.

$$\int_{2}^{\infty} \frac{dy}{y^2+2y-3}$$

10. If f is a quadratic function such that $f(0) = 1$ and $\int \frac{2f(x)}{x^2(x+1)^3}\,dx$ is a rational function, find the value of $f'(0)$.

Select the correct answer.

a. $f'(0) = 3$ b. $f'(0) = 1$ c. $f'(0) = 2$ d. $f'(0) = 0$ e. $f'(0) = 5$

11. Evaluate the integral.

$$\int_{\pi/6}^{\pi/3} \frac{\ln(\tan x)}{\sin x \cos x}\,dx$$

Select the correct answer.

a. $-\frac{1}{8}(\ln 3)^2$ b. 0 c. $\frac{1}{8}(\ln 3)^2$ d. $-\frac{1}{8}(\ln 3)$ e. $-\frac{1}{3}(\ln 8)^2$

12. Use the Table of Integrals to evaluate the integral to three decimal places.

$$\int_3^6 \frac{1}{x^2\sqrt{4x^2-4}}\,dx$$

13. Evaluate the integral if possible.

$$\int_1^\infty \frac{\ln x}{x^4}\,dx$$

14. Find $\lim_{t\to\infty} \int_{-t}^{t} -3x\,dx$.

15. Evaluate the following integral.

$$\int_0^1 3\frac{\ln 8x}{\sqrt{x}}\,dx$$

16. Use the Trapezoidal Rule to approximate $\int_2^3 e^{2/x}\,dx$ for $n = 4$. Round the result to four decimal places.

17. Use the Midpoint Rule to approximate $\int_1^5 \sqrt{x}\sin x\,dx$ for $n = 8$. Round the result to four decimal places.

18. Evaluate the integral.

$\int te^{\sqrt{t}}\,dt$

19. Find the area bounded by the curves $y = \cos x$ and $y = \cos^2 x$ between $x = 0$ and $x = \pi / 2$.

20. The region under the curve $y = 8\cos^2 x,\ 0 \le x \le \pi / 2$ is rotated about the x-axis. Find the volume of the resulting solid.

ANSWER KEY

Stewart - Calculus ET 7e Chapter 7 Form F

1. 33.58

2. $5+10\ln(2/3)$

3. $-\frac{1}{2}x\cos^2 x+\frac{1}{4}\cos x\sin x+\frac{1}{4}x+C$

4. 0

5. $\frac{\pi-2}{\pi^2}$

6. 0.003927

7. $2/15$

8. $\frac{x}{\sqrt{36-x^2}}-\arcsin\left(\frac{x}{6}\right)+C$

9. $\frac{\ln 5}{4}$

10. a

11. b

12. 0.022

13. $1/9$

14. 0

15. $6\ln(8)-12$

16. 2.2651

17. –0.5811

18. $2\left(\sqrt{t}\right)^3 e^{\sqrt{t}}-6te^{\sqrt{t}}+12\sqrt{t}e^{\sqrt{t}}-12e^{\sqrt{t}}$

19. $1-\pi/4$

20. $12\pi^2$

1. Evaluate the integral.

$$\int 20xe^{5x}\,dx$$

2. Evaluate the integral.

$$\int_1^{81} \sqrt{t}\ln t\,dx$$

3. Evaluate the integral.

$$\int_0^4 \frac{x}{x+9}\,dx$$

4. Evaluate the integral.

$$\int_0^{\pi/2} \sin^3\theta\cos^2\theta\,d\theta$$

5. Household electricity is supplied in the form of alternating current that varies from 165 V to –165 V with a frequency of 60 cycles per second (Hz). The voltage is thus given by the function $E(t)$, where t is the time in seconds. Voltmeters read the RMS (root-mean-square) voltage, which is the square root of the average value of $[E(t)]^2$ over one cycle. Calculate the RMS voltage of household current. Round your answer to the nearest integer.

$$E(t)=165\sin(120\pi t)$$

6. Evaluate the integral to six decimal places.

$$\int_0^1 \frac{x^3}{\sqrt{4-x^2}}\,dx$$

7. Find the area of the region bounded by the hyperbola $9x^2-4y^2=36$ and the line $x=6$.

8. Evaluate the integral.

$$\int x\sin x\cos x\,dx$$

9. Evaluate the integral.

$$\int_{-1}^{\sqrt{3}} \frac{e^{\arctan y}}{1+y^2}\,dy$$

10. Evaluate the integral or show that it is divergent.

$$\int_1^{\infty} \frac{\ln x}{x^4}\,dx$$

11. If f is a quadratic function such that $f(0)=1$ and $\int \frac{5f(x)}{x^2(x+1)^3}dx$ is a rational function, find the value of $f'(0)$.

Select the correct answer.

a. $f'(0)=0$ b. $f'(0)=1$ c. $f'(0)=2$ d. $f'(0)=3$ e. $f'(0)=5$

12. Evaluate the integral.

$$\int_2^{\infty} \frac{4dy}{y^2+2y-3}$$

13. Use the Midpoint Rule to approximate $\int_1^5 \sqrt{x}\sin x\,dx$ for $n=8$.

Select the correct answer. The choices are rounded to four decimal places.

a. 0.5861 b. 0.576 c. –0.5833 d. –0.5701 e. –0.5811

14. Determine how large the integer a has to be so that $\int_a^{\infty} \frac{2}{x^2+1}dx \le 0.007$.

15. Estimate the area of the shaded region in the graph by using the Trapezoidal Rule with n=4.

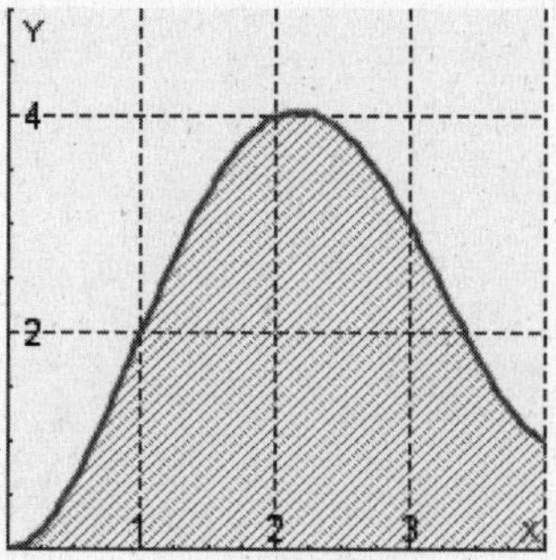

Select the correct answer.

a. 1.5 b. 7.5 c. 6.4 d. 5.9 e. 9.5

16. Evaluate the following integral.

$$I=\int_{-\infty}^{0} \frac{3}{4x-3}dx$$

Select the correct answer.

a. $I=5.3$ b. $I=3.1$ c. $I=2.2$ d. The integral is divergent

17. Evaluate the following integral.

$$\int_{-\infty}^{-7} \frac{1}{\sqrt{8-x}}\,dx$$

18. Determine whether the following integral is convergent or divergent.

$$\int_{1}^{\infty} \frac{6\ln 4x}{x}\,dx$$

Select the correct answer.

a. The integral is divergent
b. The integral is convergent

19. The region under the curve $y = 4\cos^2 x,\ 0 \le x \le \pi/2$ is rotated about the x-axis. Find the volume of the resulting solid.

20. Evaluate the integral $\int_0^1 \frac{1}{x^p}\,dx$ for different values of p. Which of the following integrals is equal to 1.25?

Select the correct answer.

a. $\int_0^1 \frac{1}{x^{0.8}}\,dx$ b. $\int_0^1 \frac{1}{x^{0.3}}\,dx$ c. $\int_0^1 \frac{1}{x^{0.2}}\,dx$ d. $\int_0^1 \frac{1}{x^{2}}\,dx$ e. none of these

ANSWER KEY

Stewart - Calculus ET 7e Chapter 7 Form G

1. $4xe^{5x} - \frac{4}{5}e^{5x} + C$

2. $1944\ln 3 - \frac{2912}{9}$

3. $4 - 9\ln 13 + 18\ln 3$

4. $2/15$

5. 117

6. 0.137181

7. $6\left(6\sqrt{2} - \ln\left(3 + 2\sqrt{2}\right)\right)$

8. $-\frac{1}{2}x\cos^2 x + \frac{1}{4}\cos x \sin x + \frac{1}{4}x$

9. $e^{\pi/3} - e^{-\pi/4}$

10. $1/9$

11. d

12. $\ln 5$

13. e

14. $a \ge 286$

15. e

16. d

17. divergent

18. a

19. $3\pi^2$

20. c

1. Make a substitution to express the integrand as a rational function and then evaluate the integral.

$$\int_{4}^{25} \frac{\sqrt{x}}{x-36}\,dx$$

Round the answer to four decimal places.

2. Evaluate the integral.

$$\int_{\pi/3}^{\pi/2} \cot^2 x\,dx$$

3. Find the area of the region bounded by the given curves.

$$y = \cos x,\ \ y = \cos^3 x,\ \ x = 0,\ \ x = \frac{\pi}{2}$$

4. Evaluate the integral to six decimal places.

$$\int_{0}^{0.5} \frac{x^3}{\sqrt{16-x^2}}\,dx$$

5. Evaluate the integral.

$$\int_{0}^{1/2} 2x\cos \pi x\,dx$$

6. Evaluate the integral using integration by parts with the indicated choices of u and dv.

$$\int 4x\ln x\,dx,\ u = 4\ln x,\ dv = x\,dx$$

Select the correct answer.

a. $2x^2\ln x + x^2 + C$

b. $2x^2\ln x - x^2 + C$

c. $2x^2\ln x - x + C$

d. $2x\ln x - x^2 + C$

e. $2x^2\ln x - 4x^2 + C$

f. none of these

7. Evaluate the integral.

$$\int \frac{1+4e^x}{1-e^x}\,dx$$

8. Evaluate the integral.

$$\int \frac{1}{e^{3x}-e^x}\,dx$$

9. Evaluate the integral.

$$\int \frac{1}{\sqrt{x+1}+\sqrt{x}}\,dx$$

10. Evaluate the integral.

$$\int \frac{1}{-e^{-x}+e^x}\,dx$$

11. Use the Trapezoidal Rule to approximate $\int_1^2 e^{3/x}\,dx$ for $n = 4$. Round the result to four decimal places.

12. Use the Midpoint Rule to approximate $\int_3^7 \sqrt{x}\sin x\,dx$ for $n = 8$. Round the result to four decimal places.

13. Estimate the area of the shaded region in the graph by using the Trapezoidal Rule with $n = 4$.

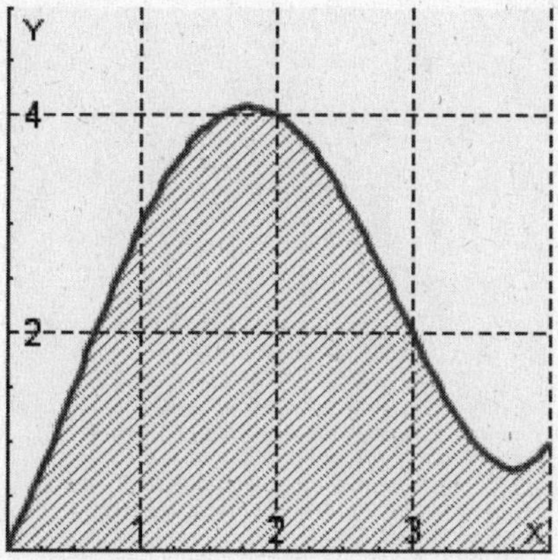

Round the answer to the nearest tenth.

14. Evaluate the integral.

$$\int_{-1/\sqrt{3}}^{\sqrt{3}} \frac{e^{\arctan y}}{1+y^2}\,dy$$

15. If f is a quadratic function such that $f(0)=1$ and $\int \frac{6f(x)}{x^2(x+1)^3}\,dx$ is a rational function, find the value of $f'(0)$.

16. Evaluate the integral.

$$\int 20xe^{4x}\,dx$$

17. Make a substitution to express the integrand as a rational function and then evaluate the integral.

$$\int \frac{3e^{6x}}{e^{6x}+3e^{3x}+2}\,dx$$

Select the correct answer.

a. $\ln\left[\left(e^{x}+2\right)^{2}/\left(e^{x}+4\right)\right]+C$

b. $\ln\left[\left(e^{3x}+1\right)/\left(e^{3x}+2\right)\right]+C$

c. $\ln\left[\left(e^{3x}+2\right)^{2}/\left(e^{3x}+1\right)\right]+C$

d. $2\ln\left[\left(e+2\right)^{2}/\left(e^{x}+1\right)\right]+C$

e. none of these

18. Evaluate the integral.

$$\int_{0}^{\pi/12} \cos^5 6x\,dx$$

19. Evaluate the integral.

$$\int e^{7x} \cos 8x \, dx$$

Select the correct answer.

a. $\dfrac{e^{7x}(7\sin 8x + 8\cos 8x)}{113}$

b. $\dfrac{e^{7x}(7\cos 8x + 8\sin 8x)}{15}$

c. $\dfrac{e^{7x}(7\cos 8x + 8\sin 8x)}{113}$

d. $\dfrac{e^{7x}(7\sin 8x - 8\cos 8x)}{113}$

e. none of these

20. The region under the curve $y = 2\cos^2 x$, $0 \le x \le \pi/2$ is rotated about the *x*-axis. Find the volume of the resulting solid.

Select the correct answer.

a. $3\pi^2/4$

b. $\pi^2/8$

c. $3\pi/4$

d. $3/8$

e. $3\pi/8$

ANSWER KEY

Stewart - Calculus ET 7e Chapter 7 Form H

1. –4.2285

2. $\dfrac{1}{\sqrt{3}}-\dfrac{\pi}{6}$

3. 1/3

4. 0.003927

5. $\dfrac{\pi-2}{\pi^2}$

6. b

7. $x-5\ln\left(\left|e^x-1\right|\right)+C$

8. $\left(e^{-x}+\dfrac{1}{2}\ln\left(\left|\dfrac{e^x-1}{e^x+1}\right|\right)\right)+C$

9. $\dfrac{2}{3}\left((x+1)^{3/2}-x^{3/2}\right)+C$

10. $\dfrac{1}{2}\ln\left(\left|e^x-1\right|\right)-\dfrac{1}{2}\ln\left(e^x+1\right)+C$

11. 9.0621

12. –3.7127

13. 9.5

14. $e^{\pi/3}-e^{-\pi/6}$

15. 3

16. $e^{4x}\left(5x-\dfrac{5}{4}\right)+C$

17. c

18. $\dfrac{4}{45}$

19. c

20. a

1. Find the length of the curve.

$$y=\frac{1}{6}(x^2+4)^{3/2},\quad 0\le x\le 3$$

2. Find the length of the curve.

$$y=2\ln\left(\sin\frac{x}{2}\right),\quad \pi/3\le x\le \pi$$

3. A steady wind blows a kite due west. The kite's height above ground from horizontal position $x=0$ to $x=50$ ft is given by $y=140-\frac{1}{40}(x-20)^2$. Find the distance traveled by the kite. Give your answer rounded to two decimal places.

4. Use Simpson's Rule with $n=6$ to estimate the length of the curve $y=2\sin x,\ 0\le x\le \pi$. Round your answer to six decimal places.

5. Set up, but do not evaluate, an integral for the area of the surface obtained by rotating the curve about the given axis.

$$y=e^x,\ 1\le y\le 5;\ y\text{-axis}$$

6. Find the area of the surface obtained by rotating the curve about the y-axis.

$$y=\frac{1}{4}x^2-\frac{1}{2}\ln x,\quad 1\le x\le 2$$

7. Find the centroid of the region bounded by the given curves.

$$y=x^3,\ x+y=2,\ x=0$$

8. Find the centroid of the region bounded by the curves.

$$y=\ln 2x,\quad y=0,\quad x=e/2$$

9. The masses m_i are located at the points P_i . Find the moments M_x and M_y and the center of mass of the system.

$$m_1=6,\ m_2=5,\ m_3=10;$$
$$P_1(1,5),\ P_2(3,-2),\ P_3(-2,-1)$$

10. A trough is filled with a liquid of density $840\,\text{kg/m}^3$. The ends of the trough are equilateral triangles with sides 8 m long and vertex at the bottom. Find the hydrostatic force on one end of the trough.

11. If $f(x)$ is the probability density function for the blood cholesterol level of men over the age of 40, where x is measured in milligrams per deciliter, express as an integral the probability that the cholesterol level of such a man lies between 170 and 240.

12. The manager of a fast-food restaurant determines that the average time that her customers wait for service is 2 minutes.

The manager wants to advertise that anybody who isn't served within a certain number of minutes gets a free hamburger. But she doesn't want to give away free hamburgers to more than 3% of her customers. What value of x must she use in the advertisement "if you aren't served within x minutes, you get a free hamburger"?

13. Find the center of mass of a lamina in the shape of a quarter-circle with radius 24 with density $\rho = 3$.

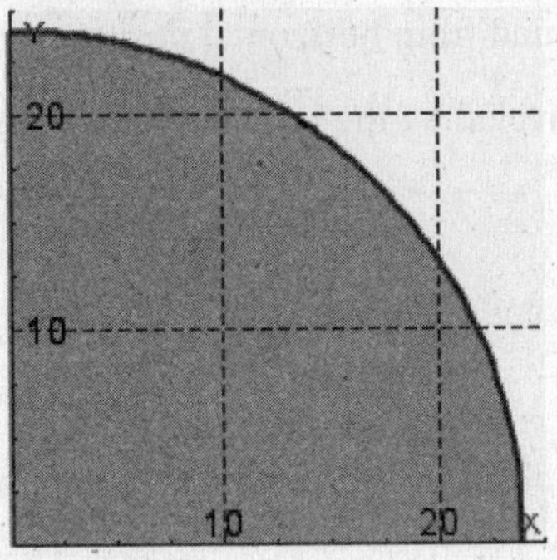

14. Find the centroid of the region shown, not by integration, but by locating the centroids of the rectangles and triangles and using additivity of moments.

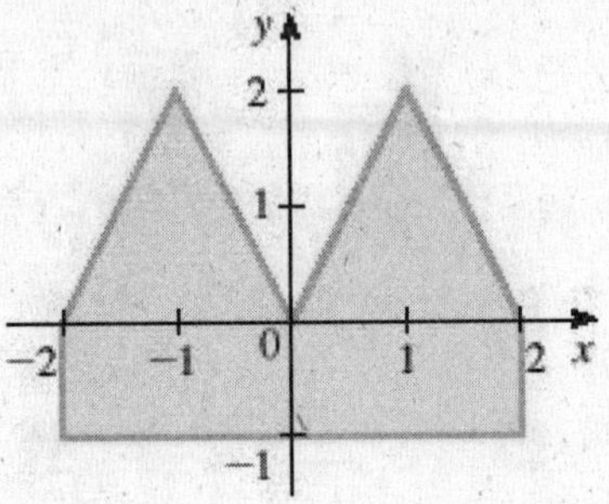

15. The standard deviation for a random variable with probability density function f and mean μ is defined by $\sigma = \left[\int_{-\infty}^{\infty} (x-\mu)^2 f(x)dx \right]^{1/2}$.

Find the standard deviation for an exponential density function with mean 9.

16. A type of lightbulb is labeled as having an average lifetime of 1,000 hours. It's reasonable to model the probability of failure of these bulbs by an exponential density function with mean $\mu = 1{,}000$. What is the median lifetime of these lightbulbs? Give your answer rounded to two decimal places.

17. The demand function for a commodity is given by $p = 2000 - 0.1x - 0.01x^2$. Find the consumer surplus when the sales level is 150.

18. Find the volume obtained when the circle of radius 1 with center (1,0) is rotated about the y-axis.

19. Let the function whose graph is shown be a probability density function. Calculate the mean.

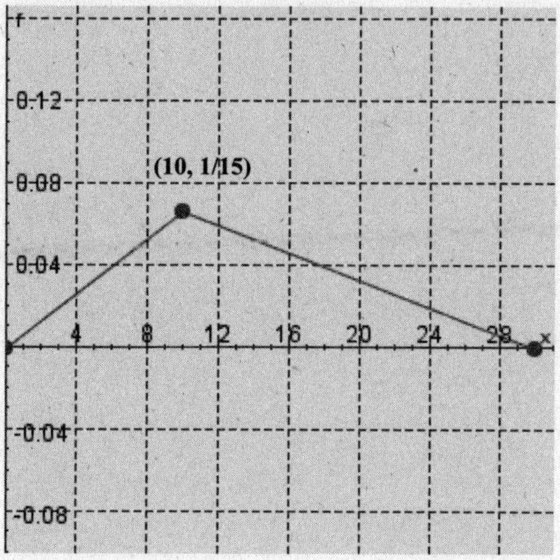

20. Let $f(x) = \dfrac{c}{\left(1+x^2\right)}$.

a) For what value of c is f a probability density function?

b) For that value of c, find $P\,(-1 < X < 1)$.

ANSWER KEY

Stewart - Calculus ET 7e Chapter 8 Form A

1. $\frac{15}{2}$

2. $2\ln(2+\sqrt{3})$

3. 61.95 ft

4. 5.258501

5. $S = \int_0^{\ln 5} 2\pi x\sqrt{1+e^{2x}}\,dx$

6. $10\pi/3$

7. $(28/75, 92/105)$

8. $\left(\frac{e^2+1}{8}, \frac{e}{2}-1\right)$

9. $M_x = 10$, $M_y = 1$, $(1/21, 10/21)$

10. $5.27\times10^5\ N$

11. $\int_{170}^{240} f(x)dx$

12. 8

13. $(32/\pi, 32/\pi)$

14. $\left(0, \frac{1}{12}\right)$

15. 9

16. 693.15

17. \$ 23,625

18. $2\pi^2$

19. $30-10\sqrt{3}\approx 12.67$

20. $a)\ 1/\pi,\ b) 1/2$

1. Find the arc length function for the curve $y = 10x^{3/2}$ with starting point P_o (1, 10).

2. Find the length of the curve.

$$y = \frac{1}{6}(x^2 + 4)^{3/2}, \quad 0 \le x \le 4$$

3. Set up, but do not evaluate, an integral for the length of the curve.

$$y = 3x + \sin x, \quad 0 \le x \le 6\pi$$

4. A steady wind blows a kite due west. The kite's height above ground from horizontal position $x = 0$ to $x = 40$ ft is given by $y = 180 - \frac{1}{40}(x - 40)^2$. Find the distance traveled by the kite. Give your answer rounded to two decimal places.

5. Find the length of the curve.

$$y = 2\ln\left(\sin\frac{x}{2}\right), \quad \pi/3 \le x \le \pi$$

6. Set up, but do not evaluate, an integral for the area of the surface obtained by rotating the curve about the given axis.

$y = \ln x$, $2 \le x \le 8$; x-axis

7. Use Simpson's Rule with $n = 6$ to estimate the length of the curve $y = \sin x$, $0 \le x \le \pi$. Round your answer to six decimal places.

8. Find the area of the surface obtained by rotating the curve about the x-axis.

$$y = \frac{x^2}{4} - \frac{\ln x}{2}, \quad 1 \le x \le 7$$

9. Find the area of the surface obtained by rotating the curve about the x-axis.

$$x = \frac{1}{3}\left(y^2 + 2\right)^{3/2}, \quad 1 \le y \le 3$$

10. Find the centroid of the region bounded by the given curves.

$y = x^3$, $x + y = 2$, $x = 0$

11. The masses m_i are located at the points P_i. Find the moments M_x and M_y and the center of mass of the system.

$m_1 = 2$, $m_2 = 4$, $m_3 = 8$;
$P_1(1,5)$, $P_2(3,-2)$, $P_3(-2,-1)$

12. The demand function for a commodity is given by $p = 2000 - 0.1x - 0.01x^2$. Find the consumer surplus when the sales level is 125.

13. Find the exact coordinates of the centroid.

$$y = e^{3x},\ \ y = 0,\ \ x = 0,\ \ x = \frac{1}{3}$$

14. Calculate the center of mass of the lamina with density $\rho = 10$.

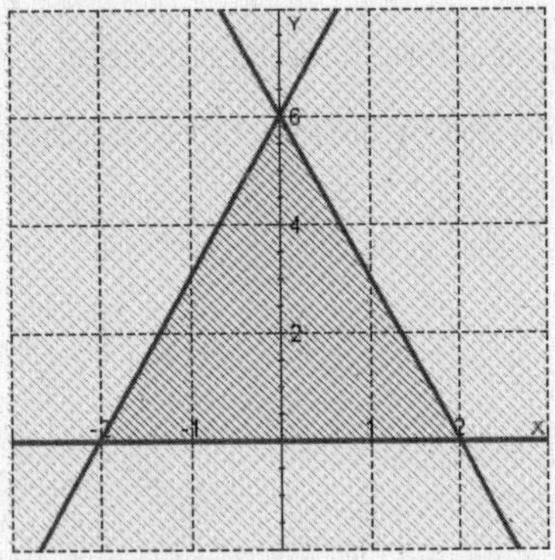

15. Find the volume obtained when the circle of radius 2 with center (2,0) is rotated about the *y*-axis.

16. A gate in an irrigation canal is constructed in the form of a trapezoid 3 ft wide at the bottom, 5 ft wide at the top, and 2 ft high. It is placed vertically in the canal, with the water extending to its top. Find the hydrostatic force on one side of the gate.

17. A demand curve is given by $p = \dfrac{300}{x+8}$.

Find the consumer surplus when the selling price is \$20.

18. For a given commodity and pure competition, the number of units produced and the price per unit are determined as the coordinates of the point of intersection of the supply and demand curves. Given the demand curve $p = 60 - \dfrac{x}{30}$ and the supply curve $p = 30 + \dfrac{x}{20}$, find the consumer surplus.

19. A movie theater has been charging \$9.00 per person and selling about 300 tickets on a typical weeknight. After surveying their customers, the theater estimates that for every \$1.00 that they lower the price, the number of moviegoers will increase by 40 per night. Find the demand function and calculate the consumer surplus when the tickets are priced at \$4.

20. Let $f(x) = \dfrac{c}{\left(1+x^2\right)}$.

a) For what value of c is f a probability density function?

b) For that value of c, find $P(-1 < X < 1)$.

ANSWER KEY

Stewart - Calculus ET 7e Chapter 8 Form B

1. $L = \frac{2}{675}\left((1+225x)^{3/2} - 226\sqrt{226}\right)$

2. $\frac{44}{3}$

3. $\int_0^{6\pi} \sqrt{\cos^2 x + 6\cos x + 10}\; dx$

4. 59.16

5. $2\ln(2+\sqrt{3})$

6. $S = \int_2^8 2\pi(\ln x)\sqrt{1+\left(\frac{1}{x}\right)^2}\; dx$

7. 3.819403

8. $\frac{\pi}{4}\left(648 - 49\ln 7 - (\ln(7))^2\right)$

9. 48π

10. $(28/75, 92/105)$

11. $M_x = -6,\ M_y = -2,\ (-1/7, -3/7)$

12. \$ 13,802.08

13. $\left(\frac{1}{3(e-1)}, \frac{e+1}{4}\right)$

14. (0, 2)

15. $16\pi^2$

16. 458 lb

17. 48.58

18. 2160

19. 3125

20. $a)\ 1/\pi,\ b) 1/2$

1. Find the length of the curve.

$$y = \frac{1}{6}(x^2+4)^{3/2}, \quad 0 \le x \le 2$$

Select the correct answer.

a. $\frac{10}{3}$ b. $\frac{15}{2}$ c. $\frac{44}{3}$ d. $\frac{3}{44}$ e. $\frac{8}{3}$

2. Find the length of the curve.

$$y = 2\ln\left(\sin\frac{x}{2}\right), \quad \pi/3 \le x \le \pi$$

Select the correct answer.

a. $\ln(\sqrt{3})$ b. $\ln(2\sqrt{3})$ c. $\ln(2)$ d. $\ln(2+\sqrt{3})$ e. none of these

3. Find the length of the curve for the interval $1 \le x \le 4$.

$$y = \int_1^x \sqrt{t^3-1}\,dt$$

Select the correct answer.

a. $L = \frac{1}{62}$ b. $L = \frac{62}{13}$ c. $L = \frac{5}{62}$ d. $L = \frac{62}{5}$ e. $L = \frac{61}{3}$

4. Set up, but do not evaluate, an integral for the area of the surface obtained by rotating the curve $y = \ln x$ about the x-axis on the interval $1 \le x \le 4$.

Select the correct answer.

a. $\int_4^1 2\pi x\sqrt{1+(1/x)^2}\,dx$

b. $\int_1^4 2\pi x\sqrt{1+(1/x)^2}\,dx$

c. $\int_1^4 2\pi x\ln(x)\sqrt{1+(1/x)^2}\,dx$

d. $\int_4^1 2\pi x\ln(x)\sqrt{1+(1/x)^2}\,dx$

e. $\int_4^1 2\pi\sqrt{x+(1/x)^2}\,dx$

5. Set up, but do not evaluate, an integral for the area of the surface obtained by rotating the curve about the given axis.

$y = e^x$, $1 \le y \le 3$; y-axis

Select the correct answer.

a. $\int_1^3 2\pi e^x \sqrt{1+e^{2x}}\, dx$

b. $\int_0^{\ln 3} 2\pi \sqrt{1+e^{2x}}\, dx$

c. $\int_0^{\ln 3} 2\pi x \sqrt{1+e^{2x}}\, dx$

d. $\int_1^3 2\pi x \sqrt{1+e^{2x}}\, dx$

e. $\int_1^3 2\pi x e^x \sqrt{1+e^x}\, dx$

6. Find the area of the surface obtained by rotating the curve about the x-axis.

$x = \frac{1}{3}\left(y^2+2\right)^{3/2}$, $1 \le y \le 3$

Select the correct answer.

a. $\frac{101\pi}{2}$ b. $\frac{99\pi}{2}$ c. 48π d. 24π e. 12π

7. Find the area of the surface obtained by rotating the curve about the y-axis.

$y = \frac{1}{4}x^2 - \frac{1}{2}\ln x$, $1 \le x \le 2$

Select the correct answer.

a. $10/3$ b. $11\pi/2$ c. $3\pi/2$ d. $8\pi/3$ e. none of these

8. Find the length of the curve.

$x = \frac{y^4}{8} + \frac{1}{4y^2}$, $1 \le y \le 2$

Select the correct answer.

a. $33/16$ b. 2 c. 3 d. $2/3$ e. none of these

9. The masses m_i are located at the points P_i. Find the moments M_x and M_y and the center of mass of the system.

$m_1 = 6,\ m_2 = 5,\ m_3 = 10;$
$P_1(1,5),\ P_2(3,-2),\ P_3(-2,-1)$

Select the correct answer.

a. $M_x = 10,\ M_y = 1,\ (1/21, 10/21)$
b. $M_x = -10,\ M_y = 1,\ (1/21, -10/21)$
c. $M_x = 10,\ M_y = -1,\ (-1/21, 10/21)$
d. $M_x = 1,\ M_y = 10,\ (1/21, 10/21)$
e. $M_x = 10,\ M_y = 1,\ (10/21, 1/21)$

10. Use Simpson's Rule with $n = 6$ to estimate the length of the curve $y = 3\sin x,\ 0 \le x \le \pi$. Round your answer to six decimal places.

Select the correct answer.

a. 6.947582 b. 6.972089 c. 6.987208 d. 6.947368 e. none of these

11. Find the area of the surface obtained by rotating the circle $x^2 + y^2 = a^2$ about the line $y = a$.

Select the correct answer.

a. $2\pi^2 a^2$ b. $3\pi^2 a^2$ c. $7\pi^2 a^2$ d. $4\pi^2 a^2$ e. $\pi^2 a^2$

12. A large tank is designed with ends in the shape of the region between the curves $y = x^2/2$ and $y = 15$, measured in feet. Find the hydrostatic force on one end of the tank if it is filled to a depth of 5 ft with gasoline. (Assume that the density of gasoline is 42.0 lb/ft^3.)

Select the correct answer.

a. 1, 771 lb b. 1, 683 lb c. 1, 855 lb d. 1, 850 lb e. 1, 785 lb f. 1, 918 lb

13. A trough is filled with a liquid of density 855 kg / m^3. The ends of the trough are equilateral triangles with sides 6 m long and vertex at the bottom. Find the hydrostatic force on one end of the trough.

Select the correct answer.

a. $2.10\times10^5\ N$ b. $1.50\times10^5\ N$ c. $2.26\times10^5\ N$ d. $3\times10^5\ N$ e. $5.10\times10^5\ N$

14. Find the centroid of the region bounded by the given curves.

$y = x^3,\ x + y = 2,\ x = 0$

Select the correct answer.

a. $(28/75, 92/105)$ b. $(9/25, 6/7)$ c. $(1/2, 6/7)$ d. $(92/105, 9/25)$ e. none of these

15. Find the centroid of the region bounded by the curves.

$y = \sin 5x, \quad y = 0, \quad x = 0, \quad x = \pi / 5$

Select the correct answer.

a. $\left(\frac{\pi}{10}, \frac{\pi}{8}\right)$ b. $\left(\frac{\pi}{10}, \pi\right)$ c. $\left(\pi, \frac{\pi}{8}\right)$ d. $\left(-\frac{\pi}{10}, \frac{\pi}{8}\right)$ e. $\left(-\frac{1}{10}, \frac{1}{8}\right)$

16. Suppose the average waiting time for a customer's call to be answered by a company representative (modeled by exponentially decreasing probability density functions) is 10 minutes. Find the median waiting time.

Select the correct answer.

a. 10.4 minutes b. 4.16 minutes c. 8.32 minutes d. 7.62 minutes e. 6.93 minutes

17. The manager of a fast-food restaurant determines that the average time that her customers wait for service is 2 minutes. Find the probability that a customer is served within the first 4 minutes.

Select the correct answer.

a. 0.86
b. 0.78
c. 0.43
d. 0.95
e. 1.085

18. The demand function for a commodity is given by $p = 2000 - 0.1x - 0.01x^2$. Find the consumer surplus when the sales level is 100.

Select the correct answer.

a. \$3, 583.31 b. \$ 7,166.67 c. \$ 9,478.33 d. \$18,478.33 e. \$3, 267.35

19. A hot, wet summer is causing a mosquito population explosion in a lake resort area. The number of mosquitoes is increasing at an estimated rate of $2{,}100 + 7e^{0.7t}$ per week (where t is measured in weeks). By how much does the mosquito population increase between the 4th and 8th weeks of summer?

Select the correct answer.

a. 14,222 b. 10,940 c. 15,316 d. 6,564 e. 7,658

20. Find the volume obtained when the circle of radius 2 with center (2, 0) is rotated about the y-axis.

Select the correct answer.

a. π^2 b. $16\pi^2$ c. 16π d. $\frac{3}{16}\pi^2$ e. $2\pi^2$

ANSWER KEY

Stewart - Calculus ET 7e Chapter 8 Form C

1. a
2. e
3. d
4. c
5. c
6. c
7. e
8. a
9. a
10. a
11. d
12. a
13. c
14. a
15. a
16. e
17. a
18. b
19. b
20. b

1. Find the length of the curve.

$$y=\frac{1}{6}(x^2+4)^{3/2},\quad 0\le x\le 2$$

Select the correct answer.

a. $\frac{10}{3}$ b. $\frac{15}{2}$ c. $\frac{44}{3}$ d. $\frac{3}{44}$ e. $\frac{8}{3}$

2. Find the length of the curve.

$$x=\frac{y^4}{8}+\frac{1}{4y^2},\quad 1\le y\le 2$$

Select the correct answer.

a. $\frac{1}{2}$ b. $\frac{8}{3}$ c. 2 d. 3 e. $\frac{33}{16}$

3. Find the area of the surface obtained by rotating the curve about the x-axis.

$$x=\frac{1}{3}\left(y^2+2\right)^{3/2},\quad 1\le y\le 3$$

Select the correct answer.

a. 12π b. 36π c. 24π d. 96π e. none of these

4. Find the area of the surface obtained by rotating the curve about the y-axis.

$$y=\frac{1}{4}x^2-\frac{1}{2}\ln x,\quad 1\le x\le 2$$

Select the correct answer.

a. $\frac{10}{3}$ b. $\frac{15\pi}{2}$ c. $\frac{8\pi}{3}$ d. $\frac{8}{3}$ e. none of these

5. Find the centroid of the region bounded by the given curves.

$$y=x^3,\ x+y=2,\ x=0$$

Select the correct answer.

a. $(28/75, 92/105)$ b. $(9/25, 6/7)$ c. $(1/2, 6/7)$ d. $(92/105, 9/25)$ e. none of these

6. Find the area of the surface obtained by rotating the circle $x^2 + y^2 = a^2$ about the line $y = a$.

Select the correct answer.

a. $2\pi^2 a^2$ b. $3\pi^2 a^2$ c. $7\pi^2 a^2$ d. $4\pi^2 a^2$ e. $\pi^2 a^2$

7. A trough is filled with a liquid of density $840\,\text{kg}/\text{m}^3$. The ends of the trough are equilateral triangles with sides 8 m long and vertex at the bottom. Find the hydrostatic force on one end of the trough.

Select the correct answer.

a. $2.10\times10^5\ N$ b. $1.50\times10^5\ N$ c. $5.27\times10^5\ N$ d. $3\times10^5\ N$ e. $5.10\times10^5\ N$

8. A gate in an irrigation canal is constructed in the form of a trapezoid 3 ft wide at the bottom, 5 ft wide at the top, and 2 ft high. It is placed vertically in the canal, with the water extending to its top. Find the hydrostatic force on one side of the gate.

Select the correct answer.

a. 229 lb b. 458 lb c. 225 lb d. 220 lb e. none of these

9. Find the volume obtained when the circle of radius 2 with center (2, 0) is rotated about the *y*-axis.

Select the correct answer.

a. π^2 b. $16\pi^2$ c. 16π d. $\frac{3}{16}\pi^2$ e. $2\pi^2$

10. *Dye dilution* is a method of measuring cardiac output. If *A* mg of dye is used and *c(t)* is the concentration of the dye at time *t*, then the cardiac output over the time interval [0, *T*] is given by

$$F = \frac{A}{\int_0^T c(t)\,dt}$$

Find the cardiac output over the time interval [0, 15] if the dye dilution method is used with 10 mg of dye and the dye concentration, in mg/L, is modeled by $c(t) = \frac{1}{2}t(15-t),\ 0 \le t \le 15$, where t is measured in seconds.

Select the correct answer.

a. 0.049778 b. 0.053333 c. 0.039111 d. 0.042667 e. 0.028444 f. 0.035556

11. If $f(x)$ is the probability density function for the blood cholesterol level of men over the age of 40, where x is measured in milligrams per deciliter, express as an integral the probability that the cholesterol level of such a man lies between 195 and 230.

Select the correct answer.

a. $\int_{195}^{230} f(x)\,dx$ b. $\int_{40}^{230} f(x)\,dx$ c. $\int_{40}^{195} f(x)\,dx$ d. $\int_{230}^{195} f(x)\,dx$ e. $\int_{0}^{230} f(x)\,dx$

12. A spinner from a board game randomly indicates a real number between 0 and 50. The spinner is fair in the sense that it indicates a number in a given interval with the same probability as it indicates a number in any other interval of the same length. Find the mean.

Select the correct answer.

a. 7.07 b. 49 c. 50 d. 25 e. 12.5 f. 2,500

13. The marginal cost function $C'(x)$ is defined to be the derivative of the cost function. If the marginal cost of manufacturing x units of a product is $C'(x) = 0.009x^2 - 1.8x + 9$ (measured in dollars per unit) and the fixed start-up cost is $C(0) = \$1{,}800{,}000$, use the Total Change Theorem to find the cost of producing the first 5,000 units.

Select the correct answer.

a. $355,009,000 b. $355,309,000 c. $354,109,000 d. $353,509,000 e. $354,345,000

14. The marginal revenue from producing x units of a certain product is $100 + x - 0.001x^2 + 0.00003x^3$ (in dollars per unit). Find the increase in revenue if the production level is raised from 1,100 units to 1,400 units.

Select the correct answer.

a. $19,541,775 b. $14,212,200 c. $10,659,150 d. $17,765,250 e. $12,435,675

15. Use Simpson's Rule with $n = 6$ to estimate the length of the curve $y = 3\sin x$, $0 \le x \le \pi$. Round your answer to six decimal places.

Select the correct answer.

a. 6.947582
b. 6.972089
c. 6.987208
d. 6.947368
e. none of these

16. A hot, wet summer is causing a mosquito population explosion in a lake resort area. The number of mosquitoes is increasing at an estimated rate of $2{,}200 + 8e^{0.8t}$ per week (where t is measured in weeks). By how much does the mosquito population increase between the 4th and 9th weeks of summer?

Select the correct answer.

a. 16,904 b. 26,564 c. 21,734 d. 24,149 e. 14,489

17. The demand function for a commodity is given by $p = 2000 - 0.1x - 0.01x^2$. Find the consumer surplus when the sales level is 110.

Select the correct answer.

a. $ 23,625 b. $ 22,625.10 c. $ 21,625.33 d. $ 10,478.33 e. $ 9,478.33

18. The manager of a fast-food restaurant determines that the average time that her customers wait for service is 5 minutes.

The manager wants to advertise that anybody who isn't served within a certain number of minutes gets a free hamburger. But she doesn't want to give away free hamburgers to more than 4% of her customers. What value of x must she use in the advertisement "If you aren't served within x minutes, you get a free hamburger"?

Select the correct answer.

a. 23 b. 17 c. 29 d. 12 e. 26 f. 31

19. According to the National Health Survey, the heights of adult males in the United States are (normally distributed with mean) 73 inches, and standard deviation of 2.8 inches. What is the probability that an adult male chosen at random is between 65 inches and 75 inches tall?

Select the correct answer.

a. 0.46 b. 0.38 c. 0.61 d. 0.76 e. 0.91 f. 0.68

20. The standard deviation for a random variable with probability density function f and mean μ is defined

by $\sigma = \left[\int_{-\infty}^{\infty} (x-\mu)^2 f(x)\, dx \right]^{1/2}$.

Find the standard deviation for an exponential density function with mean 7.

Select the correct answer.

a. 3.5 b. 8.4 c. 9.1 d. 7 e. 19.5

ANSWER KEY

Stewart - Calculus ET 7e Chapter 8 Form D

1. a
2. e
3. e
4. e
5. a
6. d
7. c
8. b
9. b
10. f
11. a
12. d
13. e
14. d
15. a
16. d
17. e
18. b
19. d
20. d

1. Use the arc length formula to find the length of the curve.

$y = 5 - 3x, \ -5 \le x \le -2$

2. Find the length of the curve for the interval $1 \le x \le 4$.

$$y = \int_1^x \sqrt{t^3 - 1}\, dt$$

Select the correct answer.

a. $L = \dfrac{1}{62}$ b. $L = \dfrac{62}{13}$ c. $L = \dfrac{5}{62}$ d. $L = \dfrac{62}{5}$ e. $L = \dfrac{61}{3}$

3. Set up, but do not evaluate, an integral for the area of the surface obtained by rotating the curve about the given axis.

$y = e^x, \ 1 \le y \le 6;$ y-axis

4. Find the area of the surface obtained by rotating the curve about the x-axis.

$y = x^3, \ 0 \le x \le 3$

Select the correct answer.

a. $\dfrac{\pi}{27}\left(731\sqrt{731} - 1\right)$

b. $\dfrac{\pi}{27}\left(730\sqrt{730} - 1\right)$

c. $\dfrac{\pi}{27}\left(733\sqrt{733} - 1\right)$

d. $\dfrac{\pi}{27}\left(728\sqrt{728} - 1\right)$

e. $\dfrac{\pi}{27}\left(707\sqrt{707} - 1\right)$

5. Find the area of the surface obtained by rotating the curve about the x-axis.

$y = \dfrac{x^2}{4} - \dfrac{\ln x}{2}, \ 1 \le x \le 3$

6. Sketch the region bounded by the curves $y = x^2, \ x = 0,$ and $y = 49$.

True or False?

The centroid of this region is $\left(\dfrac{21}{4}, \dfrac{147}{2}\right)$.

7. Use Simpson's Rule with $n = 6$ to estimate the length of the curve $y = \sin x$, $0 \le x \le \pi$. Round your answer to six decimal places.

8. The masses m_i are located at the points P_i. Find the moments M_x and M_y and the center of mass of the system.

$m_1 = 2,\ m_2 = 4,\ m_3 = 8;$
$P_1(1,5),\ P_2(3,-2),\ P_3(-2,-1)$

9. Find the centroid of the region bounded by the curves.

$y = \sin 5x,\ \ y = 0,\ \ x = 0,\ \ x = \pi / 5$

Select the correct answer.

a. $\left(-\frac{\pi}{10}, \frac{\pi}{8}\right)$ b. $\left(\frac{\pi}{10}, \frac{\pi}{8}\right)$ c. $\left(\frac{\pi}{10}, \pi\right)$ d. $\left(\pi, \frac{\pi}{8}\right)$ e. $\left(\frac{\pi}{10}, -\frac{\pi}{8}\right)$

10. Find the volume obtained when the circle of radius 3 with center (3,0) is rotated about the *y*-axis.

11. If the infinite curve $y = e^{-x}$, $x \ge 0$, is rotated about the *x*-axis, find the area of the resulting surface.

Select the correct answer.

a. $\frac{\pi}{6}\left[\sqrt{2} + \ln\left(1+\sqrt{2}\right)\right]$

b. $\frac{\pi}{4}\left[\sqrt{2} + \ln\left(1+\sqrt{2}\right)\right]$

c. $\pi\left[\sqrt{2} + \ln\left(1+\sqrt{2}\right)\right]$

d. $\frac{\pi}{3}\left[\sqrt{2} + \ln\left(1+\sqrt{2}\right)\right]$

e. $\frac{\pi}{6}\left[\sqrt{3} + \ln\left(1+\sqrt{3}\right)\right]$

12. Find the area of the surface obtained by rotating the curve about the *x*-axis.

$x = \frac{1}{2\sqrt{2}}\left(y^2 - \ln y\right),\quad 1 \le y \le 2$

13. A trough is filled with a liquid of density $840\,\text{kg/m}^3$. The ends of the trough are equilateral triangles with sides 8 m long and vertex at the bottom. Find the hydrostatic force on one end of the trough.

14. A swimming pool is 10 ft wide and 36 ft long and its bottom is an inclined plane, the shallow end having a depth of 2 ft and the deep end, 12 ft. If the pool is full of water, find the hydrostatic force on the shallow end. (Use the fact that water weighs $62.5\ \text{lb/ft}^3$.)

15. The marginal cost function $C'(x)$ is defined to be the derivative of the cost function. If the marginal cost of manufacturing x units of a product is $C'(x) = 0.009x^2 - 1.8x + 9$ (measured in dollars per unit) and the fixed start-up cost is $C(0) = \$1{,}800{,}000$, use the Total Change Theorem to find the cost of producing the first 5,000 units.

Select the correct answer.

a. \$355,009,000 b. \$355,309,000 c. \$354,109,000 d. \$353,509,000 e. \$354,345,000

16. The demand function for a commodity is given by $p = 2000 - 0.1x - 0.01x^2$. Find the consumer surplus when the sales level is 100.

17. A type of lightbulb is labeled as having an average lifetime of 2,000 hours. It's reasonable to model the probability of failure of these bulbs by an exponential density function with mean $\mu = 2{,}000$.

What is the median lifetime of these lightbulbs? Write your answer to two decimal places.

18. If $f(x)$ is the probability density function for the blood cholesterol level of men over the age of 40, where x is measured in milligrams per deciliter, express as an integral the probability that the cholesterol level of such a man lies between 190 and 235.

19. Let $f(x) = \dfrac{c}{(1+x^2)}$.

a) For what value of c is f a probability density function?

b) For that value of c, find $P(-1 < X < 1)$.

20. Boxes are labeled as containing 500 g of cereal. The machine filling the boxes produces weights that are normally distributed with standard deviation 12 g. If the target weight is 500 g, what is the probability that the machine produces a box with less than 480 g of cereal? Round your answer to four decimal places.

ANSWER KEY

Stewart - Calculus ET 7e Chapter 8 Form E

1. $3\sqrt{10}$

2. d

3. $S=\int_{0}^{\ln 6} 2\pi x\sqrt{1+e^{2x}}\,dx$

4. b

5. $\frac{\pi}{4}\left(28-9\ln 3-(\ln 3)^2\right)$

6. F

7. 3.819403

8. $M_x=-6,\ M_y=-2,\ (-1/7\ ,-3/7)$

9. b

10. $54\pi^2$

11. c

12. $\frac{\pi}{8}\left(21-8\ln 2-(\ln 2)^2\right)$

13. $5.27\times 10^5\ N$

14. 1250

15. e

16. $ 7,166.67

17. 1386.29

18. $\int_{190}^{235} f(x)\,dx$

19. $a)\ 1/\pi,\ b)\ 1/2$

20. 0.0478

1. Find the length of the curve for the interval $1 \le x \le 3$.

$$y = \frac{x^4}{4} + \frac{1}{8x^2}$$

Select the correct answer.

a. $L = \frac{181}{2}$ b. $L = 9$ c. $L = \frac{9}{181}$ d. $L = \frac{181}{9}$ e. $L = \frac{8}{9}$

2. Find the length of the curve for the interval $a \le t \le b$.

$$y = \ln\left(\frac{e^t + 1}{e^t - 1}\right)$$

3. Use Simpson's Rule with $n = 6$ to estimate the length of the curve $y = \sin x$, $0 \le x \le \pi$. Round your answer to six decimal places.

4. Set up, but do not evaluate, an integral for the length of the curve.

$$y = e^x \sin x, \quad 0 \le x \le 3\pi/2$$

Select the correct answer.

a. $L = \int_0^{3\pi/2} \sqrt{1 - e^{2x}(1 + \sin 2x)}\, dx$

b. $L = \int_0^{3\pi/2} \sqrt{1 + e^{2x}(1 + \sin 2x)}\, dx$

c. $L = \int_0^{3\pi/2} \sqrt{1 - e^{2x}(1 - \sin 2x)}\, dx$

d. $L = \int_0^{3\pi/2} \sqrt{1 + e^{2x}(1 - \sin 2x)}\, dx$

e. $L = \int_0^{3\pi/2} \sqrt{1 + e^{x}(1 - \sin x)}\, dx$

5. Set up, but do not evaluate, an integral for the length of the curve.

$$y = x\sqrt[3]{5 - x}, \quad 0 \le x \le 6$$

6. True or False?

An integral for the length of the curve $y = x\sqrt[3]{6 - x}$, $0 \le x \le 5$ is $\int_0^5 \sqrt{1 + \left[\frac{18 - 4x}{3(6 - x)^{2/3}}\right]^2}\, dx$.

7. A hawk flying at an altitude of 169 m accidentally drops its prey. The parabolic trajectory of the falling prey is described by the equation $y = 169 - \frac{x^2}{36}$ until it hits the ground, where y is its height above the ground and x is the horizontal distance traveled in meters.

True or False?

The distance traveled by the prey from the time it is dropped until the time it hits the ground is approximately 192.99 m.

8. A steady wind blows a kite due west. The kite's height above ground from horizontal position $x = 0$ to $x = 50$ ft is given by $y = 190 - \frac{1}{80}(x-40)^2$. Find the distance traveled by the kite. Write your answer to two decimal places.

9. Find the length of the curve for the interval $1 \le x \le 9$.

$$y = \int_1^x \sqrt{t^3 - 1}\, dt$$

Select the correct answer.

a. $L = \frac{5}{484}$ b. $L = \frac{484}{5}$ c. $L = \frac{484}{13}$ d. $L = \frac{1}{484}$ e. $L = \frac{1}{256}$

10. The masses m_i are located at the points P_i. Find the moments M_x and M_y and the center of mass of the system.

$m_1 = 6,\ m_2 = 5,\ m_3 = 10;$
$P_1(1,5),\ P_2(3,-2),\ P_3(-2,-1)$

11. Set up, but do not evaluate, an integral for the area of the surface obtained by rotating the curve about the given axis.

$y = e^x,\ 1 \le x \le 3$; y-axis

12. Find the area of the surface obtained by rotating the curve about the x-axis.

$$y = \frac{x^2}{4} - \frac{\ln x}{2},\quad 1 \le x \le 7$$

13. Find the volume obtained when the circle of radius 1 with center (1,0) is rotated about the y-axis.

14. If the infinite curve $y = e^x,\ x \le 0,$ is rotated about the x-axis, find the area of the resulting surface.

15. A large tank is designed with ends in the shape of the region between the curves $y = \frac{x^2}{4}$ and $y = 16$, measured in feet. Find the hydrostatic force on one end of the tank if it is filled to a depth of 7 ft with gasoline. (Assume the gasoline's density is 42.0 lb/ft^3 .)

Select the correct answer.

a. 5,808 lb b. 5,720 lb c. 5,955 lb d. 5,892 lb e. 5,887 lb

16. A trough is filled with a liquid of density 880 kg/m^3. The ends of the trough are equilateral triangles with sides 4 m long and vertex at the bottom. Find the hydrostatic force on one end of the trough.

17. For any normal distribution, find $P(\mu - 1.6\sigma \le X \le \mu + 1.6\sigma)$ to two decimal places.

18. The demand function for a commodity is given by $p = 2000 - 0.1x - 0.01x^2$. Find the consumer surplus when the sales level is 125.

19. According to the National Health Survey, the heights of adult males in the United States are (normally distributed with mean) 71 inches, and standard deviation of 2.8 inches. What is the probability that an adult male chosen at random is between 55 inches and 75 inches tall?

Select the correct answer.

a. 0.55 b. 1.2 c. 0.83 d. 0.46 e. 0.92

20. Boxes are labeled as containing 500 g of cereal. The machine filling the boxes produces weights that are normally distributed with standard deviation 12 g. If the target weight is 500 g, what is the probability that the machine produces a box with less than 485 g of cereal? Round your answer to four decimal places.

ANSWER KEY

Stewart - Calculus ET 7e Chapter 8 Form F

1. d

2. $\ln\left(\dfrac{e^{b}-e^{-b}}{e^{a}-e^{-a}}\right)$

3. 3.819403

4. b

5. $\displaystyle\int_0^6 \sqrt{1+\left(\frac{15-4x}{3(5-x)^{2/3}}\right)^2}\, dx$

6. T

7. T

8. 56.01 ft

9. b

10. $M_x = 10$, $M_y = 1$, $(1/21, 10/21)$

11. $S = \displaystyle\int_0^{\ln 3} 2\pi x\sqrt{1+e^{2x}}\, dx$

12. $\dfrac{\pi}{4}\left[\ 648-49\ln(7)-(\ln(7))^2\ \right]$

13. $2\pi^2$

14. $\pi\left(\sqrt{2}+\ln\left(1+\sqrt{2}\right)\right)$

15. a

16. 0.69×10^5

17. 0.89

18. $ 13,802.08

19. e

20. 0.1056

1. Use Simpson's Rule with $n=6$ to estimate the length of the curve $y=\sin x$, $0\le x\le \pi$. Round your answer to six decimal places.

2. Find the length of the curve for the interval $5\le x\le 7$.

$$y=\frac{x^4}{4}+\frac{1}{8x^2}$$

Select the correct answer.

a. $L=\frac{543,903}{2}$ b. $L=1,225$ c. $L=\frac{1,225}{543,903}$ d. $L=\frac{543,903}{1,225}$ e. $L=\frac{1}{1,225}$

3. Find the area of the surface obtained by rotating the curve about the y-axis.

$$y=\frac{1}{4}x^2-\frac{1}{2}\ln x,\quad 1\le x\le 2$$

Select the correct answer.

a. $10/3$ b. $15\pi/2$ c. $8\pi/3$ d. $8/3$ e. none of these

4. The masses m_i are located at the points P_i. Find the moments M_x and M_y and the center of mass of the system.

$$m_1=6,\ m_2=5,\ m_3=10;$$
$$P_1(1,5),\ P_2(3,-2),\ P_3(-2,-1)$$

5. Set up, but do not evaluate, an integral for the length of the curve.

$$y=x\sqrt[3]{4-x},\quad 0\le x\le 5$$

6. Set up, but do not evaluate, an integral for the length of the curve.

$$y=3x+\sin x,\quad 0\le x\le 3\pi$$

7. Set up, but do not evaluate, an integral that represents the length of the curve.

$$y=3^x,\quad 0\le x\le 7$$

8. A swimming pool is 14 ft wide and 36 ft long and its bottom is an inclined plane, the shallow end having a depth of 6 ft and the deep end 14 ft.

True or False?

If the pool is full of water, the hydrostatic force on the shallow end is 15,645 lb. Use the fact that water weighs $62.5\,\text{lb}/\text{ft}^3$.

9. A hawk flying at an altitude of 144 m accidentally drops its prey. The parabolic trajectory of the falling prey is described by the equation $y = 144 - \frac{x^2}{36}$ until it hits the ground, where y is its height above the ground and x is the horizontal distance traveled in meters.

True or False?

The distance traveled by the prey from the time it is dropped until the time it hits the ground is approximately 167.28 m.

10. A steady wind blows a kite due west. The kite's height above ground from horizontal position $x = 0$ to $x = 60$ ft is given by $y = 150 - \frac{1}{100}(x-40)^2$. Find the distance traveled by the kite. Write your answer to two decimal places.

11. Find the volume obtained when the circle of radius 2 with center (2,0) is rotated about the y-axis.

12. Find the area of the surface obtained by rotating the curve about the x-axis.

$y = x^3, \ 0 \le x \le 5$

13. Find the area of the surface obtained by rotating the circle $x^2 + y^2 = a^2$ about the line $y = a$.

Select the correct answer.

a. $2\pi^2 a^2$ b. $3\pi^2 a^2$ c. $7\pi^2 a^2$ d. $4\pi^2 a^2$ e. $\pi^2 a^2$

14. Find the coordinates of the centroid for the region bounded by the curves $y = x^2, \ x = 0,$ and $y = 16$.

15. Find the centroid of the region bounded by the given curves.

$y = x^3, \ x + y = 2, \ x = 0$

Select the correct answer.

a. $(28/75, 92/105)$ b. $(9/25, 6/7)$ c. $(1/2, 6/7)$ d. $(92/105, 9/25)$ e. none of these

16. The demand function for a commodity is given by $p = 2000 - 0.1x - 0.01x^2$. Find the consumer surplus when the sales level is 110.

17. The marginal cost function $C'(x)$ is defined to be the derivative of the cost function. If the marginal cost of manufacturing x units of a product is $C'(x) = 0.009x^2 - 1.8x + 9$ (measured in dollars per unit) and the fixed start-up cost is $C(0) = \$1,800,000$, use the Total Change Theorem to find the cost of producing the first 5,000 units.

Select the correct answer.

a. \$355,009,000 b. \$355,309,000 c. \$354,109,000 d. \$353,509,000 e. \$354,345,000

18. A trough is filled with a liquid of density 835 kg / m^3. The ends of the trough are equilateral triangles with sides 8 m long and vertex at the bottom. Find the hydrostatic force on one end of the trough.

Select the correct answer.

a. $1.50\times10^5\ N$
b. $5.24\times10^5\ N$
c. $2.40\times10^5\ N$
d. $0.80\times10^5\ N$
e. $1.80\times10^5\ N$

19. According to the National Health Survey, the heights of adult males in the United States are (normally distributed with mean) 73 inches, and standard deviation of 2.8 inches. What is the probability that an adult male chosen at random is between 65 inches and 75 inches tall?

Select the correct answer.

a. 0.46 b. 0.38 c. 0.61 d. 0.76 e. 0.91 f. 0.68

20. The standard deviation for a random variable with probability density function f and mean μ is defined by $\sigma = \left[\int_{-\infty}^{\infty} (x-\mu)^2 f(x)\, dx \right]^{1/2}$.

Find the standard deviation for an exponential density function with mean 3.

ANSWER KEY

Stewart - Calculus ET 7e Chapter 8 Form G

1. 3.819403

2. d

3. e

4. $M_x = 10$, $M_y = 1$, $(1/21, 10/21)$

5. $\int_0^5 \sqrt{1+\left(\frac{12-4x}{3(4-x)^{2/3}}\right)^2}\,dx$

6. $\int_0^{3\pi} \sqrt{\cos^2 x + 6\cos x + 10}\,dx$

7. $\int_0^7 \sqrt{1+(\ln(3))^2\,3^{2x}}\,dx$

8. F

9. T

10. 64.45 ft.

11. $16\pi^2$

12. $\frac{\pi}{27}\left(5626\sqrt{5626}-1\right)$

13. d

14. $\left(\frac{3}{2}, \frac{48}{5}\right)$

15. a

16. \$ 9478.33

17. e

18. b

19. d

20. 3

1. Find the length of the curve for the interval $a \le v \le b$.

$$y = \ln\left(\frac{e^v + 1}{e^v - 1}\right)$$

2. Set up, but do not evaluate, an integral for the length of the curve.

$y = e^x \sin x,\ 0 \le x \le \pi/2$

Select the correct answer.

a. $L = \int_0^{\pi/2} \sqrt{1 + e^{2x}(1 - \sin 2x)}\, dx$

b. $L = \int_0^{\pi/2} \sqrt{1 - e^{2x}(1 - \sin 2x)}\, dx$

c. $L = \int_0^{\pi/2} \sqrt{1 + e^{2x}(1 + \sin 2x)}\, dx$

d. $L = \int_0^{\pi/2} \sqrt{1 - e^{2x}(1 + \sin 2x)}\, dx$

e. $L = \int_0^{\pi} \sqrt{1 - e^{2x}(1 + \sin x)}\, dx$

3. True or False?

An integral for the length of the curve $y = x\sqrt[3]{4 - x},\ 0 \le x \le 2$ is $\int_0^2 \sqrt{1 + \left[\frac{12 - x}{3(4 - x)^{2/3}}\right]^2}\, dx.$

4. Sketch the region bounded by the curves $y = x^2,\ x = 0,$ and $y = 9$.

True or False?

The centroid of this region is $\left(\frac{9}{2}, \frac{27}{10}\right)$.

5. The masses m_i are located at the points P_i. Find the moments M_x and M_y and the center of mass of the system.

$m_1 = 2,\ m_2 = 4,\ m_3 = 8;$
$P_1(1,5),\ P_2(3,-2),\ P_3(-2,-1)$

6. Find the arc length function for the curve $y = 10x^{3/2}$ with starting point P_o (1, 10).

Select the correct answer.

a. $L = \frac{2}{675}\left((1+225x)^{1/2} - 226\sqrt{226}\right)$

b. $L = \frac{2}{675}\left((1+225x)^{5/2} + 226\sqrt{226}\right)$

c. $L = \frac{2}{675}\left((1+225x)^{3/2} + 226\right)$

d. $L = \frac{2}{675}\left((1+225x)^{3/2} - 226\sqrt{226}\right)$

e. $L = \frac{2}{225}\left((1+220x)^{3/2} - 226\sqrt{226}\right)$

7. Set up, but do not evaluate, an integral for the area of the surface obtained by rotating the curve about the given axis.

$y = e^x$, $1 \le y \le 8$; y-axis

Select the correct answer.

a. $\int_1^8 2\pi x\sqrt{1+e^{2x}}\,dx$

b. $\int_0^{\ln 8} 2\pi\sqrt{1+e^{2x}}\,dx$

c. $\int_0^{\ln 8} 2\pi x\sqrt{1+e^{2x}}\,dx$

d. $\int_1^8 2\pi e^x\sqrt{1+e^{2x}}\,dx$

e. $\int_1^{\ln 8} 2\pi e^x\sqrt{1+e^x}\,dx$

8. Find the area of the surface obtained by rotating the curve about the x-axis.

$y = \frac{x^2}{4} - \frac{\ln x}{2}$, $1 \le x \le 7$

9. Find the area of the surface obtained by rotating the curve about the x-axis.

$y = x^3,\ 0 \le x \le 2$

Select the correct answer.

a. $\pi\left(145\sqrt{145} - 1\right)/27$ b. $\sqrt{143}/27$ c. $\pi\left(143\sqrt{143} - 1\right)$ d. $146\sqrt{146} - 1$ e. none of these

10. Find the area of the surface obtained by rotating the curve about the x-axis.

$x = \frac{1}{3}\left(y^2 + 2\right)^{3/2},\ 0 \le y \le 5$

Select the correct answer.

a. $679\pi/2$ b. $675\pi/2$ c. $669\pi/2$ d. $677\pi/2$ e. none of these

11. A large tank is designed with ends in the shape of the region between the curves $y = x^2/2$ and $y = 18$, measured in feet. Find the hydrostatic force on one end of the tank if it is filled to a depth of 9 ft with gasoline. (Assume the gasoline's density is $42.0\ \text{lb}/\text{ft}^3$.)

12. Use Simpson's Rule with $n = 6$ to estimate the length of the curve $y = 3\sin x$, $0 \le x \le \pi$. Round your answer to six decimal places.

13. The end of a tank containing water is vertical and is in the shape of a semicircle with radius 10 m. Find the hydrostatic force against the end of the tank. (Use $g = 9.8$).

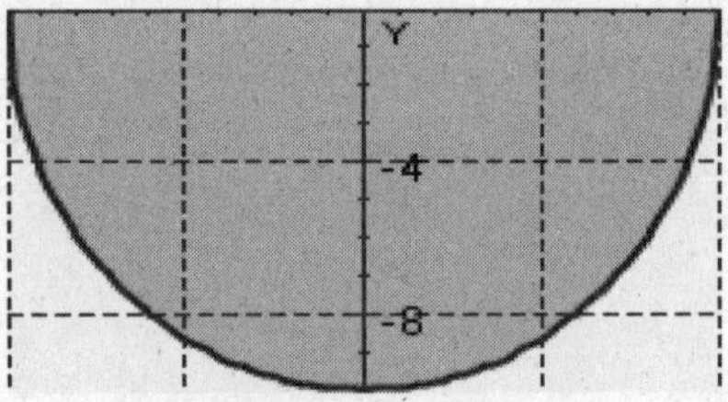

14. The end of a tank containing water is vertical and has the indicated shape, where $a = 13$, $b = 21$ and $h = 6$. Find the hydrostatic force against the end of the tank. Use the fact that the weight density of water is $62.5\ \text{lb}/\text{ft}^3$.

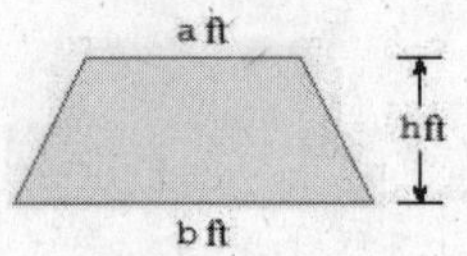

Select the correct answer.

a. 20,743.6 lb b. 20,482.9 lb c. 19,641.7 lb d. 20,729.2 lb e. 20,625.0 lb

15. Calculate the center of mass of the lamina with density $\rho = 10$ shown in the figure below.

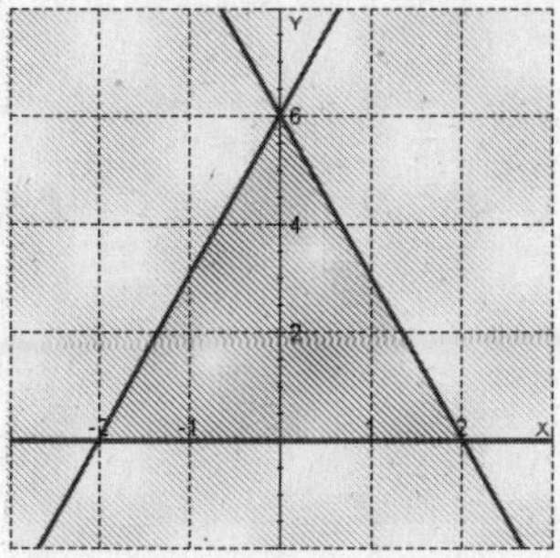

16. A hawk flying at an altitude of 225 m accidentally drops its prey. The parabolic trajectory of the falling prey is described by the equation $y = 225 - x^2/36$ until it hits the ground, where y is its height above the ground and x is the horizontal distance traveled in meters. Calculate the distance traveled by the prey from the time it is dropped until the time it hits the ground. Express your answer correct to the nearest centimeter.

17. Find the volume obtained when the circle of radius 3 with center (3,0) is rotated about the y-axis.

18. Find the centroid of the region shown, not by integration, but by locating the centroids of the rectangles and triangles and using additivity of moments.

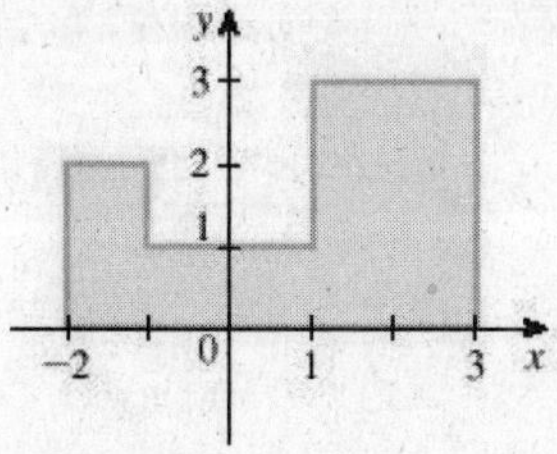

19. A steady wind blows a kite due west. The kite's height above ground from horizontal position $x = 0$ to $x = 80$ ft is given by $y = 130 - \frac{1}{100}(x-20)^2$.

True or False?

The distance traveled by the kite is approximately 92.78 ft.

20. Find the length of the curve for the interval $1 \le x \le 4$.

$$y = \int_1^x \sqrt{t^3 - 1}\, dt$$

ANSWER KEY

Stewart - Calculus ET 7e Chapter 8 Form H

1. $\ln\left(\dfrac{e^b - e^{-b}}{e^a - e^{-a}}\right)$

2. c

3. F

4. F

5. $M_x = -6,\ M_y = -2,\ (-1/7, -3/7)$

6. d

7. c

8. $\dfrac{\pi}{4}\left(648 - 49\ln 7 - (\ln 7)^2\right)$

9. a

10. b

11. 7698

12. 6.947582

13. 6533333

14. e

15. (0, 2)

16. 250.27

17. $54\pi^2$

18. $\left(\dfrac{9}{10}, \dfrac{6}{5}\right)$

19. T

20. 62/5

1. For what values of k does the function $y = \cos kt$ satisfy the differential equation $4y'' = -25y$?

2. $y = Ce^{2x^2}$ is the solution of the differential equation $y' = 4xy$. Find the solution that satisfies the initial condition $y(1) = 1$.

3. A population is modeled by the differential equation $\dfrac{dP}{dt} = 1.8P(1 - P/5{,}100)$.

For what values of P is the population decreasing?

4. A function $y(t)$ satisfies the differential equation $\dfrac{dy}{dt} = y^4 - 13y^3 + 40y^2$.

What are the constant solutions of the equation?

5. The solution of the differential equation $y' = y^3 - 4y$ satisfies the initial condition $y(0) = 0.8$.

Find the limit.

$$\lim_{t\to\infty} y(t)$$

6. Use Euler's method with step size 0.1 to estimate $y(0.5)$, where $y(x)$ is the solution of the initial-value problem. Round your answer to four decimal places.

$$y' = y(x+1), \quad y(0) = 1$$

7. Kirchhoff's Law gives us the derivative equation $Q' = 12 - 4Q$.

If $Q(0) = 0$, use Euler's method with step size 0.1 to estimate Q after 0.3 second.

8. Solve the differential equation.

$$y' = xe^{-\sin x} - y\cos x$$

9. Solve the differential equation.

$$\frac{dx}{dt} = 1 - t + x - tx$$

10. Solve the initial-value problem.

$$\frac{du}{dt} = \frac{2t + \sec^2 t}{2u}, \quad u(0) = 4$$

11. Solve the initial-value problem.

$$\frac{dr}{dt} + 2tr - r = 0, \quad r(0) = 4.$$

12. Find the orthogonal trajectories of the family of curves.

$y = kx^5$

13. **Newton's Law of Cooling** states that the rate of cooling of an object is proportional to the temperature difference between the object and its surroundings. Suppose that a roast turkey is taken from an oven when its temperature has reached 200 °F and is placed on a table in a room where the temperature is 85 °F. If $u(t)$ is the temperature of the turkey after t minutes, then Newton's Law of Cooling implies that $\frac{du}{dt} = k(u - 85)$. This could be solved as a separable differential equation. Another method is to make the change of variable $y = u - 85$. If the temperature of the turkey is 170 °F after half an hour, what is the temperature after 10 min?

14. Suppose that a population develops according to the logistic equation $\frac{dP}{dt} = 0.07P - 0.0007P^2$ where t is measured in weeks. What is the carrying capacity?

15. The Pacific halibut fishery has been modeled by the differential equation $\frac{dy}{dt} = ky\left(1 - \frac{y}{K}\right)$ where $y(t)$ is the biomass (the total mass of the members of the population) in kilograms at time t (measured in years), the carrying capacity is estimated to be $K = 30 \times 10^9$ kg and $k = 0.07$ per year. If $y(0) = 10 \times 10^9$ kg, find the biomass a year later.

16. One model for the spread of an epidemic is that the rate of spread is jointly proportional to the number of infected people and the number of uninfected people. In an isolated town of 5000 inhabitants, 160 people have a disease at the beginning of the week and 1200 have it at the end of the week. How long does it take for 80% of the population to be infected?

17. Let $\frac{dP(t)}{dt} = 0.1P\left(1 - \frac{P}{890}\right) - \frac{1,870}{89}$.

What are the equilibrium solutions?

18. Consider the differential equation $\frac{dP(t)}{dt} = 0.6P\left(1 - \frac{P}{900}\right) - c$ as a model for a fish population, where t is measured in weeks and c is a constant. For what values of c does the fish population always die out?

19. Determine whether the differential equation is linear.

$y' + y \ln x = x^3 y^3$

20. An object with mass m is dropped from rest and we assume that the air resistance is proportional to the speed of the object. If $s(t)$ is the distance dropped after t seconds, then the speed is $v = s'(t)$ and the acceleration is $a = v'(t)$. If g is the acceleration due to gravity, then the downward force on the object is $mg - cv$, where c is a positive constant, and Newton's Second Law gives $m\frac{dv}{dt} = mg - cv$.

Find the limiting velocity.

ANSWER KEY

Stewart – Calculus ET 7e Chapter 9 Form A

1. $k = \pm 5/2$

2. $\frac{1}{e^2}\left(e^{2x^2}\right)$

3. $(5100, \infty)$

4. 8, 5, 0

5. 0

6. $y(0.5) \approx 1.7616$

7. 2.352

8. $y = \left(\frac{1}{2}x^2 + C\right)e^{-\sin x}$

9. $x(t) = -1 + Ce^{t - t^2/2}$

10. $u = \sqrt{t^2 + \tan t + 16}$

11. $r(t) = 4e^{t - t^2}$

12. $x^2 + 5y^2 = C$

13. 189

14. 100

15. $10.47 \times 10^9\ kg$

16. 15 days

17. $P(t) = 340,\ \ P(t) = 550$

18. $c > 135$

19. no

20. $v = \frac{mg}{c}$

1. For what values of k does the function $y = \cos kt$ satisfy the differential equation $4y'' = -36y$?

2. Select a direction field for the differential equation $y' = y^2 - x^2$ from a set of direction fields labeled I-IV.

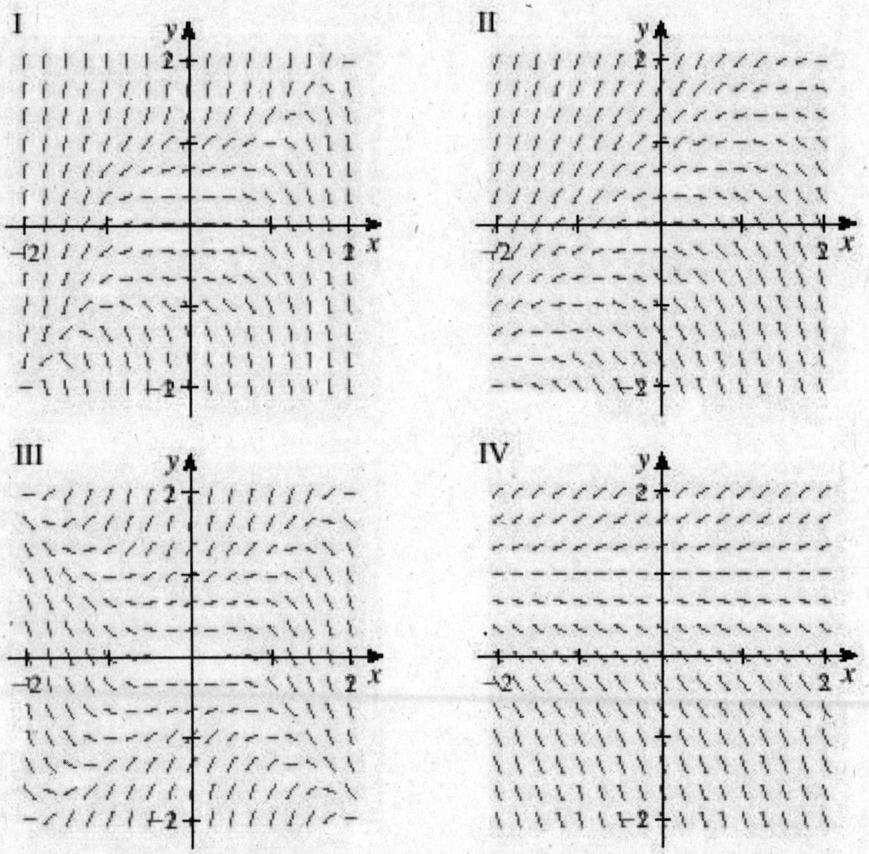

3. Use Euler's method with step size 0.2 to estimate $y(1)$, where $y(x)$ is the solution of the initial-value problem. Round your answer to four decimal places.

$$y' = y(x+1), \quad y(0) = 1$$

4. Solve the differential equation.

$$5yy' = 3x$$

5. Solve the differential equation.

$$\frac{dw}{dt} + 2e^{t+w} = 0$$

6. Solve the differential equation.

$$y' = xe^{-\sin x} - y\cos x$$

7. Solve the initial-value problem.

$$\frac{dr}{dt} = r - 2tr, \quad r(0) = 3$$

8. Write the solution of the initial-value problem and use it to find the population when $t = 20$.

$$\frac{dp}{dt} = 0.1P\left(1 - \frac{P}{2000}\right), \quad P(0) = 100$$

When does the population reach 1200?

9. A bacteria culture starts with 440 bacteria and grows at a rate proportional to its size. After 6 hours there are 5,700 bacteria. When will the population reach 24,000?

10. Experiments show that if the chemical reaction $N_2O_5 \rightarrow 2NO_2 + \frac{1}{2}O_2$ takes place at 45° C, the rate of reaction of dinitrogen pentoxide is proportional to its concentration as follows :

$$-\frac{d[N_2O_5]}{dt} = 0.0008[N_2O_5]$$

How long will the reaction take to reduce the concentration of N_2O_5 to 50% of its original value?

11. After 3 days a sample of radon-222 decayed to 58% of its original amount. How long would it take the sample to decay to 43% of its original amount?

12. A thermometer is taken from a room where the temperature is 23° C to the outdoors, where the temperature is 0° C. After one minute the thermometer reads 11° C. Use Newton's Law of Cooling to answer the following question. When will the thermometer read 10° C?

13. The rate of change of atmospheric pressure P with respect to altitude h is proportional to P provided that the temperature is constant. At 15° C the pressure is 100.9 kPa at sea level and 85.18 kPa at $h = 1,080$. What is the pressure at an altitude of 2,000 m?

14. Suppose that a population grows according to a logistic model with carrying capacity 3,000 and $k = 0.08$ per year. If the initial population is 500, write a formula, P (t, for the population after t years).

15. Biologists stocked a lake with 500 fish and estimated the carrying capacity (the maximal population for the fish of that species in that lake) to be 6,000. The number of fish tripled in the first year.

Assuming that the size of the fish population satisfies the logistic equation, how long will it take for the population to increase to 1,300?

16. Determine whether the differential equation is linear.

$$xy' + e^x - x^7 y = 0$$

17. Let $\dfrac{dP(t)}{dt} = 0.1P\left(1 - \dfrac{P}{730}\right) - \dfrac{129,000}{7,300}$.

What are the equilibrium solutions?

18. Solve the differential equation.

$$(5+t)\frac{du}{dt}+u=5+t,\ \ t>0$$

19. Solve the initial-value problem.

$$xy'=y+x^2\cos x,\qquad y(\pi/2)=0$$

20. A function $y(t)$ satisfies the differential equation $\frac{dy}{dt}=y^4-15y^3+54y^2$.

For what values of y is y decreasing?

ANSWER KEY

Stewart – Calculus ET 7e Chapter 9 Form B

1. $k = \pm 3$

2. III

3. $y(1) \approx 3.4192$

4. $y = \pm\sqrt{\frac{3}{5}x^2 + C}$

5. $w = -\ln\left(2e^t - C\right)$

6. $y = \left(\frac{1}{2}x^2 + C\right)e^{-\sin x}$

7. $r(t) = 3e^{t-t^2}$

8. 560; 33.5

9. 9.37 hours

10. 866

11. 4.65 days

12. 1.1 minutes

13. 73.7 kPa

14. $P(t) = \dfrac{3000}{1+5e^{-0.08t}}$

15. $t = 0.86$ years

16. yes

17. $P(t) = 300,\ P(t) = 430$

18. $u = \dfrac{5t + 0.5t^2 + c}{5+t}$

19. $y = x\sin x - x$

20. (6, 9)

1. Which equation does the function $y = e^{-3t}$ satisfy?

Select the correct answer.

a. $y'' + y' + 12y = 0$
b. $y'' + y' - 12y = 0$
c. $y'' - y' - 12y = 0$
d. $y'' - y' + 12y = 0$
e. $y'' - 3y' + 12y = 0$

2. Which of the following functions is a solution of the differential equation?

$$y'' + 12y' + 36y = 0$$

Select the correct answers.

a. $y = t^2 e^{-6t}$ b. $y = e^t$ c. $y = e^{-6t}$ d. $y = te^{-6t}$ e. $y = 6e^{-6t}$

3. Which of the following functions are the constant solutions of the equation

$$\frac{dy}{dt} = y^4 - 6y^3 + 8y^2$$

Select all that apply.

a. $y(t) = 2$ b. $y(t) = 0$ c. $y(t) = e^t$ d. $y(t) = 4$ e. $y(t) = 3$

4. A population is modeled by the differential equation.

$$\frac{dP}{dt} = 1.4P\left(1 - \frac{P}{4,700}\right)$$

For what values of P is the population increasing?

Select the correct answer.

a. $0 < P < 4,700$ b. $0 < P < 1.4$ c. $P < 4,700$ d. $P > 1.4$ e. $P > 47$

5. Use Euler's method with step size 0.25 to estimate $y(1)$, where $y(x)$ is the solution of the initial-value problem. Round your answer to four decimal places.

$$y' = 5x + y^2, \quad y(0) = 0$$

Select the correct answer.

a. $y(1) = 2.1307$ b. $y(1) = 1.0429$ c. $y(1) = 1.5219$ d. $y(1) = 4.5157$ e. $y(1) = 3.6127$

6. Choose the differential equation corresponding to this direction field.

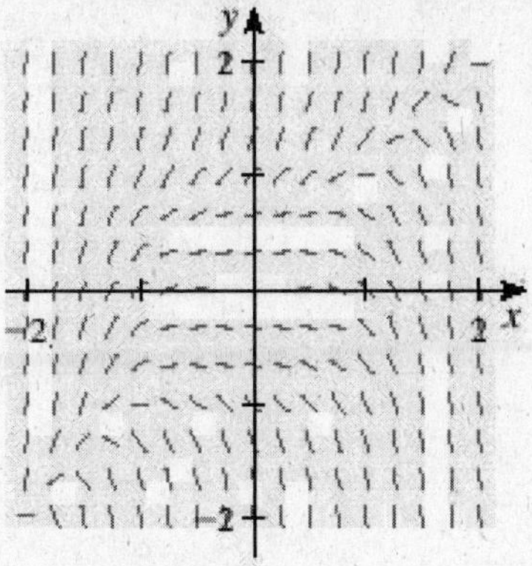

Select the correct answer.

a. $y' = y^2 - x^2$
b. $y' = y - x$
c. $y' = y - 1$
d. $y' = y^3 - x^3$
e. $y' = 2y^3 + x^3$

7. Suppose that a population develops according to the logistic equation

$\frac{dP}{dt} = 0.02P - 0.0002P^2$, where t is measured in weeks. What is the carrying capacity?

Select the correct answer.

a. $K = 0.02$
b. $K = 0.0002$
c. $K = 100$
d. $K = 200$
e. $K = 300$

8. Solve the initial-value problem.

$xy' - y = x \ln x, \quad y(1) = 2$

Select the correct answer.

a. $y(x) = \frac{1}{2}x(\ln x)^2 + 2x$

b. $y(x) = 2x \ln x + \frac{1}{2}x$

c. $y(x) = 2\ln x + \frac{1}{2}x$

d. $y(x) = \frac{1}{2}(\ln x)^2 + x$

e. $y(x) = 2x(\ln x)^2$

9. Solve the differential equation.

$$4\frac{dw}{dt}+3e^{t+w}=0$$

Select the correct answer.

a. $w=\ln\left(\frac{4}{3}+\frac{4}{3}Ce^{t}\right)-t$

b. $w=\ln\left(\frac{4}{3}t\right)-t$

c. $w=\frac{3}{4}e^{t}-C$

d. $w=-\ln\left(\frac{3e^{t}}{4}-C\right)$

e. none of these

10. Solve the differential equation.

$$7yy'=5x$$

Select the correct answer.

a. $5x^2-7y^2=C$
b. $5x^2+7y^2=C$
c. $7x^2-5y^2=C$
d. $7x^2+5y^2=C$
e. $5x^2+7y^2=12$

11. Suppose that a population grows according to a logistic model with carrying capacity 3,000 and $k=0.02$ per year. Choose the logistic differential equation for these data.

Select the correct answer.

a. $\frac{dP(t)}{dt}=0.02P\left(1+\frac{P}{3{,}000}\right)$

b. $\frac{dP(t)}{dt}=3{,}000P\left(1-\frac{P}{0.02}\right)$

c. $\frac{dP(t)}{dt}=0.02P\left(1-\frac{P}{3{,}000}\right)$

d. $\frac{dP(t)}{dt}=P\left(1-\frac{P}{3{,}000}\right)$

e. $\frac{dP(t)}{dt}=0.002P\left(1-\frac{P}{2}\right)$

12. Solve the initial-value problem.

$xy' = y + x^2 \sin x, \quad y(\pi) = 0$

Select the correct answer.

a. $y = -x\cos x - x$
b. $y = x\sin x - x$
c. $y = x\sin x$
d. $y = -x\sin x + x$
e. $y = x\cos x - \sin x$

13. Solve the differential equation.

$y' = xe^{-\sin x} - y\cos x$

Select the correct answer.

a. $y = 2Ce^{-\sin x}$
b. $y = e^{-\sin x} + 2Cx^2$
c. $y = \frac{1}{2}x + Ce^{-\cos x}$
d. $y = \left(2x^2 + C\right)e^{-x}\sin x$
e. $y = \left(\frac{1}{2}x^2 + C\right)e^{-\sin x}$

14. Solve the initial-value problem.

$r' + 2tr = r, \quad r(0) = 6$

Select the correct answer.

a. $r(t) = 6e^{2t}$ b. $r(t) = 6e^{t-2t}$ c. $r(t) = e^{t^2}/6$ d. $r(t) = e^{t-6t^2}$ e. $r(t) = 6e^{t-t^2}$

15. Solve the differential equation.

$\frac{dx}{dt} = 1 - t + x - tx$

Select the correct answer.

a. $x(t) = C + te^{t}$
b. $x(t) = 1 + Ce^{t/2}$
c. $x(t) = 1 - Ce^{t^2/2}$
d. $x(t) = Ce^{t-t^2/2}$
e. $x(t) = -1 + Ce^{t-t^2/2}$

16. Determine whether the differential equation is linear.

$y' + 3x^2 y = 6x^2$

Select the correct answer.

a. the equation is not linear
b. the equation is linear

17. A population of protozoa develops with a constant relative growth rate of 0.9264 per member per day. On day zero the population consists of 7 members. Find the population size after 4 days. Find the answer correct to the nearest whole number.

Select the correct answer.

a. P=18 b. P=285 c. P=41 d. P=275 e. P=382

18. In the circuit shown in Figure, a generator supplies a voltage of $E(t) = 20\sin 60t$ volts, the inductance is 2 H, the resistance is 40 Ω , and $I(0) = 2$ A. Find the current 0.2 s after the switch is closed. Round your answer to two decimal places.

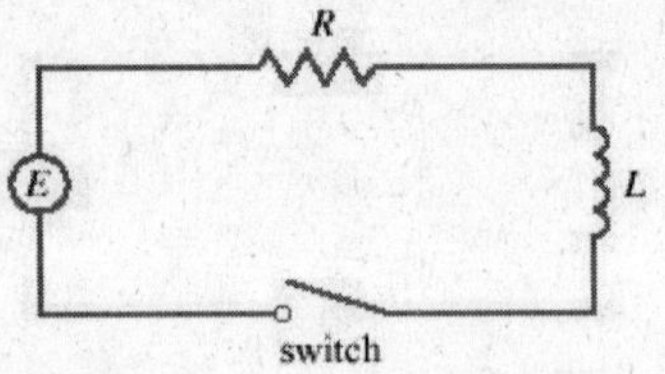

Select the correct answer.

a. –0.06 A b. –0.11 A c. –0.13 A d. –0.75 A e. –0.50 A

19. The table gives estimates of the world population, in millions, from 1750 to 2000:

Year	Population	Year	Population
1750	900	1900	1,580
1800	1,080	1950	2,280
1850	1,240	2000	6,160

Use the exponential model and the population figures for 1750 and 1800 to predict the world population in 1950.

Select the correct answer.

a. $P = 1{,}102{,}329$ b. $P = 1{,}296$ c. $P = 651{,}110{,}527$ d. $P = 1{,}866$ e. $P = 3{,}243$

20. One model for the spread of an epidemic is that the rate of spread is jointly proportional to the number of infected people and the number of uninfected people. In an isolated town of 5000 inhabitants, 160 people have a disease at the beginning of the week and 1200 have it at the end of the week. How long does it take for 80% of the population to be infected?

Select the correct answer.

a. 10 days b. 20 days c. 30 days d. 15 days e. 7 days

ANSWER KEY

Stewart – Calculus ET 7e Chapter 9 Form C

1. c

2. c, d, e

3. a, b, d

4. a

5. a

6. d

7. c

8. a

9. d

10. a

11. c

12. a

13. e

14. e

15. e

16. b

17. b

18. b

19. d

20. d

1. A curve passes through the point (4, 2) and has the property that the slope of the curve at every point P is 3 times the y-coordinate P. What is the equation of the curve?

Select the correct answer.

a. $y = e^{3x-12}/2$ b. $y = 2e^{3x+12}$ c. $y = 2e^{x-12}$ d. $y = 2e^{3x-4}$ e. $y = 2e^{3x-12}$

2. Solve the differential equation.

$$x^2 \frac{dy}{dx} - y = 2x^3 e^{-1/x}$$

Select the correct answer.

a. $y = e^{1/x}x + Ce^{1/x}$ b. $y = Ce^{-1/x}$ c. $y = e^{-1/x}x^2 + Ce^{-1/x}$ d. $y = Cxe^x$ e. none of these

3. A sum of \$3,000 is invested at 25% interest. If $A(t)$ is the amount of the investment at time t for the case of continuous compounding, write a differential equation and an initial condition satisfied by $A(t)$.

Select the correct answer.

a. $\frac{dA}{dt} = 0.25A(0),\ A(0) = 3{,}000$

b. $\frac{dA}{dt} = 25A,\ A(0) = 3{,}000$

c. $\frac{dA}{dt} = 0.25A,\ A(0) = 3{,}000$

d. $\frac{dA}{dt} = 0.25A,\ A(0) = 300$

e. $\frac{dA}{dt} = 2{,}500A,\ A(0) = 3{,}000$

4. Let c be a positive number. A differential equation of the form $\frac{dy}{dt} = ky^{1+c}$ where k is a positive constant is called a *doomsday equation* because the exponent in the expression ky^{1+c} is larger than the exponent 1 for natural growth. An especially prolific breed of rabbits has the growth term $ky^{1.05}$. If 2 such rabbits breed initially and the warren has 27 rabbits after 5 months, then when is doomsday?

Select the correct answer.

a. 40.98 months b. 38.98 months c. 1,106.35 months d. 35.98 months e. 81.95 months

5. Suppose that a population develops according to the logistic equation $\frac{dP}{dt} = 0.02P - 0.0002P^2$ where t is measured in weeks. What is the carrying capacity?

Select the correct answer.

a. $K = 0.02$ b. $K = 100$ c. $K = 0.0002$ d. $K = 200$ e. $K = 2000$

6. Suppose that a population grows according to a logistic model with carrying capacity 2,000 and $k = 0.07$ per year. Choose the logistic differential equation for these data.

Select the correct answer.

a. $\frac{dP(t)}{dt} = 0.07P\left(1 - \frac{P}{2,000}\right)$

b. $\frac{dP(t)}{dt} = 2,000P\left(1 - \frac{P}{0.07}\right)$

c. $\frac{dP(t)}{dt} = 0.07P\left(1 + \frac{P}{2,000}\right)$

d. $\frac{dP(t)}{dt} = 0.07P\left(1 + \frac{P^2}{2,000}\right)$

e. $\frac{dP(t)}{dt} = 0.02P\left(1 + \frac{P}{0.007}\right)$

7. The population of the world was about 5.3 billion in 1990. Birth rates in the 1990s range from 35 to 40 million per year and death rates range from 15 to 20 million per year. Let's assume that the carrying capacity for world population is 100 billion. Use the logistic model to predict the world population in the 2,450 year. Calculate your answer in billions to one decimal place. (Because the initial population is small compared to the carrying capacity, you can take k to be an estimate of the initial relative growth rate.)

Select the correct answer.

a. 32.9 billion b. 17.1 billion c. 24.1 billion d. 59.2 billion e. 78.3 billion

8. Determine whether the differential equation is linear.

$$y' + 3x^2y = 6x^2$$

Select the correct answer.

a. the equation is not linear
b. the equation is linear

9. In the circuit shown in Figure, a battery supplies a constant voltage of 40 V, the inductance is 2 H, the resistance is 10 Ω, and $I(0) = 0$. Find the current 1 s after the switch is closed. Round your answer to two decimal places.

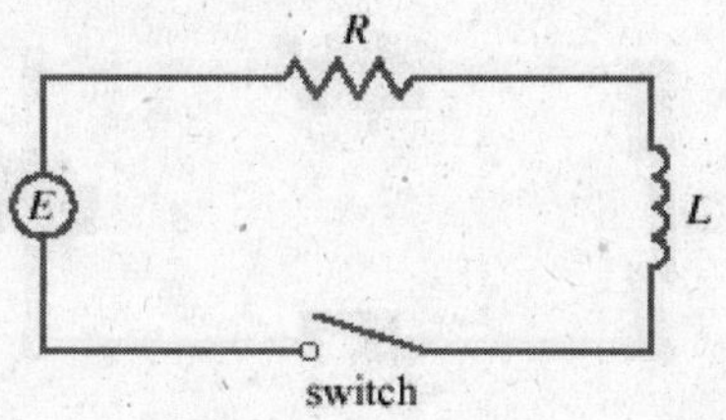

Select the correct answer.

a. 4.11 A b. 3.63 A c. 3.97 A d. 3.76 A e. 7.0 A

10. Use the Bernoulli's method to solve the differential equation.

$$y' + \frac{3y}{x} = \frac{y^3}{x^4}$$

Select the correct answer.

a. $y = \pm\left(Cx^6 + \frac{2}{9x^3}\right)^{1/2}$

b. $y = \pm\left(Cx^6 + \frac{2}{9x^3}\right)^{-1/2}$

c. $y = \left(Cx^6 \pm \frac{2}{9x^3}\right)^{1/2}$

d. $y = \left(Cx^6 \pm \frac{2}{9x^3}\right)^{-1/2}$

e. $y = \left(Cx^6 \pm \frac{2}{9x^3}\right)^{-3/2}$

11. An object with mass m is dropped from rest and we assume that the air resistance is proportional to the speed of the object. If $s(t)$ is the distance dropped after t seconds, then the speed is $v = s'(t)$ and the acceleration is $a = v'(t)$. If g is the acceleration due to gravity, then the downward force on the object is $mg - cv$, where c is a positive constant, and Newton's Second Law gives $m\frac{dv}{dt} = mg - cv$.

Find the limiting velocity.

Select the correct answer.

a. $v = \frac{g}{c}$ b. $v = \frac{c}{g}$ c. $v = \frac{mg}{c}$ d. $v = \frac{mc}{g}$ e. $v = mc$

12. We modeled populations of aphids and ladybugs with a Lotka-Volterra system. Suppose we modify those equations as follows:

$$\frac{dA}{dt} = 3A(1 - 0.0001A) - 0.01AL,$$

$$\frac{dL}{dt} = -0.5L + 0.0001AL$$

Select the correct equilibrium solution.

a. $A = 6{,}000, L = 350$
b. $A = 5{,}000, L = 150$
c. $A = 5{,}000, L = 50$
d. $A = 1{,}000, L = 350$
e. $A = 66{,}000, L = 35$

13. Solve the initial-value problem.

$$(1+\cos x)\frac{dy}{dx} = (1+e^{-y})\sin x,\ y(0)=0$$

Select the correct answer.

a. $y = \ln \dfrac{\cos x}{(1+\cos x)}$

b. $y = \ln\left((1-\cos x)(1+\cos x)\right)$

c. $y = \ln(3-\cos x) - \ln(1+\cos x)$

d. $y = \dfrac{\ln(1+\cos x)}{\ln(1-\cos x)}$

e. $y = \dfrac{(3-\cos x)}{(1+\cos x)}$

14. A phase trajectory is shown for populations of rabbits (R) and foxes (F). Describe how each population changes as time goes by.

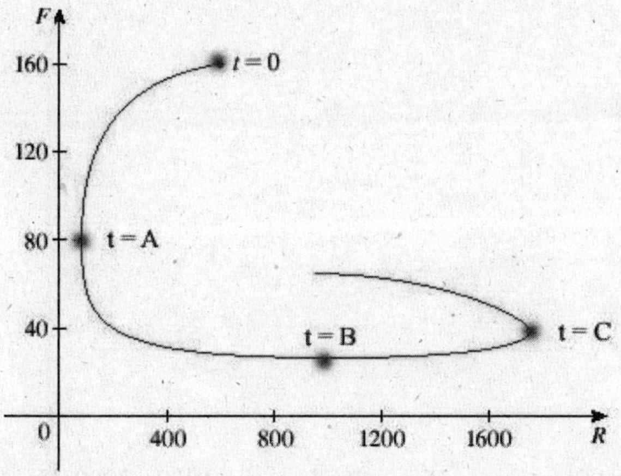

Select the correct statement.

a. At t = B the population of foxes reaches a minimum of about 30.
b. At t = B the number of rabbits rebounds to 500.
c. At t = B the number of foxes reaches a maximum of about 2400.

15. A common inhabitant of human intestines is the bacterium *Escherichia coli*. A cell of this bacterium in a nutrient-broth medium divides into two cells every 20 minutes. The initial population of a culture is 25 cells. Find the number of cells after 5 hours.

Select the correct answer.

a. $P = 1{,}000$ b. $P = 6{,}553{,}600$ c. $P = 32{,}768$ d. $P = 1{,}476{,}225$ e. $P = 819{,}194$

16. Consider a population $P = P(t)$ with constant relative birth and death rates α and β, respectively, and a constant emigration rate m, where $\alpha = 0.9$, $\beta = 0.8$ and $m = 0.7$. Then the rate of change of the population at time t is modeled by the differential equation $\frac{dP}{dt} = kP - m$ where $k = \alpha - \beta$. Find the solution of this equation with the rate of change of the population at time $t = 3$ that satisfies the initial condition $P(0) = 3{,}400$.

Select the correct answer.

a. 655.3 b. 4,602.1 c. 7,987.1 d. 4,587.1 e. 1,187.1 f. none of these

17. Solve the differential equation.

$$(2+t)\frac{du}{dt} + u = 2 + t, \ t > 0$$

Select the correct answer.

a. $u = \dfrac{2t + t^2 + C}{t+2}$

b. $u = \dfrac{t^2 + C}{t+2}$

c. $u = \dfrac{2t + \frac{1}{2}t^2}{\frac{3}{2}t + 2} + C$

d. $u = \dfrac{2t + \frac{t^2}{2} + C}{t+2}$

e. $u = 2t + \dfrac{t^2}{2} + C$

18. The table gives the population of the United States, in millions, for the years 1900 - 2000. Use the exponential model and the census figures for 1900 and 1910 to predict the population in 1950.

Year	Population	Year	Population
1900	75	1960	166
1910	91	1970	200
1920	111	1980	228
1930	126	1990	253
1940	133	2000	276
1950	126		

Select the correct answer.

a. $P = 533$
b. $P = 1{,}004$
c. $P = 239$
d. $P = 394$
e. $P = 197$

19. Solve the initial-value problem.

$xy' = y + x^2 \sin x, \quad y(\pi) = 0$

Select the correct answer.

a. $y = x \sin x$
b. $y = x \sin x - x$
c. $y = -x \cos x - x$
d. $y = -x \sin x + x$
e. $y = x \cos x - \sin x$

20. Let $P(t)$ be the performance level of someone learning a skill as a function of the training time t. The graph of P is called a *learning curve*. We propose the differential equation $\frac{dP}{dt} = r(F - P(t))$ as a reasonable model for learning, where r is a positive constant. Solve it as a linear differential equation.

Select the correct answer.

a. $P(t) = F + Ce^{-rt}$
b. $P(t) = F + Ce^{rt}$
c. $P(t) = F - Ce^{-rt}$
d. $P(t) = F - Ce^{rt}$
e. $P(t) = FCe^{rt}$

ANSWER KEY

Stewart – Calculus ET 7e Chapter 9 Form D

1. e
2. c
3. c
4. a
5. b
6. a
7. c
8. b
9. c
10. b
11. c
12. b
13. c
14. a
15. e
16. d
17. d
18. e
19. c
20. a

1. For what values of k does the function $y = \cos kt$ satisfy the differential equation $9y'' = -25y$?

   Select all that apply.

   a. $k = 5/3$ b. $k = 3/5$ c. $k = 1/5$ d. $k = -5/3$ e. $k = -1/9$

2. $y = Ce^{4x^2}$ is the family of solutions to the differential equation $y' = 8xy$. Find the solution that satisfies the initial condition $y(0) = 8$.

3. $y = \dfrac{1}{10x + C}$ is the family of solutions of the differential equation $y' = -10y^2$, find the solution that satisfies the initial condition $y(0) = 6$.

4. A population is modeled by the differential equation.

   $$\frac{dP}{dt} = 1.4P\left(1 - \frac{P}{4,700}\right)$$

   For what values of P is the population increasing?

   Select the correct answer.

   a. $0 < P < 4,700$ b. $0 < P < 1.4$ c. $P < 4,700$ d. $P > 1.4$ e. $P > 47$

5. A function $y(t)$ satisfies the differential equation $\dfrac{dy}{dt} = y^4 - 10y^3 + 21y^2$. For what values of y is y increasing?

6. One model for the spread of a rumor is that the rate of spread is proportional to the product of the fraction of the population who have heard the rumor and the fraction who have not heard the rumor. Let's assume that the constant of proportionality is $k = 0.04$. Write a differential equation that is satisfied by y.

7. Biologists stocked a lake with 450 fish and estimated the carrying capacity (the maximal population for the fish of that species in that lake) to be 11,000. The number of fish tripled in the first year. Assuming that the size of the fish population satisfies the logistic equation, find an expression for the size of the population after t years.

8. A bacteria culture starts with 150 bacteria and grows at a rate proportional to its size. After 2 hours there are 6,200 bacteria. Approximate the time it takes for the population reach 35,000?

9. Solve the differential equation.

   $$4\frac{dw}{dt} + 3e^{t+w} = 0$$

10. Use Euler's method with step size 0.05 to estimate $y(0.25)$, where $y(x)$ is the solution of the initial-value problem. Round your answer to four decimal places.

    $$y' = y(x+1), \quad y(0) = 1$$

11. Solve the initial-value problem.

$xy' - y = x \ln x,\ y(1) = 3$

12. Solve the differential equation.

$$\frac{du}{dt} = 14 + 2u + 7t + ut$$

13. Solve the initial-value problem.

$xy' = y + x^2 \cos x, \quad y(\pi / 4) = 0$

14. Solve the initial-value problem.

$$\frac{du}{dt} = \frac{2t + \sec^2 t}{2u} \quad u(0) = 7$$

15. Solve the initial-value problem.

$$\frac{dr}{dt} + 2tr - r = 0, \ \ r(0) = 4$$

16. Find the solution of the differential equation $\frac{dy}{dx} = \frac{y^2}{x^4}$ that satisfies the initial condition $y(1) = 1$.

17. Find the orthogonal trajectories of the family of curves.

$y = kx^7$

Select the correct answer.

a. $x^2 + 6y^2 = 0$ b. $x^2 - 6y^2 = 0$ c. $x^2 + 7y^2 = C$ d. $x^2 - 6y^2 = C$ e. $x^2 - 7y^2 = 0$

18. A tank contains 1,200 L of brine with 15 kg of dissolved salt. Pure water enters the tank at a rate of 14 L/min. The solution is kept thoroughly mixed and drains from the tank at the same rate. How much salt is in the tank after 15 minutes?

19. A common inhabitant of human intestines is the bacterium *Escherichia coli.* A cell of this bacterium in a nutrient-broth medium divides into two cells every 20 minutes. The initial population of a culture is 25 cells. Find the number of cells after 2 hours.

20. Find the solution of the initial-value problem and use it to find the population when $t = 20$.

$$\frac{dp}{dt} = 0.1P\left(1 - \frac{P}{2000}\right), \quad P(0) = 100$$

ANSWER KEY

Stewart – Calculus ET 7e Chapter 9 Form E

1. a, d

2. $8e^{4x^2}$

3. $\dfrac{6}{60x+1}$

4. a

5. $(-\infty,\ 0) \cup (0,\ 3) \cup (7,\ \infty)$

6. $\dfrac{dy}{dt} = 0.04y(1-y)$

7. $P(t) = \dfrac{11000}{1+23.44(0.3)^t}$

8. 2.93 hours

9. $w = -\ln\left(\dfrac{3e^t}{4} - C\right)$

10. $y(0.25) \approx 1.3069$

11. $y(x) = \dfrac{1}{2}x(\ln x)^2 + 3x$

12. $u = -7 + Ce^{\frac{t^2}{2}+2t}$

13. $y = x\sin x - \dfrac{\sqrt{2}}{2}x$

14. $u = \sqrt{t^2 + \tan t + 49}$

15. $r(t) = 4e^{t-t^2}$

16. $y = \dfrac{3x^3}{1+2x^3}$

17. c

18. 12.59 kg

19. 1600

20. 560

1. For what values of k does the function $y = \cos kt$ satisfy the differential equation $9y'' = -4y$?

2. For what values of r does the function $y = e^{rt}$ satisfy the differential equation?

$y'' - y' - 30y = 0$

3. Which of the following functions is a solution of the differential equation?

$y'' + 16y' + 64y = 0$

Select all that apply.

a. $y = t^2 e^{-8t}$

b. $y = te^{-8t}$

c. $y = e^t$

d. $y = e^{-8t}$

e. $y = -8e^{-8t}$

4. $y = Ce^{2x^2}$ is the solution of the differential equation $y' = 4xy$.

Find the solution that satisfies the initial condition $y(1) = 3$.

5. $y = \dfrac{1}{8x + C}$ is the family of solutions of the differential equation $y' = -8y^2$, find the solution that satisfies the initial condition $y(0) = 3$.

6. A population is modeled by the differential equation $\dfrac{dP}{dt} = 1.4\left(1 - \dfrac{P}{5{,}500}\right)$.

For what values of P is the population decreasing?

7. Use Euler's method with step size 0.1 to estimate $y(0.5)$, where $y(x)$ is the solution of the initial-value problem. Round your answer to four decimal places.

$y' = y(x+1),\ y(0) = 1$

8. Solve the differential equation.

$$\frac{dw}{dt} + 9e^{t+w} = 0$$

9. The solution of the differential equation $y' = y^3 - 4y$ satisfies the initial condition $y(0) = 0.2$.

Find the limit.

$$\lim_{t\to\infty} y(t)$$

10. Choose the differential equation corresponding to this direction field.

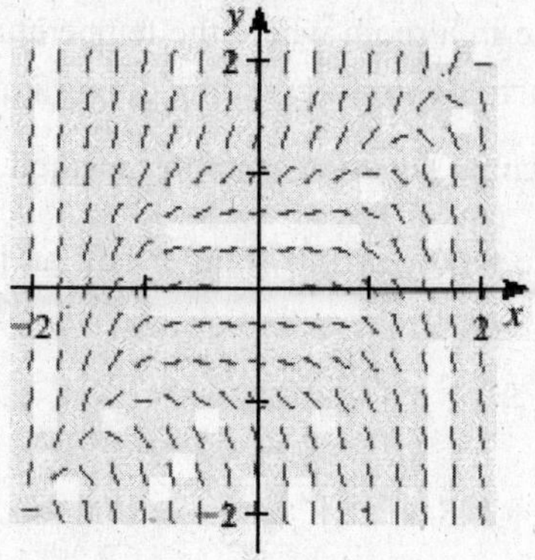

Select the correct answer.

a. $y' = y - x$
b. $y' = y^3 - x^3$
c. $y' = y - 1$
d. $y' = y^2 - x^2$
e. $y' = 2y^2 - x^3$

11. Solve the differential equation.

$y' = xe^{-\sin x} - y\cos x$

12. Scientists can determine the age of ancient objects by a method called *radiocarbon dating*. The bombardment of the upper atmosphere by cosmic rays converts nitrogen to a radioactive isotope of carbon, ^{14}C, with a half-life of about 5730 years. Vegetation absorbs carbon dioxide through the atmosphere and animal life assimilates ^{14}C through food chains. When a plant or animal dies it stops replacing its carbon and the amount of ^{14}C begins to decrease through radioactive decay. Therefore, the level of radioactivity must also decay exponentially. A parchment fragment was discovered that had about 32% as much ^{14}C radioactivity as does plant material on Earth today. Estimate the age of the parchment in years.

Select the correct answer.

a. $t = 9{,}419$
b. $t = 9{,}231$
c. $t = 9{,}041$
d. $t = 10{,}926$
e. $t = 9{,}795$

13. A curve passes through the point (9, 8) and has the property that the slope of the curve at every point P is 6 times the y-coordinate P. What is the equation of the curve?

14. Determine whether the differential equation is linear.

$y' + y\cos x = x^7 y^7$

15. **Newton's Law of Cooling** states that the rate of cooling of an object is proportional to the temperature difference between the object and its surroundings. Suppose that a roast turkey is taken from an oven when its temperature has reached 160 ° F and is placed on a table in a room where the temperature is 60 ° F. If u (t) is the temperature of the turkey after t minutes, then Newton's Law of Cooling implies that $\frac{du}{dt} = k(u-60)$. This could be solved as a separable differential equation. Another method is to make the change of variable $y = u - 60$. If the temperature of the turkey is 150 ° F after half an hour, what is the temperature after 35 min?

    Select the correct answer.

    a. $t = 298\,^\circ\text{F}$ b. $t = 95\,^\circ\text{F}$ c. $t = 143\,^\circ\text{F}$ d. $t = 148\,^\circ\text{F}$ e. none of these

16. A sum of $2,150 is invested at 14% interest. If $A(t)$ is the amount of the investment at time t for the case of continuous compounding, write a differential equation and an initial condition satisfied by $A(t)$.

17. One model for the spread of an epidemic is that the rate of spread is jointly proportional to the number of infected people and the number of uninfected people. In an isolated town of 5000 inhabitants, 160 people have a disease at the beginning of the week and 1200 have it at the end of the week. How long does it take for 80% of the population to be infected?

18. Suppose that a population grows according to a logistic model with carrying capacity 7,500 and $k = 0.07$ per year. Write the logistic differential equation for these data.

19. The Pacific halibut fishery has been modeled by the differential equation $\frac{dy}{dt} = ky\left(1 - \frac{y}{K}\right)$ where $y(t)$ is the biomass (the total mass of the members of the population) in kilograms at time t (measured in years), the carrying capacity is estimated to be $K = 20\times10^8$ kg and $k = 0.03$ per year. How long will it take for the biomass to reach 7×10^8 kg if $y(0) = 4\times10^8$?

20. One model for the spread of a rumor is that the rate of spread is proportional to the product of the fraction of the population who have heard the rumor and the fraction who have not heard the rumor. Let's assume that the constant of proportionality is $k = 0.02$. Write a differential equation that is satisfied by y.

ANSWER KEY

Stewart – Calculus ET 7e Chapter 9 Form F

1. $k = \pm 2/3$

2. 6, –5

3. b, d, e

4. $\frac{3}{e^2} e^{2x^2}$

5. $\frac{3}{24x+1}$

6. $(5500, \infty)$

7. $y(0.5) \approx 1.7616$

8. $w = -\ln\left(9e^t - C\right)$

9. 0

10. b

11. $y = \left(\frac{1}{2}x^2 + C\right)e^{-\sin x}$

12. a

13. $y = 8e^{6x-54}$

14. no

15. d

16. $\frac{dA}{dt} = 0.14A, \quad A(0) = 2150$

17. 15 days

18. $\frac{dP(t)}{dt} = 0.07P\left(1 - \frac{P}{7500}\right)$

19. 25.58 years

20. $\frac{dy}{dt} = 0.02y(1-y)$

1. For what values of k does the function $y = \cos kt$ satisfy the differential equation $4y'' = -25y$?

2. Use Euler's method with step size 0.2 to estimate $y(1)$, where $y(x)$ is the solution of the initial-value problem. Round your answer to four decimal places.

   $y' = y(x+1),\ \ y(0) = 1$

3. Solve the differential equation.

   $$\frac{dw}{dt} + 2e^{t+w} = 0$$

   Select the correct answer.

   a. $w = -\ln\left(2e^t - C\right)$

   b. $w = \ln\left(2e^t C\right)$

   c. $w = \ln\left(e^t + C\right)^{-2}$

   d. $w = -2t\ln\left(e^t - C\right)$

   e. none of these

4. Solve the initial-value problem.

   $$\frac{dr}{dt} = r - 2tr,\ \ r(0) = 3$$

5. Solve the differential equation.

   $$y' = \frac{6x^5 y}{\ln y}$$

6. Suppose that a population develops according to the logistic equation where t is measured in weeks.

   What is the carrying capacity?

   $$\frac{dP}{dt} = 0.02P - 0.0002P^2$$

7. Find the solution of the differential equation that satisfies the initial condition $y(0) = 6$.

   $$\frac{dy}{dx} = 8x^7 y$$

8. Solve the initial-value problem.

   $xy' = y + x^2 \cos x,\qquad y(\pi/2) = 0$

9. Solve the differential equation.

$$\frac{du}{dt} = 35 + 7u + 5t + ut$$

Select the correct answer.

a. $u = -5 + Ce^{t^2 - 7t}$

b. $u = -5 + Ce^{\frac{t}{2} + 7t^2}$

c. $u = -5 + Ce^{t^2 + 7t}$

d. $u = -5 + Ce^{\frac{t^2}{2} - 7t}$

e. $u = -5 + Ce^{\frac{t^2}{2} + 7t}$

10. Find the orthogonal trajectories of the family of curves.

$y = kx^6$

11. Find the orthogonal trajectories of the family of curves.

$y = (x + k)^{-8}$

12. A common inhabitant of human intestines is the bacterium *Escherichia coli*. A cell of this bacterium in a nutrient-broth medium divides into two cells every 20 minutes. The initial population of a culture is 20 cells. Find the number of cells after 2 hours.

13. A bacteria culture starts with 120 bacteria and grows at a rate proportional to its size. After 5 hours there are 5,700 bacteria. When will the population reach 32,000?

Select the correct answer.

a. t=7.2 b. t=1.4 c. t=27.9 d. t=2.1 e. none of those

14. The table gives estimates of the world population, in millions, from 1750 to 2000:

Year	Population	Year	Population
1750	620	1900	1,770
1800	930	1950	2,500
1850	1,350	2000	5,860

Use the exponential model and the population figures for 1750 and 1800 to predict the world population in 1900.

15. After 3 days a sample of radon-222 decayed to 58% of its original amount. How long would it take the sample to decay to 82% of its original amount?

16. One model for the spread of an epidemic is that the rate of spread is jointly proportional to the number of infected people and the number of uninfected people. In an isolated town of 5000 inhabitants, 160 people have a disease at the beginning of the week and 1200 have it at the end of the week. How long does it take for 80% of the population to be infected?

17. A curve passes through the point (4, 4) and has the property that the slope of the curve at every point P is 4 times the y-coordinate P. What is the equation of the curve?

18. **Newton's Law of Cooling** states that the rate of cooling of an object is proportional to the temperature difference between the object and its surroundings. Suppose that a roast turkey is taken from an oven when its temperature has reached 170 ° F and is placed on a table in a room where the temperature is 70 ° F. If $u\ (t)$ is the temperature of the turkey after t minutes, then Newton's Law of Cooling implies that $\frac{du}{dt} = k(u-70)$. This could be solved as a separable differential equation. Another method is to make the change of variable $y = u - 70$. If the temperature of the turkey is 165 ° F after half an hour, find the temperature after 45 min? Round to the nearest integer.

19. Let c be a positive number. A differential equation of the form $\frac{dy}{dt} = ky^{1+c}$ where k is a positive constant, is called a *doomsday equation* because the exponent in the expression ky^{1+c} is larger than the exponent 1 for natural growth. An especially prolific breed of rabbits has the growth term $ky^{1.01}$. If 5 such rabbits breed initially and the warren has 26 rabbits after 5 months, then when is doomsday?

20. a) Write the solution of the initial-value problem.

$$\frac{dp}{dt} = 0.1P\left(1 - \frac{P}{2000}\right), \quad P(0) = 100$$

and use it to find the population when $t = 20$

b) When does the population reach 1200?

ANSWER KEY

Stewart – Calculus ET 7e Chapter 9 Form G

1. $k = \pm 5/2$

2. $y(1) \approx 3.4192$

3. a

4. $r(t) = 3e^{t-t^2}$

5. $y = e^{\pm\sqrt{2x^6+C}}$

6. 100

7. $y = 6e^{x^8}$

8. $y = x\sin x - x$

9. e

10. $x^2 + 6y^2 = C$

11. $y = \left(\dfrac{64}{17x+C}\right)^{-8/17}$

12. 1280

13. a

14. 2093

15. 1.09 days

16. 15 days

17. $y = 4e^{4x-16}$

18. 163° F

19. 305.78

20. a) 560 , b) 33.5

1. For what nonzero values of k does the function $y = A\sin kt + B\cos kt$ satisfy the differential equation $y'' + 36y = 0$ for all values of A and B?

Select all that apply.

a. $k = -36$ b. $k = -6$ c. $k = 36$ d. $k = 1$ e. $k = 6$

2. For what values of r does the function $y = e^{rt}$ satisfy the differential equation?

$$y'' - y' - 30y = 0$$

3. Use Euler's method with step size 0.05 to estimate $y(0.25)$, where $y(x)$ is the solution of the initial-value problem. Round your answer to four decimal places.

$$y' = y(x+1),\ \ y(0) = 1$$

4. Solve the differential equation.

$$4\frac{dw}{dt} + 3e^{t+w} = 0$$

5. Kirchhoff's Law gives us the derivative equation:

$$Q' = 12 - 4Q$$

If $Q(0) = 0$, use Euler's method with step size 0.4 to estimate Q after 1.2 second.

6. Solve the differential equation.

$$5yy' = 4x$$

7. Solve the differential equation.

$$y' = \frac{7x^6 y}{\ln y}$$

8. Find the orthogonal trajectories of the family of curves.

$$y = (x+k)^{-7}$$

9. A certain small country has \$20 billion in paper currency in circulation, and each day \$70 million comes into the country's banks. The government decides to introduce new currency by having the banks replace old bills with new ones whenever old currency comes into the banks. Let $x = x(t)$ denote the amount of new currency in circulation at time t with $x(0) = 0$. Formulate and solve a mathematical model in the form of an initial-value problem that represents the "flow" of the new currency into circulation (in billions per day).

10. A population of protozoa develops with a constant relative growth rate of 0.7944 per member per day. On day zero the population consists of 2 members. Find the population size after 6 days.

11. Use the Bernoulli's method to solve the differential equation.

$$y' + \frac{6y}{x} = \frac{y^3}{x^5}$$

Select the correct answer.

a. $y = \left(Cx^{12} \pm \frac{8}{x^4} \right)^{-1/2}$

b. $y = \pm \left(Cx^{12} + \frac{1}{8x^4} \right)^{1/2}$

c. $y = \left(Cx^{8} \pm \frac{1}{8x^4} \right)^{1/2}$

d. $y = \pm \left(Cx^{12} + \frac{1}{8x^4} \right)^{-1/2}$

e. $y = \left(Cx^{8} + \frac{1}{12x^4} \right)^{-1/2}$

12. Solve the initial-value problem.

$$\frac{dr}{dt} + 2tr - r = 0, \quad r(0) = 4$$

Select the correct answer.

a. $r(t) = 4e^{t-4t^2}$

b. $r(t) = e^{4t-t^2}$

c. $r(t) = 4e^{t^2}$

d. $r(t) = 2e^{t-t^2}$

e. none of these

13. A common inhabitant of human intestines is the bacterium *Escherichia coli*. A cell of this bacterium in a nutrient-broth medium divides into two cells every 20 minutes. The initial population of a culture is 30 cells. Find the number of cells after 4 hours.

14. A bacteria culture starts with 110 bacteria and grows at a rate proportional to its size. After 3 hours there are 7,700 bacteria. When will the population reach 28,000?

15. A curve passes through the point (7, 3) and has the property that the slope of the curve at every point P is 2 times the y-coordinate P. What is the equation of the curve?

16. After 3 days a sample of radon-222 decayed to 58% of its original amount. How long would it take the sample to decay to 37% of its original amount?

17. Experiments show that if the chemical reaction $N_2O_5 \rightarrow 2NO_2 + \frac{1}{2}O_2$ takes place at 45° C, the rate of reaction of dinitrogen pentoxide is proportional to its concentration as follows :

$$-\frac{d[N_2O_5]}{dt} = 0.0008[N_2O_5]$$

How long will the reaction take to reduce the concentration of N_2O_5 to 50% of its original value?

18. A sum of $100 is invested at 27% interest. If $A(t)$ is the amount of the investment at time t for the case of continuous compounding, write a differential equation and an initial condition satisfied by $A(t)$.

19. Determine whether the differential equation is linear.

$$y' + y\cos x = x^9 y^9$$

20. Solve the initial-value problem.

$$xy' = y + x^2 \sin x, \qquad y(\pi) = 0$$

ANSWER KEY

Stewart – Calculus ET 7e Chapter 9 Form H

1. b, e

2. 6, –5

3. $y(0.25) \approx 1.3069$

4. $w = -\ln\left(\frac{3e^t}{4} - C\right)$

5. 3.648

6. $y = \pm\sqrt{\frac{4}{5}x^2 + C}$

7. $y = e^{\pm\sqrt{2x^7 + C}}$

8. $y = \left(\frac{49}{15x + C}\right)^{-7/15}$

9. $x(t) = 20\left(1 - e^{-0.0035t}\right)$

10. 235

11. d

12. e

13. 122880

14. 3.9 hours

15. $y = 3e^{2x-14}$

16. 5.48 days

17. 866

18. $\frac{dA}{dt} = 0.27A, \quad A(0) = 100$

19. no

20. $y = -x\cos x - x$

1. Eliminate the parameter to find a Cartesian equation of the curve.

$x = e^{2t} - 1, \quad y = e^{4t}$

2. Sketch the parametric curve and eliminate the parameter to find the Cartesian equation of the curve.

$x = \cos\theta,\ y = \sec\theta,\ 0 \le \theta < \pi/2$

3. Find an equation of the tangent to the curve at the point corresponding to the given value of the parameter.

$x = t\cos t, \quad y = t\sin t, \quad t = -\pi$

4. Find the points on the curve where the tangent is horizontal.

$x = t^3 - 3t, \quad y = t^3 - 3t^2$

5. Find the polar equation for the curve represented by the given Cartesian equation.

$x + y = 4$

6. Find the length of the curve.

$x = 3t^2,\ y = 2t^3,\ 0 \le t \le 3$

7. A cow is tied to a silo with radius 5 by a rope just long enough to reach the opposite side of the silo. Find the area available for grazing by the cow. Round the answer to the nearest hundredth.

8. Find d^2y/dx^2.

$x = 1 + t^2, \quad y = t - t^3$

9. True or False?

The exact length of the parametric curve $x = e^t \cos t,\ \ y = e^t \sin t,\ 0 \le t \le \dfrac{\pi}{5}$ is $\sqrt{2}e^{\pi/5}$.

10. Set up an integral that represents the length of the curve. Then use your calculator to find the length correct to four decimal places.

$x = t - 2\sin t, \quad y = t - 2\cos t, \quad 0 \le t \le 4\pi$

11. Find the exact area of the surface obtained by rotating the given curve about the x-axis.

$x = \cos^3\theta,\ y = \sin^3\theta,\quad 0 \le \theta \le \pi/2$

12. Find the points of intersection of the curves $r = 2$ and $r = 4\sin\theta$.

13. Find the area of the region that is bounded by the given curve and lies in the specified sector.

$r = \sqrt{\sin\theta},\ 0 \le \theta \le 2\pi/3$

14. Find an equation of the hyperbola with vertices $(0, \pm 6)$ and asymptotes $y = \pm\dfrac{x}{3}$.

15. Sketch the polar curve.

$r = 2\cos(\theta/2),\ -\pi \le x \le \pi$

16. Find an equation of the ellipse with foci $(\pm\sqrt{5}, 0)$ and vertices $(\pm 3, 0)$.

17. Find the area of the region that lies inside the first curve and outside the second curve.

$r = 3\cos\theta,\quad r = 1 + \cos\theta$

18. Find the area of the region that lies inside both curves.

$r = 8 + 2\sin\theta,\ r = 7$

19. Write a polar equation in r and θ of a hyperbola with the focus at the origin, with the eccentricity 9 and the directrix $x = -2$.

20. The graph of the following curve is given. Find the area that it encloses.

$r = \sin 3\theta$

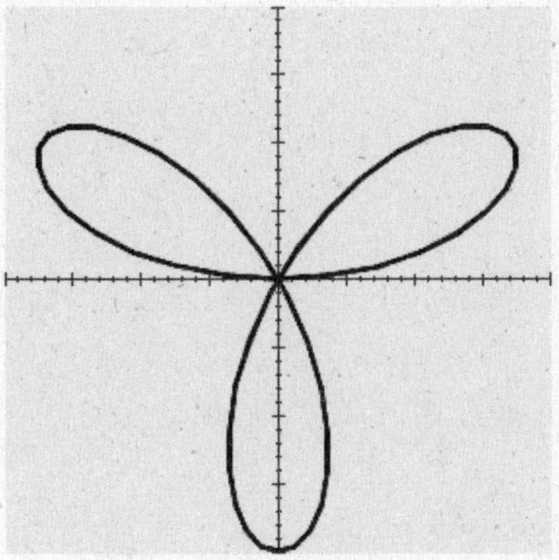

ANSWER KEY

Stewart – Calculus ET 7e Chapter 10 Form A

1. $y=(x+1)^2$

2. $y=1/x$

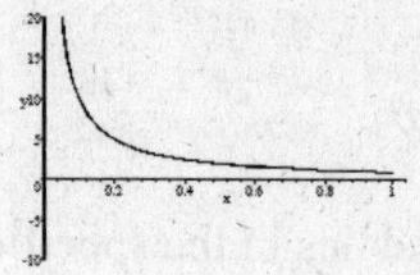

3. $y=\pi^2-\pi x$

4. $(0,0),(2,-4)$

5. $r=\dfrac{4}{\cos\theta+\sin\theta}$

6. $20\sqrt{10}-2$

7. 645.96

8. $-\dfrac{3t^2+1}{4t^3}$

9. False

10. 28.3880

11. $6\pi/5$

12. $(2,\ \pi/6),\ (2,\ 5\pi/6)$

13. 3/4

14. $\dfrac{y^2}{36}-\dfrac{x^2}{324}=1$

15.

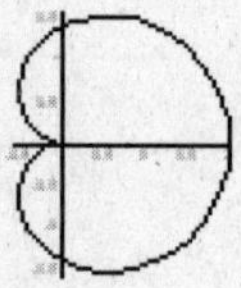

16. $\dfrac{x^2}{9}+\dfrac{y^2}{4}=1$

17. π

18. $\dfrac{164\pi}{3}-\dfrac{31\sqrt{3}}{2}$

19. $r=\dfrac{18}{(1-9\cos\theta)}$

20. $\dfrac{\pi}{4}$

1. Eliminate the parameter to find a Cartesian equation of the curve.

$x = e^t - 1, \quad y = e^{3t}$

2. Find the polar equation for the curve represented by the given Cartesian equation.

$x + y = 3$

3. Find parametric equations for the path of a particle that moves once clockwise along the circle $x^2 + (y-3)^2 = 4$, starting at (2, 3).

4. Find a Cartesian equation for the curve described by the given polar equation.

$r = 5\sin\theta$

5. Find an equation of the tangent to the curve at the point corresponding to the given value of the parameter.

$x = t\cos t, \quad y = t\sin t, \quad t = \pi$

6. Find an equation of the tangent to the curve at the point by first eliminating the parameter.

$x = e^t,\ y = (t-7)^2;\ (1,\ 49)$

7. Find the points on the curve where the tangent is vertical.

$x = t^3 - 3t, \quad y = t^3 - 3t^2$

8. Estimate the coordinates of the highest point on the curve $x = 9te^t,\ y = 7te^{-t}$.

Round the answer to the nearest hundredth.

9. Find the length of the curve.

$x = 3t^2,\ y = 2t^3,\ 0 \le t \le 1$

10. Set up an integral that represents the length of the curve. Then use your calculator to find the length correct to four decimal places.

$x = t - 2\sin t, \quad y = t - 2\cos t \quad 0 \le t \le 2\pi$

11. Find the exact area of the surface obtained by rotating the given curve about the x-axis.

$x = 2\cos^3\theta,\ y = 2\sin^3\theta,\ 0 \le \theta \le \pi/2$

12. Find a polar equation for the curve represented by the given Cartesian equation.

$x^2 = 2y$

13. Find the area enclosed by the curve $r^2 = 9\cos 5\theta$.

14. Find an equation of the parabola with focus $(9/2, 0)$ and directrix $x = -7/2$.

15. Find an equation for the conic that satisfies the given conditions.

hyperbola, vertices $(\pm 3, 0)$, asymptotes $y = \pm 3x$

16. The point in a lunar orbit nearest the surface of the moon is called perilune and the point farthest from the surface is called apolune. The Apollo 11 spacecraft was placed in an elliptical lunar orbit with perilune altitude 108 km and apolune altitude 314 km (above the moon). Find an equation of this ellipse if the radius of the moon is 1728 km and the center of the moon is at one focus.

17. Find the points of intersection of the curves $r = 2$ and $r = 4\cos\theta$.

18. Find the eccentricity of the conic.

$$r = \frac{42}{7 + 6\sin\theta}$$

19. If a projectile is fired with an initial velocity of v_0 meters per second at an angle α above the horizontal and air resistance is assumed to be negligible, then its position after t seconds is given by the parametric equations $x = (v_0 \cos\alpha)t,\ y = (v_0 \sin\alpha)t - \frac{1}{2}gt^2$, where g is the acceleration of gravity $(9.8\ m/s^2)$. If a gun is fired with $\alpha = 55^\circ$ and $v_0 = 497\ m/s$ when will the bullet hit the ground?

Round the result to the nearest tenth.

20. Find d^2y/dx^2.

$x = t + \sin t,\quad y = t - \cos t$

ANSWER KEY

Stewart – Calculus ET 7e Chapter 10 Form B

1. $y = (x+1)^3$

2. $r = \dfrac{3}{\cos\theta + \sin\theta}$

3. $x = 2\cos t,\ \ y = 3 - 2\sin t,\ \ 0 \le t \le 2\pi$

4. $x^2 + \left(y - \frac{5}{2}\right)^2 = \left(\frac{5}{2}\right)^2$

5. $y = \pi x + \pi^2$

6. $y = -14(x-1) + 49$

7. $(-2,-2), (2,-4)$

8. $(24.46,\ 2.58)$

9. $4\sqrt{2} - 2$

10. 14.1940

11. $24\pi / 5$

12. $r = 2\tan\theta\sec\theta$

13. 18

14. $y^2 = 16x - 8$

15. $\dfrac{x^2}{9} - \dfrac{y^2}{81} = 1$

16. $\dfrac{x^2}{3759721} + \dfrac{y^2}{3749112} = 1$

17. $(2, \pi/3),\ (2, -\pi/3)$

18. 6/7

19. $t \approx 83.1 s$

20. $\dfrac{\sin t + \cos t + 1}{(1+\cos t)^3}$

1. Find the point(s) on the curve where the tangent is horizontal.

$x = t^3 - 3t + 1, \quad y = t^3 - 3t^2 + 1$

Select the correct answer.

a. $(1,1), (3,-3)$ b. $(-3,3)$ c. $(-1,1), (-3,-3)$ d. $(0,0), (3,-3)$ e. none of these

2. Eliminate the parameter to find a Cartesian equation of the curve.

$x = e^t - 1, \quad y = e^{2t}$

Select the correct answer.

a. $y = \ln(x+1)$
b. $y = (x+1)^2$
c. $y = e^{2x+1}$
d. $y = (x-1)^2$
e. none of these

3. Describe the motion of a particle with position (*x*, *y*) as *t* varies in the given interval $0 \le t \le 2\pi$.

$x = 6\sin t, \quad y = 3\cos t$

Select the correct answer.

a. Moves once clockwise along the circle $(6x)^2 + (3y)^2 = 1$ starting and ending at (0, 3).

b. Moves once clockwise along the ellipse $\frac{x^2}{36} + \frac{y^2}{9} = 1$ starting and ending at (0, 3).

c. Moves once counterclockwise along the ellipse $\frac{x^2}{36} + \frac{y^2}{9} = 1$ starting and ending at (0, 3).

d. Moves once counterclockwise along the circle $x^2 + y^2 = 1$ starting and ending at (0,–3).

e. Moves once counterclockwise along the ellipse $\frac{x^2}{6} + \frac{y^2}{3} = 1$ starting and ending at (–3, 0).

4. Find a polar equation for the curve represented by the given Cartesian equation.

$x^2 = 9y$

Select the correct answer.

a. $r = 9\sin\theta$
b. $r = 9\cos\theta\sin\theta$
c. $r = 9\tan\theta\sec\theta$
d. $r = 9\tan\theta$
e. $r = 9\tan\theta\csc\theta$

5. Find the polar equation for the curve represented by the given Cartesian equation.

$x + y = 4$

Select the correct answer.

a. $r = \dfrac{2}{\cos\theta - \sin\theta}$

b. $r = \dfrac{4}{\cos\theta - \sin\theta}$

c. $r = 4(\cos\theta + \sin\theta)$

d. $r = 2(\cos\theta + \sin\theta)$

e. $r = \dfrac{4}{\cos\theta + \sin\theta}$

6. Sketch the curve with the given equation.

$r = \sin 6\theta$

Select the correct answer.

a.

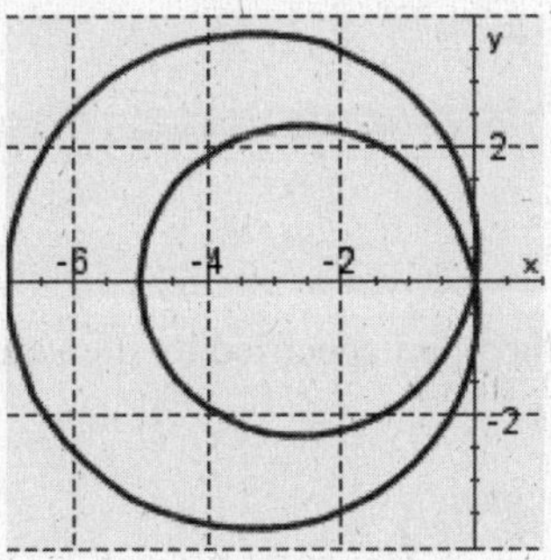

b.

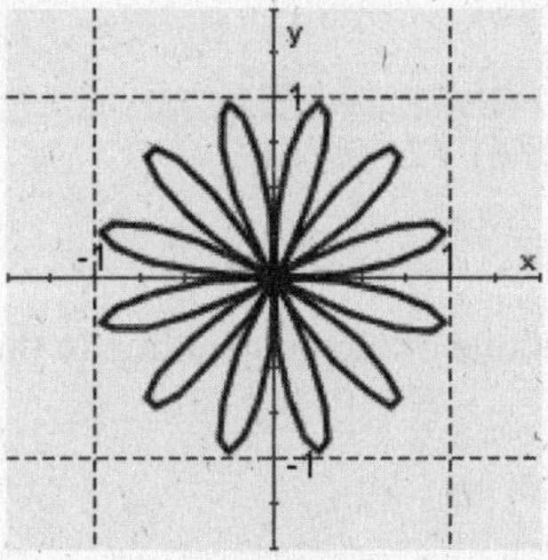

c.

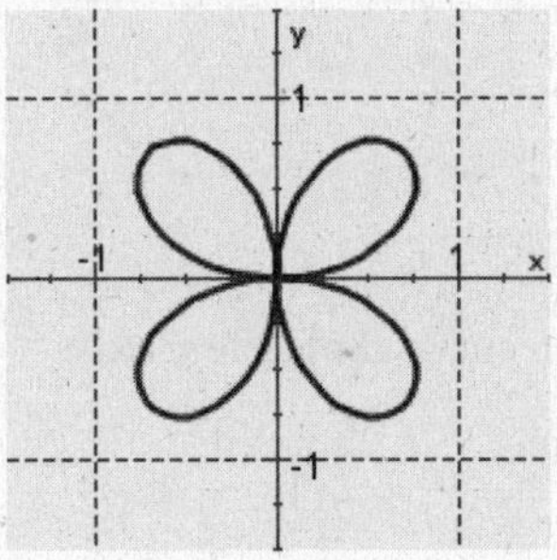

d.

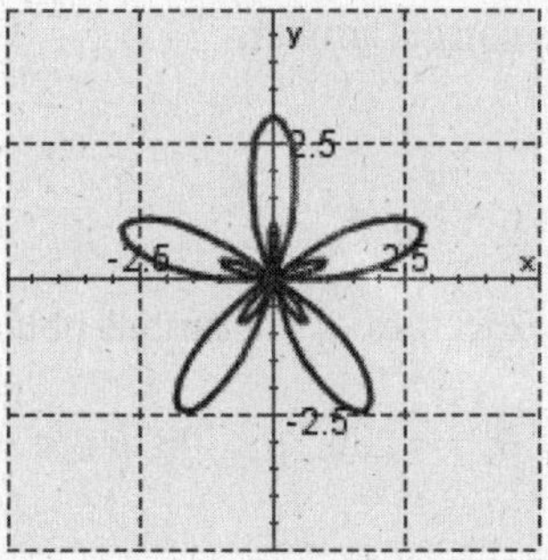

7. Find the length of the curve.

$x = 3t^2,\ y = 2t^3,\ 0 \le t \le 1$

Select the correct answer.

a. $4\sqrt{2} - 2$ b. $2\sqrt{2} - 2$ c. $4\sqrt{2}$ d. $4\sqrt{2} - 1$ e. none of these

8. Find an equation of the tangent to the curve at the point corresponding to the given value of the parameter.

$x = \cos\theta + \sin 2\theta, \quad y = \sin\theta + \cos 2\theta, \quad \theta = \pi$

Select the correct answer.

a. $y = \frac{x}{2} + 2$
b. $y = 2/x$
c. $y = \frac{x}{2} + \frac{3}{2}$
d. $y = \frac{1}{2} - \frac{x}{2}$
e. none of these

9. Find the point(s) of intersection of the curves $r = 2$ and $r = 4\cos\theta$.

Select the correct answer.

a. $(2, \pi/3), (2, -\pi/3)$
b. $(2, \pi/3)$
c. $(2, \pi/4), (2, -\pi/4)$
d. $(2, \pi/6), (2, -\pi/6)$
e. $(2, \pi/6)$

10. Find the slope of the tangent line to the given polar curve at the point specified by the value of θ.

$r = \frac{1}{\theta}, \quad \theta = \pi$

Select the correct answer.

a. -2π b. $\frac{1}{4}$ c. $-\pi$ d. 3 e. $\frac{3}{\pi}$

11. Find the exact area of the surface obtained by rotating the given curve about the *x*-axis.

$x = 2\cos^3\theta, \; y = 2\sin^3\theta, \quad 0 \le \theta \le \pi/2$

Select the correct answer.

a. $18\pi/5$ b. $24\pi/5$ c. $25\pi/4$ d. $12\pi/5$ e. none of these

12. Find the length of the polar curve.

$r = 7\cos\theta,\ 0 \le \theta \le 3\pi/4$

Select the correct answer.

a. $21/4$ b. $21\pi/4$ c. $\pi/4$ d. $21\pi/11$ e. none of these

13. Find the surface area generated by rotating the lemniscate $r^2 = 5\cos 2\theta$ about the line $\theta = \dfrac{\pi}{2}$.

Select the correct answer.

a. $\dfrac{\pi\sqrt{2}}{10}$ b. $10\sqrt{2}\pi$ c. $\dfrac{\pi}{10}$ d. $5\sqrt{2}\pi$ e. $\sqrt{2}\pi$

14. Find an equation of the parabola with focus $\left(\dfrac{9}{2}, 0\right)$ and directrix $x = -\dfrac{7}{2}$.

Select the correct answer.

a. $y = \dfrac{x^2}{8} + 2$ b. $y^2 = 8x - 16$ c. $y^2 = 16x - 8$ d. $y = \dfrac{x^2}{2} + 8$ e. $y = 16x^2 - 8$

15. Find an equation of the hyperbola with vertices $(0, \pm 6)$ and asymptotes $y = \pm\dfrac{x}{3}$.

Select the correct answer.

a. $\dfrac{y^2}{36} - \dfrac{x^2}{9} = 1$ b. $\dfrac{y^2}{324} - \dfrac{x^2}{36} = 1$ c. $\dfrac{x^2}{9} - \dfrac{y^2}{36} = 1$ d. $\dfrac{y^2}{36} - \dfrac{x^2}{324} = 1$ e. $\dfrac{x^2}{6} - \dfrac{y^2}{9} = 1$

16. Find an equation for the conic that satisfies the given conditions.

ellipse, foci $(\pm 1, 5)$, length of major axis 8

Select the correct answer.

a. $\dfrac{(x-3)^2}{16} - \dfrac{y^2}{15} = 1$ b. $\dfrac{x^2}{16} + \dfrac{y^2}{15} = 1$ c. $\dfrac{x^2}{16} + \dfrac{(y-5)^2}{15} = 1$ d. $4x^2 = y$ e. $x^2 = y$

17. A cross-section of a parabolic reflector is shown in the figure. The bulb is located at the focus and the opening at the focus is 18 cm. Find an equation of the parabola. Let V be the origin. Find the diameter of the opening $|CD|$, 19 cm from the vertex.

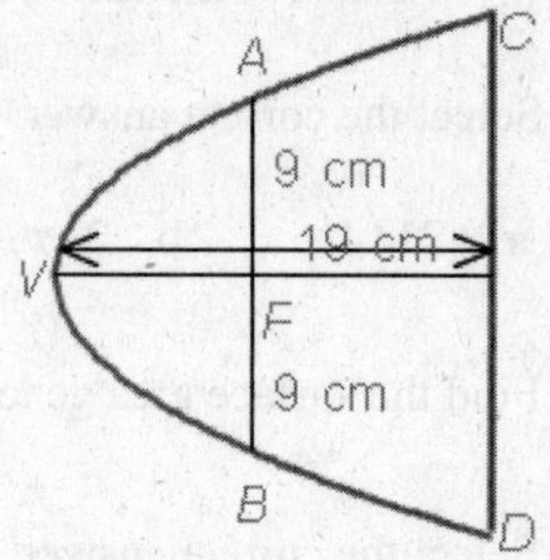

Select all that apply.

a. The equation is $y^2 - \frac{x^2}{18} = 1$

b. $|CD| = 4\sqrt{414}$

c. $|CD| = 6\sqrt{38}$

d. The equation is $y = 18x^2$

f. $|CD| = 18$

e. The equation is $y^2 = 18x$

18. In the LORAN (LOng RAnge Navigation) radio navigation system, two radio stations located at A and B transmit simultaneous signals to a ship or an aircraft located at P. The onboard computer converts the time difference in receiving these signals into a distance difference | A | – | B |, and this, according to the definition of a hyperbola, locates the ship or aircraft on one branch of a hyperbola (see the figure). Suppose that station B is located L = 400 mi due east of station A on a coastline. A ship received the signal from B 1,200 microseconds (μs) before it received the signal from A. Assuming that radio signals travel at a speed of 980 $ft / \mu s$ and if the ship is due north of B, how far off the coastline is the ship? Round your answer to the nearest mile.

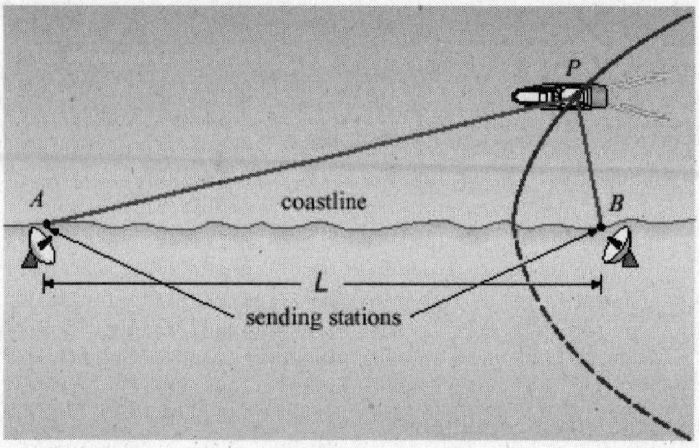

Select the correct answer.

a. 246 miles b. 243 miles c. 248 miles d. 258 miles e. 278 miles

19. Write a polar equation in r and θ of an ellipse with the focus at the origin, with the eccentricity $\frac{6}{7}$ and directrix $x = -8$.

Select the correct answer.

a. $r = \dfrac{48}{7 - 6\cos\theta}$

b. $r = \dfrac{8}{3 - 2\sin\theta}$

c. $r = \dfrac{8}{7 - 6\sin\theta}$

d. $r = \dfrac{48}{6 + 7\sin\theta}$

e. $r = \dfrac{48}{1 + 7\sin\theta}$

20. The orbit of Hale-Bopp comet, discovered in 1995, is an ellipse with eccentricity 0.995 and one focus at the Sun. The length of its major axis is 356.3 AU. [An astronomical unit (AU) is the mean distance between Earth and the Sun, about 93 million miles.] Find the maximum distance from the comet to the Sun. (The perihelion distance from a planet to the Sun is $a(1-e)$ and the aphelion distance is $a(1+e)$.) Find the answer in AU and round to the nearest hundredth.

Select the correct answer.

a. 358.40 AU b. 356.24 AU c. 355.41 AU d. 368.40 AU e. 350.60 AU

ANSWER KEY

Stewart – Calculus ET 7e Chapter 10 Form C

1. a
2. b
3. b
4. c
5. e
6. b
7. a
8. d
9. a
10. c
11. b
12. b
13. b
14. c
15. d
16. c
17. c, e
18. c
19. a
20. c

1. Find the point(s) on the curve where the tangent is vertical.

$x = t^3 - 3t + 1, \quad y = t^3 - 3t^2 + 1$

Select the correct answer.

a. $(-3,-3)$ b. $(1,1)$ c. $(-1,-1),(3,-3)$ d. $(\sqrt{3},-1),(-\sqrt{3},-3)$ e. none of these

2. Eliminate the parameter to find a Cartesian equation of the curve.

$x = e^{2t} - 1, \quad y = e^{4t}$

Select the correct answer.

a. $y = (x+1)^4$ b. $y = (x+1)^2$ c. $y = 2\ln(x+1)$ d. $y = \dfrac{\ln x}{4}$ e. none of these

3. Find the length of the curve.

$x = 3t^2,\ y = 2t^3,\ 0 \le t \le 3$

Select the correct answer.

a. $20\sqrt{10} - 2$ b. $2\sqrt{10} - 1$ c. $2\sqrt{10} - 2$ d. $10\sqrt{2} - 2$ e. $20\sqrt{2} - 2$

4. Find parametric equations to represent the line segment from (–1, 2) to (10, –6).

Select the correct answer.

a. $x = 10 - 8t,\ y = -1 + 11t,\ 0 \le t \le 1$
b. $x = -1 + 11t,\ y = 2 - 8t,\ 0 \le t \le 1$
c. $x = -1 + 11t,\ y = -6 - 8t,\ 0 \le t \le 1$
d. $x = -1 - 11t,\ y = -8t,\ 0 \le t \le 1$
e. $x = -1 + 11t,\ y = -6t,\ 0 \le t \le 1$

5. If a projectile is fired with an initial velocity of v_0 meters per second at an angle α above the horizontal and air resistance is assumed to be negligible, then its position after t seconds is given by the parametric equations $x = (v_0 \cos\alpha)t,\ y = (v_0 \sin\alpha)t - \frac{1}{2}gt^2$, where g is the acceleration of gravity $\left(9.8\ m/s^2\right)$. If a gun is fired with $\alpha = 50^\circ$ and $v_0 = 486\ m/s$ when will the bullet hit the ground?

Select the correct answer.

a. $t = 38$ s
b. $t = 744.6$ s
c. $t = 76$ s
d. $t = 58$ s
e. $t = 256.6$ s

6. Write a polar equation in r and θ of an ellipse with the focus at the origin, with the eccentricity 0.4 and vertex at (2, 0).

Select the correct answer.

a. $r = \dfrac{6}{5 + 2\cos\theta}$

b. $r = \dfrac{6}{5 - 2\cos\theta}$

c. $r = \dfrac{5}{5 - 2\cos\theta}$

d. $r = \dfrac{5}{2 + 5\cos\theta}$

e. $r = \dfrac{2}{5 - 6\cos\theta}$

7. Find an equation of the tangent to the curve at the point corresponding to the value of the parameter.

$x = t\sin t,\ \ y = t\cos t\ ;\ \ t = 11\pi$

Select the correct answer.

a. $y = \dfrac{x}{11\pi} + 12\pi$

b. $y = \dfrac{x}{11\pi} - 11\pi$

c. $y = \dfrac{x}{11\pi} + 11\pi$

d. $y = \dfrac{x}{11\pi} - 12\pi$

e. $y = \dfrac{x}{\pi} - 12\pi$

8. Find the exact area of the surface obtained by rotating the given curve about the x-axis.

$x = 3\cos^3\theta,\ y = 3\sin^3\theta,\ \ 0 \le \theta \le \pi/2$

Select the correct answer.

a. $24\pi/5$ b. $54\pi/5$ c. $9\pi/5$ d. $5/24\pi$ e. none of these

9. Find a polar equation for the curve represented by the given Cartesian equation.

$x^2 = 2y$

Select the correct answer.

a. $r = 2\tan\theta\sin\theta$ b. $r = 2\tan\theta$ c. $r = 2\tan\theta\sec\theta$ d. $r = 2\cot\theta$ e. $r = 2\sec\theta$

10. Find the polar equation for the curve represented by the given Cartesian equation.

$x + y = 4$

Select the correct answer.

a. $r = \dfrac{2}{\cos\theta - \sin\theta}$

b. $r = \dfrac{4}{\cos\theta - \sin\theta}$

c. $r = 4(\cos\theta + \sin\theta)$

d. $r = 2(\cos\theta + \sin\theta)$

e. $r = \dfrac{4}{\cos\theta + \sin\theta}$

11. Sketch the curve with the given equation.

$r = \sin(2\theta)$

Select the correct answer.

a. 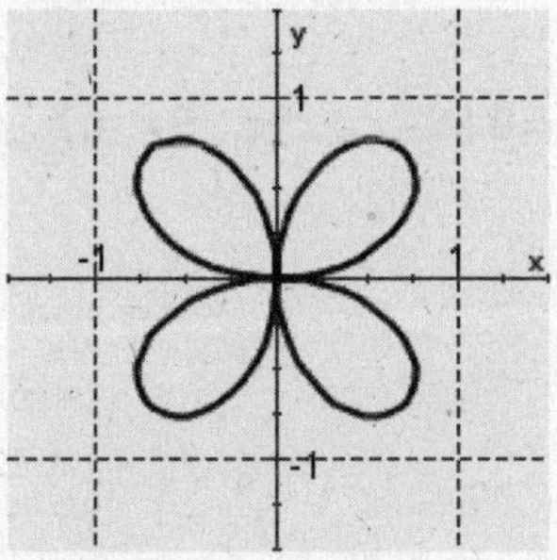

b. 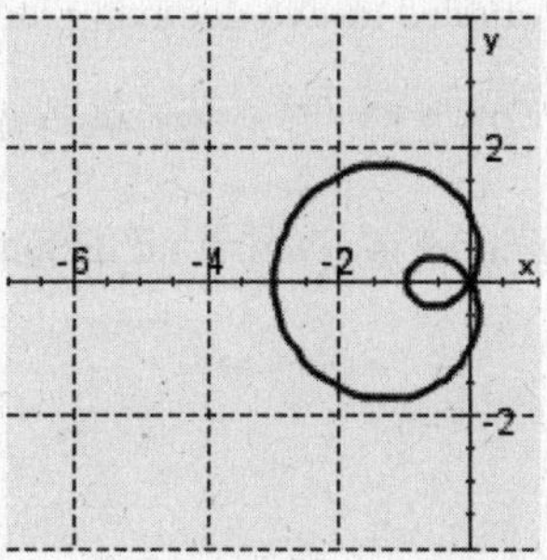

c. 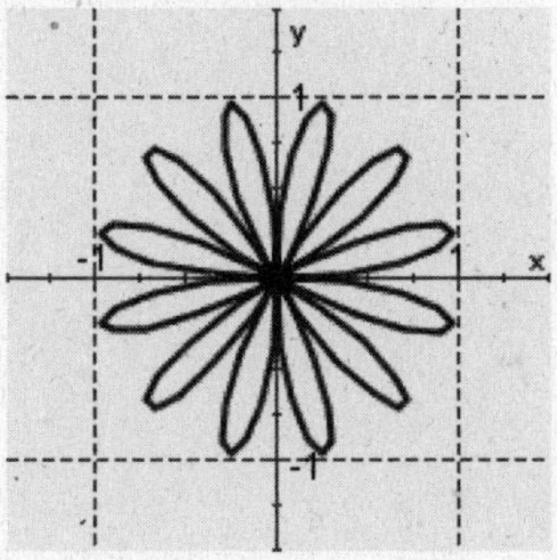

d. 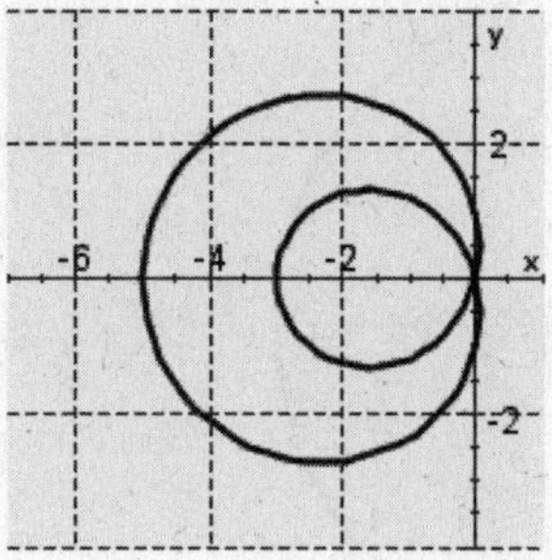

12. Find the area of the region enclosed by one loop of the curve.

$r = 7\cos 4\theta$

Select the correct answer.

a. $\dfrac{49\pi}{16}$ b. 16π c. π d. $\dfrac{49\pi}{11}$ e. $\dfrac{\pi}{11}$

13. Find the point(s) of intersection of the curves $r = 2$ and $r = 4\cos\theta$.

Select the correct answer.

a. $(2, \pi/3), (2, -\pi/3)$
b. $(2, \pi/3)$
c. $(2, \pi/4), (2, -\pi/4)$
d. $(2, \pi/6), (2, -\pi/6)$
e. $(2, \pi/6)$

14. Find the area of the region that lies inside the first curve and outside the second curve.

$r = 3\cos\theta, \ r = 1 + \cos\theta$

Select the correct answer.

a. $A = \frac{\pi}{4}$ b. $A = \pi$ c. $A = 2\pi$ d. $A = \frac{\pi}{2}$ e. $A = \frac{3\pi}{2}$

15. Use a graph to estimate the values of θ for which the curves $r = 9 + 3\sin 5\theta$ and $r = 18\sin\theta$ intersect.

Select all that apply. (rounded to two decimal places)

a. $\theta = 0.49$ b. $\theta = 2.57$ c. $\theta = 1.48$ d. $\theta = 0.58$ e. $\theta = 4.7$

16. Graph of the following curve is given. Find its length.

$r = 4\cos^2\left(\frac{\theta}{2}\right)$

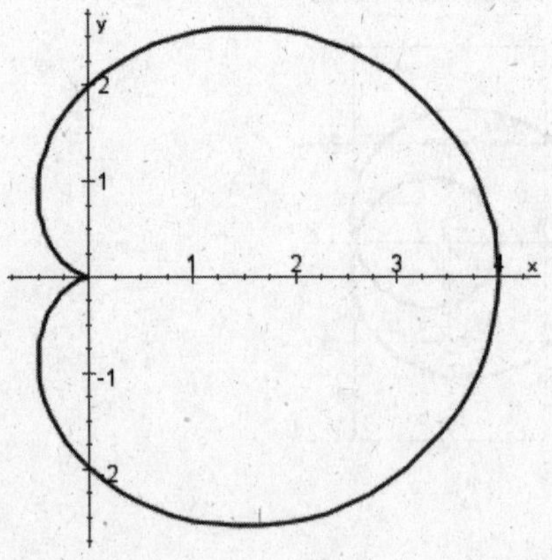

Select the correct answer.

a. $L = 17$
b. $L = 16$
c. $L = 19$
d. $L = 14$
e. $L = 22$

17. The graph of the following curve is given. Find the area that it encloses.

$r = 3 + 6\sin\theta$

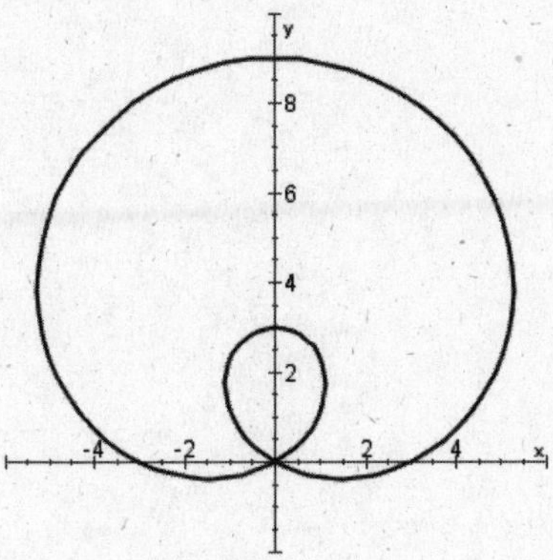

Select the correct answer.

a. $A = 18\pi + \frac{27\sqrt{5}}{2}$ b. $A = \frac{27\sqrt{5}}{2}$ c. $A = 18\pi$ d. $A = 18\pi + \frac{27\sqrt{3}}{2}$ e. $A = 18\pi + \frac{\sqrt{3}}{2}$

18. Find an equation for the conic that satisfies the given conditions.

parabola, vertex (0, 0), focus (0, −4)

Select the correct answer.

a. $y^2 = -17x$ b. $x^2 + y^2 = 16y$ c. $x^2 = -16y$ d. $x^2 = 4y$ e. $x^2 = -y$

19. Find an equation for the conic that satisfies the given conditions.

ellipse, foci $(\pm 2, 6)$, length of major axis 6

Select the correct answer.

a. $\frac{(x-5)^2}{9} - \frac{y^2}{5} = 1$ b. $\frac{x^2}{9} + \frac{(y-6)^2}{5} = 1$ c. $\frac{x^2}{9} + \frac{y^2}{5} = 1$ d. $3x^2 = y$ e. $\frac{1}{3}x^2 = y$

20. Find an equation for the conic that satisfies the given conditions.

hyperbola, foci $(0, \pm 9)$, vertices $(0, \pm 1)$

Select the correct answer.

a. $y^2 - \frac{x^2}{80} = 1$ b. $9x^2 = y$ c. $\frac{(x-9)^2}{81} - \frac{y^2}{80} = 1$ d. $\frac{x^2}{81} + \frac{y^2}{80} = 1$ e. $\frac{9}{80}x^2 = y$

ANSWER KEY

Stewart – Calculus ET 7e Chapter 10 Form D

1. c

2. b

3. a

4. b

5. c

6. b

7. b

8. b

9. c

10. e

11. a

12. a

13. a

14. b

15. b, d

16. b

17. d

18. c

19. b

20. a

1. Eliminate the parameter to find a Cartesian equation of the curve.

$x = e^t - 1, \quad y = e^{3t}$

2. Find an equation for the conic that satisfies the given conditions.

Ellipse, foci $(\pm 1, 5)$, length of major axis 8

Select the correct answer.

a. $\frac{(x-3)^2}{16} - \frac{y^2}{15} = 1$ b. $\frac{x^2}{16} + \frac{y^2}{15} = 1$ c. $\frac{x^2}{16} + \frac{(y-5)^2}{15} = 1$ d. $4x^2 = y$ e. $x^2 = y$

3. True or False?

If the parametric curve $x = f(t)$, $y = g(t)$ satisfies $g'(1) = 0$, then it has a horizontal tangent when $t = 1$.

4. Sketch the parametric curve and eliminate the parameter to find the Cartesian equation of the curve.

$x = \cos\theta, \ y = \sec\theta, \ 0 \le \theta < \pi/2$

5. Find d^2y/dx^2.

$x = 1 + t^2, \quad y = t - t^3$

6. Find the points on the curve where the tangent is horizontal.

$x = t^3 - 3t, \quad y = t^3 - 3t^2$

7. Estimate the coordinates of the highest point on the curve $x = 15te^t$, $y = 3te^{-t}$. Round the answer to the nearest hundredth.

8. Find the polar equation for the curve represented by the given Cartesian equation.

$x + y = 2$

9. Find an equation of the tangent to the curve at the point corresponding to the given value of the parameter.

$x = \cos\theta + \sin 2\theta, \quad y = \sin\theta + \cos 2\theta, \quad \theta = 0$

10. Find the points of intersection of the curves $r = 2$ and $r = 4\sin\theta$.

11. True or False?

The exact length of the parametric curve $x = e^t \cos t, \ y = e^t \sin t, \ 0 \le t \le \frac{\pi}{5}$ is $\sqrt{2}e^{\pi/5}$.

12. Set up an integral that represents the length of the curve. Then use your calculator to find the length correct to four decimal places.

$x = 2t + \cos t, \quad y = t - 2\sin t, \quad 0 \le t \le 2\pi$

13. Find the area enclosed by the curve $r^2 = 9\cos 5\theta$.

14. The graph of the following curve is given. Find the area that it encloses.

$r = 2 + \cos 6\theta$

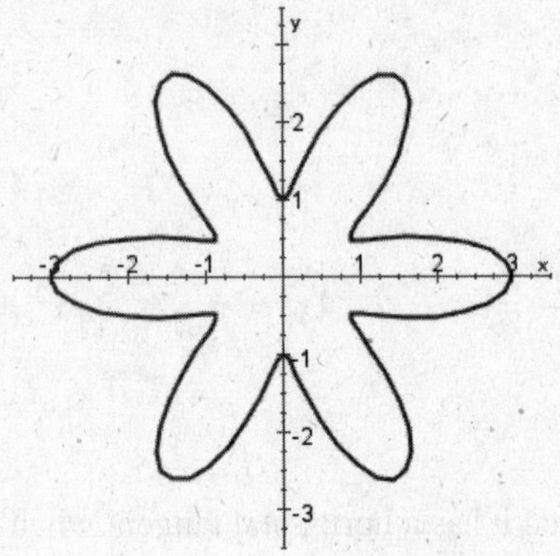

15. Find an equation of the ellipse with foci $(\pm\sqrt{5}, 0)$ and vertices $(\pm 3, 0)$.

16. Find an equation for the conic that satisfies the given conditions.

hyperbola, vertices (3, 0), (–3, 0), asymptotes $y = \pm 2x$

17. Write a polar equation in r and θ of a hyperbola with the focus at the origin, with the eccentricity 6 and the directrix $x = -2$.

18. Find the equation of the directrix of the conic.

$$r = \frac{6}{3 + \sin\theta}$$

Select the correct answer.

a. $y = 6$ b. $y = -3$ c. $x = -6$ d. $x = 3$ e. $x = 2$

19. Find the eccentricity of the conic.

$$r = \frac{9}{2 + 11\cos\theta}$$

20. Find the area of the shaded region.

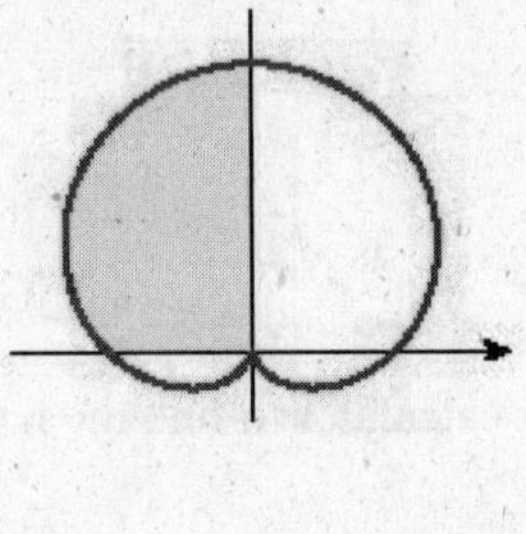

$r = 1 + \sin\theta$

ANSWER KEY

Stewart – Calculus ET 7e Chapter 10 Form E

1. $y = (x+1)^3$

2. c

3. True

4. $y = \dfrac{1}{x}$

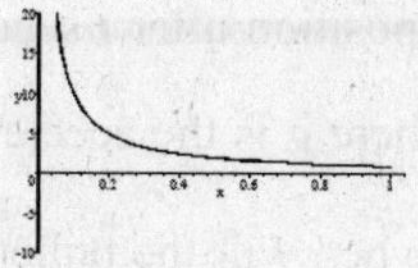

5. $-\dfrac{3t^2+1}{4t^3}$

6. $(0,0), (2,-4)$

7. (40.77, 1.10)

8. $r = \dfrac{2}{\cos\theta + \sin\theta}$

9. $y = \dfrac{1}{2}x + \dfrac{1}{2}$

10. $(2, \pi/6), (2, 5\pi/6)$

11. F

12. 16.3917

13. 18

14. $9\pi/2$

15. $\dfrac{x^2}{9} + \dfrac{y^2}{4} = 1$

16. $\dfrac{x^2}{9} - \dfrac{y^2}{36} = 1$

17. $r = \dfrac{12}{(1 - 6\cos\theta)}$

18. a

19. 11/2

20. $\dfrac{3\pi}{8} + 1$

1. Eliminate the parameter to find a Cartesian equation of the curve.

$x(t) = \cos^2 5t, \; y(t) = \sin^2 5t$

2. Find parametric equations to represent the line segment from (–9, 2) to (7, –8).

3. If a projectile is fired with an initial velocity of v_0 meters per second at an angle α above the horizontal and air resistance is assumed to be negligible, then its position after t seconds is given by the parametric equations $x = (v_0 \cos\alpha)t, \; y = (v_0 \sin\alpha)t - \frac{1}{2}gt^2$, where g is the acceleration of gravity (9.8 m/s^2). If a gun is fired with $\alpha = 20^\circ$ and $v_0 = 470 \; m/s$ when will the bullet hit the ground? Round the result to the nearest tenth.

4. True or False?

If the parametric curve $x = f(t), \; y = g(t)$ satisfies $g'(1) = 0$, then it has a horizontal tangent when $t = 1$.

5. Find the points on the curve where the tangent is vertical.

$x = t^3 - 3t, \qquad y = t^3 - 3t^2$

6. Find an equation of the tangent to the curve at the point corresponding to the given value of the parameter.

$x = \cos\theta + \sin 2\theta, \qquad y = \sin\theta + \cos 2\theta, \qquad \theta = \pi$

7. Find the exact area of the surface obtained by rotating the given curve about the x-axis.

$x = 2\cos^3\theta, \; y = 2\sin^3\theta, \quad 0 \le \theta \le \pi/2$

Select the correct answer.

a. $36/5$ b. $4/5$ c. $54\pi/5$ d. $24\pi/5$ e. none of these

8. Set up, but do not evaluate, an integral that represents the length of the parametric curve.

$x = t - t^9, \; y = \frac{9}{8}t^{8/7}, \; 3 \le t \le 12$

9. True or False?

The exact length of the parametric curve $x = e^t \cos t, \; y = e^t \sin t, \; 0 \le t \le \frac{\pi}{5}$ is $\sqrt{2}e^{\pi/5}$.

10. Find d^2y/dx^2.

$x = t + \sin t, \quad y = t - \cos t$

11. Sketch the polar curve.

$r = \cos 3\theta$

12. Find the polar equation for the curve represented by the given Cartesian equation.

$x+y=3$

13. Find the points of intersection of the curves $r=2$ and $r=4\sin\theta$.

14. Using the arc length formula, set up, but do not evaluate, an integral equal to the total arc length of the ellipse.

$x=4\sin\theta,\quad y=2\cos\theta$

15. Set up an integral that represents the area of the surface obtained by rotating the given curve about the *x*-axis. Then use your calculator to find the surface area correct to four decimal places.

$x=\sin t,\qquad y=\sin 2t,\qquad 0\le t\le \pi/2$

16. Find the area that the curve encloses.

$r=11\sin\theta$

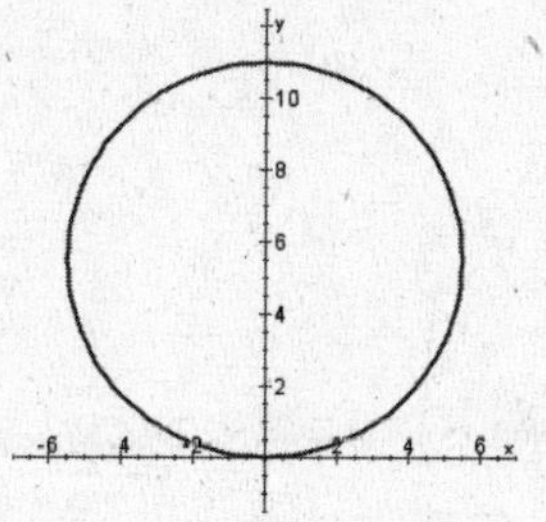

17. Find an equation of the hyperbola with vertices $(0,\pm 6)$ and asymptotes $y=\pm x/3$.

18. Find an equation of the parabola with focus $(9/2,\ 0)$ and directrix $x=-7/2$.

19. Find an equation of the ellipse with foci $(\pm\sqrt{5},0)$ and vertices $(\pm 3,0)$.

20. Write a polar equation in r and θ of an ellipse with the focus at the origin, with the eccentricity $\frac{6}{7}$ and directrix $x=-8$.

Select the correct answer.

a. $r=\dfrac{48}{7-6\cos\theta}$

b. $r=\dfrac{8}{3-2\sin\theta}$

c. $r=\dfrac{8}{7-6\sin\theta}$

d. $r=\dfrac{48}{6+7\sin\theta}$

e. $r=\dfrac{48}{1+7\sin\theta}$

ANSWER KEY

Stewart – Calculus ET 7e Chapter 10 Form F

1. $x = 1 - y$

2. $x = -9 + 16t, \quad y = 2 - 10t, \quad 0 \le t \le 1$

3. 32.8

4. True

5. $(-2, -2), (2, -4)$

6. $y = \frac{1}{2} - \frac{1}{2}x$

7. d

8. $\int_3^{12} \sqrt{(1 - 9t^8)^2 + \left(\frac{9}{7}\right)^2 t^{2/7}}\, dt$

9. False

10. $\frac{\sin t + \cos t + 1}{(1 + \cos t)^3}$

11. 

12. $r = \frac{3}{\cos\theta + \sin\theta}$

13. $(2, \pi/6), (2, 5\pi/6)$

14. $\int_0^{2\pi} \sqrt{16\cos^2\theta + 4\sin^2\theta}\, d\theta$

15. 8.0285

16. $\frac{121\pi}{4}$

17. $\frac{y^2}{36} - \frac{x^2}{324} = 1$

18. $y^2 = 16x - 8$

19. $\frac{x^2}{9} + \frac{y^2}{4} = 1$

20. a

1. Sketch the parametric curve and eliminate the parameter to find the Cartesian equation of the curve.

$x = \cos\theta,\ y = \sec\theta,\ 0 \le \theta < \pi/2$

2. Eliminate the parameter to find a Cartesian equation of the curve.

$x = e^t - 1, \quad y = e^{2t}$

Select the correct answer.

a. $y = \ln(x+1)$ b. $y = (x+1)^2$ c. $y = e^{2x+1}$ d. $y = (x-1)^2$ e. none of these

3. Find an equation of the tangent to the curve at the point corresponding to the given value of the parameter.

$x = t\cos t, \quad y = t\sin t, \quad t = -\pi$

4. Find the length of the curve.

$x = 3t^2,\ y = 2t^3,\ 0 \le t \le 1$

5. True or False?

If the parametric curve $x = f(t),\ y = g(t)$ satisfies $g'(1) = 0$, then it has a horizontal tangent when $t = 1$.

6. Using the arc length formula, set up, but do not evaluate, an integral equal to the total arc length of the ellipse.

$x = 5\sin\theta,\ y = 4\cos\theta$

7. Find d^2y/dx^2.

$x = t + \sin t, \quad y = t - \cos t$

8. Find the slope of the tangent line to the given polar curve at the point specified by the value of θ.

$r = \dfrac{1}{\theta}, \quad \theta = \pi$

9. Find a Cartesian equation for the curve described by the given polar equation.

$r = 3\sin\theta$

10. Find the polar equation for the curve represented by the given Cartesian equation.

$x + y = 4$

11. Find the point(s) of intersection of the curves $r = 2$ and $r = 4\cos\theta$.

Select the correct answer.

a. $(2, \pi/3), (2, -\pi/3)$ b. $(2, \pi/3)$ c. $(2, \pi/4), (2, -\pi/4)$ d. $(2, \pi/6), (2, -\pi/6)$ e. $(2, \pi/6)$

12. The graph of the following curve is given. Find the area that it encloses.

$r = 2 + \cos 6\theta$

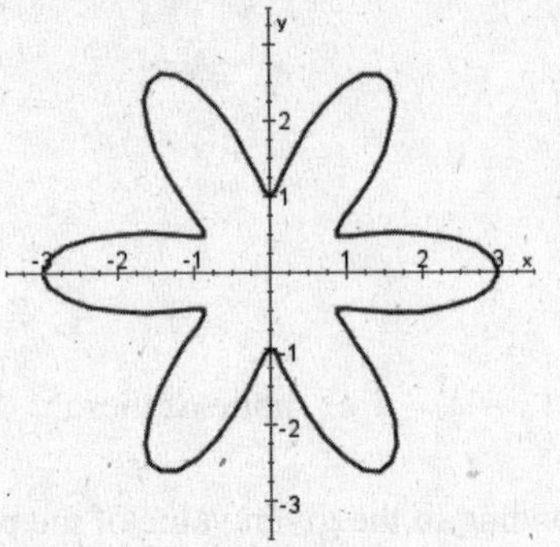

13. Set up an integral that represents the area of the surface obtained by rotating the given curve about the x-axis. Then use your calculator to find the surface area correct to four decimal places.

$x = 2\sin t, \qquad y = \sin 2t \qquad 0 \le t \le \pi/2$

14. Find the vertices, foci and asymptotes of the hyperbola.

$16x^2 - 9y^2 + 64x - 72y = 224$

Select all that apply.

a. The foci are $(-7, -4)$, $(3, -4)$

b. The vertices are $(-5, -4)$, $(1, -4)$

c. The vertices are $(\pm 1, -4)$

d. The asymptote is $y = \frac{5}{7}(x-2)$

e. The foci are $(-7, -4)$, $(6, -5)$

f. The asymptotes are $y = \pm\frac{3}{4}x$

15. Find an equation for the conic that satisfies the given conditions.

Ellipse, foci $(\pm 6, 0)$, vertices $(\pm 7, 0)$

Select the correct answer.

a. $7x^2 = y$

b. $\frac{x^2}{49} + \frac{y^2}{13} = 1$

c. $\frac{x^2}{6} + \frac{y^2}{8} = 1$

d. $\frac{x^2}{49} - \frac{y^2}{13} = 1$

e. $\frac{x^2}{49} + \frac{y^2}{8} = 1$

16. Find an equation for the conic that satisfies the given conditions.

hyperbola, foci (4, –1) and (4, 9), vertices (4, 1) and (4, 7)

17. The planet Mercury travels in an elliptical orbit with eccentricity 0.203. Its minimum distance from the Sun is 4.6×10^7 km. If the perihelion distance from a planet to the Sun is $a(1-e)$ and the aphelion distance is $a(1+e)$, find the maximum distance (in km) from Mercury to the Sun.

Select the correct answer.

a. 6.9×10^7 km b. 6.1×10^7 km c. 7×10^7 km d. 9.6×10^7 km e. 7.5×10^7 km

18. Find the eccentricity of the conic.

$$r = \frac{2}{1+3\sin\theta}$$

19. Write a polar equation in r and θ of a hyperbola with the focus at the origin, with the eccentricity 5 and directrix $r = 9\csc\theta$.

Select the correct answer

a. $r = \dfrac{45}{1-45\cos\theta}$

b. $r = \dfrac{45}{1+9\cos\theta}$

c. $r = \dfrac{14}{5+\sin\theta}$

d. $r = \dfrac{45}{1+5\sin\theta}$

e. $r = \dfrac{14}{4+5\sin\theta}$

20. Write a polar equation in r and θ of a hyperbola with the focus at the origin, with the eccentricity 6 and the directrix $y = -2$.

ANSWER KEY

Stewart – Calculus ET 7e Chapter 10 Form G

1. $y = \dfrac{1}{x}$

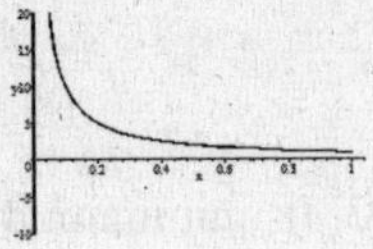

2. b

3. $y = \pi^2 - \pi x$

4. $4\sqrt{2} - 2$

5. True

6. $\displaystyle\int_0^{2\pi} \sqrt{25\cos^2(\theta) + 16\sin^2(\theta)}\, d\theta$

7. $\dfrac{\sin t + \cos t + 1}{(1+\cos t)^3}$

8. $-\pi$

9. $x^2 + \left(y - \dfrac{3}{2}\right)^2 = \left(\dfrac{3}{2}\right)^2$

10. $r = \dfrac{4}{\cos\theta + \sin\theta}$

11. a

12. $\dfrac{9\pi}{2}$

13. 11.1620

14. a, b

15. b

16. $\dfrac{(y-4)^2}{9} - \dfrac{(x-4)^2}{16} = 1$

17. a

18. 3

19. d

20. $r = \dfrac{12}{1 - 6\sin\theta}$

1. If a and b are fixed numbers, find parametric equations for the set of all points P determined as shown in the figure, using the angle *ang* as the parameter. Write the equations for $a = 10$ and $b = 4$.

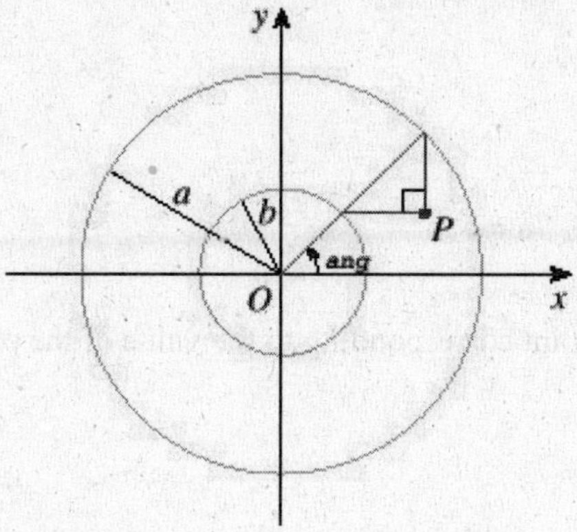

2. Find parametric equations to represent the line segment from (–5, 8) to (5, –4).

3. Find an equation for the conic that satisfies the given conditions.

ellipse, foci $(\pm 1, 5)$, length of major axis is 6

4. Find an equation for the conic that satisfies the given conditions.

hyperbola, foci (7, –1) and (7, 9), vertices (7, 1) and (7, 7)

5. Estimate the coordinates of the highest point on the curve $x = 2te^{t},\ y = 12te^{-t}$. Round the answer to the nearest hundredth.

6. If a projectile is fired with an initial velocity of v_0 meters per second at an angle α above the horizontal and air resistance is assumed to be negligible, then its position after t seconds is given by the parametric equations $x = (v_0 \cos \alpha)t,\ y = (v_0 \sin \alpha)t - \frac{1}{2}gt^2$, where g is the acceleration of gravity $(9.8\ \text{m/s}^2)$. If a gun is fired with $\alpha = 62^\circ$ and $v_0 = 264\ m/s$ when will the bullet hit the ground? Round the result to the nearest tenth.

7. Find an equation of the tangent line to the curve at the point corresponding to the value of the parameter.

$x = e^{\sqrt{t}},\ y = t - \ln t^7;\ t = 1$

8. Write a polar equation in r and θ of an ellipse with the focus at the origin, with the eccentricity $\frac{3}{4}$ and directrix $x = -5$.

9. Eliminate the parameter to find a Cartesian equation of the curve.

$x(t) = \cos^2 6t,\ y(t) = \sin^2 6t$

10. Find the eccentricity of the conic.

$$r = \frac{5}{2 - 3\sin\theta}$$

Select the correct answer.

a. $e = \frac{5}{2}$ b. $e = \frac{2}{3}$ c. $e = \frac{3}{2}$ d. $e = 5$ e. $e = \frac{5}{3}$

11. Find an equation of the tangent line to the curve at the point corresponding to the value of the parameter.

$x = t\sin t,\ \ y = t\cos t\ ;\ \ t = 3\pi$

Select the correct answer.

a. $y = \frac{x}{3\pi} - 4\pi$

b. $y = \frac{x}{3\pi} + 3\pi$

c. $y = \frac{x}{3\pi} - 3\pi$

d. $y = \frac{x}{3\pi} + 4\pi$

e. $y = \frac{x}{4\pi} + 3\pi$

12. Find the points on the curve where the tangent is vertical.

$x = t^3 - 3t + 1, \qquad y = t^3 - 3t^2 + 1$

13. The curve $x = 2 - 4\cos^2 t,\ y = \tan t(1 - 2\cos^2 t)$ cross itself at some point (x_0, y_0). Find the equations of both tangent lines at that point.

Select the correct answer.

a. $y = \frac{x}{2},\ y = -\frac{x}{2}$

b. $y = x + 6,\ y = -x + 6$

c. $y = \frac{x}{8},\ y = -\frac{x}{8}$

d. $y = \frac{x}{2} + 8,\ y = -\frac{x}{2} + 2$

e. $y = \frac{x}{2} - 8,\ y = -\frac{x}{2} - 2$

14. Find the area of the region that is bounded by the given curve and lies in the specified sector.

$r = \sqrt{\sin\theta},\ 0 \le \theta \le 2\pi/3$

15. Set up an integral that represents the length of the curve. Then use your calculator to find the length correct to four decimal places.

$x = t + \cos t, \qquad y = t - \sin t \qquad 0 \le t \le 2\pi$

16. Find d^2y/dx^2.

$x = t + \sin t, \quad y = t - \cos t$

17. Find the area of the region that lies inside both curves.

$r = 4\sin\theta, \quad r = 4\cos\theta$

18. Find the area bounded by the curve $x = t - \dfrac{1}{t}, \quad y = t + \dfrac{1}{t}$ and the line $y = 2.5$.

19. True or False?

If the parametric curve $x = f(t),\ y = g(t)$ satisfies $g'(1) = 0$, then it has a horizontal tangent when $t = 1$.

20. Find the exact area of the surface obtained by rotating the given curve about the x-axis.

$x = \cos^3\theta,\ y = \sin^3\theta, \quad 0 \le \theta \le \pi/2$

ANSWER KEY

Stewart – Calculus ET 7e Chapter 10 Form H

1. $x = 10\cos(ang),\ \ y = 4\sin(ang),\ \ 0 \le ang \le 2\pi$

2. $x = -5 + 10t,\ \ y = 8 - 12t,\ \ 0 \le t \le 1$

3. $\frac{x^2}{9} + \frac{(y-5)^2}{8} = 1$

4. $\frac{(y-4)^2}{9} - \frac{(x-7)^2}{16} = 1$

5. (5.44, 4.41)

6. 47.6

7. $y = -\frac{12}{e}(x-e)+1$

8. $r = \frac{15}{4 - 3\cos\theta}$

9. $x = 1 - y$

10. c

11. c

12. $(-1,-1),(3,-3)$

13. a

14. 3/4

15. c

16. $\frac{\sin t + \cos t + 1}{(1+\cos t)^3}$

17. $2\pi - 4$

18. $\frac{15}{4} - 4\ln 2$

19. T

20. $6\pi / 5$

1. Find a formula for the general term a_n of the sequence, assuming that the pattern of the first few terms continues.

$\{1/2, -4/3, 9/4, -16/5, 25/6, \ldots\}$

2. Use the Integral Test to determine whether the series is convergent or divergent.

$$\sum_{n=1}^{\infty} \frac{1}{8n+1}$$

3. Determine whether the sequence converges or diverges. If it converges, find the limit.

$a_n = 2e^{2n/(n+2)}$

4. Determine whether the series is convergent or divergent by expressing s_n as a telescoping sum. If it is convergent, find its sum.

$$\sum_{n=1}^{\infty} 3/(n^2+3n)$$

5. Determine whether the sequence defined as follows is convergent or divergent.

$a_1 = 1 \quad a_{n+1} = 4 - a_n \quad \text{for } n \ge 1$

6. Determine whether the series is convergent or divergent.

$$\sum_{n=1}^{\infty} \frac{1}{n^2+1}$$

7. Test the series for convergence or divergence.

$$\sum_{k=1}^{\infty} \frac{(-3)^{k+1}}{4^{2k}}$$

8. Find the values of p for which the series is convergent.

$$\sum_{n=1}^{\infty} n(1+n^2)^p$$

9. Determine whether the sequence is increasing, decreasing, or not monotonic. Is the sequence bounded?

$$a_n = \frac{1}{2n+3}$$

10. Test the series for convergence or divergence.

$$\sum_{m=1}^{\infty} (\sqrt[m]{3} - 1)^m$$

11. Determine whether the series is absolutely convergent, conditionally convergent, or divergent.

$$\sum_{n=1}^{\infty}\left(\frac{n^2+2}{3n^2+2}\right)^n$$

12. Find the interval of convergence of the series.

$$\sum_{n=1}^{\infty}\frac{6x^n}{\sqrt[5]{n}}$$

13. Find the radius of convergence of the series.

$$\sum_{n=1}^{\infty}\frac{8^n x^n}{(n+5)^2}$$

14. Use the sum of the first 10 terms to approximate the sum of the series. Estimate the error.

$$\sum_{n=1}^{\infty}\frac{1}{1+2^n}$$

15. Find a power series representation for the function and determine the radius of convergence.

$$f(x)=\arctan(x/3)$$

16. Find the sum of the series.

$$\sum_{n=2}^{\infty} n(n-1)x^{n+1} \quad |x|<1$$

17. Find the Maclaurin series for *f* and its radius of convergence.

$$f(x)=\ln(1-x)$$

18. Evaluate the indefinite integral as an infinite series.

$$\int\frac{e^x-1}{x}\,dx$$

19. Find the Taylor series for $f(x)$ centered at the given value of a. Assume that *f* has a power series expansion. Also find the associated radius of convergence.

$$f(x)=x^4-3x^2+1, \quad a=1$$

20. Find the sum of the series.

$$\sum_{n=0}^{\infty}\frac{2^n}{3^n n!}$$

ANSWER KEY

Stewart - Calculus ET 7e Chapter 11 Form A

1. $a_n = \dfrac{(-1)^{n+1} n^2}{n+1}$

2. divergent

3. $2e^2$

4. converges; $11/6$

5. divergent

6. converges

7. convergent

8. $p < -1$

9. Decreasing, yes

10. convergent

11. absolutely convergent by the Root Test

12. $[-1, 1)$

13. 1/8

14. 0.76352, error < 0.001

15. $\sum_{n=0}^{\infty} (-1)^n \dfrac{(x/3)^{2n+1}}{2n+1}$; $R = 3$

16. $\dfrac{2x^3}{(1-x)^3}$

17. $-\sum_{n=0}^{\infty} \dfrac{x^n}{n}$, $R = 1$

18. $C + \sum_{n=1}^{\infty} \dfrac{x^n}{n \cdot n!}$, $R = \infty$

19. $-1 - 2(x-1) + 3(x-1)^2 + 4(x-1)^3 + (x-1)^4$; $R = \infty$

20. $e^{2/3}$

1. Find a formula for the general term a_n of the sequence, assuming that the pattern of the first few terms continues.

$$\left\{-\frac{1}{2}, \frac{4}{3}, -\frac{9}{4}, \frac{16}{5}, -\frac{25}{6}, \ldots\right\}$$

2. Find the value of the limit for the sequence.

$$\left\{\arctan\left(\frac{3n}{3n+8}\right)\right\}$$

3. Find the exact value of the limit of the sequence defined by $a_1 = \sqrt{3},\ a_{n+1} = \sqrt{3+a_n}$.

4. Determine whether the series is convergent or divergent.

$$\sum_{n=1}^{\infty} \frac{4}{n^2+4}$$

5. Determine whether the sequence converges or diverges. If it converges, find the limit.

$$a_n = 3e^{3n/(n+3)}$$

6. Find the partial sum s_7 of the series $\sum_{m=1}^{\infty} \frac{3}{10+7^m}$. Give your answer to five decimal places.

7. How many terms of the series $\sum_{m=2}^{\infty} \frac{18}{9m(\ln m)^2}$ would you need to add to find its sum to within 0.02?

8. Find all positive values of b for which the series $\sum_{n=1}^{\infty} 4b^{\ln 3n}$ converges.

9. Write the partial sum of the converging series which represent the decimal number 0.2523.

10. Test the series for convergence or divergence.

$$\sum_{n=2}^{\infty} (-1)^n \frac{n}{5\ln n}$$

11. Approximate the sum to the indicated accuracy.

$$\sum_{n=1}^{\infty} \frac{(-1)^{n-1}}{n^7} \quad \text{(five decimal places)}$$

12. Approximate the sum to the indicated accuracy.

$$\sum_{n=0}^{\infty} \frac{(-1)^n}{3^n n!} \qquad \text{(four decimal places)}$$

13. Test the series for convergence or divergence.

$$\sum_{k=5}^{\infty} \frac{5}{k(\ln k)^6}$$

14. Test the series for convergence or divergence.

$$\sum_{m=1}^{\infty} \frac{3^m m^5}{m!}$$

15. Test the series for convergence or divergence.

$$\sum_{k=1}^{\infty} \cos k$$

16. Test the series for convergence or divergence.

$$\sum_{m=1}^{\infty} (-1)^m \frac{\ln m}{\sqrt{m}}$$

17. Find the sum of the series.

$$\sum_{n=0}^{\infty} \frac{3^n}{5^n n!}$$

18. Find the Taylor series for $f(x)$ centered at the given value of a. Assume that f has a power series expansion. Also find the associated radius of convergence.

$$f(x) = x^4 - 4x^2 + 1, \quad a = 1$$

19. A car is moving with speed 23 m/s and acceleration 2m/s^2 at a given instant. Using a second-degree Taylor polynomial, estimate how far the car moves in the next second.

20. The resistivity of a conducting wire is the reciprocal of the conductivity and is measured in units of ohm-meters. The resistivity of a given metal depends on the temperature according to the equation $\rho(t) = \rho_{27} e^{\alpha(t-27)}$ where t is the temperature in C. There are tables that list the values of α (called the temperature coefficient) and ρ_{27} (the resistivity at 27° C) for various metals. Except at very low temperatures, the resistivity varies almost linearly with temperature and so it is common to approximate the expression for $\rho(t)$ by its first-degree Taylor polynomial at $t = 27$. Find the expression for this linear approximation.

ANSWER KEY

Stewart - Calculus ET 7e Chapter 11 Form B

1. $a_n = \dfrac{(-1)^n n^2}{n+1}$

2. $\dfrac{\pi}{4}$

3. $\dfrac{1+\sqrt{13}}{2}$

4. converges

5. $3e^3$

6. 0.23727

7. $m > e^{100}$

8. $b < \dfrac{1}{e}$

9. $\dfrac{1}{5} + \dfrac{5}{10^2} + \dfrac{2}{10^3} + \dfrac{3}{10^4}$

10. divergent

11. 0.99259

12. 0.7165

13. convergent

14. convergent

15. divergent

16. convergent

17. $e^{3/5}$

18. $-2-4(x-1)+2(x-1)^2+4(x-1)^3+(x-1)^4$; $R=\infty$

19. 24

20. $\rho_{27}(1+\alpha(t-27))$

1. Determine whether the sequence converges or diverges. If it converges, find the limit.

$a_n = e^{n/(n+3)}$

Select the correct answer.

a. e b. $\ln 3$ c. $\ln(1/3)$ d. e^3 e. diverges

2. Find the value of the limit for the sequence given.

$$\left\{ \frac{1 \cdot 9 \cdot 17 \cdots (8n+1)}{(8n)^2} \right\}$$

Select the correct answer.

a. π b. -1 c. 3 d. 0 e. 1

3. A sequence $\{a_n\}$ is defined recursively by the equation $a_n = 0.5(a_{n-1} + a_{n-2})$ for $n \geq 3$ where $a_1 = 18,\ a_2 = 9$.

Use your calculator to guess the limit of the sequence.

Select the correct answer.

a. 12 b. 13 c. 6 d. 17 e. 26

4. Find the partial sum s_7 of the series $\sum_{n=1}^{\infty} \frac{1}{2+5^n}$. Give your answer to five decimal places.

Select the correct answer.

a. $s_7 = 0.18976$ b. $s_7 = 0.18985$ c. $s_7 = 1.60976$ d. $s_7 = 0.18975$ e. $s_7 = 0.19176$

5. Given the series $\sum_{m=1}^{\infty} \frac{3m}{4^m(3m+5)}$ estimate the error in using the partial sum s_8 by comparison with the series $\sum_{m=9}^{\infty} \frac{1}{4^m}$.

Select the correct answer.

a. $R_8 \geq 0.0000051$ b. $R_8 \leq 2.6130051$ c. $R_8 \leq 0.0000051$ d. $R_8 \leq 0.000005$ e. $R_8 \geq 0.0000052$

6. Find all positive values of u for which the series $\sum_{m=1}^{\infty} 4u^{\ln 7m}$ converges.

Select the correct answer.

a. $u < 4$ b. $4 < u < \frac{7}{e}$ c. $u > 7$ d. $0 < u < \frac{1}{e}$ e. $u > \ln 7$

7. Evaluate the function $f(x) = \cos x$ by a Taylor polynomial of degree 4 centered at $a = 0$, and $x = 2$.

Select the correct answer.

a. 0.67 b. –0.33 c. –1.33 d. 0.28 e. –0.44

8. Given the series :

$$A = \sum_{k=1}^{\infty} \frac{1}{k^5 + 9} \text{ and } B = \sum_{k=1}^{\infty} \frac{1}{k^4 - k}$$

Select the correct answer.

a. Both series are convergent.
b. Both series are divergent.
c. Series A diverges by the Integral Test.
d. Series B and A converges by the Limit Comparison Test.
e. Series B diverges by the Integral Test.

9. Determine whether the series is convergent or divergent by expressing s_n as a telescoping sum. If it is convergent, find its sum.

$$\sum_{n=1}^{\infty} \frac{2}{n^2 + 2n}$$

Select the correct answer.

a. $2/3$ b. $3/2$ c. $1/3$ d. 2 e. diverges

10. Use the power series for $f(x) = \sqrt[3]{5+x}$ to estimate $\sqrt[3]{5.08}$ correct to four decimal places.

Select the correct answer.

a. 1.7156 b. 1.7189 c. 1.7195 d. 1.7200 e. 1.7190

11. How many terms of the series do we need to add in order to find the sum to the indicated accuracy?

$$\sum_{n=1}^{\infty} \frac{(-1)^{n+1}}{n^2} \quad (|\,error\,|) < 0.0399$$

Select the correct answer.

a. $n = 12$ b. $n = 5$ c. $n = 13$ d. $n = 6$ e. $n = 8$

12. Which of the given series are absolutely convergent?

Select the correct answer.

a. $\sum_{n=1}^{\infty} \frac{\sin 3n}{n}$ b. $\sum_{n=1}^{\infty} \frac{\cos \frac{\pi n}{8}}{n\sqrt{n}}$

13. Determine whether the series is absolutely convergent, conditionally convergent, or divergent.

$$\sum_{n=1}^{\infty} \frac{(-1)^n \arctan n}{n^5}$$

Select the correct answer.

a. divergent b. absolutely convergent c. conditionally convergent

14. Test the series for convergence or divergence.

$$\sum_{m=1}^{\infty} \frac{(-6)^{m+1}}{4^{5m}}$$

Select the correct answer.

a. The series is convergent b. The series is divergent

15. Test the series for convergence or divergence.

$$\sum_{m=1}^{\infty} (\sqrt[m]{5} - 1)^m$$

Select the correct answer.

a. The series is divergent b. The series is convergent

16. Find the interval of convergence of the series.

$$\sum_{n=1}^{\infty} \frac{(-1)^n x^n}{n+4}$$

Select the correct answer.

a. [–1, 1) b. [–1, 1] c. (–1, 1] d. (–1, 1) e. diverges everywhere

17. Suppose that the radius of convergence of the power series $\sum_{n=0}^{\infty} c_n x^n$ is 16. What is the radius of convergence of the power series $\sum_{n=0}^{\infty} c_n x^{2n}$?

Select the correct answer.

a. 256
b. 4
c. 1
d. 16
e. 252

18. Evaluate the indefinite integral as a power series.

$$\int \tan^{-1}(t^2)\, dt$$

Select the correct answer.

a. $C+\sum_{n=0}^{\infty} \frac{(-1)^n t^{4n+3}}{(2n+1)(4n+3)}$

b. $C+\sum_{n=0}^{\infty} \frac{(-1)^n t^{4n+3}}{(4n+3)}$

c. $C+\sum_{n=0}^{\infty} \frac{(-1)^n t^{4n+2}}{(2n+1)(4n+3)}$

d. $C+\sum_{n=0}^{\infty} \frac{(-1)^n t^{2n+2}}{(2n+1)}$

e. $C+\sum_{n=0}^{\infty} \frac{(-1)^n t^{2n+3}}{(2n+3)}$

19. Find the sum of the series.

$$\frac{2}{1\cdot 3}-\frac{2^2}{2\cdot 3^2}+\frac{2^3}{3\cdot 3^3}-\frac{2^4}{4\cdot 3^4}+\ldots$$

Select the correct answer.

a. $e^{5/3}$ b. $5e/3$ c. $\ln(1/3)$ d. $\ln(4/3)$ e. $\ln(5/3)$

20. Find the Maclaurin series for $f(x)$ using the definition of the Maclaurin series.

$$f(x)=x\cos(4x)$$

Select the correct answer.

a. $\sum_{n=0}^{\infty} \frac{(-1)^n 4^{2n} x^{2n+1}}{n!}$

b. $\sum_{n=0}^{\infty} \frac{(-1)^n 4^{2n} x^{2n+1}}{(2n)!}$

c. $\sum_{n=0}^{\infty} \frac{(-1)^n 4^{2n} x^{2n}}{(2n)!}$

d. $\sum_{n=0}^{\infty} \frac{(-1)^{n+1} 4^{2n} x^{2n+1}}{(2n)!}$

e. $\sum_{n=0}^{\infty} \frac{(-1)^n 4^n x^{2n+1}}{(2n)!}$

ANSWER KEY

Stewart - Calculus ET 7e Chapter 11 Form C

1. a
2. d
3. a
4. a
5. c
6. d
7. b
8. a
9. b
10. e
11. b
12. b
13. b
14. a
15. b
16. c
17. b
18. a
19. e
20. b

1. Determine whether the sequence converges or diverges. If it converges, find the limit.

$a_n = 3e^{3n/(n+3)}$

Select the correct answer.

a. e b. $\ln 3$ c. $\ln(1/3)$ d. $3e^3$ e. diverges

2. Determine whether the sequence is increasing, decreasing, or not monotonic. Is the sequence bounded?

$$a_n = \frac{1}{2n+1}$$

Select all that apply.

a. decreasing b. not monotonic c. increasing d. bounded

3. Find the value of the limit of the sequence defined by $a_1 = 1,\ a_{n+1} = 3 - \dfrac{1}{a_n}$.

Select the correct answer.

a. $\dfrac{3+\sqrt{5}}{2}$ b. $\dfrac{3-\sqrt{5}}{2}$ c. $\dfrac{3-\sqrt{10}}{2}$ d. $\dfrac{3+\sqrt{10}}{2}$ e. $3+\sqrt{10}$

4. Determine whether the series is convergent or divergent by expressing s_n as a telescoping sum. If it is convergent, find its sum.

$$\sum_{n=2}^{\infty} \frac{2}{n\left(n^2-1\right)}$$

Select the correct answer.

a. 1 b. $1/2$ c. 2 d. $1/4$ e. diverges

5. Given the two series $A = 1 + \dfrac{1}{4} + \dfrac{1}{9} + \dfrac{1}{16} + \dfrac{1}{25} + \ldots$ and $B = \sum\limits_{n=1}^{\infty} n^5 e^{-n^6}$ determine whether each series is convergent or divergent and choose the correct statement.

Select the correct answer.

a. Both series are divergent.
b. Series A is convergent, series B is divergent.
c. Both series are convergent.
d. Series A is divergent, series B is convergent.

6. Find the partial sum s_7 of the series $\sum_{k=1}^{\infty} \frac{3}{4+5^k}$. Give your answer to five decimal places.

Select the correct answer.

a. $s_7 = 0.46301$ b. $s_7 = 0.47999$ c. $s_7 = 2.276$ d. $s_7 = 0.466$ e. $s_7 = 0.566$

7. Given the series:

$$A = \sum_{m=1}^{\infty} \frac{\sin^2 5m}{m^{10}\sqrt{m}} \text{ and } B = \sum_{m=1}^{\infty} 8\cos\left(\frac{1}{7m}\right)$$

Determine whether each series is convergent or divergent.

a. A is convergent, B is divergent.
b. A is divergent, B is convergent.
c. The both series are convergent.
d. The both series are divergent.

8. Find the interval of convergence of the series.

$$\sum_{n=1}^{\infty} \frac{x^n}{n8^n}$$

Select the correct answer.

a. $(-8, 8]$ b. $(-1,1)$ c. $[-1, 1]$ d. $[-8, 8]$ e. $[-8, 8)$ f. diverges everywhere

9. Find the radius of convergence of the series.

$$\sum_{n=1}^{\infty} \frac{n^3 x^n}{3^n}$$

Select the correct answer.

a. $R = \infty$ b. $R = 0$ c. $R = \frac{1}{3}$ d. $R = 1$ e. $R = 3$

10. Find the interval of convergence of the series.

$$\sum_{n=1}^{\infty} (-1)^n \frac{(x+8)^n}{n6^n}$$

Select the correct answer.

a. $(2, 14]$ b. $(-14, -2)$ c. $[-1,1]$ d. $(-8, 6]$ e. $[-14, -2)$

11. Find a power series representation for

$f(t) = \ln(10 - t)$

Select the correct answer.

a. $\sum_{n=0}^{\infty} \frac{t^n}{n10^n}$

b. $\sum_{n=1}^{\infty} \frac{10t^n}{n^n}$

c. $\ln 10 - \sum_{n=1}^{\infty} \frac{t^n}{10^n}$

d. $\ln 10 - \sum_{n=1}^{\infty} \frac{t^n}{n10^n}$

e. $\ln 10 + \sum_{n=1}^{\infty} \frac{t^{2n}}{10^n}$

12. Find a power series representation for the function.

$f(y) = \ln\left(\frac{7+y}{7-y}\right)$

Select the correct answer.

a. $\sum_{n=0}^{\infty} 14y^{2n+1}$

b. $\sum_{n=0}^{\infty} \frac{y^{2n+1}}{7}$

c. $\sum_{n=7}^{\infty} \frac{14y^{2n+1}}{14}$

d. $\sum_{n=0}^{\infty} \frac{2y^{2n+1}}{7^{n+1}(2n+1)}$

e. $\sum_{n=0}^{\infty} \frac{y^{2n+1}}{7^{n+1}(n+1)}$

13. Use series to approximate the definite integral to within the indicated accuracy.

$\int_0^{0.9} x^2 e^{-x^2}\,dx \quad |error| < 0.001$

Select the correct answer.

a. 0.1529 b. 0.0125 c. 0.1447 d. 0.0625 e. 0.2774

14. Use series to evaluate the limit correct to three decimal places.

$$\lim_{x\to 0}\frac{7x-\tan^{-1}7x}{x^3}$$

Select the correct answer.

a. 114.133 b. 114.333 c. 34.3233 d. 115.933 e. 118.933

15. Find the sum of the series.

$$\frac{3}{1\cdot 5}-\frac{3^2}{2\cdot 5^2}+\frac{3^3}{3\cdot 5^3}-\frac{3^4}{4\cdot 5^4}+\ldots$$

Select the correct answer.

a. $\ln(8/5)$ b. $\ln(5/3)$ c. $\ln(7/4)$ d. $e^{8/5}$ e. $8e/5$

16. Use the binomial series to expand the function as a power series. Find the radius of convergence.

$$\frac{x}{\sqrt{16+x^2}}$$

Select the correct answer.

a. $|x|<8$ b. $|x|<1$ c. $|x|<4$ d. $|x|<10$ e. $|x|<1.8$

17. Find the Taylor polynomial T_3 for the function f at the number $a=1$.

$f(x)=\ln x$

Select the correct answer.

a. $(x-1)-\frac{1}{2}(x-1)^2+\frac{1}{3}(x-1)^3$
b. $(x-1)+\frac{1}{5}(x-1)^2+\frac{1}{4}(x-1)^3$
c. $(x+1)-\frac{1}{4}(x+1)^2+\frac{1}{3}(x+1)^3$
d. $(x+1)-\frac{1}{5}(x+1)^2+\frac{1}{7}(x+1)^3$
e. $(x-1)-\frac{1}{5}(x-1)^2-\frac{1}{7}(x-1)^3$

18. Find the Taylor polynomial T_3 for the function $f(x)$ at the number $a = 9$.

$f(x) = \cos x$

Select the correct answer.

a. $\cos(9) - \sin(9)(x+9) - \frac{\cos(9)}{2}(x+9)^2 + \frac{\sin(9)}{6}(x+9)^3$
b. $\cos(9) - \sin(9)(x-9) - \frac{\cos(9)}{2}(x-9)^2 + \frac{\sin(9)}{6}(x-9)^3$
c. $\cos(9) + \sin(9)(x-9) + \frac{\cos(9)}{2}(x-9)^2 + \frac{\sin(9)}{6}(x-9)^3$
d. $\cos(6) + \sin(6)(x-9) + \frac{\cos(6)}{6}(x-9)^2 + \frac{\sin(6)}{9}(x-9)^3$
e. $\cos(6) + \sin(6)(x-9) + \frac{\cos(2)}{2}(x-9)^2 + \frac{\sin(2)}{6}(x-9)^3$

19. Use Taylor's Inequality to estimate the accuracy $|R_2|$ of the approximation $f(x)$ at the number $a = 1$, when $0.71 \le x \le 1.29$.

$f(x) = \frac{1}{x^2}$

Select the correct answer.

a. 1.0407
b. 0.5407
c. 1.5407
d. 1.7407
e. 1.8407

20. Estimate $\sin(35^\circ)$ correct to five decimal places.

Select the correct answer.

a. 1.07358
b. 1.57358
c. 0.57358
d. 1.77358
e. 2.57358

ANSWER KEY

Stewart - Calculus ET 7e Chapter 11 Form D

1. d

2. a, d

3. a

4. b

5. c

6. d

7. a

8. e

9. e

10. e

11. d

12. d

13. a

14. b

15. a

16. c

17. a

18. b

19. b

20. c

1. Determine whether the series is convergent or divergent.

$$\sum_{n=1}^{\infty} \frac{1}{n^2 - 6n + 10}$$

Select the correct answer.

a. converges
b. diverges

2. If \$1,600 is invested at 7% interest, compounded annually, then after n years the investment is worth $a_n = 1{,}600(1.07)^n$ dollars. Find the size of investment after 7 years.

3. Determine whether the series is convergent or divergent. If it is convergent, write its sum. Otherwise write *divergent.*

$$\sum_{n=1}^{\infty} 7\left(\frac{3}{4}\right)^{n-1}$$

4. Express the number $0.\overline{87}$ as a ratio of integers.

5. Use the binomial series to expand the function as a power series. Find the radius of convergence.

$$\sqrt[4]{1 + x^6}$$

6. When money is spent on goods and services, those that receive the money also spend some of it. The people receiving some of the twice-spent money will spend some of that, and so on. Economists call this chain reaction the multiplier effect. In a hypothetical isolated community, the local government begins the process by spending D dollars. Suppose that each recipient of spent money spends $100c\%$ and saves $100s\%$ of the money that he or she receives. The values c and s are called the marginal propensity to consume and the marginal propensity to save and, of course, $c + s = 1$.
The number $k = 1/s$ is called the multiplier. What is the multiplier if the marginal propensity to consume is 80%?

Select the correct answer.

a. 6 b. 4 c. 5 d. 7 e. 3

7. Determine whether the series is convergent or divergent by expressing s_n as a telescoping sum. If it is convergent, find its sum.

$$\sum_{n=1}^{\infty} \frac{3}{n^2 + 3n}$$

8. Use the sum of the first 9 terms to approximate the sum of the following series:

$$\sum_{n=1}^{\infty} \frac{6}{n^6 + n^2}$$

Write your answer to six decimal places.

9. Determine whether the series is absolutely convergent, conditionally convergent, or divergent.

$$\sum_{n=1}^{\infty} \left(\frac{2n^3 + 3}{3n^3 + 2} \right)^n$$

10. For what values of k does the series $\sum_{n=3}^{\infty} \frac{1}{n^k \ln n}$ converge?

11. Test the series for convergence or divergence.

$$\sum_{n=2}^{\infty} \frac{(-1)^{n-1}}{\sqrt[3]{7 \ln n}}$$

12. Find the radius of convergence of the series.

$$\sum_{n=1}^{\infty} \frac{5^n x^n}{(n+8)^3}$$

13. Find the Maclaurin series for $f(x)$ using the definition of a Maclaurin series.

$$f(x) = (2 + x)^{-3}$$

14. Find the Taylor series for $f(x)$ centered at the given value of a. Assume that f has a power series expansion. Also find the associated radius of convergence.

$$f(x) = x^4 - 5x^2 + 1, \quad a = 1$$

15. Find the sum of the series.

$$\sum_{n=0}^{\infty} \frac{4^n}{7^n n!}$$

16. Find the Maclaurin series for $f(x)$.

$$f(x) = x \cos(6x)$$

17. Use multiplication or division of power series to find the first three nonzero terms in the Maclaurin series for the function.

$f(x) = e^{-x^2} \cos 4x$

Select the correct answer.

a. $1-17x^2+\frac{115}{6}x^4$ b. $1-9x^2+\frac{97}{6}x^4$ c. $1-9x^2+\frac{115}{6}x^4$ d. $1-9x+\frac{115}{6}x^2$ e. $1-17x^2+\frac{67}{6}x^4$

18. Use the binomial series to expand the function as a power series. Find the radius of convergence.

$$\frac{1}{(5+x)^6}$$

19. The following table contains the evaluation of the Taylor polynomial centered at $a = 1$ for $f(x) = 1/x$.

What is the degree of this polynomial?

x	*T(x)*
0.5	1.88
0.7	1.42
1.7	0.45
2.8	–3.39
3	–5.00

Select the correct answer.

a. 3 b. 2 c. 1 d. 5 e. 4

20. Use the Alternating Series Estimation Theorem or Taylor's Inequality to estimate the range of values of x for which the given approximation is accurate to within the stated error.

$$\cos x \approx 1 - \frac{x^2}{2} + \frac{x^4}{24} \quad |error| < 0.08$$

Write a such that $-a < x < a$.

ANSWER KEY

Stewart - Calculus ET 7e Chapter 11 Form E

1. a

2. 2569.25

3. 28

4. 29/33

5. $|x| < 1$

6. c

7. 11/6

8. 3.098422

9. absolutely convergent by the Root Test

10. $k > 1$

11. convergent

12. 1/5

13. $\sum_{n=0}^{\infty} \frac{(-1)^n (n+1)(n+2)\left(\frac{x}{2}\right)^n}{2^4}$

14. $-3-6(x-1)+(x-1)^2+4(x-1)^3+(x-1)^4;\quad R=\infty$

15. $e^{4/7}$

16. $\sum_{n=0}^{\infty} \frac{(-1)^n 6^{2n} x^{2n+1}}{(2n)\,!}$

17. c

18. $|x| < 5$

19. a

20. $-1.965 < x < 1.965$

1. Find a formula for the general term a_n of the sequence, assuming that the pattern of the first few terms continues.

$$\left\{\frac{1}{2}, -\frac{4}{3}, \frac{9}{4}, -\frac{16}{5}, \frac{25}{6}, \ldots\right\}$$

2. Determine whether the sequence converges or diverges. If it converges, find the limit.

$$a_n = 3e^{3n/(n+3)}$$

3. If $600 is invested at 4% interest, compounded annually, then after n years the investment is worth $a_n = 600(1.04)^n$ dollars. Find the size of investment after 7 years.

Select the correct answer.

a. $789.56 b. $430.21 c. $1,321.06 d. $1,230.81 e. $1,860.81

4. Find the value of the limit of the sequence defined by $a_1 = 1,\ a_{n+1} = 3 - \dfrac{1}{a_n}$.

Select the correct answer.

a. $\dfrac{3+\sqrt{10}}{2}$ b. $\dfrac{3-\sqrt{10}}{2}$ c. $\dfrac{3-\sqrt{5}}{2}$ d. $\dfrac{3+\sqrt{5}}{2}$ e. $\dfrac{2+\sqrt{5}}{3}$

5. Use Taylor's Inequality to estimate the accuracy $|R_3|$ of the approximation $f(x)$ at the number $a = 0$, when $0 \le x \le 0.5$.

$$f(x) = \tan x$$

6. A right triangle ABC is given with $\theta = 1.1$ and $|AC| = b = 4$. CD is drawn perpendicular to AB, DE is drawn perpendicular to BC, EF $\perp$ AB and this process is continued indefinitely as shown in the figure. Find the total length of all the perpendiculars $|CD| + |DE| + |EF| + |FG| + \ldots$

Write your answer to two decimal places.

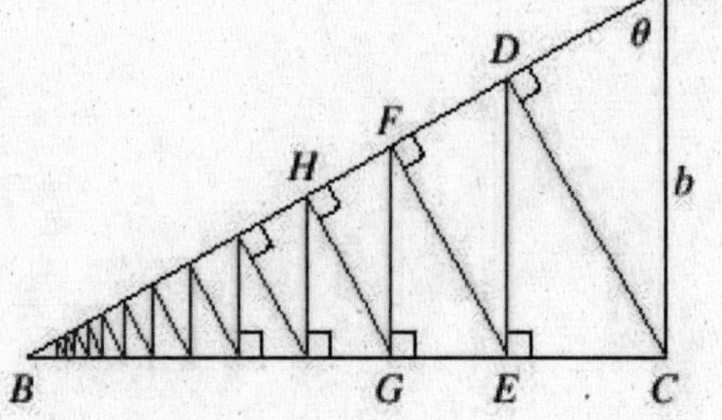

7. Let $A = \sum_{n=10}^{\infty} \frac{3}{n^{4.6}}$ and $B = \int_{9}^{\infty} \frac{3}{x^{4.6}}\, dx$. Compare A and B.

Select the correct answer.

a. $A \geq B$ b. $A \leq B$ c. $A < B$ d. $A > B$ e. $A = B$

8. Given the two series

$A = 1 + \frac{1}{16} + \frac{1}{81} + \frac{1}{256} + \frac{1}{625} + \ldots$ and $B = \sum_{n=1}^{\infty} n^8 e^{-n^9}$ determine whether each series is convergent or divergent and choose the correct statement.

Select the correct answer.

a. Series A is divergent, series B is convergent.
b. Both series are convergent.
c. Series A is convergent, series B is divergent.
d. Both series are divergent.

9. Find the values of s for which the series is convergent.

$$\sum_{k=5}^{\infty} \frac{1}{m \ln m [\ln(\ln m)]^{s}}$$

10. Find the partial sum s_{10} of the series $\sum_{n=1}^{\infty} \frac{7}{n^3}$.

Approximate the answer to the nearest thousandth.

11. Determine whether the series is absolutely convergent, conditionally convergent, or divergent.

$$\sum_{n=1}^{\infty} \left(\frac{3n^2+2}{2n^2+3} \right)^n$$

12. Determine whether the series is convergent or divergent.

$$\sum_{n=1}^{\infty} \frac{1}{n^2 - 6n + 10}$$

13. Determine which series is convergent.

Select the correct answer.

a. $\frac{7}{6} - \frac{7}{7} + \frac{7}{8} - \frac{7}{9} + \frac{7}{10} - \ldots$

b. $-\frac{1}{6} + \frac{2}{7} - \frac{3}{8} + \frac{4}{9} - \frac{5}{10} + \ldots$

14. Determine whether the series is convergent or divergent by expressing s_n as a telescoping sum. If it is convergent, find its sum.

$$\sum_{n=1}^{\infty} \frac{2}{n^2 + 2n}$$

15. Approximate the sum to the indicated accuracy.

$$\sum_{n=0}^{\infty} \frac{(-1)^n}{3^n n\,!} \quad \text{(four decimal places)}$$

16. The terms of a series are defined recursively by the equations $a_1 = 5,\ a_{n+1} = \dfrac{7n+1}{6n+3} a_n$

Determine whether $\sum a_n$ converges or diverges.

17. Estimate $\sin(33^\circ)$ correct to five decimal places.

Select the correct answer.

a. 1.54464 b. 1.04464 c. 0.54464 d. 2.04464 e. 3.54464

18. Find the sum of the series.

$$\sum_{n=0}^{\infty} \frac{3^n}{5^n n!}$$

19. For which positive integers k is the series $\sum_{n=1}^{\infty} \dfrac{(n!)^6}{(kn)!}$ convergent?

Select the correct answer.

a. $k \geq 1$
b. $k \leq 0$
c. $k \geq 0$
d. $k \geq 6$
e. $k \leq -6$

20. Find the Taylor series for $f(x)$ centered at the given value of a. Assume that f has a power series expansion. Also find the associated radius of convergence.

$$f(x) = x^4 - 3x^2 + 1, \quad a = 1$$

ANSWER KEY

Stewart - Calculus ET 7e Chapter 11 Form F

1. $a_n = \dfrac{(-1)^{n+1} n^2}{n+1}$

2. $3e^3$

3. a

4. d

5. 0.0428

6. 32.77

7. c

8. b

9. $(1, \infty)$

10. 8.383

11. divergent by the Root Test

12. converges

13. a

14. converges; $3/2$

15. 0.7165

16. diverges

17. c

18. $e^{3/5}$

19. d

20. $-1-2(x-1)+3(x-1)^2+4(x-1)^3+(x-1)^4$; $R=\infty$

1. Find a formula for the general term a_n of the sequence, assuming that the pattern of the first few terms continues.

$$\left\{-4, \frac{9}{2}, -\frac{16}{3}, \frac{25}{4}, -\frac{36}{5}, \ldots\right\}$$

2. Determine whether the sequence converges or diverges. If it converges, find the limit.

$$a_n = 2e^{2n/(n+2)}$$

3. Find the exact value of the limit of the sequence defined by $a_1 = 1,\ a_{n+1} = 6 - \frac{1}{a_n}$

4. A right triangle ABC is given with $\theta = 1.4$ and |AC| = b = 10. CD is drawn perpendicular to AB, DE is drawn perpendicular to BC, EF $\perp$ AB and this process is continued indefinitely as shown in the figure.

Find the total length of all the perpendiculars |CD| + |DE| + |EF| + |FG| + ...

Write your answer to two decimal places.

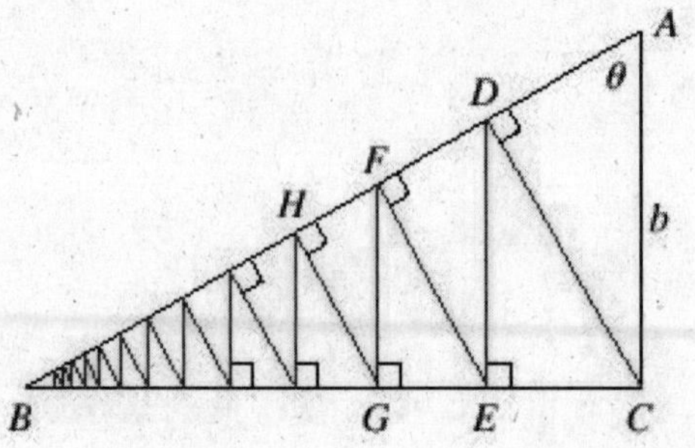

5. A sequence $\{a_n\}$ is defined recursively by the equation $a_n = 0.5(a_{n-1} + a_{n-2})$ for $n \ge 3$ where $a_1 = 21,\ a_2 = 21$. Use your calculator to guess the limit of the sequence.

6. Determine whether the series is convergent or divergent.

$$\sum_{n=1}^{\infty} \frac{4}{n^2 + 4}$$

Select the correct answer.

a. diverges
b. converges

7. Which of the following series is convergent?

Select the correct answer(s).

a. $\sum_{m=1}^{\infty} \frac{10}{m^8 + 3}$ b. $\sum_{m=1}^{\infty} 10\frac{\ln 6m}{m^2}$ c. $\sum_{m=1}^{\infty} \frac{5}{m \ln 3m}$

8. Find the partial sum s_{10} of the series $\sum_{m=1}^{\infty} \frac{5}{m^3}$. Approximate the answer to the nearest thousandth.

9. Find all positive values of u for which the series $\sum_{n=1}^{\infty} 8u^{\ln 5n}$ converges.

10. A car is moving with speed 16 m/s and acceleration 6m/s^2 at a given instant. Using a second-degree Taylor polynomial, estimate how far the car moves in the next second.

Select the correct answer.

a. 19.5 m b. 19 m c. 20 m d. 25.5 m e. 30 m

11. Find the Taylor polynomial T_3 for the function f at the number $a = 1$.

$f(x) = \ln x$

Select the correct answer.

a. $(x+1)-\frac{1}{3}(x+1)^2+\frac{1}{2}(x+1)^3$

b. $(x-1)-\frac{1}{2}(x-1)^2+\frac{1}{3}(x-1)^3$

c. $(x-1)+\frac{1}{4}(x-1)^2+\frac{1}{2}(x-1)^3$

d. $(x-1)+\frac{1}{4}(x-1)^2+\frac{1}{2}(x-1)^3$

e. $(x-1)+\frac{1}{3}(x-1)^2+\frac{1}{4}(x-1)^3$

12. Use Taylor's Inequality to estimate the accuracy $|R_4|$ of the approximation $f(x)$ at the number $a = 1.5$, when $0 \le x \le 3$.

$f(x) = \cos x$

13. How many terms of the series do we need to add in order to find the sum to the indicated accuracy?

$$\sum_{n=1}^{\infty} \frac{(-1)^n n}{2^n} \quad (|error| < 0.1562)$$

14. Approximate the sum to the indicated accuracy.

$$\sum_{n=1}^{\infty} \frac{(-1)^{n-1}}{n^7} \quad \text{(five decimal places)}$$

Select the correct answer.

a. 0.99219 b. 0.99249 c. 0.97269 d. 0.99259 e. 0.98259

15. Which of the partial sums of the alternating series $\sum_{n=1}^{\infty} \frac{(-1)^{n-1}}{n}$ are overestimates of the total sum?

Select the correct answer(s).

a. s_{100} b. s_{67} c. s_{82} d. s_{91} e. s_{55}

16. Determine whether the series is absolutely convergent, conditionally convergent, or divergent.

$$\sum_{n=1}^{\infty} \left(\frac{3n^2+2}{2n^2+3} \right)^n$$

Select the correct answer.

a. divergent b. absolutely convergent c. conditionally convergent

17. Find the sum of the series.

$$\sum_{n=0}^{\infty} \frac{4^n}{5^n n!}$$

18. Find the Maclaurin series for the function $f(x)$.

$f(x) = x \cos 7x$

19. Use multiplication or division of power series to find the first three nonzero terms in the Maclaurin series for the function.

$f(x) = e^{-x^2} \cos 4x$

20. Use the binomial series to expand the function as a power series. Find the radius of convergence.

$\sqrt[4]{1+x^5}$

ANSWER KEY

Stewart - Calculus ET 7e Chapter 11 Form G

1. $a_n = \frac{(-1)^n (n+1)^2}{n}$

2. $2e^2$

3. $3+2\sqrt{2}$

4. 677.27

5. 21

6. b

7. a, b

8. 5.988

9. $u < \frac{1}{e}$

10. b

11. b

12. 0.0633

13. 5

14. d

15. b, d, e

16. a

17. $e^{4/5}$

18. $\sum_{n=0}^{\infty} \frac{(-1)^n \cdot 7^{2n} \cdot x^{2n+1}}{(2n)!}$

19. $1-9x^2+\frac{115}{6}x^4$

20. $|x| < 1$

1. Find a formula for the general term a_n of the sequence, assuming that the pattern of the first few terms continues.

$$\left\{4, -\frac{9}{2}, \frac{16}{3}, -\frac{25}{4}, \frac{36}{5}, \ldots\right\}$$

2. Use the sum of the first 9 terms to approximate the sum of the following series:

$$\sum_{n=1}^{\infty} \frac{6}{n^6 + n^2}$$

Write your answer to six decimal places.

3. Determine whether the series is convergent or divergent.

$$\sum_{n=1}^{\infty} \frac{1}{n^2 - 6n + 10}$$

4. Use multiplication or division of power series to find the first three nonzero terms in the Maclaurin series for the function.

$$f(x) = e^{-x^2} \cos 4x$$

Select the correct answer.

a. $1 - 17x^2 + \frac{115}{6}x^4$ b. $1 - 9x^2 + \frac{97}{6}x^4$ c. $1 - 9x^2 + \frac{115}{6}x^4$ d. $1 - 9x + \frac{115}{6}x^2$ e. $1 - 17x^2 + \frac{67}{6}x^4$

5. Use the binomial series to expand the function as a power series. Find the radius of convergence.

$$\frac{1}{(5+x)^6}$$

6. Determine whether the sequence converges or diverges. If it converges, find the limit.

$$a_n = 3e^{3n/(n+3)}$$

7. Find the value of the limit for the sequence.

$$\left\{\frac{1 \cdot 8 \cdot 15 \cdots (7n+1)}{(7n)^2}\right\}$$

8. Determine whether the series is convergent or divergent by expressing s_n as a telescoping sum. If it is convergent, find its sum.

$$\sum_{n=2}^{\infty} \frac{2}{n\left(n^2 - 1\right)}$$

9. A right triangle ABC is given with $\theta = 1.1$ and $|AC| = b = 4$. CD is drawn perpendicular to AB, DE is drawn perpendicular to BC, EF $\perp$ AB and this process is continued indefinitely as shown in the figure. Find the total length of all the perpendiculars $|CD| + |DE| + |EF| + |FG| + \ldots$

   Write your answer to two decimal places.

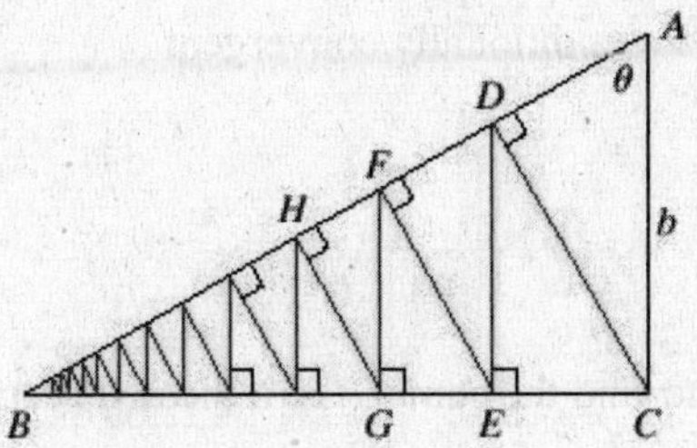

10. Find the partial sum s_{10} of the series $\sum_{n=1}^{\infty} \frac{7}{n^3}$. Approximate the answer to the nearest thousandth.

11. The terms of a series are defined recursively by the equations $a_1 = 5$, $a_{n+1} = \frac{7n+1}{6n+3} a_n$

    Determine whether $\sum a_n$ converges or diverges.

12. Find the Taylor series for $f(x)$ centered at the given value of a. Assume that f has a power series expansion. Also find the associated radius of convergence.

    $f(x) = x^4 - 4x^2 + 1, \quad a = 1$

13. Approximate the sum to the indicated accuracy.

    $\sum_{n=1}^{\infty} \frac{(-1)^{n-1}}{n^7}$ (five decimal places)

    Select the correct answer.

    a. 0.99219 b. 0.99249 c. 0.97269 d. 0.99259 e. 0.98259

14. Which of the partial sums of the alternating series $\sum_{n=1}^{\infty} \frac{(-1)^{n-1}}{n}$ are overestimates of the total sum?

    Select the correct answer(s).

    a. s_{100} b. s_{67} c. s_{82} d. s_{91} e. s_{55}

15. Determine whether the series is absolutely convergent, conditionally convergent, or divergent.

$$\sum_{n=1}^{\infty} \frac{(-1)^n \arctan n}{n^2}$$

Select the correct answer.

a. absolutely convergent   b. divergent   c. conditionally convergent

16. Find the Maclaurin series for the function $f(x)$.

$f(x) = x\cos 7x$

17. How many terms of the series do we need to add in order to find the sum to the indicated accuracy?

$$\sum_{n=1}^{\infty} \frac{(-1)^n n}{2^n} \quad (\,|\mathit{error}| < 0.1562\,)$$

18. Test the series for convergence or divergence.

$$\sum_{m=1}^{\infty} (-1)^m \frac{\ln m}{\sqrt{m}}$$

19. The resistivity of a conducting wire is the reciprocal of the conductivity and is measured in units of ohm-meters. The resistivity of a given metal depends on the temperature according to the equation $\rho(t) = \rho_{27} e^{\alpha(t-27)}$ where t is the temperature in C. There are tables that list the values of α (called the temperature coefficient) and ρ_{27} (the resistivity at 27° C) for various metals. Except at very low temperatures, the resistivity varies almost linearly with temperature and so it is common to approximate the expression for $\rho(t)$ by its first-degree Taylor polynomial at $t = 27$. Find the expression for this linear approximation.

20. Find the sum of the series.

$$\frac{3}{1\cdot 4} - \frac{3^2}{2\cdot 4^2} + \frac{3^3}{3\cdot 4^3} - \frac{3^4}{4\cdot 4^4} + \ldots$$

ANSWER KEY

Stewart - Calculus ET 7e Chapter 11 Form H

1. $a_n = \dfrac{(-1)^{n+1}(n+1)^2}{n}$

2. 3.098422

3. converges

4. c

5. $|x| < 5$

6. $3e^3$

7. 0

8. Converges; $1/2$

9. 32.77

10. 8.383

11. diverges

12. $-2-4(x-1)+2(x-1)^2+4(x-1)^3+(x-1)^4; \quad R=\infty$

13. d

14. b, d,e

15. a

16. $\displaystyle\sum_{n=0}^{\infty} \frac{(-1)^n \cdot 7^{2n} \cdot x^{2n+1}}{(2n)!}$

17. 5

18. convergent

19. $\rho_{27}(1+\alpha(t-27))$

20. $\ln(7/4)$

1. a. Find an equation of the sphere that passes through the point (6, −2, 3) and has center (−1, 2, 1).

   b. Find the curve in which this sphere intersects the *xy*-plane.

2. Find the center and radius of the sphere.

   $x^2+6x-8+y^2-8y+z^2-8z=0$

3. Write an inequality to describe the half-space consisting of all points to the left of a plane parallel to the *xz*-plane and 9 units to the right of it.

4. Write inequalities to describe the solid rectangular box in the first octant bounded by the planes $x=1, y=6$, and $z=4$.

5. Write an inequality to describe the region consisting of all points between (but not on) the spheres of radius 5 and 7 centered at the origin.

6. Find the values of x such that the vectors $\langle 3, 2, x\rangle$ and $\langle 2x, 4, x\rangle$ are orthogonal.

7. Calculate the given quantities if $\mathbf{a}=\mathbf{i}-\mathbf{j}$ and $\mathbf{b}=-\mathbf{j}+2\mathbf{k}$.

   I. $\mathbf{a}\bullet\mathbf{b}$

   II. $\mathbf{a}\times\mathbf{b}$

   III. The angle between **a** and **b** (correct to the nearest degree)

8. Find, correct to the nearest degree, the angle between the planes.

   $2x+y+z=1, \quad x-3y+5z=5$

9. A woman walks due west on the deck of a ship at 4 mi/h. The ship is moving north at a speed of 20 mi/h. Find the speed of the woman relative to the surface of the water. Round the result to the nearest tenth.

10. The tension ***T*** at each end of the chain has magnitude 30 N and makes an angle $\angle a=35^\circ$ with the horizontal. What is the weight of the chain? Round the result to the nearest hundredth.

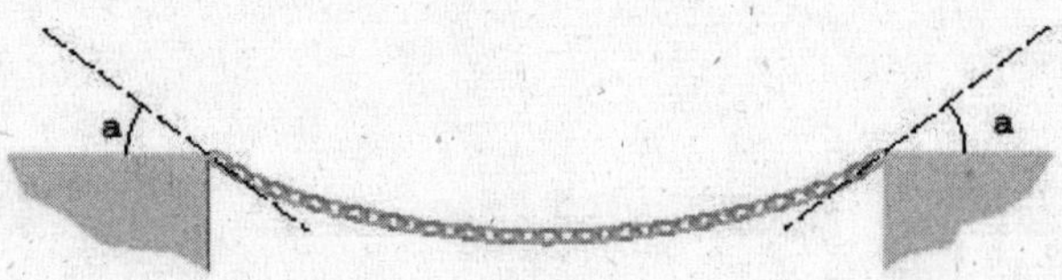

11. Velocities have both direction and magnitude and thus are vectors. The magnitude of a velocity vector is called *speed*. Suppose that a wind is blowing from the direction N 67° W at a speed of 23 km/h. (This means that the direction from which the wind blows is 67° west of the northerly direction.) A pilot is steering a plane in the direction N 24° E at an airspeed (speed in still air) of 230 km/h. The *true course*, or *track*, of the plane is the direction of the resultant of the velocity vectors of the plane and the wind. The *ground speed* of the plane is the magnitude of the resultant. Find the *ground speed* of the plane. Round the result to the nearest hundredth.

12. Find the unit vectors that are parallel to the tangent line to the curve $y=3x^2$ at the point (1,3).

13. Find the work done by a force $\mathbf{F}=7\mathbf{i}-8\mathbf{j}+10\mathbf{k}$ that moves an object from the point (0,10,8) to the point (6,12,20) along a straight line. The distance is measured in meters and the force in newtons.

14. Find the distance between the planes.

$5x-2y+z-1=0$, $5x-2y+z+4=0$

15. Find an equation of the plane through $(1, 1, -2)$, $(-3, -4, 2)$ and $(-3, 4, 1)$.

16. Find a nonzero vector orthogonal to the plane through the points P, Q, and R.

$P(1,0,-3)$, $Q(5,2,0)$, $R(0,3,1)$

17. Find the equation of the line through $(2, -2, 4)$ and perpendicular to the plane $-x+2y+5z=12$.

18. Find the rectangular coordinates of the point whose cylindrical coordinates are $(7, \pi/2, 6)$.

19. Change from spherical to cylindrical coordinates.

$(4, 0, 0)$

20. Write the equation in spherical coordinates.

$5x^2+5y^2-9z^2=4$

ANSWER KEY

Stewart - Calculus ET 7e Chapter 12 Form A

1. a. $(x+1)^2+(y-2)^2+(z-1)^2=69$, b. $(x+1)^2+(y-2)^2=68$

2. $C(-3, 4, 4)$, $r=7$

3. $y<9$

4. $0\le x\le 1,\ 0\le y\le 6,\ 0\le z\le 4$

5. $25<x^2+y^2+z^2<49$

6. $x=-2,\ x=-4$

7. $\mathbf{a}\bullet\mathbf{b}=1$
$\mathbf{a}\times\mathbf{b}=-2\mathbf{i}-2\mathbf{j}-\mathbf{k}$
72°

8. 74° or 106°

9. 20.4

10. 34.41

11. 230.75

12. $\pm(\mathbf{i}+6\mathbf{j})/\sqrt{37}$

13. 146 J

14. $\dfrac{\sqrt{30}}{6}$

15. $27x+4y+32z=-33$

16. $-\mathbf{i}-19\mathbf{j}+14\mathbf{k}$

17. $x=2-t,\ y=-2+2t,\ z=4+5t$

18. (0, 7, 6)

19. (0, 0, 4)

20. $\rho^2(5(\sin(\phi))^2-9(\cos(\phi))^2)=4$

1. a. Find an equation of the sphere that passes through the point (6, −2, 3) and has center (−1, 2, 1).

   b. Find the curve in which this sphere intersects the *xz*-plane.

2. Find the center and radius of the sphere.

   $x^2+6x-8+y^2-8y+z^2-8z=0$

3. Write an equation or inequality that represents all points on or inside a circular cylinder of radius 9 with the *y*-axis as its axis.

4. Write an inequality to describe the half-space consisting of all points to the left of a plane parallel to the *xz*-plane and 2 units to the right of it.

5. Write inequalities to describe the solid rectangular box in the first octant bounded by the planes $x=4$, $y=7$, and $z=8$.

6. Find the values of *x* such that the vectors $\langle x, 1, x\rangle$ and $\langle 8, 7, x\rangle$ are orthogonal.

7. Find an equation of the set of all points equidistant from the points $A(0, 7, 1)$ and $B(3, 3, 5)$.

8. Calculate the given quantities if $\mathbf{a}=2\mathbf{i}-\mathbf{j}$ and $\mathbf{b}=-\mathbf{j}+\mathbf{k}$.

   I. $\mathbf{a}\cdot\mathbf{b}$

   II. $\mathbf{a}\times\mathbf{b}$

   III. The angle between **a** and **b** (correct to the nearest degree)

9. Find the unit vectors that are perpendicular to the tangent line to the curve $y=3x^2$ at the point $(1,3)$.

10. Two forces F_1 and F_2 with magnitudes 10 lb and 18 lb act on an object at a point *P* as shown in the figure. Find the magnitude of the resultant force *F* acting at *P*. Round the result to the nearest tenth.

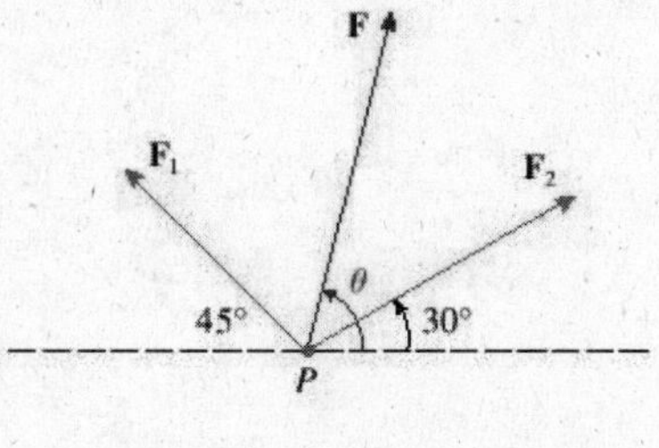

11. Find an equation of the plane through $(1, 1, -2)$, $(-3, -4, 2)$ and $(-3, 4, 1)$.

12. Find the equation of the line through $(2, -2, 4)$ and perpendicular to the plane $-x+2y+5z=12$.

13. Find the work done by a force $\mathbf{F}=4\mathbf{i}+5\mathbf{j}+8\mathbf{k}$ that moves an object from the point $(1,0,2)$ to the point $(5,3,8)$ along a straight line. The distance is measured in meters and the force in newtons.

14. Change from rectangular to cylindrical coordinates.

    $(3, -3, 6)$

15. Find, correct to the nearest degree, the angle between the planes.

$2x+3y+4z=1,\quad 4x-3y+2z=5$

16. Write the equation in spherical coordinates.

$7x^2+7y^2-2z^2=17$

17. An ellipsoid is created by rotating the ellipse $4x^2+y^2=16$ about the x-axis. Find the equation of the ellipsoid.

18. The tension $\boldsymbol{T}$ at each end of the chain has magnitude 22 N and makes an angle $\angle a=42^\circ$ with the horizontal. What is the weight of the chain? Round the result to the nearest hundredth.

19. Find parametric equations for the line through (–2, 1, 1) and (2, 3, 5) .

20. Find a nonzero vector orthogonal to the plane through the points P, Q, and R.

$P(1,0,0),\ Q(5,2,0),\ R(0,3,1)$

ANSWER KEY

Stewart - Calculus ET 7e Chapter 12 Form B

1. a. $(x+1)^2+(y-2)^2+(z-1)^2=69$, b. $(x+1)^2+(z-1)^2=65$

2. $C(-3, 4, 4)$, $r=7$

3. $x^2+z^2\le 81$

4. $y<2$

5. $0\le x\le 4,\ 0\le y\le 7,\ 0\le z\le 8$

6. $x=-1,\ x=-7$

7. $-3x+4y-4z=3.5$

8. $\mathbf{a}\cdot\mathbf{b}=1$
   $\mathbf{a}\times\mathbf{b}=-\mathbf{i}-2\mathbf{j}-2\mathbf{k}$
   72°

9. $\pm(6\mathbf{i}-\mathbf{j})/\sqrt{37}$

10. 18.2 lb

11. $27x+4y+32z=-33$

12. $x=2-t,\ y=-2+2t,\ z=4+5t$

13. 79 J

14. $\left(3\sqrt{2},\ \frac{7\pi}{4},\ 6\right)$

15. 76° or 104°

16. $\rho^2(7(\sin\phi)^2-2(\cos\phi)^2)=17$

17. $4x^2+y^2+z^2=16$

18. 29.44

19. $x=-2+4t,\ y=1+2t,\ z=1+4t$

20. $2\mathbf{i}-4\mathbf{j}+14\mathbf{k}$

1. Suppose you start at the origin, move along the x-axis a distance of 8 units in the positive direction, and then move downward a distance of 1 units. What are the coordinates of your position?

Select the correct answer.

a. (8, 0, 1) b. (0, 8, 1) c. (8, −1, 0) d. (8, 0, −1) e. (8, 1, 0)

2. Find that the midpoint of the line segment from $P1(-10, 10, 5)$ to $P2(2, 8, 3)$.

Select the correct answer.

a. (−4, 9, 4) b. (6, 0, −1) c. (−6, 0, 1) d. (4, −9, −4) e. (1, 9, −4)

3. Find an equation of the set of all points equidistant from the points $A(7, -8, -9)$ and $B(-4, 2, -10)$.

Select the correct answer.

a. $11x - 10y + z = -37$
b. $10x - 37y = 0$
c. $-11x - 10y + z = 37$
d. $11x - 10y - z = 37$
e. $11x - 10y + z = 37$

4. Find the center and radius of the sphere.

$$x^2 - 2x - 38 + y^2 + 8y + z^2 - 6z = 0$$

Select the correct answer.

a. $C(1, -4, 3)$, $r = 4$
b. $C(4, -4, 3)$, $r = 2\sqrt{2}$
c. $C(1, 4, 3)$, $r = \sqrt{2}$
d. $C(1, -4, 2)$, $r = 2$
e. none of these

5. Find the values of x such that the vectors $\langle 4x, x, 3\rangle$ and $\langle 2, x, 5\rangle$ are orthogonal.

Select the correct answer.

a. $x = -3$, $x = -5$
b. $x = -1$, $x = -5$
c. $x = 3$, $x = -3$
d. $x = 1$, $x = -1$
e. $x = 5$, $x = -5$

6. Calculate the angle between **a** and **b** (correct to the nearest degree).

$$\mathbf{a}=\mathbf{i}-2\mathbf{j}, \quad \mathbf{b}=-\mathbf{j}+\mathbf{k}$$

Select the correct answer.

a. 1°
b. 2°
c. 72°
d. 75°
e. none of these

7. Two forces F_1 and F_2 with magnitudes 8 lb and 12 lb act on an object at a point P as shown in the figure. Find the magnitude of the resultant force F acting at P. Round the result to the nearest tenth.

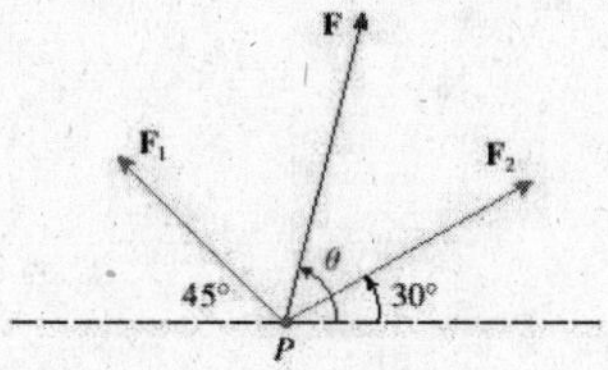

Select the correct answer.

a. 13.6 lb b. 12.6 lb c. 11.5 lb d. 10.6 lb e. 14.6 lb

8. Find the unit vectors that are parallel to the tangent line to the curve $y=2x^2$ at the point $(1,2)$.

Select the correct answer.

a. $\pm(\mathbf{i}+2\mathbf{j})/\sqrt{17}$
b. $\pm(4\mathbf{i}-\mathbf{j})/4$
c. $\pm(\mathbf{i}-4\mathbf{j})/4$
d. $\pm(\mathbf{i}+4\mathbf{j})/\sqrt{17}$
e. $\pm(\mathbf{i}+\mathbf{j})/\sqrt{17}$

9. Find the work done by a force $\mathbf{F}=\mathbf{i}+5\mathbf{j}+7\mathbf{k}$ that moves an object from the point $(1,0,2)$ to the point $(5,3,8)$ along a straight line. The distance is measured in meters and the force in newtons.

Select the correct answer.

a. 120 J b. 61 J c. 104 J d. 103 J e. 57 J

10. Find the cross product $\mathbf{a}\times\mathbf{b}$.

$$\mathbf{a}=\langle 3,\ 5,\ 1\rangle,\ \mathbf{b}=\langle -5,\ 2,\ -2\rangle$$

Select the correct answer. $\langle -16,-23,\ 25\rangle$

a. $\langle -10,-5,\ 6\rangle$ b. $\langle -12,1,31\rangle$ c. $\langle 2,-6,-25\rangle$ d. $\langle -8,-11,-19\rangle$ e. $\langle -16,-23,\ 25\rangle$

11. Let $\mathbf{v} = 7\,\mathbf{j}$ and let $\mathbf{u}$ be a vector with length 5 that starts at the origin and rotates in the *xy* - plane. Find the maximum value of the length of the vector $|\mathbf{u}\times\mathbf{v}|$.

Select the correct answer.

a. $|\mathbf{u}\times\mathbf{v}| = 12$ b. $|\mathbf{u}\times\mathbf{v}| = 140$ c. $|\mathbf{u}\times\mathbf{v}| = 30$ d. $|\mathbf{u}\times\mathbf{v}| = 1$ e. $|\mathbf{u}\times\mathbf{v}| = 35$

12. Find the distance between the planes.

$5x-2y+z-1=0$, $5x-2y+z+4=0$

Select the correct answer.

a. $\frac{1}{6}$ b. $\frac{\sqrt{30}}{6}$ c. $\frac{5}{6}$ d. $\sqrt{30}$ e. $\frac{5\sqrt{30}}{6}$

13. Identify the planes that are perpendicular.

Select the correct answer.

a. $x+10y-z=6,\ -9x-y-19z=2$

b. $x=5x+3y,\ -10x-6y+2z=-1$

c. $8x+5y=-3,\ 9y+6z=-1$

d. $8x+5y=-3,\ y+6z=1$

e. $8x+5y=-3,\ y+6z=-1$

14. Find, correct to the nearest degree, the angle between the planes.

$x+y-z=1,\quad 2x-3y+4z=5$

Select the correct answer.

a. 122° b. 60° c. 50° d. 116° e. none of these

15. Find a nonzero vector orthogonal to the plane through the points *P*, *Q*, and *R*.

$P(1,0,0),\ Q(3,2,0),\ R(0,2,1)$

Select the correct answer.

a. $2\mathbf{i}-2\mathbf{j}+6\mathbf{k}$ b. $5\mathbf{i}-2\mathbf{j}+\mathbf{k}$ c. $-2\mathbf{i}+\mathbf{j}+6\mathbf{k}$ d. $\mathbf{i}-7\mathbf{j}+4\mathbf{k}$ e. none of these

16. Find $|\mathbf{u}\times\mathbf{v}|$ correct to three decimal places where $|\mathbf{u}|=9,\ |\mathbf{v}|=3,\ \angle\theta=85^\circ$.

Select the correct answer.

a. 26.897 b. 31.897 c. 2.989 d. 2.353 e. 8.966

17. Classify the surface.

$$25x^2 + y^2 - z^2 - 6y + 6z = 0$$

Select the correct answer.

a. A cone with axis parallel to the z-axis and vertex (0, 3, 3).
b. A circular paraboloid with vertex (0, 3, 1) and axis the z-axis.
c. A hyperboloid of one sheet with center (–5, 3, –1) and axis parallel to the z-axis.

18. Change from rectangular to cylindrical coordinates.

$(9, -9, 2)$

Select the correct answer.

a. $\left(9\sqrt{2}, \frac{7\pi}{4}, 2\right)$ b. $\left(9\sqrt{2}, \frac{\pi}{4}, 2\right)$ c. $\left(9\sqrt{2}, 0, 2\right)$ d. $\left(9, \frac{7\pi}{4}, 2\right)$ e. $\left(-9\sqrt{2}, \frac{\pi}{4}, 2\right)$

19. Change from spherical to cylindrical coordinates.

$(8, 0, 0)$

Select the correct answer.

a. $(0, 0, -8)$ b. $(8, 0, 8)$ c. $(-8, 0, -8)$ d. $(0, 0, 8)$ e. $(8, 0, 0)$

20. Write the equation in cylindrical coordinates:

$$2x^2 + 2y^2 + z^2 = 15$$

Select the correct answer.

a. $2r + z = 15$
b. $2r^2 - z^2 = 15$
c. $2r^2 + z^2 = 15$
d. $4r^2 + z^2 = 15$
e. $2r^2 + z^2 = 225$

ANSWER KEY

Stewart - Calculus ET 7e Chapter 12 Form C

1. d
2. a
3. e
4. e
5. a
6. c
7. b
8. d
9. b
10. b
11. e
12. b
13. a
14. a
15. a
16. a
17. a
18. a
19. d
20. c

1. Find the distance from $(-10, 2, -8)$ to the xy-plane.

Select the correct answer.

a. 10 b. 8 c. 2 d. 16 e. 4

2. Find an equation of the sphere with center $(8, -4, 8)$ that touches the xy-plane.

Select the correct answer.

a. $(x-8)^2+(y+4)^2+(z-8)^2=4096$
b. $(x-8)^2+(y+4)^2+(z-8)^2=64$
c. $(x-8)^2+(y-4)^2+(z-8)^2=8$
d. $(x+8)^2+(y-4)^2+(z+8)^2=64$
e. $(x+8)^2-(y-4)^2-(z+8)^2=64$

3. Write an equation that represents all points on and inside a circular cylinder of radius 6 with the y-axis as its axis.

Select the correct answer.

a. $y^2+z^2<36$
b. $x^2+z^2\le 36$
c. $x^2+z^2\ge 36$
d. $x^2+y^2\le 36$
e. $x^2+y^2\le 6$

4. Calculate the angle between **a** and **b** (correct to the nearest degree).
$\mathbf{a}=\mathbf{i}-\mathbf{j},\quad \mathbf{b}=-\mathbf{j}+2\mathbf{k}$

Select the correct answer.

a. 1° b. 2° c. 72° d. 75° e. none of these

5. Find the values of x such that the vectors $\langle 3, 2, x\rangle$ and $\langle 2x, 4, x\rangle$ are orthogonal.

Select the correct answer.

a. $x=-2, x=2$ b. $x=-2, x=-4$ c. $x=-2, x=4$ d. $x=2, x=-4$ e. $x=-4, x=4$

6. Find the unit vectors that are perpendicular to the tangent line to the curve $y=2x^2$ at the point $(1,2)$.

Select the correct answer.

a. $\pm(\mathbf{i}+\mathbf{j})/\sqrt{17}$ b. $\pm(4\mathbf{i}-\mathbf{j})/4$ c. $\pm(4\mathbf{i}-\mathbf{j})/\sqrt{2}$ d. $\pm(\mathbf{i}+\mathbf{j})/17$ e. $\pm(4\mathbf{i}-\mathbf{j})/\sqrt{17}$

7. Two forces F_1 and F_2 with magnitudes 10 lb and 6 lb act on an object at a point P as shown in the figure. Find the magnitude of the resultant force F acting at P. Round the result to the nearest tenth.

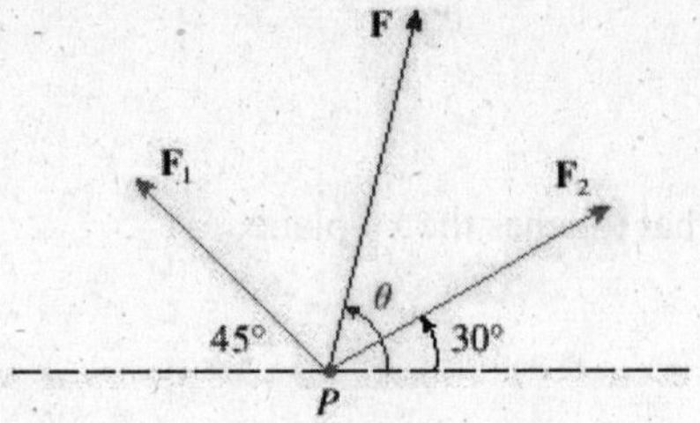

Select the correct answer.

a. 9.1 lb b. 11.3 lb c. 10.2 lb d. 12.4 lb e. 8.2 lb

8. Find the work done by a force $\mathbf{F} = 7\mathbf{i} - 8\mathbf{j} + 10\mathbf{k}$ that moves an object from the point $(0,10,8)$ to the point $(6,12,20)$ along a straight line. The distance is measured in meters and the force in newtons.

Select the correct answer.

a. 146 J b. 164 J c. 24 J d. 64 J e. 42 J

9. Find the point at which the line given by the parametric equations below intersects the plane.

$2x + 4y - 3z = -48$; $x = 10 + 7t,\ \ y = -10,\ \ z = 7t$

Select the correct answer.

a. (−38, −10, 28) b. (43, −10, −18) c. (38, −10, 28) d. (−43, −10, 18) e. (38, −10, −28)

10. Find, correct to the nearest degree, the angle between the planes.

$2x + y + z = 1,\quad x - 3y + 5z = 5$

Select the correct answer.

a. 1° b. 174° c. 47° d. 72° e. 74°

11. Find the distance (correct to two decimal places) between the given parallel planes.

$6x + 7y - 2z = 10$ and $12x + 14y - 4z = 60$

Select the correct answer.

a. 3.42
b. 2.13
c. 2.12
d. 3.14
e. 5.12

12. Reduce the equation to one of the standard forms.

$z^2 = 6x^2 + 2y^2 - 12$

Select the correct answer.

a. $x^2 + y^2 - \frac{z^2}{3} = 1$

b. $(x-1)^2 + \frac{y^2}{(1/3)^2} + z^2 = 1$

c. $\frac{x^2}{2} + \frac{y^2}{6} - \frac{z^2}{12} = 1$

d. $x^2 + \frac{y^2}{6} - \frac{z^2}{12} = 1$

e. $\frac{x^2}{2} + \frac{y^2}{6} - z^2 = 1$

13. Find a nonzero vector orthogonal to the plane through the points P, Q, and R.

$P(1,0,0)$, $Q(3,2,0)$, $R(0,3,1)$

Select the correct answer.

a. $2\mathbf{i} - 2\mathbf{j}$ b. $2\mathbf{i} - 2\mathbf{j} + 8\mathbf{k}$ c. $-2\mathbf{j} + 8\mathbf{k}$ d. $2\mathbf{i} + 8\mathbf{k}$ e. none of these

14. Find an equation for the surface consisting of all points that are equidistant from the point (0, –3, 0) and the plane $y = 3$.

Select the correct answer.

a. $x^2 + 12y^2 + z^2 = 1$ b. $x^2 + y^2 = z$ c. $z^2 - y^2 = x$ d. $z^2 + x^2 = -12y$ e. $z^2 - x^2 = -12y$

15. Find an equation for the surface consisting of all points P for which the distance from P to the x-axis is three times the distance from P to the yz-plane.

Select the correct answer.

a. $x^2 - y^2 - z^2 = 3$ b. $x^2 + y^2 + z^2 = 9$ c. $9x^2 = y^2 + z^2$ d. $3x^2 = y^2 - 3z^2$ e. $3x^2 = y^2 + 3z$

16. Plot the point whose cylindrical coordinates are $(9, \pi/2, 7)$. Then find the rectangular coordinates of the point.

Select the correct answer.

a. (0, 7, 9) b. (7, 0, 7) c. (9, 9, 7) d. (0, 9, 7) e. (0, 0, 7)

17. Change (7, 0, 0) from spherical to cylindrical coordinates.

Select the correct answer.

a. (0, 0, 7) b. (0, 0, –7) c. (–7, 0, –7) d. (7, 0, 7) e. (7, 0, 0)

18. The sketch of the solid is given below. Given $a = 8$, write the inequalities that describe it.

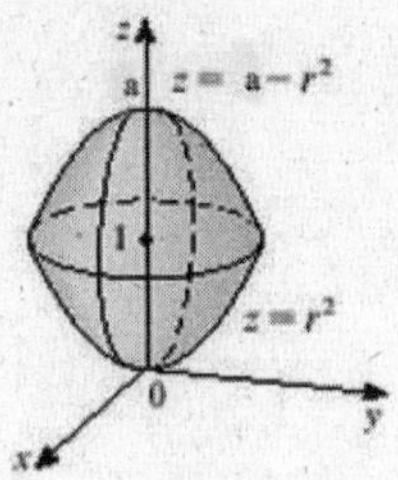

Select the correct answer.

a. $r^2 \le z \le 8 - r^2$ b. $r^2 \le z \le 8 + r^2$ c. $r^2 \le z \le 8$ d. $r^2 - 8 \le z \le r^2$ e. none of these

19. A solid lies above the cone $z = 9\sqrt{x^2 + y^2}$ and below the sphere $x^2 + y^2 + z^2 = 6z$.

Describe the solid in terms of inequalities involving spherical coordinates.

Select the correct answer.

a. $0 \le \rho \le 6\cos\phi,\ 0 \le \theta \le 2\pi,\ 0 \le \phi \le \arctan(1/9)$
b. $0 \le \rho \le 9\cos\phi,\ 0 \le \theta \le 2\pi,\ 0 \le \phi \le \arctan(6)$
c. $0 \le \rho \le 12\cos\phi,\ 0 \le \theta \le 2\pi,\ 0 \le \phi \le \arctan(9)$
d. $0 \le \rho \le 6\cos\phi,\ 0 \le \theta \le \pi,\ 0 \le \phi \le \arctan(9)$
e. $0 \le \rho \le 2\cos\phi,\ 0 \le \theta \le \pi,\ 0 \le \phi \le \arctan(9)$

20. An ellipsoid is created by rotating the ellipse $4x^2 + y^2 = 16$ about the x-axis. Find the equation of the ellipsoid.

Select the correct answer.

a. $4x^2 + y^2 + z^2 = 16$
b. $4x^2 + y^2 - z^2 = 16$
c. $4x^2 - 4y^2 + z^2 = 16$
d. $4x^2 + 4y^2 + z^2 = 1$
e. $4x^2 + y^2 + z^2 = 1$

ANSWER KEY

Stewart - Calculus ET 7e Chapter 12 Form D

1. b
2. b
3. b
4. c
5. b
6. e
7. c
8. a
9. c
10. e
11. c
12. c
13. b
14. d
15. c
16. d
17. a
18. a
19. a
20. a

1. Find the length of the median of side AB of the triangle with vertices $A(-2, 8, -7)$, $B(-6, -8, -3)$ and $C(2, -4, 9)$.

2. Find the center and radius of the sphere.

$$x^2 - 2x - 38 + y^2 + 8y + z^2 - 6z = 0$$

3. Write an equation or inequality that represents a plane containing all points with equal x and z coordinates.

4. Write an equation or inequality that represents all points on or inside a circular cylinder of radius 1 with the y-axis as its axis.

5. Calculate the given quantities if $\mathbf{a} = 2\mathbf{i} - \mathbf{j}$ and $\mathbf{b} = -\mathbf{j} + \mathbf{k}$.

   I. $\mathbf{a} \cdot \mathbf{b}$

   II. $\mathbf{a} \times \mathbf{b}$

   III. The angle between **a** and **b** (correct to the nearest degree)

6. Find the unit vectors that are parallel to the tangent line to the curve $y = 3x^2$ at the point $(1,3)$.

7. Find the values of x such that the vectors $\langle 4x, x, 3\rangle$ and $\langle 2, x, 5\rangle$ are orthogonal.

8. A bicycle pedal is pushed by a foot with a force of aN as shown. The shaft of the pedal is 15 cm long.

   Find the magnitude of the torque about P correct to two decimal places. Let $a = 70$, $b = 58°$, $c = 7°$.

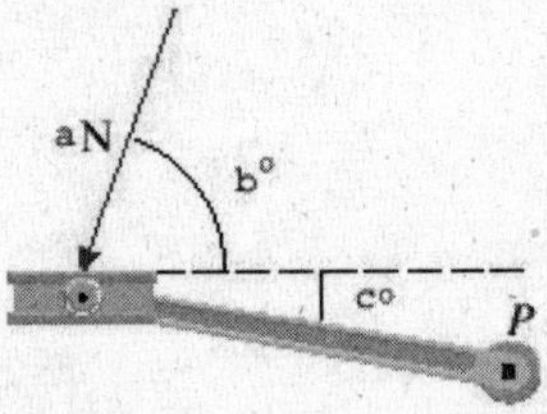

9. Find the work done by a force $\mathbf{F} = 4\mathbf{i} + 5\mathbf{j} + 8\mathbf{k}$ that moves an object from the point $(1,0,2)$ to the point $(5,3,8)$ along a straight line. The distance is measured in meters and the force in newtons.

10. Find the magnitude of the torque about P correct to two decimal places if a d-lb force is applied as shown. Let $a = 1$ ft, $b = 1$ ft, $c = 30°$, $d = 44$ lb.

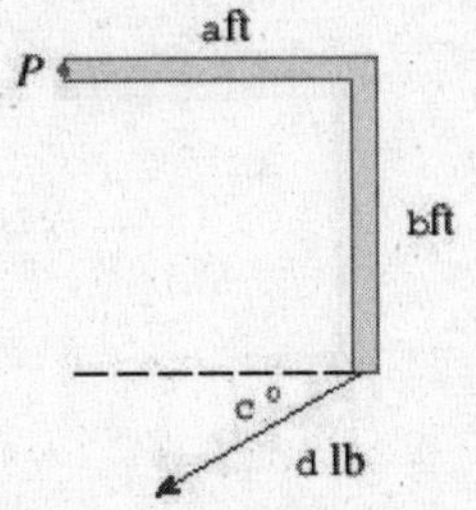

11. Find parametric equations for the line through the points $(5, 1, 10)$ and $(-6, -9, 6)$.

12. Find, correct to the nearest degree, the angle between the planes.

$2x+2y+z=1, \quad x-4y+4z=5$

13. Find an equation of the plane that passes through the line of intersection of the planes $x-z=2$ and $y+3z=7$, and is perpendicular to the plane $5x+3y-2z=8$.

14. Find an equation of the plane with x-intercept = 1, y-intercept = 10, and z-intercept = –10.

15. Find parametric equations for the line through the point $(4, 5, 2)$ that is parallel to the plane $x+y+z=-15$ and perpendicular to the line $x=15+t, \ y=12-t, \ z=3t$.

Select the correct answer.

a. $x=4t+4, \ y=-2t+5, \ z=-2t+2$

b. $x=2t+4, \ y=-4t+5, \ z=2t+2$

c. $x=4t-4, \ y=-2t-5, \ z=-2t+2$

d. $x=4t, \ y=2t-5, \ z=-2t$

e. $x=4t-4, \ y=-2t, \ z=-2t+5$

16. Find the distance between the planes.

$5x-2y+z-1=0, \ 5x-2y+z+4=0$

Select the correct answer.

a. $\frac{\sqrt{30}}{5}$ b. $5\sqrt{6}$ c. $\frac{5}{6}$ d. $\frac{\sqrt{30}}{6}$ e. $\frac{1}{6}$

17. Find an equation for the surface obtained by rotating the parabola $y=x^2$ about the y-axis.

Select the correct answer.

a. $y^2+x^2=z$ b. $z^2+x^2=y$ c. $z^2-x^2=y$ d. $z^2+x^2+y^2=1$ e. $z^2-x^2-y^2=1$

18. An ellipsoid is created by rotating the ellipse $4x^2+y^2=16$ about the x-axis. Find the equation of the ellipsoid.

19. Change from rectangular to cylindrical coordinates.

$(4, -4, 2)$

20. Write the equation in spherical coordinates.

$x^2+y^2=2y$

ANSWER KEY

Stewart - Calculus ET 7e Chapter 12 Form E

1. $2\sqrt{62}$

2. $C(1,-4,3),\ r=8$

3. $x=z$

4. $x^2+z^2\le 1$

5. $\mathbf{a}\cdot\mathbf{b}=1$
   $\mathbf{a}\times\mathbf{b}=-\mathbf{i}-2\mathbf{j}-2\mathbf{k}$
   72°

6. $\pm(\mathbf{i}+6\mathbf{j})/\sqrt{37}$

7. $x=-3,\ x=-5$

8. 9.52

9. 79 J

10. 60.11

11. $x=5+11t,\ \ y=1+10t,\ \ z=10+4t$

12. 97° or 83°

13. $3x+7y+18z=55$

14. $10x+y-z=10$

15. a

16. d

17. b

18. $4x^2+y^2+z^2=16$

19. $\left(4\sqrt{2},\ \dfrac{7\pi}{4},\ 2\right)$

20. $\rho\sin\phi=2\sin\theta$

1. Suppose you start at the origin, move along the x-axis a distance of 4 units in the positive direction, and then move downward a distance of 8 units. What are the coordinates of your position?

Select the correct answer.

a. (4, 0, –8)   b. (0, 4, 8)   c. (4, 8, 0)   d. (4, 0, 8)   e. (4, –8, 0)

2. Find the length of the side AB of the triangle with vertices $A(5,5,-10)$, $B(-3,-6,1)$ and $C(-9,-2,-1)$.

3. Find an equation of the sphere that passes through the point (7, –4, 9) and has center $(-4, 5, -5)$.

4. Given the following equation, find the radius of the sphere.

$$x^2+y^2+z^2=6x+2y+4z$$

5. Find the midpoint of the line segment from $P1(8, 10, -3)$ to $P2(-2, 10, 7)$.

Select the correct answer.

a. (–5, 0, 5)   b. (–3, –10, –2)   c. (5, 0, –5)   d. (3, 10, 2)   e. (–3, 10, 2)

6. Write an equation or inequality that represents a plane containing all points with equal x and y coordinates.

Select the correct answer.

a. $y \neq z$ b. $x \leq y$ c. $x = y$ d. $x \geq y$ e. $y = z$

7. Write inequalities to describe the solid rectangular box in the first octant bounded by the planes $x = 4$, $y = 8$, and $z = 5$.

8. Calculate the given quantities if $\mathbf{a}=\mathbf{i}-2\mathbf{j}$ and $\mathbf{b}=-\mathbf{j}+\mathbf{k}$.

I. $\mathbf{a}\cdot\mathbf{b}$

II. $\mathbf{a}\times\mathbf{b}$

III. The angle between **a** and **b** (correct to the nearest degree)

9. Find the unit vectors that are perpendicular to the tangent line to the curve $y=3x^2$ at the point $(1,3)$.

10. Find the work done by a force $\mathbf{F}=8\mathbf{i}-6\mathbf{j}+9\mathbf{k}$ that moves an object from the point $(0,10,8)$ to the point $(6,12,20)$ along a straight line. The distance is measured in meters and the force in newtons.

11. Find, correct to the nearest degree, the angle between the planes.

$$2x+3y+4z=1, \quad 4x-3y+2z=5$$

12. Find the volume of the parallelepiped with adjacent edges PQ, PR, and PS.

$$P(1, 2, 3),\ Q(3, 5, 4),\ R(3, 2, 5),\ S(4, 2, 3)$$

13. Find a parametric equation for the line through the point (–6, 9, 3) and parallel to the vector $\langle 7,3,-7\rangle$.

14. Find the point of intersection.

$$L_1 : \frac{x-17}{3}=\frac{y-58}{8}=\frac{z-23}{2}, \quad L_2 : \frac{x-49}{7}=\frac{y-26}{4}=z-15$$

15. Find an equation of the plane that passes through the line of intersection of the planes $x-z=10$ and $y+5z=9$, and is perpendicular to the plane $3x+2y-2z=7$.

16. Find an equation of the plane with x-intercept = 9, y-intercept = 1, and z-intercept = –3.

17. Find a nonzero vector orthogonal to the plane through the points P, Q, and R.

$P(1,0,-3),\ Q(5,2,0),\ R(0,3,1)$

18. Change from rectangular to cylindrical coordinates.

(9, –9, 1)

19. Identify the correct statement(s) below.

Select all that apply.

a. $r=3$ is a circular cylinder, radius 3, axis the z-axis
b. $\rho=7$ is a circular cylinder, radius 7, axis the z-axis
c. $\varphi=\pi/9$ is a half-cone
d. $\theta=\pi/5$ is a half-cone
e. none of these

20. The sketch of the solid is given below. Given a = 2, write the inequalities that describe it.

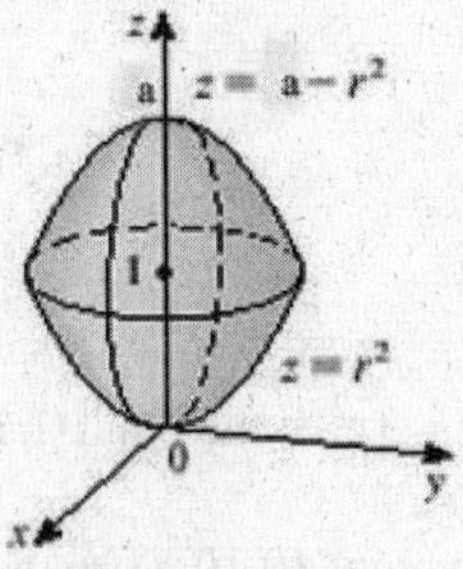

Select the correct answer.

a. $r^2 \le z \le 2+r^2$
b. $r^2 \le z \le 2-r^2$
c. $r^2 \le z \le 2$
d. $r \le z \le 2-r$
e. $r^2-2 \le z \le r^2$

ANSWER KEY

Stewart - Calculus ET 7e Chapter 12 Form F

1. a

2. $\sqrt{306}$

3. $(x+4)^2+(y-5)^2+(z+5)^2=398$

4. $\sqrt{14}$

5. d

6. c

7. $0 \le x \le 4,\ 0 \le y \le 8,\ 0 \le z \le 5$

8. $\mathbf{a} \cdot \mathbf{b} = 2$
$\mathbf{a} \times \mathbf{b} = -2\mathbf{i} - \mathbf{j} - \mathbf{k}$
51°

9. $\pm(6\mathbf{i}-\mathbf{j})/\sqrt{37}$

10. 144 J

11. 76° or 104°

12. 18

13. $x=-6+7t,\ y=9+3t,\ z=3-7t$

14. $(-7,\ -6,\ 7)$

15. $8x+5y+17z=125$

16. $-3x-27y+9z=-27$

17. $-\mathbf{i}-19\mathbf{j}+14\mathbf{k}$

18. $\left(9\sqrt{2},\ \frac{7\pi}{4},\ 1\right)$

19. a, c

20. b

1. Draw a rectangular box with the origin and (6, 6, 3) as opposite vertices and with its faces parallel to the coordinate planes. Find the length of the diagonal of the box.

2. Find an equation of the sphere that passes through the point (–6, –2, 5) and has center (9, –9, 2).

3. Find the center of the sphere.

$x^2 + y^2 + z^2 = 4x + 10y - 10z$

Select the correct answer.

a. (–2, –5, 5) b. (2, 5, –5) c. (4, 10, –10) d. (2, 5, 5) e. (2, 4, 10)

4. Find the point at which the line given by the parametric equations below intersects the plane.

$10x + 4y - 4z = -32$

$x = -4 + 4t,\ \ y = 2,\ \ z = -7t$

5. Find the values of x such that the vectors $\langle x, 1, x \rangle$ and $\langle 8, 7, x \rangle$ are orthogonal.

6. A bicycle pedal is pushed by a foot with a force of a–N as shown. The shaft of the pedal is 15 cm long.

Find the magnitude of the torque about P correct to two decimal places.

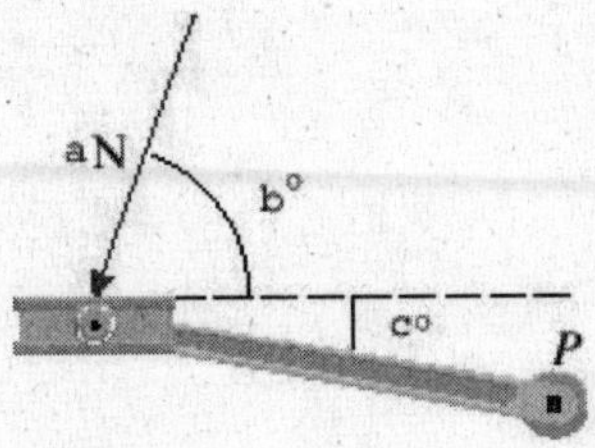

$a = 60,\ \ b = 55°,\ \ c = 5°$

7. Find a nonzero vector orthogonal to the plane through the points P, Q, and R.

$P(1,0,0),\ Q(3,2,0),\ R(0,3,1)$

8. Find an equation of the plane through the points (0, 3, 3), (3, 0, 3) and (3, 3, 0).

Select the correct answer.

a. $x + y + z = 6$
b. $9x - 6y - 9z = 1$
c. $x + y + z = 3$
d. $x + 3y + z = 1$
e. $x - y + z = 1$

9. Find an equation of the plane with x-intercept = 7, y-intercept = 6 and z-intercept = 3.

Select the correct answer.

a. $\frac{x}{7}+\frac{y}{6}+\frac{z}{3}=1$

b. $7x+6y+3z=1$

c. $\frac{x}{7}+\frac{y}{6}+\frac{z}{3}=0$

d. $7x+6y+3z=0$

e. $\frac{7x}{3}+6y+z=0$

10. Which of the given lines is parallel to the line $x=8+t,\ y=t,\ z=-7-10t$?

Select the correct answer.

a. $r=\langle -6,\ -10,\ 0\rangle + t\langle 2,\ 2,\ -20\rangle$

b. $x+8=y-2=-9-z$

c. $x=-5+t,\ y=10+t,\ z=-1-t$

d. $x=-5t,\ y=10t,\ z=-1-t$

e. $x=-5+3t,\ y=10+t,\ z=-2-t$

11. Find the distance between the point (9, 9, 5) and the plane $10x-3y-8z=10$.

Select the correct answer.

a. 0.99 b. 2.51 c. 0.08 d. 1.51 e. 0.8

12. Find the distance between the given parallel planes. Round to two decimal places.

$3x+3y-6z=3$ and $6x+6y-12z=30$

13. Find an equation for the surface obtained by rotating the parabola $x=z^2$ about the x-axis.

Select the correct answer.

a. $y^2+z^2=x$

b. $x^2+z^2=y$

c. $x^2+y^2+z^2=1$

d. $y^2-z^2=x$

e. $y^2-2z^2=3x$

14. Find an equation for the surface consisting of all points that are equidistant from the point (0, –5, 0) and the plane $y=5$.

15. Find an equation for the surface consisting of all points P for which the distance from P to the x-axis is three times the distance from P to the yz-plane.

Select the correct answer.

a. $3x^2 = y^2 - 3z^2$

b. $9x^2 = y^2 + z^2$

c. $x^2 - y^2 - z^2 = 3$

d. $x^2 + y^2 + z^2 = 9$

e. $x^2 + 2y^2 - z^2 = 0$

16. Write the equation in cylindrical coordinates.

$5x^2 + 5y^2 + z^2 = 11$

17. Identify the correct statement(s) below.

Select all that apply.

a. $\phi = \frac{\pi}{3}$ is a half-cone

b. $\rho = 4$ is a circular cylinder, radius 4, axis the z-axis

c. $\theta = \frac{\pi}{6}$ is a half-cone

d. $r = 1$ is a circular cylinder, radius 1, axis the z-axis

e. none of these

18. Change from spherical to cylindrical coordinates.

(4, 0, 0)

Select the correct answer.

a. (–4, 0, –4) b. (0, 0, –4) c. (4, 0, 0) d. (4, 0, 4) e. (0, 0, 4)

19. Write the equation in spherical coordinates.

$7x^2 + 7y^2 - 4z^2 = 12$

20. Change from rectangular to cylindrical coordinates.

(3, –3, 1)

ANSWER KEY

Stewart - Calculus ET 7e Chapter 12 Form G

1. 9

2. $(x-9)^2+(y+9)^2+(z-2)^2=283$

3. b

4. (–4, 2, 0)

5. $x=-1$, $x=-7$

6. 7.79

7. $2\mathbf{i}-2\mathbf{j}+8\mathbf{k}$

8. a

9. a

10. a

11. a

12. 1.63

13. a

14. $x^2+z^2=-20y$

15. b

16. $5r^2+z^2=11$

17. a, d

18. e

19. $\rho^2(7\sin^2\phi-4\cos^2\phi)=12$

20. $\left(3\sqrt{2},\dfrac{7\pi}{4},1\right)$

1. Suppose you start at the origin, move along the x-axis a distance of 7 units in the positive direction, and then move downward a distance of 1 units. What are the coordinates of your position?

2. a. Find an equation of the sphere that passes through the point $(6, -2, 3)$ and has center $(-1, 2, 1)$.

   b. Find the curve in which this sphere intersects the xz-plane.

3. Write inequalities to describe the solid rectangular box in the first octant bounded by the planes $x = 8$, $y = 3$, and $z = 5$.

4. Write inequalities to describe the solid upper hemisphere of the sphere of radius 2 centered at the origin.

5. Calculate the given quantities if $\mathbf{a} = \mathbf{i} - \mathbf{j}$ and $\mathbf{b} = -\mathbf{j} + 2\mathbf{k}$.

   I. $\mathbf{a} \cdot \mathbf{b}$

   II. $\mathbf{a} \times \mathbf{b}$

   III. The angle between **a** and **b** (correct to the nearest degree)

6. Find the unit vectors that are parallel to the tangent line to the curve $y = 2x^2$ at the point $(1, 2)$.

7. Find the values of x such that the vectors $\langle 3, 2, x \rangle$ and $\langle 2x, 4, x \rangle$ are orthogonal.

8. Find the work done by a force $\mathbf{F} = \mathbf{i} + 5\mathbf{j} + 7\mathbf{k}$ that moves an object from the point $(1, 0, 2)$ to the point $(5, 3, 8)$ along a straight line. The distance is measured in meters and the force in newtons.

9. Find an equation for the surface obtained by rotating the line $x = 4z$ about the x-axis.

10. Find parametric equations for the line through the point $(6, 0, 10)$ and perpendicular to the plane $-3x + 2y - 4z = 2$.

11. Find parametric equations for the line through the points $(-6, 2, 1)$ and $(-9, -4, 3)$.

12. Find an equation of the plane through the origin and parallel to the plane $-9x + 6y - 9z = -1$.

13. Find an equation of the plane that passes through the point $(1, 0, -3)$ and contains the line $x = 6 - 7t,\ \ y = 6 + 5t,\ \ z = 4 + 8t$.

14. Find an equation of the plane that passes through the line of intersection of the planes $x - z = 3$ and $y + 7z = 10$, and is perpendicular to the plane $3x + 5y - 4z = 4$.

15. Find, correct to the nearest degree, the angle between the planes.

    $2x + y + z = 1, \quad x - 3y + 5z = 5$

16. An ellipsoid is created by rotating the ellipse $4x^2 + y^2 = 16$ about the x-axis. Find the equation of the ellipsoid.

17. A solid lies above the cone $z = 7\sqrt{x^2 + y^2}$ and below the sphere $x^2 + y^2 + z^2 = 9z$. Describe the solid in terms of inequalities involving spherical coordinates.

18. Identify the planes that are perpendicular.

Select the correct answer(s).

a. $4x+8y=3,\ 10y+8z=5$
b. $x+5y-z=2,\ -2x-y-7z=2$
c. $x=5x+5y,\ -20x-20y+4z=5$
d. $5x-2y+z-1=0,\ 5x-2y+z+4=0$
e. none of these

19. Write the equation in spherical coordinates.

$x^2+y^2=9y$

Select the correct answer.

a. $\rho\cos\phi=9\sin\theta$
b. $\rho\sin\phi=9\sin\phi$
c. $\rho\sin\phi=9\sin\theta$
d. $\rho\sin\phi=9\cos\phi$
e. $\rho^2\sin\theta=9\cos\phi$

20. Find a nonzero vector orthogonal to the plane through the points *P*, *Q*, and *R*.

$P(1,0,0),\ Q(3,2,0),\ R(0,3,1)$

Select the correct answer.

a. $2\mathbf{i}-2\mathbf{j}+8\mathbf{k}$
b. $8\mathbf{k}$
c. $-2\mathbf{j}+\mathbf{k}$
d. $3\mathbf{i}-2\mathbf{j}+5\mathbf{k}$
e. $-2\mathbf{i}+3\mathbf{j}+\mathbf{k}$

ANSWER KEY

Stewart - Calculus ET 7e Chapter 12 Form H

1. $(7, 0, -1)$

2. a. $(x+1)^2+(y-2)^2+(z-1)^2=69$, b. $(x+1)^2+(z-1)^2=65$

3. $0 \le x \le 8,\ 0 \le y \le 3,\ 0 \le z \le 5$

4. $0 \le x^2+y^2+z^2 \le 4,\ z \ge 0$

5. $\mathbf{a} \cdot \mathbf{b} = 1$
$\mathbf{a} \times \mathbf{b} = -2\mathbf{i} - 2\mathbf{j} - \mathbf{k}$
72°

6. $\pm(\mathbf{i}+4\mathbf{j})/\sqrt{17}$

7. $x=-2,\ x=-4$

8. 61 J

9. $y^2+z^2=\dfrac{x^2}{16}$

10. $x=6-3t,\ y=2t,\ z=10-4t$

11. $x=-6+3t,\ y=2+6t,\ z=1-2t$

12. $-9x+6y-9z=0$

13. $13x-89y+67z=-188$

14. $23x+7y+26z=139$

15. 74° or 106°

16. $4x^2+y^2+z^2=16$

17. $0 \le \rho \le 9\cos\phi,\ 0 \le \phi \le \arctan\left(\dfrac{1}{7}\right)$

18. b

19. c

20. a

1. Find the following limit.

$$\lim_{t\to\infty}\left\langle \arctan t,\, e^{-7t},\, \frac{\ln t}{t}\right\rangle$$

2. Find a vector function that represents the curve of intersection of the two surfaces:
The cylinder $x^2+y^2=16$ and the surface $z=xy$.

3. Find a vector function that represents the curve of intersection of the two surfaces:
The cone $z=\sqrt{x^2+y^2}$ and the plane $z=2+y$.

4. If $\mathbf{r}(t)=t\,\mathbf{i}+t\cos\pi t\,\mathbf{j}+\sin\pi t\,\mathbf{k}$, evaluate $\int_0^1 \mathbf{r}(t)\,dt$.

5. Find $\mathbf{r}'(t)$ for the function given.

$\mathbf{r}(t)=2\mathbf{i}+\sin t\,\mathbf{j}+\cos t\,\mathbf{k}$

6. Find the point of intersection of the tangent lines to the curve $\mathbf{r}(t)=\langle \sin\pi t,\, 6\sin\pi t,\, \cos\pi t\rangle$, at the points where $t=0$ and $t=0.5$.

7. The helix $\mathbf{r}_1(t)=\cos t\,\mathbf{i}+\sin t\,\mathbf{j}+t\,\mathbf{k}$ intersects the curve $\mathbf{r}_2(t)=(1+t)\mathbf{i}+t^2\mathbf{j}+t^3\,\mathbf{k}$ at the point (1, 0, 0).

Find the angle of intersection.

8. Evaluate the integral.

$\int\left(e^{6t}\mathbf{i}+8t\,\mathbf{j}+\ln t\,\mathbf{k}\right)dt$

9. If $\mathbf{u}(t)=\mathbf{i}-9t^2\mathbf{j}+3t^3\mathbf{k}$ and $\mathbf{v}(t)=t\,\mathbf{i}-\cos t\,\mathbf{j}+\sin t\,\mathbf{k}$, find $\frac{d}{dt}[\mathbf{u}(t)\cdot\mathbf{v}(t)]$.

10. Use *Simpson's Rule* with $n = 10$ to estimate the length of the arc of the twisted cubic $x=t,\ y=t^2,\ z=t^3$ from the origin to the point (2, 4, 8). Round your answer to four decimal places.

11. Find the unit tangent vector for the curve given by $\mathbf{r}(t)=\left\langle \frac{1}{4}t^4, \frac{1}{3}t^3, t\right\rangle$.

12. Find the curvature of the curve $y=x^3$ at the point $(-1, -1)$.

13. A particle moves with position function $\mathbf{r}(t)=2\sqrt{2}\,t\,\mathbf{i}+e^{2t}\mathbf{j}+e^{-2t}\mathbf{k}$. Find the acceleration of the particle.

14. A particle moves with position function $\mathbf{r}(t)=2\cos t\mathbf{i}+2\sin t\mathbf{j}+2t\mathbf{k}$.

Find the normal component of the acceleration vector.

15. Find an expression for $\frac{d}{dt}[x(t)\cdot(y(t)\times z(t))]$.

16. At what point on the curve $x = t^3,\ y = 3t,\ z = t^4$ is the normal plane parallel to the plane $9x + 9y - 12z = 7$?

17. Find the velocity of a particle with the given position function.

$\mathbf{r}(t) = 13e^{15t}\mathbf{i} + 10e^{-18t}\mathbf{j}$

18. Let $\mathbf{r}(t) = \left\langle \sqrt{t-3},\ (e^{2t} - 1)/t,\ \ln(2t+1) \right\rangle$.

Find the domain of $\mathbf{r}$.

19. Find equations of the normal plane to $x = t,\ y = t^2,\ z = t^3$ at the point (3, 9, 27).

20. A particle moves with position function $\mathbf{r}(t) = (9t - 3t^3 - 2)\mathbf{i} + 9t^2\mathbf{j}$.

Find the tangential component of the acceleration vector.

ANSWER KEY

Stewart - Calculus ET 7e Chapter 13 Form A

1. $\mathbf{r}(t) = \frac{\pi}{2}\mathbf{i}$

2. $\mathbf{r}(t) = 4\cos(t)\mathbf{i} + 4\sin(t)\mathbf{j} + 16\sin(t)\cos(t)\mathbf{k}$

3. $\mathbf{r}(t) = t\mathbf{i} + \frac{(t^2-4)}{4}\mathbf{j} + \frac{(t^2+4)}{4}\mathbf{k}$

4. $\frac{1}{2}\mathbf{i} - \left(\frac{2}{\pi^2}\right)\mathbf{j} + \left(\frac{2}{\pi}\right)\mathbf{k}$

5. $\mathbf{r}'(t) = \cos t\,\mathbf{j} - \sin t\,\mathbf{k}$

6. (1, 6, 1)

7. $\pi/2$

8. $\frac{e^{6t}}{6}\mathbf{i} + 4t^2\mathbf{j} + t(\ln t - 1)\mathbf{k} + C$

9. $1 + 18t\cos t + 3t^3\cos t$

10. 9.5706

11. $\frac{\langle t^3, t^2, 1\rangle}{\sqrt{t^6 + t^4 + 1}}$

12. $\frac{3\sqrt{10}}{50}$

13. $a(t) = 4e^{2t}\mathbf{j} + 4e^{-2t}\mathbf{k}$

14. 2

15. $\frac{dx(t)}{dt}\cdot(y(t)\times z(t)) - \frac{dy(t)}{dt}(x(t)\times z(t)) + \frac{dz(t)}{dt}(x(t)\times y(t))$

16. (–1, –3, 1)

17. $v = 195e^{15t}\mathbf{i} - 180e^{-18t}\mathbf{j}$

18. $[3, \infty)$

19. $x + 6y + 27z - 786 = 0$

20. $18t$

1. Find the following limit.

$$\lim_{t\to\infty}\left\langle \arctan t,\ e^{-7t},\ \frac{\ln t}{t}\right\rangle$$

2. Let $\mathbf{r}(t)=\left\langle \sqrt{3-t},\ (e^t-1)/t,\ \ln(2t+1)\right\rangle$.

   Find the domain of $\mathbf{r}$.

3. If $\mathbf{r}(t)=t^3\mathbf{i}+t\cos\pi t\,\mathbf{j}+\sin\pi t\,\mathbf{k}$, evaluate $\int_0^1 \mathbf{r}(t)\,dt$.

4. Find a vector function that represents the curve of intersection of the two surfaces:

   The paraboloid $z=4x^2+y^2$ and the parabolic cylinder $y=x^2$.

5. Find the unit tangent vector for the curve given by $\mathbf{r}(t)=\left\langle \frac{1}{2}t^2,\ t,\ 1\right\rangle$.

6. What force is required so that a particle of mass m has the following position function?

   $\mathbf{r}(t)=5t^3\mathbf{i}+2t^2\mathbf{j}+7t^3\mathbf{k}$

7. Find $\mathbf{r}''(t)$ for the function given.

   $\mathbf{r}(t)=2\mathbf{i}+\sin t\,\mathbf{j}+\cos t\,\mathbf{k}$

8. Find the point of intersection of the tangent lines to the curve $\mathbf{r}(t)=\left\langle \sin\pi t,\ 6\sin\pi t,\ \cos\pi t\right\rangle$, at the points where $t=0$ and $t=0.5$.

9. Find the curvature of the curve $y=x^4$ at the point (1, 1).

10. Find the velocity of a particle with the given position function.

    $\mathbf{r}(t)=4e^{12t}\mathbf{i}+14e^{-8t}\mathbf{j}$

11. The curves $\mathbf{r}_1(t)=\left\langle t,\ t^6,\ t^7\right\rangle$ and $\mathbf{r}_2(t)=\left\langle \sin t,\ \sin 5t,\ t\right\rangle$ intersect at the origin. Find their angle of intersection correct to the nearest degree.

12. Evaluate the integral.

    $$\int (e^{6t}\mathbf{i}+8t\mathbf{j}+\ln t\mathbf{k})\ dt$$

13. If $\mathbf{u}(t)=\mathbf{i}-9t^2\mathbf{j}+3t^3\mathbf{k}$ and $\mathbf{v}(t)=t\mathbf{i}-\cos t\mathbf{j}+\sin t\mathbf{k}$, find $\frac{d}{dt}[\mathbf{u}(t)\cdot\mathbf{v}(t)]$.

14. Use *Simpson's Rule* with $n = 10$ to estimate the length of the arc of the twisted cubic $x = t,\ y = t^2,\ z = t^3$ from the origin to the point (2, 4, 8).

Round the answer to four decimal places.

15. Find the velocity of a particle with the given position function.

$\mathbf{r}(t) = 13e^{15t}\mathbf{i} + 10e^{-18t}\mathbf{j}$

16. A particle moves with position function $\mathbf{r}(t) = 2\sqrt{2}\,t\,\mathbf{i} + e^{2t}\mathbf{j} + e^{-2t}\mathbf{k}$. Find the speed of the particle.

17. A force with magnitude 40 N acts directly upward from the xy-plane on an object with mass 5 kg. The object starts at the origin with initial velocity $\mathbf{v}(0) = 5\mathbf{i} - 4\mathbf{j}$. Find its position function.

18. A ball is thrown at an angle of $15°$ to the ground. If the ball lands 67 m away, what was the initial speed of the ball? Let $g = 9.8\,\text{m/s}^2$.

19. A particle moves with position function $\mathbf{r}(t) = (12t - 4t^3 - 2)\mathbf{i} + 12t^2\mathbf{j}$.

Find the tangential component of the acceleration vector.

20. A particle moves with position function $\mathbf{r}(t) = 8\cos t\,\mathbf{i} + 8\sin t\,\mathbf{j} + 8t\,\mathbf{k}$.

Find the normal component of the acceleration vector.

ANSWER KEY

Stewart - Calculus ET 7e Chapter 13 Form B

1. $\mathbf{r}(t) = \frac{\pi}{2}\mathbf{i}$

2. $(-1/2, 0) \cup (0, 3]$

3. $\frac{1}{4}\mathbf{i} - \left(\frac{2}{\pi^2}\right)\mathbf{j} + \left(\frac{2}{\pi}\right)\mathbf{k}$

4. $\mathbf{r}(t) = t\mathbf{i} + t^2\mathbf{j} + (4t^2 + t^4)\mathbf{k}$

5. $\frac{\langle t, 1, 0\rangle}{\sqrt{t^2+1}}$

6. $\mathbf{F} = m(30t\mathbf{i} + 4\mathbf{j} + 42t\mathbf{k})$

7. $r''(t) = -\sin t\,\mathbf{j} - \cos t\,\mathbf{k}$

8. $(1, 6, 1)$

9. $12/17^{3/2}$

10. $v = 48e^{12t}\mathbf{i} - 112e^{-8t}\mathbf{j}$

11. $79°$

12. $\frac{e^{6t}}{6}\mathbf{i} + 4t^2\mathbf{j} + t(\ln t - 1)\mathbf{k} + C$

13. $1 + 18t\cos t + 3t^3\cos t$

14. 9.5706

15. $v = 195e^{15t}\mathbf{i} - 180e^{-18t}\mathbf{j}$

16. $|v(t)| = 2(e^{2t} + e^{-2t})$

17. $\mathbf{r}(t) = 5t\mathbf{i} - 4t\mathbf{j} + 4t^2\mathbf{k}$

18. 36.2

19. $24t$

20. 8

1. Find the limit.

$\lim_{t\to 0^+} \langle 2\cos t,\ 6\sin t,\ 3t\ln t\rangle$

Select the correct answer.

a. $\mathbf{r}(t) = 2\mathbf{i}$ b. $\mathbf{r}(t) = 2\mathbf{i}+6\mathbf{j}+3\mathbf{k}$ c. $\mathbf{r}(t) = 2\mathbf{i}-3\mathbf{k}$ d. $\mathbf{r}(t) = 2\mathbf{j}$ e. $\mathbf{r}(t) = 2\mathbf{k}$

2. Let $\mathbf{r}(t) = \left\langle \sqrt{2-t},\ (e^t-1)/t,\ \ln(t+1)\right\rangle$.

Find the domain of $\mathbf{r}$.

Select the correct answer.

a. $(-1,0)\cup(0,2]$ b. $[-1,0)\cup(0,3)$ c. $[2,\infty)$ d. $(-\infty,-1)$ e. $(-1,2]$

3. A particle moves with position function $\mathbf{r}(t) = (21t-7t^3-2)\mathbf{i}+21t^2\mathbf{j}$.

Find the tangential component of the acceleration vector.

Select the correct answer.

a. $a_T = 42t+2$ b. $a_T = 21t$ c. $a_T = -42t$ d. $a_T = 42t$ e. $a_T = 242t$

4. Find a vector function that represents the curve of intersection of the two surfaces:

The circular cylinder $x^2+y^2=4$ and the parabolic cylinder $z = x^2$.

Select the correct answer.

a. $\mathbf{r}(t) = 2\cos t\,\mathbf{i}+2\sin t\,\mathbf{j}+4\cos^2 t\,\mathbf{k}$
b. $\mathbf{r}(t) = 4\cos t\,\mathbf{i}+4t\,\mathbf{j}+4\cos^2 t\,\mathbf{k}$
c. $\mathbf{r}(t) = \cos t\,\mathbf{i}+\sin t\,\mathbf{j}-4\cos^2 t\,\mathbf{k}$
d. $\mathbf{r}(t) = 4\cos t\,\mathbf{i}-\sin t\,\mathbf{j}-4\cos^2 t\,\mathbf{k}$
e. $\mathbf{r}(t) = \mathbf{i}+\mathbf{j}+16\cos^2 t\,\mathbf{k}$

5. A force with magnitude 12 N acts directly upward from the *xy*-plane on an object with mass 3 kg. The object starts at the origin with initial velocity $\mathbf{v}(0) = 3\mathbf{i}-4\mathbf{j}$. Find its position function.

Select the correct answer.

a. $\mathbf{r}(t) = 3t\mathbf{i}-4t\mathbf{j}+2t^2\mathbf{k}$
b. $\mathbf{r}(t) = 3t^2\mathbf{i}-4t^2\mathbf{j}+2t^3\mathbf{k}$
c. $\mathbf{r}(t) = 3t\mathbf{i}-4t\mathbf{j}+4t^2\mathbf{k}$
d. $\mathbf{r}(t) = 3\mathbf{i}-4\mathbf{j}+2t^2\mathbf{k}$
e. $\mathbf{r}(t) = 3t^3\mathbf{i}-4\mathbf{j}+2t^2\mathbf{k}$

6. The figure shows a curve C given by a vector function $\mathbf{r}(t)$. Choose the correct expression for $\mathbf{r}'(4)$.

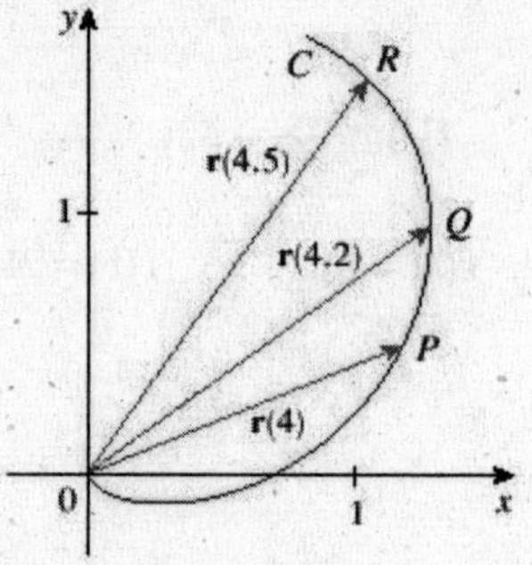

Select the correct answer.

a. $\lim_{h\to 0} \dfrac{\mathbf{r}(4+h)+\mathbf{r}(4)}{h}$

b. $\lim_{h\to 0} \dfrac{\mathbf{r}(4-h)-\mathbf{r}(4)}{h}$

c. $\lim_{h\to 0} \dfrac{\mathbf{r}(4-h)+\mathbf{r}(4)}{h}$

d. $\lim_{h\to 0} \dfrac{\mathbf{r}(4+h)-\mathbf{r}(4)}{h}$

e. $\lim_{h\to 0} \dfrac{\mathbf{r}(4+h)-\mathbf{r}(h)}{h}$

7. If $\mathbf{r}(t)=\langle t, t^7, t^9\rangle$, find $\mathbf{r}''(t)$.

Select the correct answer.

a. $\langle 0, 42t^5, 72t^7\rangle$ b. $\langle 0, 42t^6, 72t^8\rangle$ c. $\langle 1, 42t^5, 72t^7\rangle$ d. $\langle 0, 7t^5, 9t^7\rangle$ e. $\langle 1, 7t^6, 9t^8\rangle$

8. The helix $\mathbf{r}_1(t)=\cos t\,\mathbf{i}+\sin t\,\mathbf{j}+t\,\mathbf{k}$ intersects the curve $\mathbf{r}_2(t)=(1+t)\mathbf{i}+t^2\mathbf{j}+t^3\,\mathbf{k}$ at the point (1, 0, 0). Find the angle of intersection.

Select the correct answer.

a. 0 b. $\pi/4$ c. $\pi/2$ d. $\pi/3$ e. none of these

9. Find $\mathbf{r}(t)$ if $\mathbf{r}'(t)=\sin t\mathbf{i}-\cos t\mathbf{j}+6t\mathbf{k}$ and $r(0)=\mathbf{i}+\mathbf{j}+5\mathbf{k}$.

Select the correct answer.

a. $(-\cos t+2)\mathbf{i}-(\sin t-1)\mathbf{j}+(3t^2+5)\mathbf{k}$

b. $(-\cos t+2)\mathbf{i}+(\sin t+1)\mathbf{j}+(3t^2+5)\mathbf{k}$

c. $(\cos t)\mathbf{i}-(\sin t-1)\mathbf{j}+(3t^2+5)\mathbf{k}$

d. $(\cos t)\mathbf{i}+(\sin t+1)\mathbf{j}+(3t^2+5)\mathbf{k}$

e. $(-\cos t+1)\mathbf{i}-(\sin t-1)\mathbf{j}+(3t^2+5)\mathbf{k}$

10. Evaluate the integral.

$$\int (e^{7t}\mathbf{i}+4t\mathbf{j}+\ln t\mathbf{k})\ dt$$

Select the correct answer.

a. $\dfrac{e^{7t}}{7}\mathbf{i}+2t^2\mathbf{j}+(\ln t-1)\mathbf{k}+\mathbf{C}$

b. $\dfrac{e^{7t}}{7}\mathbf{i}+4t^2\mathbf{j}+(\ln t-1)\mathbf{k}+\mathbf{C}$

c. $e^{7t}\mathbf{i}+2t^2\mathbf{j}+(\ln t-1)\mathbf{k}+\mathbf{C}$

d. $\dfrac{e^{7t}}{7}\mathbf{i}+2t^2\mathbf{j}+t(\ln t-1)\mathbf{k}+\mathbf{C}$

e. $e^{7t}\mathbf{i}+4t^2\mathbf{j}+(\ln t-1)\mathbf{k}+\mathbf{C}$

11. Reparametrize the curve with respect to arc length measured from the point where $t=0$ in the direction of increasing t.

$$\mathbf{r}(t)=(7+3t)\mathbf{i}+(8+9t)\mathbf{j}-(6t)\mathbf{k}$$

Select the correct answer.

a. $\mathbf{r}(t(s))=(7+\dfrac{3}{\sqrt{116}}s)\mathbf{i}+(8+\dfrac{9}{\sqrt{116}}s)\mathbf{j}-(6s)\mathbf{k}$

b. $\mathbf{r}(t(s))=(7+\dfrac{3}{\sqrt{136}}s)\mathbf{i}+(8+\dfrac{9}{\sqrt{136}}s)\mathbf{j}-(6s)\mathbf{k}$

c. $\mathbf{r}(t(s))=(7+\dfrac{3}{\sqrt{126}}s)\mathbf{i}+(8+\dfrac{9}{\sqrt{126}}s)\mathbf{j}-(\dfrac{6s}{\sqrt{126}})\mathbf{k}$

d. $\mathbf{r}(t(s))=(7-\dfrac{3}{\sqrt{126}}s)\mathbf{i}-(8+\dfrac{9}{\sqrt{126}}s)\mathbf{j}+(\dfrac{6s}{\sqrt{126}})\mathbf{k}$

e. $\mathbf{r}(t(s))=(7-\dfrac{3}{\sqrt{116}}s)\mathbf{i}-(8+\dfrac{s}{\sqrt{116}})\mathbf{j}+(\dfrac{6s}{\sqrt{126}})\mathbf{k}$

12. Find the acceleration of a particle with the following position function.

$$\mathbf{r}(t)=\left\langle 4t^2-2,\ 8t\right\rangle$$

Select the correct answer.

a. $\mathbf{a}(t)=(4+2t)\mathbf{i}-8\mathbf{j}$
b. $\mathbf{a}(t)=4\mathbf{i}-\mathbf{j}$
c. $\mathbf{a}(t)=8\mathbf{i}$
d. $\mathbf{a}(t)=8t\mathbf{i}+8\mathbf{j}$
e. $\mathbf{a}(t)=4t\mathbf{i}+8\mathbf{j}$

13. Find the curvature of $y = x^7$.

Select the correct answer.

a. $\dfrac{7x^6}{(1+49x^{12})^{3/2}}$ b. $\dfrac{42|x|^5}{(1+7x^6)^{3/2}}$ c. $\dfrac{42|x|^5}{(1+49x^{12})^{3/2}}$ d. $\dfrac{49|x|^5}{(1+7x^{12})^{3/2}}$ e. $\dfrac{|x|^5}{(1+x^6)^{3/2}}$

14. Find the unit tangent vector $\mathbf{T}(t)$.

$\mathbf{r}(t) = \langle 3\sin t,\ 6t,\ 3\cos t \rangle$

Select the correct answer.

a. $\left\langle -\dfrac{\cos t}{\sqrt{5}}, \dfrac{2}{\sqrt{5}}, \dfrac{3\sin t}{\sqrt{5}} \right\rangle$

b. $\langle 3\cos t,\ 6,\ -3\sin t \rangle$

c. $\left\langle \dfrac{\cos t}{\sqrt{5}}, \dfrac{2}{\sqrt{5}}, -\dfrac{\sin t}{\sqrt{5}} \right\rangle$

d. $\langle \cos t,\ 1,\ -\sin t \rangle$

e. $\langle 3\sqrt{5}\cos t,\ 6,\ -3\sqrt{5}\sin t \rangle$

15. Find the velocity of a particle with the given position function.

$\mathbf{r}(t) = 10e^{7t}\mathbf{i} + 7e^{-12t}\mathbf{j}$

Select the correct answer.

a. $\mathbf{v}(t) = 70e^{t}\mathbf{i} - 84e^{-t}\mathbf{j}$
b. $\mathbf{v}(t) = 10e^{7t}\mathbf{i} - 7e^{-12t}\mathbf{j}$
c. $\mathbf{v}(t) = 70e^{7t}\mathbf{i} - 84e^{-12t}\mathbf{j}$
d. $\mathbf{v}(t) = 17e^{7t}\mathbf{i} + 19e^{-12t}\mathbf{j}$
e. $\mathbf{v}(t) = 17e^{7t}\mathbf{i} + e^{-12t}\mathbf{j}$

16. Find the acceleration of a particle with the given position function.

$\mathbf{r}(t) = 6\sin t\,\mathbf{i} + 10t\,\mathbf{j} - 8\cos t\,\mathbf{k}$

Select the correct answer.

a. $\mathbf{a}(t) = -6\cos t\,\mathbf{i} + 8\sin t\,\mathbf{k}$
b. $\mathbf{a}(t) = -6\sin t\,\mathbf{i} + 8\cos t\,\mathbf{k}$
c. $\mathbf{a}(t) = -6\sin t\,\mathbf{i} + 8\cos t\,\mathbf{j}$
d. $\mathbf{a}(t) = 6\sin t\,\mathbf{i} - 8\cos t\,\mathbf{k}$
e. $\mathbf{a}(t) = 6\sin t\,\mathbf{i} - 8t\,\mathbf{k}$

17. Find the speed of a particle with the given position function.

$\mathbf{r}(t) = 5\sqrt{2}t\,\mathbf{i} + e^{5t}\mathbf{j} - e^{-5t}\mathbf{k}$

Select the correct answer.

a. $|\mathbf{v}(t)| = (e^{5t} + e^{-5t})$

b. $|\mathbf{v}(t)| = \sqrt{10 + 5e^{t} + 5e^{-t}}$

c. $|\mathbf{v}(t)| = \sqrt{10 + e^{10t} + e^{-10t}}$

d. $|\mathbf{v}(t)| = 5(e^{5t} + e^{-5t})$

e. $|\mathbf{v}(t)| = 5(e^{t} + e^{-t})$

18. Find the velocity of a particle that has the given acceleration and the given initial velocity.

$\mathbf{a}(t) = 2\mathbf{k},\ \mathrm{v}(0) = 10\mathbf{i} - 9\mathbf{j}$

Select the correct answer.

a. $\mathbf{v}(t) = (10t - 9)\mathbf{i} + 2t\mathbf{k}$

b. $\mathbf{v}(t) = 10\mathbf{i} - 9\mathbf{j} + 2\mathbf{k}$

c. $\mathbf{v}(t) = 9\mathbf{i} - 10\mathbf{j} + 2t\mathbf{k}$

d. $\mathbf{v}(t) = 10\mathbf{i} - 9\mathbf{j} + 2t\mathbf{k}$

e. $\mathbf{v}(t) = 10\mathbf{i} - \mathbf{j} + 2t\mathbf{k}$

19. For the curve given by $\mathbf{r}(t) = \langle 2\sin t,\ 5t,\ 2\cos t\rangle$, find the unit normal vector.

Select the correct answer.

a. $\langle \sqrt{29}\sin t,\ 0,\ -\sqrt{29}\cos t\rangle$

b. $\left\langle -\dfrac{\sin t}{\sqrt{29}},\ 0,\ -\dfrac{\cos t}{\sqrt{29}}\right\rangle$

c. $\langle -\sin t,\ 0,\ -\cos t\rangle$

d. $\langle \sin t, 5, -\cos t\rangle$

e. none of these

20. The position function of a particle is given by

$\mathbf{r}(t) = \langle 7t^2,\ 7t,\ 7t^2 - 140t\rangle$

When is the speed a minimum?

Select the correct answer.

a. $t = 5$ b. $t = 0$ c. $t = 20$ d. $t = 10$ e. $t = 30$

ANSWER KEY

Stewart - Calculus ET 7e Chapter 13 Form C

1. a
2. a
3. d
4. a
5. a
6. d
7. a
8. c
9. a
10. d
11. c
12. c
13. c
14. c
15. c
16. b
17. d
18. d
19. c
20. a

1. Find the following limit.

$$\lim_{t\to 0^+}\left\langle 2\cos t,\ 6\sin t,\ 3t\ln t\right\rangle$$

Select the correct answer.

a. $\mathbf{r}(t)=2\mathbf{i}$ b. $\mathbf{r}(t)=2\mathbf{i}+6\mathbf{j}+3\mathbf{k}$ c. $\mathbf{r}(t)=2\mathbf{i}-3\mathbf{k}$ d. $\mathbf{r}(t)=2\mathbf{j}$ e. $\mathbf{r}(t)=2\mathbf{k}$

2. Let $\mathbf{r}(t)=\left\langle \sqrt{3-t},\ (e^t-1)/t,\ \ln(2t+1)\right\rangle$.

Find the domain of $\mathbf{r}$.

Select the correct answer.

a. $(-1/2,0)\cup(0,3]$ b. $[-1,0)\cup(0,3)$ c. $[2,\infty)$ d. $(-\infty,-1)$ e. $(-1,2]$

3. What force is required so that a particle of mass m has the following position function?

$\mathbf{r}(t)=3t^3\mathbf{i}+7t^2\mathbf{j}+9t^3\mathbf{k}$

Select the correct answer.

a. $\mathbf{F}(t)=9mt^2\mathbf{i}+14mt\mathbf{j}+27mt^2\mathbf{k}$
b. $\mathbf{F}(t)=mt^2\mathbf{i}+4mt\mathbf{j}+27mt^2\mathbf{k}$
c. $\mathbf{F}(t)=18mt\mathbf{i}+14m\mathbf{j}+54t\mathbf{k}$
d. $\mathbf{F}(t)=18mt\mathbf{i}+14m\mathbf{j}+54mt\mathbf{k}$
e. $\mathbf{F}(t)=27mt\mathbf{i}+14m\mathbf{j}+18mt\mathbf{k}$

4. A projectile is fired with an initial speed of 287 m/s and angle of elevation 16°. Find the range of the projectile.

Select the correct answer.

a. $d\approx 10$ km b. $d\approx 28$ km c. $d\approx 40$ km d. $d\approx 4.4$ km e. $d\approx 16$ km

5. A force with magnitude 12 N acts directly upward from the *xy*-plane on an object with mass 3 kg. The object starts at the origin with initial velocity $\mathbf{v}(0)=3\mathbf{i}-4\mathbf{j}$. Find its position function.

Select the correct answer.

a. $\mathbf{r}(t)=3t\mathbf{i}-4t\mathbf{j}+2t^2\mathbf{k}$
b. $\mathbf{r}(t)=3t^2\mathbf{i}-4t^2\mathbf{j}+2t^3\mathbf{k}$
c. $\mathbf{r}(t)=3t\mathbf{i}-4t\mathbf{j}+4t^2\mathbf{k}$
d. $\mathbf{r}(t)=3\mathbf{i}-4\mathbf{j}+2t^2\mathbf{k}$
e. $\mathbf{r}(t)=3t^3\mathbf{i}-4\mathbf{j}+2t^2\mathbf{k}$

6. Find a vector function that represents the curve of intersection of the two surfaces: the top half of the ellipsoid $x^2 + 6y^2 + 6z^2 = 36$ and the parabolic cylinder $y = x^2$.

Select the correct answer.

a. $\mathbf{r}(t) = t\mathbf{i} + t^2\mathbf{j} + \sqrt{\dfrac{6 - t^2 - 6t^4}{6}}\mathbf{k}$

b. $\mathbf{r}(t) = t\mathbf{i} + t^4\mathbf{j} + \sqrt{\dfrac{36 - t^2 - 6t}{6}}\mathbf{k}$

c. $\mathbf{r}(t) = t\mathbf{i} + t^2\mathbf{j} + \sqrt{\dfrac{36 - t^2 - 6t^4}{6}}\mathbf{k}$

d. $\mathbf{r}(t) = t\mathbf{i} + t^2\mathbf{j} + \sqrt{\dfrac{36 - t^2 - 6t}{6}}\mathbf{k}$

e. $\mathbf{r}(t) = t\mathbf{i} - t^2\mathbf{j} - \sqrt{\dfrac{36 - t^2 - 6t}{6}}\mathbf{k}$

7. A particle moves with position function $\mathbf{r}(t) = (21t - 7t^3 - 2)\mathbf{i} + 21t^2\mathbf{j}$.

Find the tangential component of the acceleration vector.

Select the correct answer.

a. $a_T = 42t + 2$ b. $a_T = 21t$ c. $a_T = -42t$ d. $a_T = 42t$ e. $a_T = 242t$

8. Find $\mathbf{r}(t)$ if $\mathbf{r}'(t) = \sin t\mathbf{i} - \cos t\mathbf{j} + 6t\mathbf{k}$ and $\mathbf{r}(0) = \mathbf{i} + \mathbf{j} + 5\mathbf{k}$.

Select the correct answer.

a. $(-\cos t + 2)\mathbf{i} - (\sin t - 1)\mathbf{j} + (3t^2 + 5)\mathbf{k}$
b. $(-\cos t + 2)\mathbf{i} + (\sin t + 1)\mathbf{j} + (3t^2 + 5)\mathbf{k}$
c. $(\cos t)\mathbf{i} - (\sin t - 1)\mathbf{j} + (3t^2 + 5)\mathbf{k}$
d. $(\cos t)\mathbf{i} + (\sin t + 1)\mathbf{j} + (3t^2 + 5)\mathbf{k}$
e. $(-\cos t + 1)\mathbf{i} - (\sin t - 1)\mathbf{j} + (3t^2 + 5)\mathbf{k}$

9. Use Simpson's Rule with $n = 4$ to estimate the length of the arc of the curve with equations $x = \sqrt{t}$, $y = \dfrac{4}{t}$, $z = t^2 + 1$, from (1, 4, 2) to (2, 1, 17). Round your answer to four decimal places.

Select the correct answer.

a. 7.4106
b. 7.2041
c. 14.824
d. 6.5706
e. none of these

10. If $\mathbf{r}(t)=\mathbf{i}+t\cos\pi t\,\mathbf{j}+\sin\pi t\,\mathbf{k}$, evaluate $\int_0^1 \mathbf{r}(t)\,dt$.

Select the correct answer.

a. $\mathbf{i}-\frac{2}{\pi^2}\mathbf{j}+\frac{2}{\pi}\mathbf{k}$

b. $\frac{2}{\pi^2}\mathbf{j}+\frac{2}{\pi}\mathbf{k}$

c. $\frac{2}{\pi^2}\mathbf{i}-\mathbf{j}+\frac{\pi}{2}\mathbf{k}$

d. $\mathbf{i}-\frac{1}{\pi}\mathbf{j}+\frac{1}{\pi}\mathbf{k}$

e. $2\mathbf{i}-\frac{1}{\pi^2}\mathbf{j}+\frac{\pi}{2}\mathbf{k}$

11. Reparametrize the curve with respect to arc length measured from the point where $t=0$ in the direction of increasing t.

$\mathbf{r}(t)=(7+3t)\mathbf{i}+(8+9t)\mathbf{j}-(6t)\mathbf{k}$

Select the correct answer.

a. $\mathbf{r}(t(s))=(7+\frac{3}{\sqrt{116}}s)\mathbf{i}+(8+\frac{9}{\sqrt{116}}s)\mathbf{j}-(6s)\mathbf{k}$

b. $\mathbf{r}(t(s))=(7+\frac{3}{\sqrt{136}}s)\mathbf{i}+(8+\frac{9}{\sqrt{136}}s)\mathbf{j}-(6s)\mathbf{k}$

c. $\mathbf{r}(t(s))=(7+\frac{3}{\sqrt{126}}s)\mathbf{i}+(8+\frac{9}{\sqrt{126}}s)\mathbf{j}-(\frac{6s}{\sqrt{126}})\mathbf{k}$

d. $\mathbf{r}(t(s))=(7-\frac{3}{\sqrt{126}}s)\mathbf{i}-(8+\frac{9}{\sqrt{126}}s)\mathbf{j}+(\frac{6s}{\sqrt{126}})\mathbf{k}$

e. $\mathbf{r}(t(s))=(7-\frac{3}{\sqrt{116}}s)\mathbf{i}-(8+\frac{s}{\sqrt{116}})\mathbf{j}+(\frac{6s}{\sqrt{126}})\mathbf{k}$

12. Find parametric equations for the tangent line to the curve with the given parametric equations at the specified point.

$x=\cos t,\ y=4e^{6t},\ z=4e^{-6t};\ (1,\ 4,\ 4)$

Select the correct answer.

a. $x=t,\ y=4+24t,\ z=4-24t$

b. $x=1,\ y=4-24t,\ z=4+24t$

c. $x=t,\ y=4+24t,\ z=4+24t$

d. $x=1,\ y=4+24t,\ z=4-24t$

e. $x=0,\ y=4+6t,\ z=4-6t$

13. A particle moves with position function $\mathbf{r}(t) = 2\sqrt{2}\,t\,\mathbf{i} + e^{2t}\mathbf{j} + e^{-2t}\mathbf{k}$. Find the speed of the particle.

Select the correct answer.

a. $2(e^{2t} + e^{2t})$ b. $2(e^{2t} + e^{-2t})$ c. $2e^{2t} + e^{-2t}$ d. $e^{2t} + e^{-2t}$ e. $e^{2t} - 2e^{-2t}$

14. A particle moves with position function $\mathbf{r}(t) = (18t - 6t^3 + 2)\mathbf{i} + 18t^2\mathbf{j}$.

Find the tangential component of the acceleration vector.

Select the correct answer.

a. $a_T = 36\,t + 2$ b. $a_T = 36\,t$ c. $a_T = 18\,t$ d. $a_T = -36\,t$ e. $a_T = -48\,t$

15. Find $\mathbf{r}''(t)$ for the function given.

$\mathbf{r}(t) = 2\mathbf{i} + \sin t\,\mathbf{j} + \cos t\,\mathbf{k}$

Select the correct answer.

a. $\mathbf{r}''(t) = \cos t\,\mathbf{j} - \sin t\,\mathbf{k}$
b. $\mathbf{r}''(t) = -\cos t\,\mathbf{j} - \sin t\,\mathbf{k}$
c. $\mathbf{r}''(t) = -\sin t\,\mathbf{j} - \cos t\,\mathbf{k}$
d. $\mathbf{r}''(t) = \sin t\,\mathbf{j} - \cos t\,\mathbf{k}$
e. $\mathbf{r}''(t) = -\sin t\,\mathbf{j} + \cos t\,\mathbf{k}$

16. The curvature of the curve given by the vector function $\mathbf{r}$ is

$$\mathbf{k}(t) = \frac{|\mathbf{r}'(t) \times \mathbf{r}''(t)|}{|\mathbf{r}'(t)|^3}$$

Find the curvature of $\mathbf{r}(t) = \left\langle \sqrt{15}t,\, e^t,\, e^{-t} \right\rangle$ at the point (0, 1, 1).

Select the correct answer.

a. $\sqrt{2}/19$ b. $17\sqrt{2}$ c. $\sqrt{2}/17$ d. 1/17 e. $\sqrt{15}/17$

17. Find the velocity of a particle that has the given acceleration and the given initial velocity.

$\mathbf{a}(t) = 2\mathbf{k},\ \ \mathbf{v}(0) = 10\mathbf{i} - 9\mathbf{j}$

Select the correct answer.

a. $\mathbf{v}(t) = (10t - 9)\mathbf{i} + 2t\mathbf{k}$
b. $\mathbf{v}(t) = 10\mathbf{i} - 9\mathbf{j} + 2\mathbf{k}$
c. $\mathbf{v}(t) = 9\mathbf{i} - 10\mathbf{j} + 2t\mathbf{k}$
d. $\mathbf{v}(t) = 10\mathbf{i} - 9\mathbf{j} + 2t\mathbf{k}$
e. $\mathbf{v}(t) = 10\mathbf{i} - \mathbf{j} + 2t\mathbf{k}$

18. Find the unit tangent vector for the curve given by $\mathbf{r}(t) = \left\langle \frac{1}{5}t^5, \frac{1}{2}t^2, t \right\rangle$.

Select the correct answer.

a. $\dfrac{\langle 5t^4, 2t, t \rangle}{\sqrt{25t^8 + 4t^2 + 1}}$ b. $\dfrac{\langle t^5, t^2, 1 \rangle}{\sqrt{t^{10} + t^2 + 1}}$ c. $\dfrac{\langle t^4, t, 1 \rangle}{\sqrt{t^{16} + t^2 + 1}}$ d. $\dfrac{\langle t^4, t, 1 \rangle}{\sqrt{t^8 + t^2 + 1}}$ e. none of these

19. The helix $\mathbf{r}_1(t) = \cos t\,\mathbf{i} + \sin t\,\mathbf{j} + t\,\mathbf{k}$ intersects the curve $\mathbf{r}_2(t) = (1+t)\mathbf{i} + t^2\mathbf{j} + t^3\,\mathbf{k}$ at the point (1, 0, 0). Find the angle of intersection.

Select the correct answer.

a. 0 b. $1/2$ c. π d. $\pi/4$ e. $\pi/2$

20. The figure shows a curve C given by a vector function **r**(t). Choose the correct expression for $\mathbf{r}'(4)$.

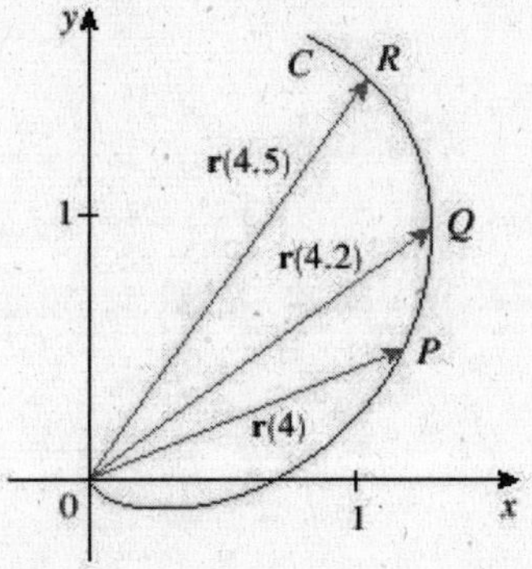

Select the correct answer.

a. $\lim\limits_{h \to 0} \dfrac{\mathbf{r}(4-h) - \mathbf{r}(4)}{h}$

b. $\lim\limits_{h \to 0} \dfrac{\mathbf{r}(4+h) - \mathbf{r}(4)}{h}$

c. $\lim\limits_{h \to 0} \dfrac{\mathbf{r}(4+h) + \mathbf{r}(4)}{h}$

d. $\lim\limits_{h \to 0} \dfrac{\mathbf{r}(4-h) + \mathbf{r}(4)}{h}$

e. $\lim\limits_{h \to 0} \dfrac{\mathbf{r}(4-h) + \mathbf{r}(h)}{h}$

ANSWER KEY

Stewart - Calculus ET 7e Chapter 13 Form D

1. a
2. a
3. d
4. d
5. a
6. c
7. d
8. a
9. e
10. a
11. c
12. d
13. b
14. b
15. c
16. c
17. d
18. d
19. e
20. b

1. Let $\mathbf{r}(t) = \left\langle \sqrt{t+3},\ (e^{2t}-1)/t,\ \ln(2t-1) \right\rangle$.

Find the domain of $\mathbf{r}$.

Select the correct answer.

a. $(1/2, \infty)$
b. $(1/2, 3]$
c. $[1/2, 0) \cup (0, 3]$
d. $[-3, 0) \cup (0, 1/2]$
e. none of these

2. Find a vector function that represents the curve of intersection of the two surfaces. The circular cylinder $x^2 + y^2 = 4$ and the parabolic cylinder $z = x^2$.

3. Find the derivative of the vector function.

$\mathbf{r}(t) = \mathbf{a} + t\,\mathbf{b} + t^2\mathbf{c}$

4. Find parametric equations for the tangent line to the curve with the given parametric equations at the specified point.

$x = t^8,\ \ y = t^3,\ \ z = t^7;\ \ (1, 1, 1)$

Select the correct answer.

a. $x = 1 - 7t,\ \ y = 1 - 2t,\ \ z = 1 - 6t$
b. $x = 1 + 7t,\ \ y = 1 + 2t,\ \ z = 1 + 6t$
c. $x = 1 + 8t,\ \ y = 1 + 3t,\ \ z = 1 + 7t$
d. $x = 1 - 8t,\ \ y = 1 - 3t,\ \ z = 1 - 7t$
e. $x = 8t,\ \ y = 3t,\ \ z = 7t$

5. The curves $\mathrm{r}_1(t) = \langle t, t^5, t^3 \rangle$ and $\mathrm{r}_2(t) = \langle \sin t, \sin 4t, t \rangle$ intersect at the origin.

Find their angle of intersection correct to the nearest degree.

6. Find $\mathbf{r}(t)$ if $\mathbf{r}'(t) = t^9\mathbf{i} + 4t^3\mathbf{j} - t^5\mathbf{k}$ and $\boldsymbol{r}(0) = \mathbf{j}$.

7. If $\mathbf{u}(t) = \mathbf{i} - 3t^2\mathbf{j} + 6t^3\mathbf{k}$ and $\mathbf{v}(t) = t\mathbf{i} - \cos t\mathbf{j} + \sin t\mathbf{k}$, find $\dfrac{d}{dt}[\mathbf{u}(t)\cdot\mathbf{v}(t)]$.

8. Use Simpson's Rule with $n = 10$ to estimate the length of the arc of the twisted cubic $x = t,\ y = t^2\ z = t^3$, from the origin to the point (2, 4, 8). Round your answer to four decimal places.

Select the correct answer.

a. 9.5706 b. 19.5706 c. 7.5706 d. 8.5706 e. 10.5706

9. Reparametrize the curve with respect to arc length measured from the point where $t = 0$ in the direction of increasing t.

$\mathbf{r}(t) = 8\sin t\mathbf{i} + t\mathbf{j} + 8\cos t\mathbf{k}$

10. Find the unit tangent vector $T(t)$.

$\mathbf{r}(t) = \langle 4\sin t, 9t, 4\cos t \rangle$

11. A force with magnitude 40 N acts directly upward from the xy-plane on an object with mass 5 kg. The object starts at the origin with initial velocity $\mathbf{v}(0) = 5\mathbf{i} - 4\mathbf{j}$. Find its position function.

12. Find the curvature of the curve $y = x^4$ at the point $(-1, 1)$.

Select the correct answer.

a. $\frac{3}{16}$ b. $\frac{16}{3^{3/2}}$ c. $\frac{12}{17^{3/2}}$ d. $\frac{-12}{17^{2/3}}$ e. none of these

13. At what point on the curve $x = t^3,\ y = 3t,\ z = t^4$ is the normal plane parallel to the plane $9x + 9y - 12z = 7$?

14. Find the velocity of a particle with the given position function.

$\mathbf{r}(t) = 13e^{15t}\mathbf{i} + 10e^{-18t}\mathbf{j}$

15. What force is required so that a particle of mass m has the following position function?

$\mathbf{r}(t) = 5t^3\mathbf{i} + 2t^2\mathbf{j} + 7t^3\mathbf{k}$

16. Find the speed of a particle with the given position function.

$\mathbf{r}(t) = t\mathbf{i} + 6t^2\mathbf{j} + 2t^6\mathbf{k}$

Select the correct answer.

a. $|v(t)| = \sqrt{1 + 12t + 12t^5}$

b. $|v(t)| = 1 + 144t^2 + 144t^{10}$

c. $|v(t)| = 1 + 12t + 12t^5$

d. $|v(t)| = \sqrt{1 + 144t^2 + 144t^{10}}$

e. $|v(t)| = \sqrt{1 + 144t + 144t^5}$

17. The position function of a particle is given by $\mathbf{r}(t) = \langle 8t^2, 2t, 8t^2 - 96t \rangle$.

When is the speed a minimum?

18. A ball is thrown at an angle of 15° to the ground. If the ball lands 67 m away, what was the initial speed of the ball? Let $g = 9.8\ \text{m/s}^2$.

19. A particle moves with position function $\mathbf{r}(t) = (12t - 4t^3 - 2)\mathbf{i} + 12t^2\mathbf{j}$.

Find the tangential component of the acceleration vector.

20. A particle moves with position function $\mathbf{r}(t) = 8\cos t\mathbf{i} + 8\sin t\mathbf{j} + 8t\mathbf{k}$.

Find the normal component of the acceleration vector.

ANSWER KEY

Stewart - Calculus ET 7e Chapter 13 Form E

1. a

2. $\mathbf{r}(t) = 2\cos t\,\mathbf{i} + 2\sin t\,\mathbf{j} + 4\cos^2 t\,\mathbf{k}$

3. $\mathbf{b} + 2t\mathbf{c}$

4. c

5. 76°

6. $\frac{t^{10}}{10}\mathbf{i} + (t^4 + 1)\mathbf{j} - \frac{t^6}{6}\mathbf{k}$

7. $1 + 6t\cos t + 15t^2 \sin t + 6t^3 \cos t$

8. a

9. $\mathbf{r}(t(s)) = 8\sin\left(\frac{s}{\sqrt{65}}\right)\mathbf{i} + \left(\frac{s}{\sqrt{65}}\right)\mathbf{j} + 8\cos\left(\frac{s}{\sqrt{65}}\right)\mathbf{k}$

10. $\left\langle \frac{4}{\sqrt{97}}\cos t, \frac{9}{\sqrt{97}}, \frac{-4}{\sqrt{97}}\sin t \right\rangle$

11. $\mathbf{r}(t) = 5t\mathbf{i} - 4t\mathbf{j} + 4t^2\mathbf{k}$

12. c

13. (–1, –3, 1)

14. $\mathbf{v} = 195e^{15t}\mathbf{i} - 180e^{-18t}\mathbf{j}$

15. $\mathbf{F} = m(30t\mathbf{i} + 4\mathbf{j} + 42t\mathbf{k})$

16. d

17. $t = 3$

18. 36.2

19. $24t$

20. 8

1. Let $\mathbf{r}(t) = \left\langle \sqrt{2-t},\ (e^t - 1)/t,\ \ln(t+1) \right\rangle$.

   Find the domain of $\mathbf{r}$.

2. Find the following limit:

   $\lim_{t\to\infty} \left\langle \arctan t,\ e^{-4t},\ (\ln t)/t \right\rangle$

3. A particle moves with position function $\mathbf{r}(t) = 2\cos t\mathbf{i} + 2\sin t\mathbf{j} + 2t\mathbf{k}$.

   Find the normal component of the acceleration vector.

4. Find the unit tangent vector for the curve given by $\mathbf{r}(t) = \left\langle \frac{1}{5}t^5,\ \frac{1}{2}t^2,\ t \right\rangle$.

   Select the correct answer.

   a. $\dfrac{\langle 5t^4, 2t, t\rangle}{\sqrt{25t^8 + 4t^2 + 1}}$ b. $\dfrac{\langle t^5, t^2, 1\rangle}{\sqrt{t^{10} + t^2 + 1}}$ c. $\dfrac{\langle t^4, t, 1\rangle}{\sqrt{t^{16} + t^2 + 1}}$ d. $\dfrac{\langle t^4, t, 1\rangle}{\sqrt{t^8 + t^2 + 1}}$ e. none of these

5. What force is required so that a particle of mass m has the following position function?

   $\mathbf{r}(t) = 3t^3\mathbf{i} + 7t^2\mathbf{j} + 9t^3\mathbf{k}$

   Select the correct answer.

   a. $\mathbf{F}(t) = 9mt^2\mathbf{i} + 14mt\mathbf{j} + 27mt^2\mathbf{k}$
   b. $\mathbf{F}(t) = mt^2\mathbf{i} + 4mt\mathbf{j} + 27mt^2\mathbf{k}$
   c. $\mathbf{F}(t) = 18mt\mathbf{i} + 14m\mathbf{j} + 54t\mathbf{k}$
   d. $\mathbf{F}(t) = 18mt\mathbf{i} + 14m\mathbf{j} + 54mt\mathbf{k}$
   e. $\mathbf{F}(t) = 27mt\mathbf{i} + 14m\mathbf{j} + 18mt\mathbf{k}$

6. Find a vector function that represents the curve of intersection of the two surfaces:
   The top half of the ellipsoid $x^2 + 6y^2 + 6z^2 = 36$ and the parabolic cylinder $y = x^2$.

   Select the correct answer.

   a. $\mathbf{r}(t) = t\mathbf{i} + t^2\mathbf{j} + \sqrt{\dfrac{6 - t^2 - 6t^4}{6}}\mathbf{k}$

   b. $\mathbf{r}(t) = t\mathbf{i} + t^4\mathbf{j} + \sqrt{\dfrac{36 - t^2 - 6t}{6}}\mathbf{k}$

   c. $\mathbf{r}(t) = t\mathbf{i} + t^2\mathbf{j} + \sqrt{\dfrac{36 - t^2 - 6t^4}{6}}\mathbf{k}$

   d. $\mathbf{r}(t) = t\mathbf{i} + t^2\mathbf{j} + \sqrt{\dfrac{36 - t^2 - 6t}{6}}\mathbf{k}$

   e. $\mathbf{r}(t) = t\mathbf{i} - t^2\mathbf{j} - \sqrt{\dfrac{36 - t^2 - 6t}{6}}\mathbf{k}$

7. Find a vector function that represents the curve of intersection of the two surfaces:

The cylinder $x^2 + y^2 = 9$ and the surface $z = xy$.

8. Find a vector function that represents the curve of intersection of the two surfaces:

The circular cylinder $x^2 + y^2 = 4$ and the parabolic cylinder $z = x^2$.

9. Find the derivative of the vector function.

$\mathbf{r}(t) = \mathbf{a} + t\,\mathbf{b} + t^2\mathbf{c}$

10. Find the point of intersection of the tangent lines to the curve $\mathbf{r}(t) = \langle \sin \pi t,\ 5\sin \pi t,\ \cos \pi t \rangle$, at the points where $t = 0$ and $t = 0.5$.

11. The curves $\mathbf{r}_1(t) = \langle t,\ t^6,\ t^7 \rangle$ and $\mathbf{r}_2(t) = \langle \sin t,\ \sin 5t,\ t \rangle$ intersect at the origin. Find their angle of intersection correct to the nearest degree.

12. If $\mathbf{r}(t) = t^2\mathbf{i} + t\cos \pi t\,\mathbf{j} + \sin \pi t\,\mathbf{k}$, evaluate $\int_0^1 \mathbf{r}(t)\,dt$.

13. Reparametrize the curve with respect to arc length measured from the point where $t = 0$ in the direction of increasing t.

$\mathbf{r}(t) = 8\sin t\mathbf{i} + t\mathbf{j} + 8\cos t\mathbf{k}$

14. The curvature of the curve given by the vector function $\mathbf{r}$ is

$$k(t) = \frac{|\mathbf{r}'(t) \times \mathbf{r}''(t)|}{|\mathbf{r}'(t)|^3}$$

Find the curvature of $\mathbf{r}(t) = \left\langle \sqrt{15}t,\ e^t,\ e^{-t} \right\rangle$ at the point (0, 1, 1).

15. Find the velocity of a particle with the given position function.

$\mathbf{r}(t) = 10e^{7t}\mathbf{i} + 7e^{-12t}\mathbf{j}$

Select the correct answer.

a. $\mathbf{v}(t) = 70e^{t}\mathbf{i} - 84e^{-t}\mathbf{j}$

b. $\mathbf{v}(t) = 10e^{7t}\mathbf{i} - 7e^{-12t}\mathbf{j}$

c. $\mathbf{v}(t) = 70e^{7t}\mathbf{i} - 84e^{-12t}\mathbf{j}$

d. $\mathbf{v}(t) = 17e^{7t}\mathbf{i} + 19e^{-12t}\mathbf{j}$

e. $\mathbf{v}(t) = 17e^{7t}\mathbf{i} + e^{-12t}\mathbf{j}$

16. Find equations of the normal plane to $x = t,\ y = t^2,\ z = t^3$ at the point (3, 9, 27).

17. Find the acceleration of a particle with the given position function.

$\mathbf{r}(t) = -2\sin t\mathbf{i} + 6t\mathbf{j} - 4\cos t\mathbf{k}$

18. A projectile is fired with an initial speed of 834 m/s and angle of elevation 38°. Find the range of the projectile.

Select the correct answer.

a. $d \approx 42$ km
b. $d \approx 34$ km
c. $d \approx 11$ km
d. $d \approx 69$ km
e. $d \approx 58$ km

19. A ball is thrown at an angle of 15° to the ground. If the ball lands 126 m away, what was the initial speed of the ball? Let $g = 9.8\ \text{m/s}^2$.

Select the correct answer.

a. $v_0 \approx$ 49.7 m/s
b. $v_0 \approx$ 16.6 m/s
c. $v_0 \approx$ 99.4 m/s
d. $v_0 \approx$ 24.8 m/s
e. $v_0 \approx$ 24.1 m/s

20. A particle moves with position function $\mathbf{r}(t) = (9t - 3t^3 - 2)\mathbf{i} + 9t^2\mathbf{j}$.

Find the tangential component of the acceleration vector.

ANSWER KEY

Stewart - Calculus ET 7e Chapter 13 Form F

1. $(-1,0)\cup(0,2]$

2. $\mathbf{r}(t)=\frac{\pi}{2}\mathbf{i}$

3. 2

4. d

5. d

6. c

7. $\mathbf{r}(t)=3\cos t\mathbf{i}+3\sin t\mathbf{j}+9\sin t\cos t\mathbf{k}$

8. $\mathbf{r}(t)=2\cos t\,\mathbf{i}+2\sin t\,\mathbf{j}+4\cos^2 t\,\mathbf{k}$

9. $\mathbf{b}+2t\mathbf{c}$

10. $\left(1,\ 5,\ 1\right)$

11. 79°

12. $\frac{1}{3}\mathbf{i}-\left(\frac{2}{\pi^2}\right)\mathbf{j}+\left(\frac{2}{\pi}\right)\mathbf{k}$

13. $\mathbf{r}(t(s))=8\sin\left(\frac{s}{\sqrt{65}}\right)\mathbf{i}+\left(\frac{s}{\sqrt{65}}\right)\mathbf{j}+8\cos\left(\frac{s}{\sqrt{65}}\right)\mathbf{k}$

14. $\frac{\sqrt{2}}{17}$

15. c

16. $x+6y+27z-786=0$

17. $\mathbf{a}(t)=2\sin t\mathbf{i}+4\cos t\mathbf{k}$

18. d

19. a

20. $18t$

1. Find the following limit.

$$\lim_{t \to 0^+} \langle 2\cos t,\ 6\sin t,\ 3t\ln t \rangle$$

Select the correct answer.

a. $\mathbf{r}(t) = 2\mathbf{i}$ b. $\mathbf{r}(t) = 2\mathbf{i} + 6\mathbf{j} + 3\mathbf{k}$ c. $\mathbf{r}(t) = 2\mathbf{i} - 3\mathbf{k}$ d. $\mathbf{r}(t) = 2\mathbf{j}$ e. $\mathbf{r}(t) = 2\mathbf{k}$

2. If $\mathbf{r}(t) = t^3\mathbf{i} + t\cos\pi t\,\mathbf{j} + \sin\pi t\,\mathbf{k}$, evaluate $\int_0^1 \mathbf{r}(t)\,dt$.

3. Find $\mathbf{r}'(t)$ for the function given.

$\mathbf{r}(t) = 2\mathbf{i} + \sin t\,\mathbf{j} + \cos t\,\mathbf{k}$

4. The curves $\mathbf{r}_1(t) = \langle t, t^6, t^7 \rangle$ and $\mathbf{r}_2(t) = \langle \sin t, \sin 5t, t \rangle$ intersect at the origin. Find their angle of intersection correct to the nearest degree.

5. A force with magnitude 24 N acts directly upward from the *xy*-plane on an object with mass 4 kg. The object starts at the origin with initial velocity $\mathbf{v}(0) = 8\mathbf{i} - 2\mathbf{j}$. Find its position function.

6. Find a vector function that represents the curve of intersection of the two surfaces: The circular cylinder $x^2 + y^2 = 4$ and the parabolic cylinder $z = x^2$.

Select the correct answer.

a. $\mathbf{r}(t) = 2\cos t\,\mathbf{i} + 2\sin t\,\mathbf{j} + 4\cos^2 t\,\mathbf{k}$

b. $\mathbf{r}(t) = 4\cos t\,\mathbf{i} + 4t\,\mathbf{j} + 4\cos^2 t\,\mathbf{k}$

c. $\mathbf{r}(t) = \cos t\,\mathbf{i} + \sin t\,\mathbf{j} - 4\cos^2 t\,\mathbf{k}$

d. $\mathbf{r}(t) = 4\cos t\,\mathbf{i} - \sin t\,\mathbf{j} - 4\cos^2 t\,\mathbf{k}$

e. $\mathbf{r}(t) = \mathbf{i} + \mathbf{j} + 16\cos^2 t\,\mathbf{k}$

7. Use Simpson's Rule with $n = 4$ to estimate the length of the arc of the curve with equations $x = \sqrt{t}$, $y = \dfrac{4}{t}$, $z = t^2 + 1$, from (1, 4, 2) to (2, 1, 17). Round your answer to four decimal places.

Select the correct answer.

a. 7.4106 b. 7.2041 c. 14.8241 d. 6.5706 e. none of these

8. Find the point of intersection of the tangent lines to the curve $\mathbf{r}(t) = \langle \sin\pi t,\ 8\sin\pi t,\ \cos\pi t \rangle$, at the points where $t = 0$ and $t = 0.5$.

9. The curvature of the curve given by the vector function $\mathbf{r}$ is

$$\mathbf{k}(t) = \frac{|\mathbf{r}'(t) \times \mathbf{r}''(t)|}{|\mathbf{r}'(t)|^3}$$

Find the curvature of $\mathbf{r}(t) = \langle \sqrt{15}t, e^t, e^{-t} \rangle$ at the point (0, 1, 1).

10. Find the curvature of the curve $y = x^3$ at the point (1, 1) .

11. At what point on the curve $x = t^3,\ y = 3t,\ z = t^4$ is the normal plane parallel to the plane $3x + 3y - 4z = 9$?

Select the correct answer.

a. (–1, –3, 9)
b. (–1, –3, 1)
c. (–9, 3, 1)
d. (9, 3, –2)
e. (–1, 3, 9)

12. Find the unit tangent vector for the curve given by $\mathbf{r}(t) = \langle t^4/4,\ t^3/3,\ t \rangle$.

13. Find the speed of a particle with the given position function.

$\mathbf{r}(t) = 5\sqrt{2}t\mathbf{i} + e^{5t}\mathbf{j} - e^{-5t}\mathbf{k}$

Select the correct answer.

a. $|\mathbf{v}(t)| = (e^{5t} + e^{-5t})$
b. $|\mathbf{v}(t)| = \sqrt{10 + 5e^{t} + 5e^{-t}}$
c. $|\mathbf{v}(t)| = \sqrt{10 + e^{10t} + e^{-10t}}$
d. $|\mathbf{v}(t)| = 5(e^{5t} + e^{-5t})$
e. $|\mathbf{v}(t)| = 5(e^{t} + e^{-t})$

14. A force with magnitude 40 N acts directly upward from the *xy*-plane on an object with mass 5 kg. The object starts at the origin with initial velocity $\mathbf{v}(0) = 5\mathbf{i} - 4\mathbf{j}$. Find its position function.

15. Find the position vector of a particle that has the given acceleration and the given initial velocity and position.

$\mathbf{a}(t) = -4\mathbf{k},\ \mathbf{v}(0) = \mathbf{i} + \mathbf{j} - 10\mathbf{k},\ \mathbf{r}(0) = 2\mathbf{i} + 9\mathbf{j}$

16. The position function of a particle is given by $\mathbf{r}(t) = \langle 5t^2,\ 10t,\ 5t^2 - 40t \rangle$. When is the speed a minimum?

17. What force is required so that a particle of mass *m* has the following position function?

$\mathbf{r}(t) = 3t^3\mathbf{i} + 7t^2\mathbf{j} + 9t^3\mathbf{k}$

Select the correct answer.

a. $\mathbf{F}(t) = 9mt^2\mathbf{i} + 14mt\mathbf{j} + 27mt^2\mathbf{k}$
b. $\mathbf{F}(t) = mt^2\mathbf{i} + 4mt\mathbf{j} + 27mt^2\mathbf{k}$
c. $\mathbf{F}(t) = 18mt\mathbf{i} + 14m\mathbf{j} + 54t\mathbf{k}$
d. $\mathbf{F}(t) = 18mt\mathbf{i} + 14m\mathbf{j} + 54mt\mathbf{k}$
e. $\mathbf{F}(t) = 27mt\mathbf{i} + 14m\mathbf{j} + 18mt\mathbf{k}$

18. A projectile is fired with an initial speed of 748 m/s and angle of elevation 28°. Find the range of the projectile in kilometers. Round your answer to the nearest integer.

19. A particle moves with position function $\mathbf{r}(t) = (9t - 3t^3 - 2)\mathbf{i} + 9t^2\mathbf{j}$.

Find the tangential component of the acceleration vector.

20. A particle moves with position function $\mathbf{r}(t) = 8\cos t\mathbf{i} + 8\sin t\mathbf{j} + 8t\mathbf{k}$.

Find the normal component of the acceleration vector.

ANSWER KEY

Stewart - Calculus ET 7e Chapter 13 Form G

1. a

2. $\frac{1}{4}\mathbf{i}-\left(\frac{2}{\pi^2}\right)\mathbf{j}+\left(\frac{2}{\pi}\right)\mathbf{k}$

3. $\mathbf{r}'(t)=\cos t\,\mathbf{j}-\sin t\,\mathbf{k}$

4. 79°

5. $\mathbf{r}(t)=8t\mathbf{i}\text{-}2t\mathbf{j}+3t^2\mathbf{k}$

6. a

7. e

8. (1, 8, 1)

9. $\frac{\sqrt{2}}{17}$

10. $\frac{3\sqrt{10}}{50}$

11. b

12. $\frac{\langle t^3, t^2, 1\rangle}{\sqrt{t^6+t^4+1}}$

13. d

14. $\mathbf{r}(t)=5t\mathbf{i}-4t\mathbf{j}+4t^2\mathbf{k}$

15. $\mathbf{r}(t)=(t+2)\mathbf{i}+(t+9)\mathbf{j}-(2t^2+10t)\mathbf{k}$

16. $t=2$

17. d

18. 47 km

19. $18t$

20. 8

1. Find a vector function that represents the curve of intersection of the two surfaces.
The circular cylinder $x^2 + y^2 = 4$ and the parabolic cylinder $z = x^2$.

2. Choose the point that is not on the given curve.

$\mathbf{r}(t) = (8+t)\mathbf{i} + 2t\mathbf{j} + t\mathbf{k}$

Select the correct answer.

a. (12, 8, 4) b. (6, –2, –1) c. (8, 0, 0) d. (11, 6, 3) e. (4, –8, –4)

3. If $\mathbf{r}(t) = \mathbf{i} + t\cos\pi t\,\mathbf{j} + \sin\pi t\,\mathbf{k}$, evaluate $\int_0^1 \mathbf{r}(t)\,dt$.

4. Find the point of intersection of the tangent lines to the curve $\mathbf{r}(t) = \langle \sin\pi t,\ 4\sin\pi t,\ \cos\pi t \rangle$, at the points where $t = 0$ and $t = 0.5$.

5. The curves $\mathbf{r}_1(t) = \langle t, t^6, t^7 \rangle$ and $\mathbf{r}_2(t) = \langle \sin t, \sin 5t, t \rangle$ intersect at the origin. Find their angle of intersection correct to the nearest degree.

6. If $\mathbf{u}(t) = \mathbf{i} - 3t^2\mathbf{j} + 6t^3\mathbf{k}$ and $\mathbf{v}(t) = t\mathbf{i} - \cos t\mathbf{j} + \sin t\mathbf{k}$, find $\frac{d}{dt}[\mathbf{u}(t)\cdot\mathbf{v}(t)]$.

7. Find the unit tangent vector $\mathbf{T}(t)$.

$\mathbf{r}(t) = \langle 4\sin t,\ 9t,\ 4\cos t \rangle$

8. Use *Simpson's Rule* with $n = 10$ to estimate the length of the arc of the twisted cubic $x = t,\ y = t^2,\ z = t^3$ from the origin to the point (2, 4, 8). Round the answer to four decimal places.

9. The curvature of the curve given by the vector function $\mathbf{r}$ is

$$\mathbf{k}(t) = \frac{|\mathbf{r}'(t)\times\mathbf{r}''(t)|}{|\mathbf{r}'(t)|^3}$$

Use the formula to find the curvature of $\mathbf{r}(t) = \langle \sqrt{15}t,\ e^t,\ e^{-t} \rangle$ at the point (0, 1, 1).

Select the correct answer.

a. $\frac{\sqrt{2}}{19}$ b. $17\sqrt{2}$ c. $\frac{\sqrt{2}}{17}$ d. $\frac{1}{17}$ e. $\frac{\sqrt{15}}{17}$

10. The position function of a particle is given by $\mathbf{r}(t) = \langle 8t^2,\ 2t,\ 8t^2 - 96t \rangle$. When is the speed a minimum?

11. Find the curvature of the curve $y = x^3$ at the point (1, 1).

12. Find the speed of a particle with the given position function.

$\mathbf{r}(t) = 5\sqrt{2}t\mathbf{i} + e^{5t}\mathbf{j} - e^{-5t}\mathbf{k}$

Select the correct answer.

a. $|\mathbf{v}(t)| = (e^{5t} + e^{-5t})$
b. $|\mathbf{v}(t)| = \sqrt{10 + 5e^{t} + 5e^{-t}}$
c. $|\mathbf{v}(t)| = \sqrt{10 + e^{10t} + e^{-10t}}$
d. $|\mathbf{v}(t)| = 5(e^{5t} + e^{-5t})$
e. $|\mathbf{v}(t)| = 5(e^{t} + e^{-t})$

13. Find the following limit.

$$\lim_{t\to\infty}\left\langle \arctan t,\ e^{-7t},\ \frac{\ln t}{t}\right\rangle$$

14. Find the unit tangent vector for the curve given by $\mathbf{r}(t) = \left\langle \frac{1}{3}t^3, \frac{1}{2}t^2, t\right\rangle$.

15. Find parametric equations for the tangent line to the curve with the given parametric equations at the specified point.

$x = t^8,\ y = t^3,\ z = t^7;\ (1, 1, 1)$

Select the correct answer.

a. $x = 1 - 7t,\ y = 1 - 2t,\ z = 1 - 6t$
b. $x = 1 + 7t,\ y = 1 + 2t,\ z = 1 + 6t$
c. $x = 1 + 8t,\ y = 1 + 3t,\ z = 1 + 7t$
d. $x = 1 - 8t,\ y = 1 - 3t,\ z = 1 - 7t$
e. $x = 8t,\ y = 3t,\ z = 7t$

16. Find the following limit.

$$\lim_{t\to 0^+}\langle 2\cos t,\ 6\sin t,\ 3t\ln t\rangle$$

Select the correct answer.

a. $\mathbf{r}(t) = 2\mathbf{i}$
b. $\mathbf{r}(t) = 2\mathbf{i} + 6\mathbf{j} + 3\mathbf{k}$
c. $\mathbf{r}(t) = 2\mathbf{i} - 3\mathbf{k}$
d. $\mathbf{r}(t) = 2\mathbf{j}$
e. $\mathbf{r}(t) = 2\mathbf{k}$

17. Let $\mathbf{r}(t) = \left\langle \sqrt{t-3},\ (e^{2t}-1)/t,\ \ln(2t+1) \right\rangle$.

Find the domain of $\mathbf{r}$.

18. Evaluate the integral.

$$\int (e^{6t}\mathbf{i} + 8t\mathbf{j} + \ln t\mathbf{k})\ dt$$

19. A ball is thrown at an angle of 75° to the ground. If the ball lands 53 m away, what was the initial speed of the ball? Let $g = 9.8\ \mathrm{m/s^2}$.

20. The following table gives coordinates of a particle moving through space along a smooth curve.

t	x	y	z
0.5	5.8	9.1	4.3
1	12.6	14.9	16.8
1.5	25.6	21.2	29.4
2	39.2	39.5	37.9
2.5	42.4	42.4	43

Find the average velocity over the time interval [0.5, 2.5].

Select the correct answer.

a. $\mathbf{v} = 18.3\ \mathbf{i} + 16.65\ \mathbf{j} + 19.35\ \mathbf{k}$
b. $\mathbf{v} = 26.6\ \mathbf{i} - 24.6\ \mathbf{j} - 21.1\ \mathbf{k}$
c. $\mathbf{v} = 13.6\ \mathbf{i} - 11.6\ \mathbf{j} + 25\ \mathbf{k}$
d. $\mathbf{v} = 19.8\ \mathbf{i} + 12.1\ \mathbf{j} - 25.1\ \mathbf{k}$
e. $\mathbf{v} = 21.1\ \mathbf{i} + 12.1\ \mathbf{j} - 11.6\ \mathbf{k}$

ANSWER KEY

Stewart - Calculus ET 7e Chapter 13 Form H

1. $\mathbf{r}(t) = 2\cos t\,\mathbf{i} + 2\sin t\,\mathbf{j} + 4\cos^2 t\,\mathbf{k}$

2. b

3. $\mathbf{i} - \left(\frac{2}{\pi^2}\right)\mathbf{j} + \left(\frac{2}{\pi}\right)\mathbf{k}$

4. (1, 4, 1)

5. 79 °

6. $1 + 6t\cos t + 15t^2 \sin t + 6t^3 \cos t$

7. $\left\langle \frac{4}{\sqrt{97}}\cos t, \frac{9}{\sqrt{97}}, \frac{-4}{\sqrt{97}}\sin t \right\rangle$

8. 9.5706

9. c

10. $t = 3$

11. $\frac{3\sqrt{10}}{50}$

12. d

13. $\mathbf{r}(t) = \frac{\pi}{2}\mathbf{i}$

14. $\frac{\langle t^2, t, 1 \rangle}{\sqrt{t^4 + t^2 + 1}}$

15. c

16. a

17. $[3, \infty)$

18. $\frac{e^{6t}}{6}\mathbf{i} + 4t^2\mathbf{j} + t(\ln t - 1)\mathbf{k} + C$

19. 32.2

20. a

1. The *temperature-humidity index I* (or humidex, for short) is the perceived air temperature when the actual temperature is T and the relative humidity is h, so we can write $I = f(T, h)$. The following table of values of I is an excerpt from a table compiled by the National Oceanic and Atmospheric Administration. For what value of T is $f(T, 50) = 82$?

T ↓ \ h →	20	30	40	50	60	70
80	74	76	78	82	83	86
85	81	82	84	86	90	94
90	86	90	93	96	101	106
95	94	94	98	107	111	125
100	99	101	109	122	129	138

2. Evaluate the limit.

$$\lim_{(x,y)\to(1,1)} \frac{3x^2y}{\sqrt{x^2+2y^2}}$$

3. Find $h(x, y) = g(f(x, y))$, if $g(t) = t^2 + \sqrt{t}$ and $f(x, y) = 8x + 7y - 6$.

4. Find f_x for $f(x, y) = 3x^5 + 2x^3y^2 + 9xy^4$.

5. Find the first partial derivatives of the function.

$$c = \ln\left(a + \sqrt{a^2 + b^2}\right)$$

6. Find the linearization $L(x, y)$ of the function at the given point.

$$f(x, y) = x\sqrt{y}, \quad (-5,\ 4)$$

Round the answers to the nearest hundredth.

7. Find the differential of the function.

$$u = e^{5t}\sin 3x$$

8. Find f_x for $f(x, y) = 7x^5 + 6x^3y^2 + 7xy^4$.

9. Find $\dfrac{\partial^2 z}{\partial x^2}$ for $z = y\tan 8x$.

10. The length l, width w and height h of a box change with time. At a certain instant the dimensions are $l = 3$ and $w = h = 5$, and l and w are increasing at a rate of 10 m/s while h is decreasing at a rate of 1 m/s. At that instant find the rates at which the surface area is changing.

11. Find the gradient of the function $f(x, y, z) = z^2 e^{2x\sqrt{y}}$.

12. Find the directional derivative of $f(x, y) = 2\sqrt{x} - y^2$ at the point (1, 3) in the direction toward the point (3, 1).

13. Find the maximum rate of change of $f(x, y) = x^2 y + \sqrt{y}$ at the point (1,1). In what direction does it occur?

14. Find f_x for $f(x, y) = \int_y^x \cos(t^8)\, dt$.

15. Find the equation of the tangent plane to the given surface at the specified point.

$5x^2 + 3y^2 + 8z^2 = 353$, (3, 6, 5)

16. Find all the second partial derivatives of

$f(x, y) = 4x^3 y - 7xy^2$

17. Find the critical points of the function.

$$f(x, y) = 5 + 76xy + 38x^2 + 240y + \frac{y^4}{4}$$

18. Find the local maximum, and minimum value and saddle points of the function.

$f(x, y) = x^2 - xy + y^2 - 9x + 6y + 10$

19. Find the dimensions of a rectangular box of maximum volume such that the sum of the lengths of its 12 edges is 24.

20. Use Lagrange multipliers to find the maximum and the minimum of f subject to the given constraint(s).

$f(x, y) = xyz$; $x^2 + y^2 + z^2 = 3$

ANSWER KEY

Stewart - Calculus ET 7e Chapter 14 Form A

1. $T = 80$

2. $\sqrt{3}$

3. $64x^2 + 49y^2 + 112xy + 36 - 96x - 84y + \sqrt{8x + 7y - 6}$

4. $15x^4 + 6x^2y^2 + 9y^4$

5. $\dfrac{1}{\sqrt{a^2+b^2}}, \dfrac{b}{a\sqrt{a^2+b^2} + a^2 + b^2}$

6. $L = 2x - 1.25y + 5$

7. $du = 5e^{5t}\sin(3x)dt + 3e^{5t}\cos(3x)dx$

8. $35x^4 + 18x^2y^2 + 7y^4$

9. $128y\sec^2 8x\tan 8x$

10. 344

11. $ze^{2x\sqrt{y}}\langle 2z\sqrt{y}, xz/\sqrt{y}, 2\rangle$

12. $7\sqrt{2}/2$

13. $5/2, \langle 2, 3/2\rangle$

14. $\cos(x^8)$

15. $15x + 18y + 40z = 353$

16. $f_{xy} = 12x^2 - 14y$ $\quad f_{yx} = 12x^2 - 14y$
    $f_{xx} = 24xy$ $\quad f_{yy} = -14x$

17. (-6, 6), (-4, 4), (10, -10)

18. Min at $(-4,1)$, $f(-4,1) = 73$, Max point - none, Saddle point - none

19. 2, 2, 2

20. maximum = 1, minimum = – 1

1. Find the limit.

$$\lim_{(x,y)\to(9,-5)} x^5 + 8x^3y - 2xy^2$$

2. Find the directional derivative of $f(x,y) = 2\sqrt{x} - y^3$ at the point (1, 5) in the direction toward the point (4, 1).

3. Find the maximum rate of change of $f(x,y) = xy^2 + \sqrt{y}$ at the point (1,1). In what direction does it occur?

4. Find the direction in which the function $f(x,y) = x^4y - x^3y^2$ decreases fastest at the point (2, -1).

5. Find equation of the tangent plane to the given surface at the specified point.

$$5x^2 + 3y^2 + 8z^2 = 353, \ (3, 6, 5)$$

6. Find the equation of the tangent plane to the given surface at the specified point.

$$f(x,y) = 4x^3y - 7xy^2 \ , \ (1, 1, -3)$$

7. Find the critical points of the function.

$$f(x,y) = 5 + 76xy + 38x^2 + 240y + \frac{y^4}{4}$$

8. Find f_x for $f(x,y) = 7x^5 + 6x^3y^2 + 7xy^4$.

9. Find the first partial derivatives of the function.

$$c = \ln(a + \sqrt{a^2 + b^2})$$

10. Find f_x for $f(x,y) = \int_y^x \cos(t^8)\, dt$.

11. Find $\frac{\partial^2 z}{\partial x^2}$ for $z = y \tan 8x$.

12. Use Lagrange multipliers to find the maximum and the minimum of f subject to the given constraint(s).

$$f(x,y) = xyz; \qquad x^2 + y^2 + z^2 = 27$$

13. Find an equation of the tangent plane to the given surface at the specified point.

$$z = \sqrt{18 - x^2 - 2y^2}, \ (3, 2, -2)$$

14. Find the gradient of the function $f(x,y,z) = ze^{x^2}\sqrt{y}$.

15. Find the differential of the function.

$u = e^{5t} \sin 3x$

16. The length l, width w and height h of a box change with time. At a certain instant the dimensions are $l = 3$ and $w = h = 5$, and l and w are increasing at a rate of 10 m/s while h is decreasing at a rate of 1 m/s. At that instant find the rates at which the surface area is changing.

17. Use differentials to estimate the amount of tin in a closed tin can with diameter 8 cm and height 11 cm if the tin is 0.04 cm thick.

18. Find the point at which the function achieves its minimum.

$f(x, y) = x^2 + 2y^2 + 2xy + 2x + 3y$ subject to $x^2 - y = 1$

19. Find f_x for $f(x, y) = 3x^5 + 2x^3y^2 + 9xy^4$.

20. Find all the second partial derivatives of $f(x, y) = 4x^3y - 7xy^2$.

ANSWER KEY

Stewart - Calculus ET 7e Chapter 14 Form B

1. 29439

2. $303/5$

3. $\sqrt{29}/2, \langle 1, 5/2 \rangle$

4. $\langle 44, -32 \rangle$

5. $15x+18y+40z=353$

6. $z=5x-10y+2$

7. (-6, 6), (-4, 4), (10, -10)

8. $35x^4+18x^2y^2+7y^4$

9. $\dfrac{1}{\sqrt{a^2+b^2}}, \dfrac{b}{a\sqrt{a^2+b^2}+a^2+b^2}$

10. $\cos(x^8)$

11. $128y\sec^2 8x\tan 8x$

12. maximum = 27 , minimum = −27

13. $z=-3x-4y+15$

14. $e^{x^2\sqrt{y}}\langle 2xz\sqrt{y}, x^2z/(2\sqrt{y}), 1\rangle$

15. $du=5e^{5t}\sin(3x)dt+3e^{5t}\cos(3x)dx$

16. 344

17. 15.08

18. Min at $(-3/4,-7/16)$

19. $15x^4+6x^2y^2+9y^4$

20. $f_{xy}=12x^2-14y \qquad f_{yx}=12x^2-14y$
$f_{xx}=24xy \qquad f_{yy}=-14x$

1. Evaluate the limit.

$$\lim_{(x,y)\to(1,1)} \frac{3x^2 y}{\sqrt{x^2+2y^2}}$$

Select the correct answer.

a. $\sqrt{3}$ b. 0 c. $\sqrt{2}$ d. $\sqrt{3}/3$ e. $3/\sqrt{2}$

2. Two contour maps are shown. One is for a function f whose graph is a cone. The other is for a function g whose graph is a paraboloid. Which is the contour map of a cone?

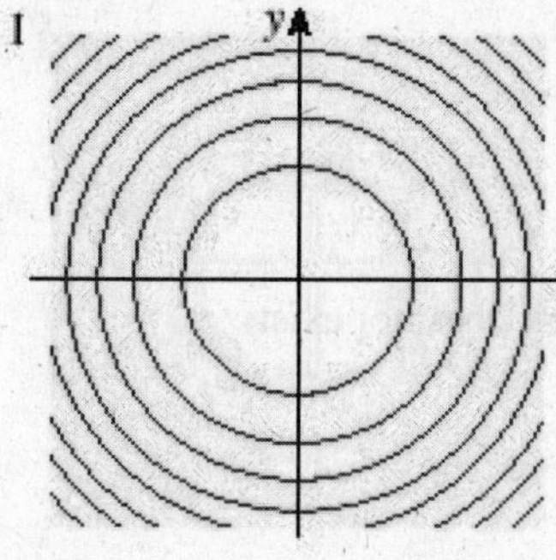

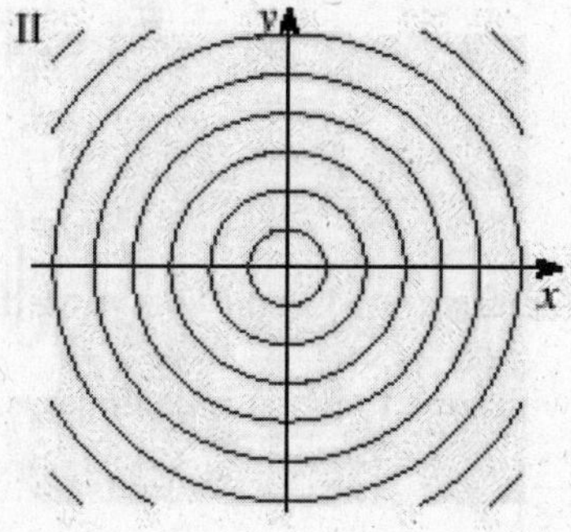

Select the correct answer.

a. II
b. I
c. impossible to determine

3. A contour map for a function f is shown. Use it to estimate the value of $f(-3, 3)$.

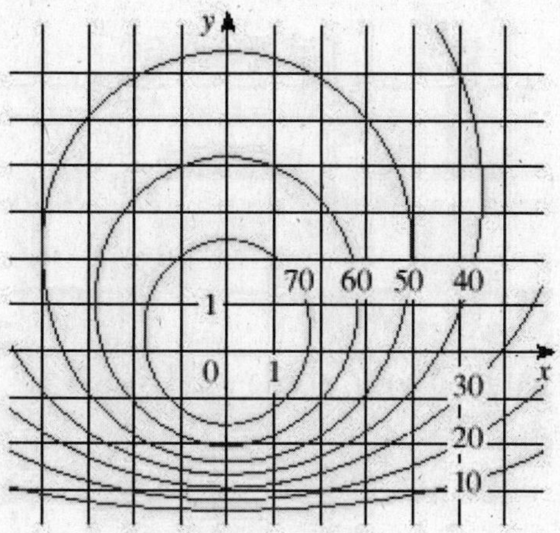

Select the correct answer.

a. 56 b. 48 c. 28 d. 65 e. 78

4. Use a table of numerical values of $f(x, y)$ for (x, y) near the origin to make a conjecture about the value of the limit of $f(x, y)$ as $(x, y) \to (0, 0)$.

$$f(x,y)=\frac{x^2y^3+x^3y^2-3}{1-xy}$$

Select the correct answer.

a. -1 b. 3 c. -3 d. 1 e. the value cannot be determined

5. Find the limit, if it exists.

$$\lim_{(x,y)\to(0,0)}\frac{6xy^2}{x^2+y^2}$$

Select the correct answer.

a. 0 b. 6 c. 2 d. 1 e. the limit does not exist

6. Determine the largest set on which the function is continuous.

$F(x,y)=\arctan(10x+8\sqrt{y-3})$

Select the correct answer.

a. $\left\{ (x,y) \mid y\geq 3, \left|10x+8\sqrt{y}\right|\leq 1 \right\}$
b. $\{ (x,y) \mid y\geq 3 \}$
c. $\{ (x,y) \mid y\leq 0 \}$
d. $\{ (x,y) \mid x\geq 0 \}$
e. $\{ (x,y) \mid x\geq 1 \}$

7. Find $f_y(-36, 6)$ for $f(x, y)=\sin(2x+12y)$.

Select the correct answer.

a. 2 b. 12 c. -2 d. 0 e. -12

8. Use the definition of partial derivatives as limits to find $f_x(x, y)$ if $f(x,y)=4x^2-9xy+2y^2$.

Select the correct answer.

a. $8x-9xy$
b. $8x-9y$
c. $8x-9$
d. $4y-9x$
e. $4x-9y$

9. Find the indicated partial derivative.

$f(x, y) = x^2y^4 - 3x^4y$; f_{xxx}

Select the correct answer.

a. $f_{xxx} = 3xy$ b. $f_{xxx} = -3xy$ c. $f_{xxx} = 72x^2y$ d. $f_{xxx} = -72xy$ e. $f_{xxx} = -45xy$

10. Find the indicated partial derivative.

$u = x^a y^b z^c$; $\dfrac{\partial^6 u}{\partial x \partial y^2 \partial z^3}$, $a > 1,\ b > 2,\ c > 3$

Select the correct answer.

a. $\dfrac{\partial^6 u}{\partial x \partial y^2 \partial z^3} = x^{a-1}y^{b-2}z^{c-3}$

b. $\dfrac{\partial^6 u}{\partial x \partial y^2 \partial z^3} = x^{b-1}y^{c-2}z^{a-3}$

c. $\dfrac{\partial^6 u}{\partial x \partial y^2 \partial z^3} = ab(b-1)c(c-1)(c-2)x^{a-1}y^{b-2}z^{c-3}$

d. $\dfrac{\partial^6 u}{\partial x \partial y^2 \partial z^3} = cb(b-1)c(a-1)(a-2)x^{c-1}y^{b-2}z^{a-3}$

e. $\dfrac{\partial^6 u}{\partial x \partial y^2 \partial z^3} = acb(a-1)(a-2)x^{a-1}y^{b-2}z^{c-3}$

11. Use the Chain Rule to find $\dfrac{\partial z}{\partial s}$.

$z = e^r \cos(\theta),\ r = 10st,\ \theta = \sqrt{s^2 + t^2}$

Select the correct answer.

a. $\dfrac{\partial z}{\partial s} = e^r\left(10t\cos(\theta) - \dfrac{s\sin(\theta)}{\sqrt{s^2+t^2}}\right)$

b. $\dfrac{\partial z}{\partial s} = e^r\left(t\cos(\theta) - \dfrac{s\sin(\theta)}{\sqrt{s^2+t}}\right)$

c. $\dfrac{\partial z}{\partial s} = e^r\left(10t\cos(\theta) + \dfrac{s\sin(\theta)}{\sqrt{s^2-t^2}}\right)$

d. $\dfrac{\partial z}{\partial s} = e^t\left(\cos(\theta) + \dfrac{s\sin(\theta)}{\sqrt{s^2-t^2}}\right)$

e. $\dfrac{\partial z}{\partial s} = \left(10t\cos(\theta) + \dfrac{se^r\sin(\theta)}{\sqrt{s^2+t^2}}\right)$

12. Use the Chain Rule to find $\dfrac{\partial u}{\partial p}$.

$$u = \frac{x+y}{y+z}$$

$$x = p+6r+5t, \quad y = p-6r+5t, \quad z = p+6r-5t$$

Select the correct answer.

a. $\dfrac{\partial u}{\partial p} = \dfrac{5t}{p}$ b. $\dfrac{\partial u}{\partial p} = -\dfrac{20t}{p^3}$ c. $\dfrac{\partial u}{\partial p} = -\dfrac{5t}{p^2}$ d. $\dfrac{\partial u}{\partial p} = -\dfrac{25t}{p^2}$ e. $\dfrac{\partial u}{\partial p} = \dfrac{25t}{p^2} + t$

13. Find the directional derivative of $f(x,y) = 2\sqrt{x} - y^3$ at the point (1, 3) in the direction toward the point (3, 1).

Select the correct answer.

a. $14\sqrt{2}$ b. $\sqrt{2}$ c. $7\sqrt{2}$ d. 28 e. none of these

14. Find the direction in which the maximum rate of change of f at the given point occurs.

$f(x,y) = \sin(xy), \ (1, 0)$

Select the correct answer.

a. $\langle 1/\sqrt{2}, 1/\sqrt{2} \rangle$ b. $\langle 0, 1 \rangle$ c. $\langle 1, 0 \rangle$ d. $\langle \sqrt{2}, 0 \rangle$ e. $\langle 1, -\sqrt{2} \rangle$

15. Find the equation of the normal line to the given surface at the specified point.

$2x^2 + 8y^2 + 3z^2 = 235, \ (4, 4, 5)$

Select the correct answer.

a. $\dfrac{x-4}{55} = \dfrac{y-4}{55} = \dfrac{z-5}{55}$

b. $\dfrac{x+4}{16} = \dfrac{y+4}{64} = \dfrac{z+5}{30}$

c. $\dfrac{x-4}{16} = \dfrac{y-4}{64} = \dfrac{z-5}{30}$

d. $16x + 64y + 30z = 235$

e. $2x + 8y + 3z = 1$

16. At what point is the following function a local minimum?

$f(x,y) = 6x^2 + 3y^2$

Select the correct answer.

a. (6, 3) b. (3, 0) c. (0, 0) d. (6, 0) e. (6, -3)

17. Find the equation of the tangent plane to the given surface at the specified point.

$z+5=xe^{y}\cos z$, (5, 0, 0)

Select the correct answer.

a. $x+5y+z=5$
b. $x+y-5z=5$
c. $5x+y-z=5$
d. $x+5y-z=5$
e. $x+y-z=5$

18. Find the critical points of the function.

$$f(x,y)=8+76xy+38x^2+240y+\frac{y^4}{4}$$

Select the correct answer.

a. (-4, 4), (-6, 6), (10, -10)
b. (-6,6), (-8,8), (8, -8)
c. (-4,6), (-6,-10), (10, 4)
d. (4, 4), (6, 6), (-10, 0)
e. (-4,6), (-8,6), (8, -6)

19. Use *Lagrange multipliers* to find the maximum value of the function subject to the given constraint.

$f(x,y)=8x^2-4y^2,\ 8x^2+4y^2=9$

Select the correct answer.

a. $f(x,y)=\frac{1}{9}$ b. $f(x,y)=\frac{1}{4}$ c. $f(x,y)=\frac{1}{8}$ d. $f(x,y)=8$ e. $f(x,y)=9$

20. Use *Lagrange multipliers* to find the maximum value of the function subject to the given constraint.

$f(x,y,z)=14x+8y+12z,\ x^2+y^2+z^2=101$

Select the correct answer.

a. $f(20,\ 9,\ 18)=568$
b. $f(14,\ 8,\ 12)=404$
c. $f(8,\ 17,\ 5)=308$
d. $f(7,\ 4,\ 6)=202$
e. $f(8,\ 4,\ 12)=212$

ANSWER KEY

Stewart - Calculus ET 7e Chapter 14 Form C

1. a
2. a
3. a
4. c
5. a
6. b
7. b
8. b
9. d
10. c
11. a
12. c
13. a
14. b
15. c
16. c
17. d
18. a
19. e
20. d

1. Find f_{xy} for the function $f(x,y)=4x^3y-7xy^2$.

Select the correct answer.

a. $f_{xy}=24x^2-14y$
b. $f_{xy}=12x^2+14y$
c. $f_{xy}=14x^2-12y$
d. $f_{xy}=12x^2-14y$
e. $f_{xy}=14x^2+12y$

2. The ellipsoid $8x^2+3y^2+z^2=14$ intersects the plane $y=2$ in an ellipse. Find parametric equations for the tangent line to this ellipse at the point (1, 2, 2).

Select the correct answer.

a. $x=1+t,\ y=2,\ z=4t-2$
b. $x=1+t,\ y=1,\ z=4t+2$
c. $x=1+t,\ y=2,\ z=-4t+2$
d. $x=1+t,\ y=2, z=-4t-2$
e. $x=t,\ y=2, z=-4t+2$

3. How many *nth* - order partial derivatives does a function of two variables have?

Select the correct answer.

a. $\frac{n}{2}$ b. $2n$ c. n^2 d. 2^n e. $n2^n$

4. Use a table of numerical values of $f(x, y)$ for (x, y) near the origin to make a conjecture about the value of the limit of $f(x, y)$ as $(x, y) \to (0, 0)$.

$$f(x,y)=\frac{x^2y^3+x^3y^2-3}{1-xy}$$

Select the correct answer.

a. -1 b. 3 c. -3 d. 1 e. the value cannot be determined

5. Evaluate the limit.

$$\lim_{(x,y)\to(1,1)}\frac{3x^2y}{\sqrt{x^2+2y^2}}$$

Select the correct answer.

a. $\sqrt{3}$ b. 0 c. $\sqrt{2}$ d. $\sqrt{3}/3$ e. $3/\sqrt{2}$

6. If R is the total resistance of three resistors, connected in parallel, with resistances $R_1,\ R_2,\ R_3$, then $\frac{1}{R}=\frac{1}{R_1}+\frac{1}{R_2}+\frac{1}{R_3}$. If the resistances are measured in ohms as $R_1 = 30\ \Omega,\ R_2 = 35\ \Omega$ and $R_3 = 50\ \Omega$, with a possible error of 0.8% in each case, estimate the maximum error in the calculated value of R.

Select the correct answer.

a. 0.291 Ω   b. 0.957 Ω   c. 0.347 Ω   d. 0.476 Ω   e. 0.098 Ω

7. Use the equation $\frac{dy}{dx}=-\frac{\frac{\partial F}{\partial x}}{\frac{\partial F}{\partial y}}=-\frac{F_x}{F_y}$ to find $\frac{dy}{dx}$.

$\cos(x-9y)=xe^{3y}$

Select the correct answer.

a. $\frac{dy}{dx}=\frac{\sin(x-9y)+e^{3y}}{\sin(x-9y)-xe^{3y}}$

b. $\frac{dy}{dx}=\frac{\sin(x-y)+e^{3y}}{9\sin(x-9y)-xe^{3y}}$

c. $\frac{dy}{dx}=\frac{\sin(x-9y)+e^{3y}}{9\sin(x-9y)-3xe^{3y}}$

d. $\frac{dy}{dx}=\frac{\sin(x-y)+e^{3y}}{\sin(x-y)-xe^{y}}$

e. $\frac{dy}{dx}=\frac{9\sin(x-y)+e^{3y}}{\sin(x-9y)-9xe^{y}}$

8. Find the direction in which the maximum rate of change of f at the given point occurs.

$f(x,y)=\sin(xy),\ \ (0,\ 1)$

Select the correct answer.

a. $\langle 0, 1\rangle$ b. $\langle 1, 0\rangle$ c. $\left\langle \frac{1}{\sqrt{2}}, \frac{1}{\sqrt{2}}\right\rangle$ d. $\left\langle 0, \frac{1}{\sqrt{2}}\right\rangle$ e. $\left\langle \frac{1}{\sqrt{2}}, 1\right\rangle$

9. Suppose that over a certain region of space the electrical potential V is given by $V(x,y,z)=8x^2-7xy+7xyz$.

Find the rate of change of the potential at (-1, 1, -1) in the direction of the vector $\mathbf{v}=8\mathbf{i}+10\mathbf{j}-8\mathbf{k}$.

Select the correct answer.

a. -15.099   b. 20   c. 14.569856   d. -2.91   e. 44

10. Find the critical points of the function.

$$f(x, y) = 8 + 76xy + 38x^2 + 240y + \frac{y^4}{4}$$

Select the correct answer.

a. (-4, 4), (-6, 6), (10, -10)
b. (-6,6), (-8,8), (8, -8)
c. (-4,6), (-6,-10), (10, 4)
d. (4, 4), (6, 6), (-10, 0)
e. (-4,6), (-8,6), (8, -6)

11. Suppose (1, 1) is a critical point of a function f with continuous second derivatives. In the case of $f_{xx}(1, 1) = 7$, $f_{xy}(1, 1) = 8$, $f_{yy}(1, 1) = 10$ what can you say about f ?

Select the correct answer.

a. f has a local maximum at (1,1)
b. f has a saddle point at (1,1)
c. f has a local minimum at (1,1)

12. At what point is the following function a local maximum?

$$f(x, y) = 3 - 10x + 12y - 5x^2 - 6y^2$$

Select the correct answer.

a. (1, -1) b. (-1, 1) c. (3, 1) d. (0, 1) e. (1, 1)

13. At what point is the following function a local minimum?

$$f(x, y) = 2x^2 + 2y^2 + 2x^2y + 6$$

Select the correct answer.

a. (-1, 2) b. (1, 6) c. (0, 0) d. (-1, 6) e. (-1, -6)

14. Find all the saddle points of the function.

$$f(x, y) = x\sin\frac{y}{3}$$

Select the correct answer.

a. $(0, 3\pi n)$ b. $\left(0, \frac{\pi n}{3}\right)$ c. $(3\pi n, 1)$ d. $\left(\frac{3n}{\pi}, 0\right)$ e. $(3\pi n, 0)$

15. Find the gradient of the function $f(x,y,z)=ze^{x\sqrt{y}}$.
Select the correct answer.

a. $ze^{x\sqrt{y}}\left\langle z\sqrt{y},\ xz/(2\sqrt{y}),\ 2\right\rangle$
b. $ze^{2x\sqrt{y}}\left\langle 2z\sqrt{y},\ xz/\sqrt{y},2\right\rangle$
c. $e^{x^2\sqrt{y}}\left\langle 2xz\sqrt{y},\ x^2z/(2\sqrt{y}),\ 2\right\rangle$
d. $e^{x^2\sqrt{y}}\left\langle 2xz\sqrt{y},\ x^2z/(2\sqrt{y}),1\right\rangle$
e. $e^{x\sqrt{y}}\left\langle z\sqrt{y},\ xz/(2\sqrt{y}),1\right\rangle$

16. Find the point at which the function achieves its minimum.

$f(x,y)=x^2+2y^2+2xy+2x+3y$ subject to $x^2-y=1$

Select the correct answer.

a. $(-1/4,-1/16)$ b. $(-1,-7/16)$ c. $(-3,-7)$ d. $(3/4,7/16)$ e. $(-3/4,-7/16)$

17. Find three positive numbers whose sum is 360 and whose product is a maximum.

Select the correct answer.

a. 120, 120, 120 b. 179.5, 179.5, 1 c. 358, 1, 1

18. Use *Lagrange multipliers* to find three positive numbers whose sum is 297 and whose product is a maximum.

Select the correct answer.

a. $x=y=z=99$
b. $x=129, y=79, z=89$
c. $x=99, y=z=-99$
d. $x=109, y=99, z=89$
e. $x=100, y=108, z=89$

19. Use *Lagrange multipliers* to find the dimensions of the rectangular box with largest volume if the total surface area is given as 54 cm^2.

Select the correct answer.

a. $x=9$ cm, $y=z=3$ cm
b. $x=y=z=9$ cm
c. $x=6$ cm, $y=6$ cm, $z=2$ cm
d. $x=y=z=3$ cm

20. Use *Lagrange multipliers* to find the shortest distance from the point (3, 9, 8) to the plane $3x+9y+4z=16$.

Select the correct answer.

a. $D=106$ b. $D=90$ c. $D=\sqrt{106}$ d. $D=\sqrt{61}$ e. $D=61$

ANSWER KEY

Stewart - Calculus ET 7e Chapter 14 Form D

1. d
2. c
3. d
4. c
5. a
6. e
7. c
8. b
9. d
10. a
11. c
12. b
13. c
14. a
15. e
16. e
17. a
18. a
19. d
20. c

1. Use the contour map of f to estimate the value of $f(-3, 3)$.

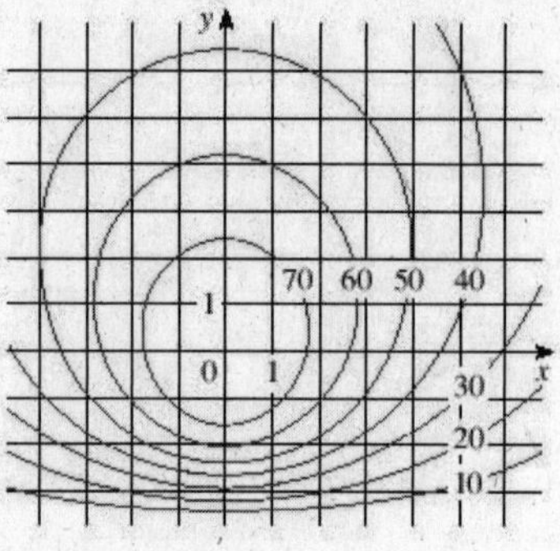

2. Evaluate the limit.

$$\lim_{(x,y)\to(1,1)} \frac{3x^2 y}{\sqrt{x^2+2y^2}}$$

Select the correct answer.

a. $\sqrt{2}$ b. $\sqrt{2}/2$ c. $\sqrt{3}/3$ d. 0 e. none of these

3. Determine the largest set on which the function is continuous.

$$f(x,y,z)=\frac{xyz}{7x^2+2y^2-z}$$

4. A cardboard box without a lid is to have a volume of 6,912 cm^2. Find the dimensions that minimize the amount of cardboard used.

5. Find the point at which the function achieves its minimum.

$f(x,y)=x^2+2y^2+2xy+2x+3y$ subject to $x^2-y=1$

6. Find $f_y(-24, 8)$ for $f(x,y)=\sin(2x+6y)$.

Select the correct answer.

a. 6 b. 2 c. 0 d. -6 e. -2

7. Use implicit differentiation to find $\partial z/\partial x$.

$$9x^2+8y^2-3z^2=2x(y+z)$$

8. Find $\dfrac{\partial^2 z}{\partial x^2}$ for $z=y\tan 8x$.

9. Find the indicated partial derivative.

$f(x,y)=x^2y^9-2x^4y$; f_{xxx}

10. The ellipsoid $6x^2 + 3y^2 + z^2 = 14$ intersects the plane $y = 2$ in an ellipse. Find parametric equations for the tangent line to this ellipse at the point (1, 2, 2).

11. Use differentials to estimate the amount of metal in a closed cylindrical can that is 13 cm high and 6 cm in diameter if the metal in the top and bottom is 0.09 cm thick and the metal in the sides is 0.01 cm thick.

Select the correct answer. (rounded to the nearest hundredth.)

a. 8.34 cm^3 b. 4.58 cm^3 c. 6.99 cm^3 d. 6.91 cm^3 e. 6.7 cm^3

12. Use the Chain Rule to find $\dfrac{\partial w}{\partial s}$ where $s = 3$, $t = 0$.

$w = x^2 + y^2 + z^2$, $x = st$, $y = s\cos t$, $z = s\sin t$

13. Find the directional derivative of $f(x, y) = 2\sqrt{x} - y^2$ at the point (1, 5) in the direction toward the point (4, 1).

14. Find the maximum rate of change of $f(x, y) = xy^2 + \sqrt{y}$ at the point (2,1).
In what direction does it occur?

Select the correct answer.

a. $\sqrt{85}/2, \langle 1, 9/2 \rangle$
b. $\sqrt{29}/2, \langle 1, 5/2 \rangle$
c. $85/2, \langle 2, 7/2 \rangle$
d. $29/2, \langle 1, 9/2 \rangle$
e. none of these

15. Find the dimensions of a rectangular box of maximum volume such that the sum of the lengths of its 12 edges is 96.

16. Find the equation of the tangent plane to the given surface at the specified point.

$f(x, y) = 4x^3y - 7xy^2$, (1, 1, -3)

17. If $f(x, y) = x^2 + 9y^2$, use the gradient vector $\nabla f(-5, 10)$ to find the tangent line to the level curve $f(x, y) = 925$ at the point $(-5, 10)$.

18. Find all the saddle points of the function $f(x, y) = x\sin(y/5)$.

19. Find the absolute minimum value of the function $f(x, y) = 6 + 3xy - 2x - 4y$ on the set D. D is the region bounded by the parabola $y = x^2$ and the line $y = 4$.

Select the correct answer.

a. 0 b. -34 c. -36 d. -30 e. 30

20. Find all the second partial derivatives of $f(x, y) = 4x^3y - 7xy^2$.

ANSWER KEY

Stewart - Calculus ET 7e Chapter 14 Form E

1. 56

2. e

3. $\{ (x, y),\ z \neq 7x^2 + 2y^2 \}$

4. 24, 24, 12

5. $(-3/4, -7/16)$

6. a

7. $\dfrac{9x - y - z}{x + 3z}$

8. $\dfrac{128y\sin(8x)}{\cos^3(8x)}$

9. $-48xy$

10. $x = 1 + t,\ \ y = 2,\ \ z = -3t + 2$

11. b

12. 6

13. 43/5

14. a

15. 8, 8, 8

16. $z = 5x - 10y + 2$

17. $-5x + 90y = 925$

18. $(0, 5\pi n)$

19. d

20. $f_{xy} = 12x^2 - 14y \qquad f_{yx} = 12x^2 - 14y$
$f_{xx} = 24xy \qquad f_{yy} = -14x$

1. The *temperature-humidity index* I (or humidex, for short) is the perceived air temperature when the actual temperature is T and the relative humidity is h, so we can write $I = f(T, h)$. The following table of values of I is an excerpt from a table compiled by the National Oceanic and Atmospheric Administration. For what value of h is $f(95, h) = 96$?

T ↓ / h →	20	30	40	50	60	70
80	70	75	80	81	83	86
85	80	84	85	86	89	94
90	88	93	96	100	102	104
95	93	96	99	103	114	123
100	99	102	112	121	128	144

2. A contour map for a function f is shown. Use it to estimate the value of $f(-3, 3)$.

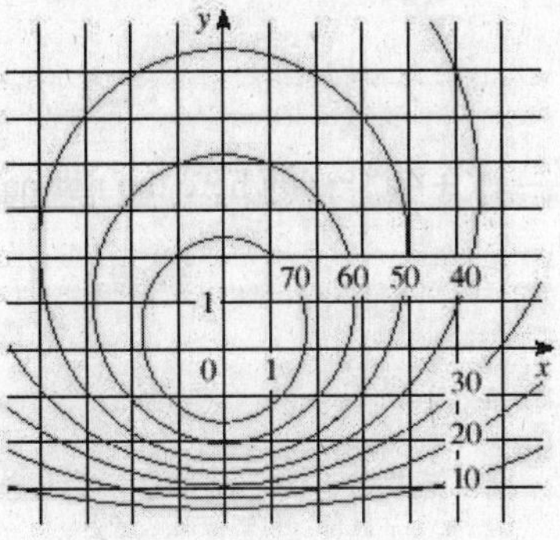

3. The radius of a right circular cone is increasing at a rate of 5 in/s while its height is decreasing at a rate of 3.6 in/s. At what rate is the volume of the cone changing when the radius is 115 in. and the height is 140 in.?

Select the correct answer.

a. $117,741.73 \text{ in}^3/\text{s}$
b. $119,741.73 \text{ in}^3/\text{s}$
c. $118,741.73 \text{ in}^3/\text{s}$
d. $123,741.73 \text{ in}^3/\text{s}$
e. $136,741.73 \text{ in}^3/\text{s}$

4. Find the gradient of the function $f(x, y, z) = z^2 e^{2x\sqrt{y}}$.

5. Evaluate the gradient of f at the point P.

$f(x, y, z) = xy^2z^3,\ P(-1, 3, -1)$

6. Find the directional derivative of $f(x, y) = 2\sqrt{x} - y^3$ at the point (1, 5) in the direction toward the point (4, 1).

7. Suppose that over a certain region of space the electrical potential V is given by

$V(x,y,z)=2x^2-2xy+8xyz$

Find the rate of change of the potential at $(-4,\ -6,\ -1)$ in the direction of the vector $v=7\mathbf{i}+10\mathbf{j}-8\mathbf{k}$.

8. Find the equation of the normal line to the given surface at the specified point.

$z+2=xe^y\cos z,\ \ (2,\ 0,\ 0)$

9. If $f(x,y)=x^2+9y^2$, use the gradient vector $\nabla f(10,\ 2)$ to find the tangent line to the level curve $f(x,y)=136$ at the point (10, 2).

Select the correct answer.

a. $10x+18y=136$
b. $100x+36y=136$
c. $10x+18y=12$
d. $100x-36y=12$
e. $100x-18y=12$

10. Which of the given points are the points on the hyperboloid $x^2-y^2+4z^2=4$ where the normal line is parallel to the line that joins the points (-1, 1, 3) and (0, 2, 5).

Select all that apply.

a. (-2, 2, 1)
b. (2, -2, 1)
c. (-2, 2, -1)
d. (2, -2, -1)
e. (2, 2, 1)

11. At what point is the following function a local minimum?

$f(x,y)=8x^2+8y^2+8x^2y+6$

12. Find the equation of the tangent plane to the given surface at the specified point.

$f(x,y)=4x^3y-7xy^2$, (1, 1, -3)

13. Find the points on the surface $z^2=xy+49$ that are closest to the origin.

Select the correct answer.

a. (0, 0, 7)
b. (0, 0, 49) (0, 0, -49)
c. (0, 0, 7) (0, 0, -7)
d. (0, 0, -49)
e. (0, 0, 28)

14. Find three positive numbers whose sum is 500 and whose product is a maximum.

15. Use Lagrange multipliers to find the maximum and the minimum of f subject to the given constraint(s).

$f(x, y) = xyz$; $\quad x^2 + y^2 + z^2 = 9$

16. Find f_{yx} for the function $f(x, y) = 4x^3 y - 7xy^2$.

17. Find the point at which the function achieves its minimum.

$f(x, y) = x^2 + 2y^2 + 2xy + 2x + 3y$ subject to $x^2 - y = 1$

18. Find all the saddle points of the function.

$f(x, y) = x \sin \frac{y}{5}$

19. Find the gradient of the function.

$f(x, y, z) = x^2 e^y \sqrt{z}$

20. Use *Lagrange multipliers* to find the volume of the largest rectangular box with edges parallel to the axes that can be inscribed in the ellipsoid $9x^2 + 4y^2 + 9z^2 = 324$.

ANSWER KEY

Stewart - Calculus ET 7e Chapter 14 Form F

1. $h = 30$

2. 56

3. c

4. $ze^{2x\sqrt{y}}\left\langle 2z\sqrt{y},\ xz/\sqrt{y}\ ,2\right\rangle$

5. $\left\{ -9,\ 6,\ -27 \right\}$

6. $303/5$

7. -56.734

8. $x-2=\dfrac{y}{2}=-z$

9. a

10. b, c

11. (0, 0)

12. $z=5x-10y+2$

13. c

14. $\dfrac{500}{3},\ \dfrac{500}{3},\ \dfrac{500}{3}$

15. maximum = $3\sqrt{3}$, minimum = $-\ 3\sqrt{3}$

16. $f_{yx} = 12x^2 - 14y$

17. Min at $(-3/4, -7/16)$

18. $(0,\ 5\pi n)$

19. $\left\langle 2xe^y\sqrt{z},\ x^2e^y\sqrt{z},\ \dfrac{x^2e^y}{2\sqrt{z}}\right\rangle$

20. $36\sqrt{3}$

1. Evaluate the limit.

$$\lim_{(x,y)\to(1,1)} \frac{3x^2y}{\sqrt{x^2+2y^2}}$$

2. Use a table of numerical values of $f(x, y)$ for (x, y) near the origin to make a conjecture about the value of the limit of $f(x, y)$ as $(x, y) \to (0, 0)$.

$$f(x,y)=\frac{x^2y^3+x^3y^2-2}{1-xy}$$

Select the correct answer.

a. -2
b. 1
c. -1
d. 2
e. cannot determine the value from the given information

3. Find the limit.

$$\lim_{(x,y)\to(14,7)} xy\cos(x-2y)$$

4. Determine the largest set on which the function is continuous.

$$F(x,y)=\arctan\left(10x+2\sqrt{y-3}\right)$$

5. Use polar coordinates to find the limit.

$$\lim_{(x,y)\to(0,0)} \frac{x^4+y^4}{x^3+y^3}$$

6. Use spherical coordinates to find the limit.

$$\lim_{(x,y)\to(0,0)} \frac{5xyz}{x^2+y^2+z^2}$$

7. At what point is the following function a local minimum?

$$f(x,y)=8x^2+9y^2$$

Select the correct answer.

a. (8, 9) b. (0, 0) c. (9, 0) d. (8, 0) e. (-8, 0)

8. Find the directional derivative of $f(x,y)=2\sqrt{x}-y^2$ at the point (1, 3) in the direction toward the point (3,1).

9. Find the critical points of the function.

$$f(x,y)=\frac{x^4}{4}-14x^2+5y^2+48x+10$$

Select the correct answer.

a. (-4, 0), (-6,0), (-2, 0)
b. (4, 0), (-6,0)
c. (4, 0), (6, 0), (2, 0)
d. (4, 0), (-6, 0), (2, 0)
e. (1, 0), (6, 0), (0, 0)

10. Find the points on the surface $z^2 = xy+4$ that are closest to the origin.

11. Find the dimensions of the rectangular box with largest volume if the total surface area is given as 294 cm^2.

Select the correct answer.

a. 28 cm, 1.75 cm, 1.75 cm
b. 7 cm, 7 cm, 7 cm
c. 294 cm, 7 cm, 7 cm
d. 14 cm, 14 cm, 3.5 cm
e. 714 cm, 14 cm, 1.75 cm

12. Find the dimensions of a rectangular box of maximum volume such that the sum of the lengths of its 12 edges is 96.

Select the correct answer

a. 4, 8, 16
b. 8, 8, 8
c. 8, 96, 8
d. 32, 32, 32
e. 32, 8, 16

13. Find the equation of the tangent plane to the given surface at the specified point.

$$f(x,y)=4x^3y-7xy^2\ , \quad (1, 1, -3)$$

14. Find the gradient of the function $f(x,y,z)=ze^{x^2\sqrt{y}}$.

15. Use *Lagrange multipliers* to find the maximum and the minimum of f subject to the given constraint(s).

$$f(x,y)=xyz\,; \qquad x^2+y^2+z^2=27$$

16. Use *Lagrange multipliers* to find the minimum value of the function subject to the given constraints.

$$f(x,y,z,t)=7x+7y+7z+7t,\ \ 7(x^2+y^2+z^2+t^2)=9$$

17. Use *Lagrange multipliers* to find the maximum value of the function subject to the given constraints.

$f(x, y, z) = x + 3y$; $x + y + z = 4$, $y^2 + z^2 = 4$

18. Use *Lagrange multipliers* to find the shortest distance from the point (8, 10, 8) to the plane $8x + 10y + 4z = 16$.

Select the correct answer

a. $D = \sqrt{59}$ b. $D = \sqrt{180}$ c. $D = 19$ d. $D = 180$ e. $D = 18$

19. Use *Lagrange multipliers* to find three positive numbers whose sum is 279 and whose product is a maximum.

Select the correct answer.

a. $x = 103, y = 93, z = 83$
b. $x = 123, y = 73, z = 83$
c. $x = 93, y = z = -93$
d. $x = y = z = 93$
e. $x = 92, y = 93, z = 94$

20. Use *Lagrange multipliers* to find the dimensions of the rectangular box with largest volume if the total surface area is given as $150\ \text{cm}^2$.

ANSWER KEY

Stewart - Calculus ET 7e Chapter 14 Form G

1. $\sqrt{3}$

2. a

3. 98

4. $\{\ (x, y),\ \ y \geq 3\ \}$

5. 0

6. 0

7. b

8. $7\sqrt{2}/2$

9. d

10. (0, 0, 2), (0, 0, -2)

11. b

12. b

13. $z=5x-10y+2$

14. $e^{x^2\sqrt{y}}\left\langle 2xz\sqrt{y},\ x^2z/(2\sqrt{y}),\ 1\right\rangle$

15. maximum = 27, minimum = −27

16. $6\sqrt{7}$

17. $4+2\sqrt{5}$

18. b

19. d

20. $x=5,\ \ y=5,\ \ z=5$

1. Find the limit.

$$\lim_{(x,y)\to(4,-8)} x^5 + 2x^3y - 5xy^2$$

Select the correct answer.

a. -1,280
b. 1,024
c. 3,328
d. -2,304
e. -2,256

2. Use implicit differentiation to find $\partial z / \partial x$.

$$6x^2 + 3y^2 - 2z^2 = 2x(y+z)$$

3. Use implicit differentiation to find $\partial z / \partial x$ and $\partial z / \partial y$.

$$xyz = \sin(x + y + z)$$

4. Find all the second partial derivatives.

$$f(x, y) = x^4 - 8x^2y^3$$

5. Find the indicated partial derivative.

$$u = x^a y^b z^c; \quad \frac{\partial^6 u}{\partial x \partial y^2 \partial z^3}, \quad a > 1, \; b > 2, \; c > 3$$

6. Find an equation of the tangent plane to the given surface at the specified point.

$$z = \sqrt{192 - x^2 - 8y^2}, \quad (12, 2, -3)$$

7. Use the linearization $L(x, y)$ of the function.

$f(x, y) = \sqrt{9 - x^2 - 2y^2}$ at (-1, 1) to approximate $f(-0.91, 0.82)$.

8. Find the maximum rate of change of $f(x, y) = x^2y + \sqrt{y}$ at the point (2,1).
In what direction does it occur?

9. If $z = x^2 - xy + 7y^2$ and (x, y) changes from (2, 1) to (1.95, 1.07), find dz.

10. A boundary stripe 2 in. wide is painted around a rectangle whose dimensions are 100 ft by 240 ft. Use differentials to approximate the number of square feet of paint in the stripe.

Select the correct answer.

a. 113.23ft^2 b. 113.89ft^2 c. 113ft^2 d. 113.33ft^2 e. 113.81ft^2

11. Find $\dfrac{\partial z}{\partial y}$.

$$xe^{4y} + 4yz + ze^{8x} = 0$$

12. The wind-chill index I is the perceived temperature when the actual temperature is T and the wind speed is v so we can write $I = f(T, v)$. The following table of values is an excerpt from a table compiled by the National Atmospheric and Oceanic Administration. Use the table to find a linear approximation $L(T, v)$ to the wind chill index function when T is near 16° C and v is near 30 kmh.

T ↓ **v** →	**10**	**20**	**30**	**40**	**50**
20	**18**	**17**	**14**	**13**	**12**
16	**15**	**12**	**10**	**7**	**8**
12	**8**	**6**	**2**	**2**	**-1**
8	**5**	**1**	**-2**	**-6**	**-7**

13. Find the maximum rate of change of f at the given point.

$$f(x, y, z) - x^4 y^3 z^2, \ \ (1, -1, 1)$$

14. Find the absolute minimum value of the function f on the set D. D is the region bounded by the parabola $y = x^2$ and the line $y = 4$.

$$f(x, y) = 5 + 8xy - 2x - 4y$$

Select the correct answer.

a. -76 b. -75 c. -71 d. 0 e. 4

15. Find the directional derivative of $f(x, y) = 2\sqrt{x} - y^2$ at the point (1, 5) in the direction toward the point (4, 1).

16. Use Lagrange multipliers to find the maximum and the minimum of f subject to the given constraint(s).

$$f(x, y) = xyz; \qquad x^2 + y^2 + z^2 = 1$$

17. Use Lagrange multipliers to find the maximum value of the function subject to the given constraints.

$$f(x, y, z) = x + 3y, \ \ x + y + z = 2, \ \ y^2 + z^2 = 25$$

Select the correct answer.

a. $f_{\max} = 2 + 5\sqrt{5}$ b. $f_{\max} = 2 - 5\sqrt{5}$ c. $f_{\max} = 2 + 6\sqrt{5}$ d. $f_{\max} = 7 - 5\sqrt{19}$ e. $f_{\max} = 2 + \sqrt{5}$

18. Use Lagrange multipliers to find the maximum and minimum values of the function $f(x,y,z)=5x-y-5z$ subject to the constraints $x+2y-z=0$ and $x^2+4y^2=1$.

19. Use *Lagrange multipliers* to find the shortest distance from the point (1, 5, -5) to the plane $2x+9y-3z=6$.

20. Find the local maximum, and minimum value and saddle points of the function.

$$f(x,y)=x^2-xy+y^2-9x+6y+10$$

Stewart - Calculus ET 7e Chapter 14 Form H

1. a

2. $\dfrac{6x-y-z}{x+2z}$

3. $\dfrac{-(yz-\cos(x+y+z))}{(xy-\cos(x+y+z))}, \dfrac{-(xz-\cos(x+y+z))}{(xy-\cos(x+y+z))}$

4. $12x^2-16y^3,\ -48xy^2,\ -48xy^2,\ -48x^2y$

5. $ab(b-1)c(c-1)(c-2)x^{a-1}y^{b-2}z^{c-3}$

6. $z=-3x-4y+41$

7. 2.63

8. $\sqrt{145}/2,\ \langle 4, 9/2\rangle$

9. $dz=0.69$

10. d

11. $\dfrac{\partial z}{\partial y}=-\dfrac{4xe^{4y}+4z}{4y+e^{8x}}$

12. $L=-6.5+1.5T-0.25v$

13. $\sqrt{29}$

14. c

15. 43/5

16. maximum $=\sqrt{3}/9$, minimum $=-\sqrt{3}/9$

17. a

18. $f_{\min}=\dfrac{-11}{2},\ f_{\max}=\dfrac{11}{2}$

19. $\dfrac{28\sqrt{94}}{47}$

20. Min at $(-4,1)$, $f(-4,1)=73$, Max point - none, Saddle point - none

1. Find an approximation for the integral.

$$\iint_R (4x - 5y^2)\, dA$$

Use a double Riemann sum with $m = n = 2$ and the sample point in the upper right corner to approximate the double integral, where $R = \{\, (x, y) \mid 0 \le x \le 8,\ 0 \le y \le 4 \,\}$.

2. Find $\int_0^5 f(x, y)\, dx$, if $f(x, y) = 8x + 3x^2 y$.

3. Calculate the iterated integral.

$$\int_1^4 \int_0^3 (1 + 2xy)\, dx dy$$

4. Find the volume of the given solid.

Under the paraboloid $z = x^2 + 3y^2$ and above the rectangle $R = [0,3] \times [1,5]$

5. Find the average value of $f(x, y) = x^2 y$ over the rectangle with vertices $(-4,0)$, $(-4,3)$, $(4,3)$, $(4,0)$.

6. Calculate the iterated integral.

$$\int_0^1 \int_0^1 xe^{xy}\, dx\, dy$$

7. Evaluate the double integral.

$$\iint_D x \cos y\ dA$$

D is bounded by $y = 0$, $y = x^2$, and $x = 2$.

8. Evaluate the integral by changing to polar coordinates.

$$\iint_D e^{-x^2 - y^2}\, dA$$

D is the region bounded by the semicircle $x = \sqrt{16 - y^2}$ and the y-axis.

9. Calculate the iterated integral.

$$\int_0^1 \int_0^y \cos(y^2)\, dx dy$$

10. A cylindrical drill with radius 1 is used to bore a hole through the center of a sphere of radius 5. Find the volume of the ring-shaped solid that remains. Round the answer to the nearest hundredth.

11. An agricultural sprinkler distributes water in a circular pattern of radius 100 ft. It supplies water to a depth of e^{-r} feet per hour at a distance of r feet from the sprinkler. What is the total amount of water supplied per hour to the region inside the circle of radius 10 feet centered at the sprinkler?

Round the answer to the nearest thousandth.

12. Find the mass of the lamina that occupies the region D and has the given density function, if D is bounded by the parabola $x = y^2$ and the line $y = x - 2$.

$\rho(x, y) = 7$

13. Find the mass of the lamina that occupies the region D and has the given density function. Round your answer to two decimal places.

$$R = \left\{ (x, y) \mid 0 \le x \le \frac{\pi}{2},\ 0 \le y \le \cos x \right\} \quad \rho(x, y) = 10x$$

14. Find the area of the part of the plane $6x + 5y + z = 9$ that lies inside the cylinder $x^2 + y^2 = 49$.

15. Find the area of the surface. Round your answer to three decimal places.

$$z = \frac{2}{3}\left(x^{3/2} + y^{3/2} \right),\ 0 \le x \le 3,\ 0 \le y \le 3$$

16. Describe the region whose area is given by the integral.

$$\int_0^{\pi/4} \int_0^{\cos 2\theta} r\, dr\, d\theta$$

17. Use spherical coordinates.

Evaluate $\iiint_B (x^2 + y^2 + z^2)^2\, dV$, where B is the ball with center the origin and radius 4.

18. Express the volume of the wedge in the first octant that is cut from the cylinder $y^2 + z^2 = 3$ by the planes $y = x$ and $x = 4$ as an iterated integral with respect to z, then to y, then to x.

19. Calculate the iterated integral.

$$\int_0^{2\pi} \int_0^1 \int_0^{\sqrt{1-y^2}} y \sin x\, dz\, dy\, dx$$

20. The joint density function for random variables X, Y and Z is $f(x, y, z) = C\,xyz$ for $0 \le x \le 2,\ 0 \le y \le 4,\ 0 \le z \le 1$, and $f(x, y, z) = 0$ otherwise. Find the value of the constant C.

Round the answer to the nearest thousandth.

ANSWER KEY

Stewart - Calculus ET 7e Chapter 15 Form A

1. -832

2. $100+125y$

3. 76.5

4. 408

5. 8

6. $e-2$

7. $\dfrac{1-\cos(4)}{2}$

8. $\dfrac{\left(1-e^{-16}\right)\pi}{2}$

9. $\dfrac{1}{2}\sin(1)$

10. 492.5

11. 6.28

12. 63/2

13. 5.71

14. $49\pi\sqrt{62}$

15. 17.771

16. half the region inside the loop of the four-leaved $\cos 2\theta$ in quadrant I and IV

17. $65536\pi/7$

18. $\int_0^4\int_0^x\int_0^{\sqrt{3-y^2}} dzdxdy$

19. 0

20. 0.125

1. Find $\int_0^2 f(x,y)\ dx$ if $f(x,y) = 8x + 6x^2 y$.

2. Calculate the iterated integral.

$$\int_2^4 \int_0^3 (3 + 2xy)\ dxdy$$

3. Calculate the iterated integral.

$$\int_0^1 \int_1^2 xe^{xy}\, dxdy$$

4. Find the volume of the solid bounded by the surface $z = x\sqrt{3x^2 + 3y}$ and the planes $x = 1,\ x = 0,$ $y = 1,\ y = 0$, and $z = 0$. Round your answer to two decimal places.

5. Find the volume of the given solid.

Under the paraboloid $z = x^2 + 3y^2$ and above the rectangle $R = [0,2] \times [1,4]$

6. Evaluate $\iint_D x^2 y^2 dA$ where D is the figure bounded by $y = 1,\ y = 2,\ x = 0,\ and\ x = y$.

7. Evaluate the double integral.

$$\iint_D x\cos y\ dA,$$

D is bounded by $y = 0$, $y = x^2$, and $x = 2$.

8. Evaluate the double integral

$$\iint_D (5x - y)\ dA$$

D is bounded by the circle with center the origin and radius 9.

9. Evaluate the integral by reversing the order of integration.

$$\int_0^1 \int_{\arcsin y}^{\pi/2} \cos x\sqrt{1 + \cos^2 x}\ dx\, dy$$

10. Compute $\iint_D \sqrt{25 - x^2 - y^2}\ dA$, where D is the disk $x^2 + y^2 \le 25$, by first identifying the integral as the volume of a solid.

11. Use polar coordinates to find the volume of the solid under the paraboloid $z = x^2 + y^2$ and above the disk $x^2 + y^2 \le 4$.

12. Find the exact area of the surface $z = x^2 + 2y$, $0 \le x \le 1$, $0 \le y \le 2$.

13. A cylindrical drill with radius 3 is used to bore a hole through the center of a sphere of radius 5. Find the volume of the ring-shaped solid that remains. Round the answer to the nearest hundredth.

14. Use polar coordinates to evaluate.

$$\int_{-\sqrt{\pi}}^{\sqrt{\pi}} \int_{-\sqrt{\pi-y^2}}^{\sqrt{\pi-y^2}} \sin(x^2 + y^2)\,dx\,dy$$

15. An agricultural sprinkler distributes water in a circular pattern of radius 100 ft. It supplies water to a depth of e^{-r} feet per hour at a distance of *r* feet from the sprinkler. What is the total amount of water supplied per hour to the region inside the circle of radius 85 feet centered at the sprinkler?

16. Find the mass of the lamina that occupies the region *D* and has the given density function, if *D* is bounded by the parabola $x = y^2$ and the line $y = x - 2$.

$$\rho(x, y) = 7$$

17. The joint density function for a pair of random variables *X* and *Y* is given.

$$f(x, y) = \begin{cases} Cx(1+y), & 0 \le x \le 2,\ 0 \le y \le 4 \\ 0, & \text{otherwise} \end{cases}$$

Find the value of the constant *C*.

18. Find the area of the part of the plane $6x + 6y + z = 6$ that lies in the first octant.

19. Calculate the iterated integral.

$$\int_0^{\pi/4} \int_0^1 \int_0^{\sqrt{1-y^2}} y \sin x \, dz\, dy\, dx$$

20. Evaluate the triple integral. Round your answer to one decimal place.

$$\iiint_E 3xy \ dV$$

E lies under the plane $z = 5 + x + y$ and above the region in the *xy*-plane bounded by the curves $y = \sqrt{x}$, $y = 0$, and $x = 4$.

ANSWER KEY

Stewart - Calculus ET 7e Chapter 15 Form B

1. $16+16y$

2. 72

3. e^2-e-1

4. 0.84

5. 134

6. $7/2$

7. $\dfrac{1-\cos(4)}{2}$

8. 0

9. $\frac{1}{3}\left(2\sqrt{2}-1\right)$

10. $\dfrac{250}{3}\pi$

11. 8π

12. $3+\frac{5}{4}\ln(5)$

13. 268.08

14. 2π

15. 6.283

16. $63/2$

17. $C=\dfrac{1}{24}$

18. $\dfrac{\sqrt{73}}{2}$

19. $\dfrac{2-\sqrt{2}}{6}$

20. 292.6

1. Estimate the volume of the solid that lies above the square $R=[0, 4]\times[0, 4]$ and below the elliptic paraboloid $f(x, y)=68-2x^2-2y^2$.

   Divide R into four equal squares and use the Midpoint rule.

   Select the correct answer.

   a. 836 b. 778 c. 768 d. 192 e. 762

2. Evaluate the double integral by first identifying it as the volume of a solid.

   $$\iint_R (15-2x)\ dA\ ,\ R=\{\ (x,y)\,|\,3\le x\le 7,\ 3\le y\le 8\ \}$$

   Select the correct answer.

   a. 200 b. -300 c. 100 d. -100 e. -200

3. Find the volume of the given solid.

   Under the paraboloid $z=x^2+4y^2$ and above the rectangle $R=[0,2]\times[1,4]$

   Select the correct answer.

   a. 220 b. 272 c. 176 d. 200 e. 74

4. Find the volume of the solid bounded by the surface $z=5+(x-4)^2+2y$ and the planes $x=3, y=4$ and coordinate planes.

   Select the correct answer.

   a. $V=384$ b. $V=768$ c. $V=192$ d. $V=576$ e. $V=256$

5. Calculate the iterated integral.

   $$\int_{-1}^{1}\int_{0}^{1} ye^{xy}\ dx\, dy$$

   Select the correct answer.

   a. $(2e^2+2e-1)/e$ b. $(e^2-2e-1)/e$ c. e^2-2e-1 d. e^2-e e. $(2e-1)/e$

6. Find the volume under $z=x^5+y^5$ and above the region bounded by $y=x^2$ and $x=y^2$.

   Select the correct answer.

   a. $\frac{1}{5}$ b. $\frac{3}{52}$ c. $\frac{1}{32}$ d. $\frac{3}{32}$ e. $\frac{5}{32}$

7. For which of the following regions would you use rectangular coordinates?

Select the correct answer.

a.

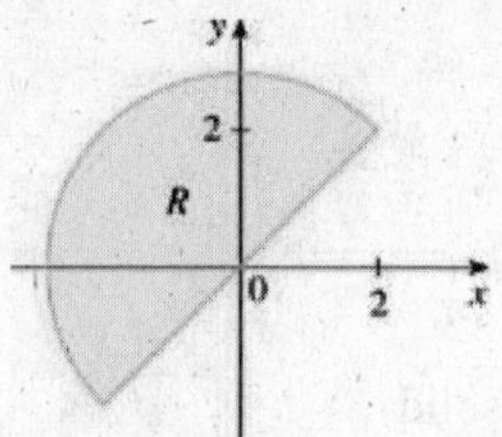

b.

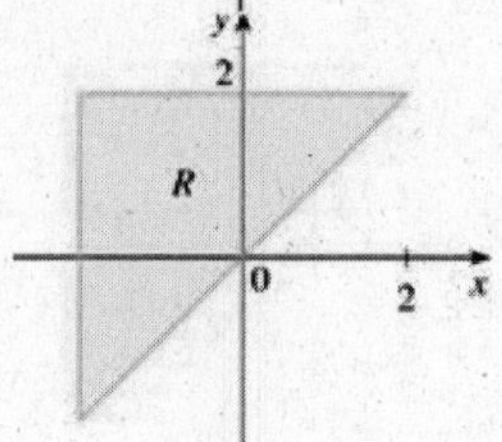

c.

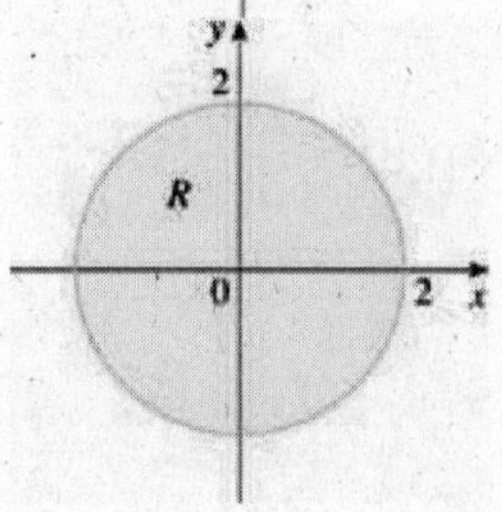

8. Use polar coordinates to find the volume of the solid under the paraboloid $z = x^2 + y^2$ and above the disk $x^2 + y^2 \le 9$.

Select the correct answer.

a. 40.5π b. 7.5π c. 68.5π d. 140.5π e. 43.5π

9. Use polar coordinates to find the volume of the solid bounded by the paraboloid $z = 7 - 6x^2 - 6y^2$ and the plane $z = 1$.

Select the correct answer.

a. 13π b. 6π c. 4.5π d. 2π e. 3π

10. Evaluate the iterated integral by converting to polar coordinates. Round the answer to two decimal places.

$$\int_{-2}^{2} \int_{0}^{\sqrt{4-y^2}} (x^2 + y^2)^{3/2}\, dx\, dy$$

Select the correct answer.

a. 20.11 b. 28.67 c. 11.03 d. 10.52 e. 19.65

11. A swimming pool is circular with a 20-ft diameter. The depth is constant along east-west lines and increases linearly from 4 ft at the south end to 9 ft at the north end. Find the volume of water in the pool.

Select the correct answer.

a. 650π ft^3 b. 600π ft^3 c. 696.5π ft^3 d. 628π ft^3 e. 714.5π ft^3

12. Find the center of mass of a lamina in the shape of an isosceles right triangle with equal sides of length $a = 5$ if the density at any point is proportional to the square of the distance from the vertex opposite the hypotenuse. Assume the vertex opposite the hypotenuse is located at (0, 0), and that the sides are along the positive axes.

Select the correct answer.

a. (5, 3) b. (2, 2) c. (2, 4) d. (3, 3) e. none of these

13. Find the exact area of the surface.

$z = x^2 + 2y,\ 0 \le x \le 1,\ 0 \le y \le 2$

Select the correct answer.

a. $3 + \frac{5}{4}\ln(5)$

b. $\frac{5\ln(3)}{4}$

c. $3 - \ln(5)$

d. $\frac{5}{4}$

e. $2 + \frac{5}{3}\ln(4)$

14. Find the area of the part of hyperbolic paraboloid $z = y^2 - x^2$ that lies between the cylinders $x^2 + y^2 = 1$ and $x^2 + y^2 = 16$.

Select the correct answer.

a. $\pi\frac{65\sqrt{65} - 5\sqrt{5}}{3}$

b. $\pi\frac{\sqrt{65} - \sqrt{5}}{6}$

c. $\pi\frac{65\sqrt{65} - 5\sqrt{5}}{6}$

d. $\pi\frac{\sqrt{65} - \sqrt{5}}{3}$

e. $\pi\frac{32\sqrt{65} - 4\sqrt{5}}{3}$

15. Find the area of the surface. Round your answer to three decimal places.

$z = \frac{2}{3}\left(x^{3/2} + y^{3/2}\right),\ 0 \le x \le 5,\ 0 \le y \le 3$

Select the correct answer.

a. 36.238 b. 38.031 c. 31.017 d. 29.973 e. 33.018

16. Find the area of the surface. The part of the sphere $x^2 + y^2 + z^2 = 64$ that lies above the plane z = 3.

Select the correct answer.

a. $80 - \pi$ b. 80π c. π d. $\pi / 80$ e. 80

17. Use spherical coordinates.

Evaluate $\iiint_B (x^2 + y^2 + z^2)^2 \, dV$, where *B* is the ball with center the origin and radius 3.

Select the correct answer.

a. $559872\pi / 7$ b. $8748\pi / 7$ c. $4374\pi / 7$ d. $4374 / 7$ e. none of these

18. Calculate the iterated integral.

$$\int_0^{\pi} \int_0^{1} \int_0^{\sqrt{1-y^2}} y \sin x \, dz \, dy \, dx$$

Select the correct answer.

a. 2/3 b. 4/3 c. 1/2 d. 0 e. none of these

19. Use a triple integral to find the volume of the solid bounded by $x = y^2$ and the planes $z = 0$ and $x + z = 3$.

Select the correct answer.

a. 2.5 b. 11.3 c. 8.3 d. 15.3 e. 18.3

20. Find the Jacobian of the transformation.

$x = 5\alpha \sin \beta,\ \ y = 4\alpha \cos \beta$

Select the correct answer.

a. $\frac{\partial(x, y)}{\partial(\alpha, \beta)} = 9\alpha$ b. $\frac{\partial(x, y)}{\partial(\alpha, \beta)} = -20\alpha \sin \beta \cos \beta$ c. $\frac{\partial(x, y)}{\partial(\alpha, \beta)} = -20\alpha$

d. $\frac{\partial(x, y)}{\partial(\alpha, \beta)} = -\alpha$ e. $\frac{\partial(x, y)}{\partial(\alpha, \beta)} = 36\alpha$

ANSWER KEY

Stewart - Calculus ET 7e Chapter 15 Form C

1. c
2. c
3. c
4. c
5. b
6. b
7. b
8. a
9. e
10. a
11. a
12. b
13. a
14. c
15. e
16. b
17. b
18. a
19. c
20. c

1. Use the transformation $x = \sqrt{5}u - \sqrt{\frac{5}{3}}v$, $y = \sqrt{5}u + \sqrt{\frac{5}{3}}v$ to evaluate the integral $\iint_R \left(x^2 - xy + y^2\right)\, dA$, where R is the region bounded by the ellipse $x^2 - xy + y^2 = 5$.

Select the correct answer.

a. $\frac{100\pi}{3^{3/2}}$ b. $\frac{25}{\sqrt{3}}$ c. $\frac{25\pi}{\sqrt{3}}$ d. $\frac{5\pi^2}{\sqrt{3}}$ e. $\frac{5\pi}{\sqrt{3}}$

2. A swimming pool is circular with a 20-ft diameter. The depth is constant along east-west lines and increases linearly from 4 ft at the south end to 9 ft at the north end. Find the volume of water in the pool.

Select the correct answer.

a. 650π ft³ b. 600π ft³ c. 696.5π ft³ d. 628π ft³ e. 714.5π ft³

3. Use a triple integral to find the volume of the solid bounded by $x = y^2$ and the planes $z = 0$ and $x + z = 3$.

Select the correct answer.

a. 2.5 b. 11.3 c. 8.3 d. 18.3 e. 15.3

4. Find the volume under $z = x^5 + y^5$ and above the region bounded by $y = x^2$ and $x = y^2$.

Select the correct answer.

a. $\frac{1}{36}$ b. $\frac{3}{52}$ c. $\frac{1}{32}$ d. $\frac{3}{32}$ e. $\frac{5}{36}$

5. Use polar coordinates to find the volume of the solid bounded by the paraboloid $z = 7 - 6x^2 - 6y^2$ and the plane $z = 1$.

Select the correct answer.

a. 13π b. 6π c. 4.5π d. 2π e. 3π

6. Use a computer algebra system to find the value of the integral.

$$\iint_R x^5 y^3 e^{xy}\, dA\ ,\quad R = [0,\ 2] \times [0,\ 2]$$

Select the correct answer.

a. 815.97 b. 13,045.96 c. 791.97 d. 12,067.96 e. 706.97

7. Find the volume of the solid bounded by the surface $z = 5 + (x-4)^2 + 2y$ and the planes $x = 3, y = 4$ and coordinate planes.

Select the correct answer.

a. $V = 384$ b. $V = 768$ c. $V = 192$ d. $V = 576$ e. $V = 525$

8. Find the area of the surface. The part of the sphere $x^2 + y^2 + z^2 = 64$ that lies above the plane $z = 3$.

Select the correct answer.

a. $80 - \pi$ b. 80π c. π d. $\pi / 80$ e. $7\pi / 80$

9. Find the Jacobian of the transformation.

$x = 5\alpha \sin \beta, \quad y = 4\alpha \cos \beta$

Select the correct answer.

a. $\dfrac{\partial(x, y)}{\partial(\alpha, \beta)} = 9\alpha$ b. $\dfrac{\partial(x, y)}{\partial(\alpha, \beta)} = -20\alpha \sin \beta$ c. $\dfrac{\partial(x, y)}{\partial(\alpha, \beta)} = -20\alpha$

d. $\dfrac{\partial(x, y)}{\partial(\alpha, \beta)} = -2\alpha$ e. $\dfrac{\partial(x, y)}{\partial(\alpha, \beta)} = \alpha$

10. Find the area of the surface. Round your answer to three decimal places.

$z = \frac{2}{3}\left(x^{3/2} + y^{3/2}\right), \quad 0 \le x \le 5, \ 0 \le y \le 3$

Select the correct answer.

a. 36.238 b. 38.031 c. 31.017 d. 29.973 e. 33.018

11. Calculate the iterated integral.

$$\int_0^{\pi/4} \int_0^1 \int_0^{\sqrt{1-y^2}} y \sin x \, dz \, dy \, dx$$

Select the correct answer.

a. $\dfrac{\sqrt{2}}{6}$ b. $\dfrac{1}{3}$ c. $\dfrac{2}{3}$ d. $\dfrac{1-\sqrt{3}}{6}$ e. none of these

12. Find the volume of the given solid.

Under the paraboloid $z = x^2 + 3y^2$ and above the rectangle $R = [0, 2] \times [1, 4]$

Select the correct answer.

a. 25 b. 200 c. 134 d. 256 e. 252

13. For which of the following regions would you use rectangular coordinates?

a.

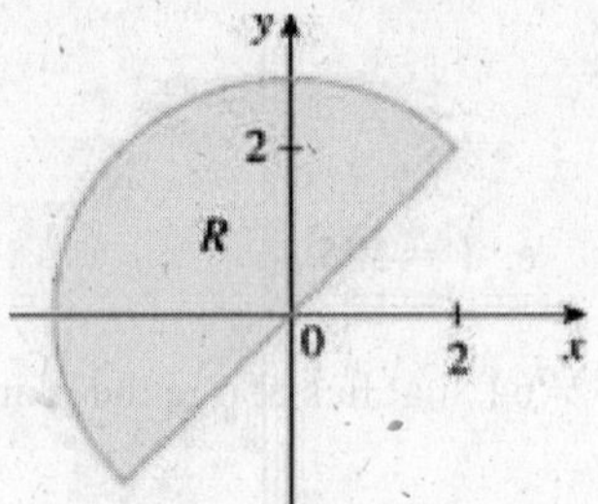

b.

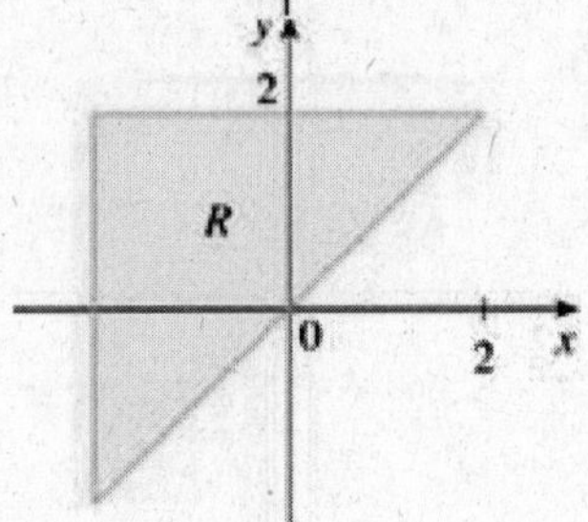

c.

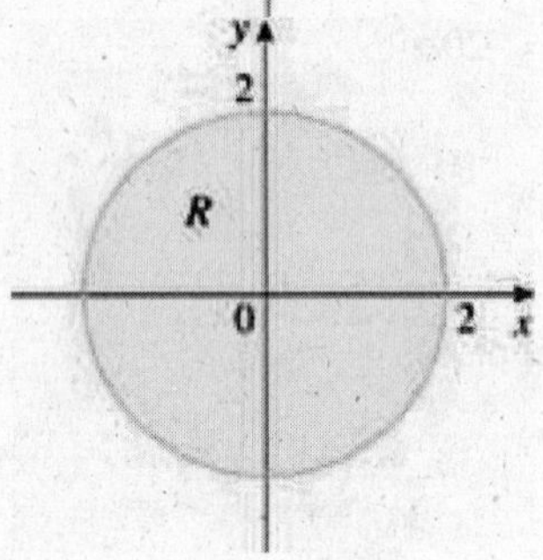

14. Use spherical coordinates.

Evaluate $\iiint_B (x^2 + y^2 + z^2)^2 \, dV$, where B is the ball with center the origin and radius 2.

Select the correct answer.

a. $252\pi / 7$ b. $128\pi / 7$ c. $512 / 7$ d. $256\pi / 7$ e. $512\pi / 7$

15. Calculate the double integral.

$$\iint_R (3x^2 y^3 - 4x^4) \, dA, \quad R = \{ (x, y) \mid 0 \le x \le 4, \ 0 \le y \le 4 \}$$

Select the correct answer.

a. 409.6 b. 273.7 c. 819.2 d. 204.8 e. 215.8

16. Use polar coordinates to find the volume of the solid under the paraboloid $z = x^2 + y^2$ and above the disk $x^2 + y^2 \le 9$.

Select the correct answer.

a. 40.5π b. 7.5π c. 68.5π d. 140.5π e. 43.5π

17. Evaluate the iterated integral by converting to polar coordinates. Round the answer to two decimal places.

$$\int_{-2}^{2} \int_{0}^{\sqrt{4-y^2}} (x^2 + y^2)^{3/2} \, dxdy$$

Select the correct answer.

a. 20.11 b. 28.67 c. 11.03 d. 10.52 e. 19.65

18. Evaluate the iterated integral.

$$\int_{1}^{3} \int_{y}^{3} xy \, dxdy$$

Select the correct answer.

a. 18.1 b. 8 c. 5 d. 10 e. 10.3

19. Use polar coordinates to find the volume of the sphere of radius 6. Round to two decimal places.

Select the correct answer.

a. 824.54 b. 924.54 c. 913.26 d. 964.54 e. 904.78

20. Use a computer algebra system to find the moment of inertia I_0 of the lamina that occupies the region D and has the density function $\rho(x, y) = 3xy$, if $D = \{ (x, y) \mid 0 \le x \le \pi,\ 0 \le y \le \sin(x) \}$.

Select the correct answer.

a. 8.313 b. 34.138 c. 24.105 d. 28.5 e. none of these

ANSWER KEY

Stewart - Calculus ET 7e Chapter 15 Form D

1. c

2. a

3. c

4. b

5. e

6. a

7. c

8. b

9. c

10. e

11. e

12. c

13. b

14. e

15. c

16. a

17. a

18. b

19. e

20. a

1. Calculate the iterated integral.

$$\int_0^1 \int_{-1}^1 xe^{xy}\,dx\,dy$$

2. Compute $\iint_D \sqrt{16 - x^2 - y^2}\,dA$, where D is the disk $x^2 + y^2 \le 16$, by first identifying the integral as the volume of a solid.

3. Use polar coordinates to find the volume of the solid under the paraboloid $z = x^2 + y^2$ and above the disk $x^2 + y^2 \le 49$.

Select the correct answer.

a. $1{,}277.5\pi$ b. $1{,}205.5\pi$ c. $1{,}200.5\pi$ d. $1{,}163.5\pi$ e. $1{,}267.5\pi$

4. Use polar coordinates to find the volume of the sphere of radius 6. Round to two decimal places.

Select the correct answer.

a. 824.54 b. 924.54 c. 913.26 d. 964.54 e. 904.78

5. A cylindrical drill with radius 5 is used to bore a hole through the center of a sphere of radius 7. Find the volume of the ring-shaped solid that remains.

6. Find the volume of the given solid.

Under the paraboloid $z = x^2 + 4y^2$ and above the rectangle $R = [0,3] \times [1,5]$

7. Find the center of mass of the lamina that occupies the region D and has the given density function, if D is bounded by the parabola $y = 64 - x^2$ and the x-axis.

$\rho(x, y) = y$

Select the correct answer.

a. (0, 36.57) b. (16, 56.57) c. (9, 40.57) d. (8, 46.57) e. none of these

8. Find the area of the surface.

The part of the sphere $x^2 + y^2 + z^2 = 9$ that lies above the plane $z = 2$.

9. Find the area of the part of the sphere $x^2 + y^2 + z^2 = 4z$ that lies inside the paraboloid $z = x^2 + y^2$.

10. Calculate the iterated integral.

$$\int_0^{2\pi} \int_0^1 \int_0^{\sqrt{1-y^2}} y \sin x\,dz\,dy\,dx$$

11. Use polar coordinates to evaluate.

$$\int_{-\sqrt{\pi}}^{\sqrt{\pi}} \int_{-\sqrt{\pi-y^2}}^{\sqrt{\pi-y^2}} \sin(x^2+y^2)\,dx\,dy$$

12. Find the moment of inertia about the y-axis for a cube of constant density 3 and side length 5 if one vertex is located at the origin and three edges lie along the coordinate axes.

13. Find the region E for which the triple integral $\iiint_E (1-4x^2-5y^2-6z^2)\,dV$ is a maximum.

14. Use cylindrical coordinates to evaluate the triple integral $\iiint_E y\,dV$ where E is the solid that lies between the cylinders $x^2+y^2=3$ and $x^2+y^2=7$ above the xy-plane and below the plane $z=x+4$.

Select the correct answer.

a. 3.4 b. 9.19 c. 0 d. 8.57 e. 0.54

15. Use spherical coordinates to evaluate the triple integral $\iiint_E xe^{(x^2+y^2+z^2)^2}\,dV$ where E is the solid that lies between the spheres $x^2+y^2+z^2=9$ and $x^2+y^2+z^2=16$ in the first octant.

16. Use spherical coordinates to evaluate $\iiint_B (x^2+y^2+z^2)^2\,dV$, where B is the ball with center the origin and radius 4.

17. Use spherical coordinates to find the moment of inertia of the solid homogeneous hemisphere of radius 3 and density 1 about a diameter of its base.

Select the correct answer.

a. 203.58 b. 198.08 c. 205.13 d. 213.5 e. 195.22

18. Use cylindrical or spherical coordinates, whichever seems more appropriate, to evaluate $\iiint_E z\,dV$ where E lies above the paraboloid $z=x^2+y^2$ and below the plane $z=4y$.

Select the correct answer.

a. 160.28 b. 176.38 c. 167.55 d. 175.93 e. 175.37

19. Find the Jacobian of the transformation.

$$x=\frac{u}{2u+7v},\quad y=\frac{v}{4u-8v}$$

20. Use spherical coordinates to find the volume above the cone $z^2=x^2+y^2$ and inside the sphere $x^2+y^2+z^2=2az$.

ANSWER KEY

Stewart - Calculus ET 7e Chapter 15 Form E

1. $(e^2 - 2e - 1)/e$

2. $\frac{128}{3}\pi$

3. c

4. e

5. 492.5

6. 532

7. a

8. 6π

9. 4π

10. 0

11. 2π

12. 6250

13. $4x^2 + 5y^2 + 6z^2 = 1$

14. c

15. $\frac{\pi}{16}\left(e^{256} - e^{81}\right)$

16. $65536\pi/7$

17. a

18. c

19. 0

20. πa^3

1. Calculate the iterated integral.

$$\int_0^1\int_0^1 xe^{xy}\,dx\,dy$$

2. Find the volume of the given solid.

Under the paraboloid $z = x^2 + 3y^2$ and above the rectangle $R = [0,3]\times[1,5]$

3. Evaluate the integral by making an appropriate change of variables. Round the answer to two decimal places.

$\iint_R e^{x+y}\,dA$, where R is given by the inequality $|x|+|y| \le 3$

4. Calculate the double integral. Round your answer to two decimal places.

$$\iint_R \frac{4+x^2}{1+y^2}\,dA,\quad R=\left\{ (x,y) \mid 0\le x\le 9,\ 0\le y\le 1 \right\}$$

5. Calculate the double integral. Round your answer to two decimal places.

$$\iint_R x\sin(x+y)\,dA,\quad R=\left[0,\ \frac{\pi}{4}\right]\times\left[0,\ \frac{\pi}{6}\right]$$

6. Calculate the double integral. Round your answer to two decimal places.

$$\iint_R xye^{y}\,dA,\quad R=\left\{ (x,y) \mid 0\le x\le 1,\ 0\le y\le 1 \right\}$$

7. Find the volume of the solid in the first octant bounded by the cylinder $z = 9 - y^2$ and the plane $x = 1$.

8. Use the given transformation to evaluate the integral.

$\iint_R (x+y)\,dA$, where R is the square with vertices (0, 0), (2, 3), (3, -2), (5, 1) and

$x = 2u + 3v,\ \ y = 3u - 2v$

9. A lamina occupies the part of the disk $x^2 + y^2 \le 25$ in the first quadrant. Find its center of mass if the density at any point is proportional to its distance from the x-axis.

10. Evaluate the iterated integral.

$$\int_1^5\int_y^5 xy\,dxdy$$

11. Evaluate $\iint_D x^2y^2\,dA$ where D is the figure bounded by $y = 1,\ y = 2,\ x = 0,\ and\ x = y$.

12. Evaluate the double integral.

$\iint_D y^3\, dA$, where D is the triangular region with vertices (0, 1), (7, 0) and (1, 1).

13. Find the volume bounded by the cylinders $x^2 + y^2 = 25$ and $y^2 + z^2 = 25$.

14. Evaluate the integral by reversing the order of integration.

$$\int_0^1 \int_{4y}^4 e^{x^2}\, dx dy$$

15. Use spherical coordinates.

Evaluate $\iiint_B (x^2 + y^2 + z^2)^2\, dV$, where B is the ball with center the origin and radius 3.

16. Evaluate the integral by changing to polar coordinates.

$\iint_D e^{-x^2-y^2}\, dA$, where D is the region bounded by the semicircle $x = \sqrt{4 - y^2}$ and the y-axis.

17. Use polar coordinates to find the volume of the solid inside the cylinder $x^2 + y^2 = 9$ and the ellipsoid $2x^2 + 2y^2 + z^2 = 36$.

Select the correct answer.

a. 260.31 b. 301.74 c. 261.29 d. 292.45 e. 284.22

18. Find the Jacobian of the transformation.

$x = 6uv, \quad y = 4vw, \quad z = 5uw$

19. Find the mass of the lamina that occupies the region D and has the given density function, if D is bounded by the parabola $x = y^2$ and the line $y = x - 2$.

$\rho(x, y) = 3$

Select the correct answer.

a. $\frac{27}{2}$ b. $\frac{9}{2}$ c. $\frac{3}{2}$ d. $\frac{7}{2}$ e. none of these

20. Find the area of the surface. The part of the surface $z = 9 - x^2 - y^2$ that lies above the xy-plane.

ANSWER KEY

Stewart - Calculus ET 7e Chapter 15 Form F

1. $e-2$

2. 408

3. 60.11

4. 219.13

5. 0.11

6. 0.5

7. 18

8. 39

9. $\left(\frac{15}{8}, \frac{15\pi}{16}\right)$

10. 72

11. $7/2$

12. $\frac{1}{5}$

13. $1000/3$

14. $\frac{e^{16}-1}{8}$

15. $8748\pi/7$

16. $\frac{\left(1-e^{-4}\right)\pi}{2}$

17. d

18. $240uvw$

19. a

20. $\frac{\pi}{6}(37\sqrt{37}-1)$

1. Find the volume of the given solid.

Under the paraboloid $z = x^2 + 3y^2$ and above the rectangle $R = [0,2] \times [1,4]$

Select the correct answer.

a. 25 b. 200 c. 134 d. 256 e. 252

2. Find $\int_0^2 f(x,y)\, dx$, if $f(x,y) = 2x + 6x^2 y$.

3. Calculate the iterated integral. Round your answer to two decimal places.

$$\int_0^6 \int_0^3 \sqrt{x+y}\; dxdy$$

Select the correct answer.

a. 18.56 b. 111.38 c. 37.13 d. 74.26 e. 79.26

4. Calculate the iterated integral.

$$\int_0^{\ln 4} \int_0^{\ln 5} e^{5x-y}\; dxdy$$

5. Calculate the double integral.

$$\iint_R (3x^2y^3 - 5x^4)\, dA,\quad R = \{ (x,y) \mid 0 \le x \le 1,\ 0 \le y \le 4 \}$$

Select the correct answer.

a. 30 b. 60 c. 15 d. 20 e. 25

6. Calculate the double integral. Round your answer to two decimal places.

$$\iint_R \frac{xy^2}{x^2+4}\, dA,\quad R = \{ (x,y) \mid 0 \le x \le 2,\ -1 \le y \le 1 \}$$

7. Calculate the double integral.

$$\iint_R xye^y\, dA,\quad R = \{ (x,y) \mid 0 \le x \le 2, 0 \le y \le 1 \}$$

Select the correct answer.

a. 4.19 b. -2 c. 12.87 d. 2 e. 2.57

8. Find the area of the surface.

The part of the surface $z = 1 - x^2 - y^2$ that lies above the *xy*-plane.

Select the correct answer.

a. $\frac{\pi}{6}(5\sqrt{5} - 1)$

b. $\frac{\pi}{3}(5\sqrt{5} - 1)$

c. $\frac{1}{6}(5\sqrt{5} - 1)$

d. $\frac{\pi}{6}(\sqrt{5} - 1)$

e. $\frac{\pi}{5}(6\sqrt{5} - 1)$

9. Find the area of the surface. The part of the sphere $x^2 + y^2 + z^2 = 9$ that lies above the plane z = 1.

Select the correct answer.

a. $\frac{\pi}{12}$

b. 12π

c. $12 - \pi$

d. π

e. $\frac{1}{12}$

10. Calculate the iterated integral.

$$\int_0^{\pi} \int_0^{1} \int_0^{\sqrt{1-y^2}} y \sin x \, dz \, dy \, dx$$

11. Find the Jacobian of the transformation.

$$x = \frac{u}{10u + 3v}, \quad y = \frac{v}{10u - 3v}$$

12. Find the mass of the solid *S* bounded by the paraboloid $z = 6x^2 + 6y^2$ and the plane $z = 5$ if *S* has constant density 3.

Select the correct answer.

a. 24.91 b. 16.25 c. 19.63 d. 13.92 e. 15.07

13. Use spherical coordinates to evaluate the triple integral $\iiint_E xe^{(x^2+y^2+z^2)^2} \, dV$ where *E* is the solid that lies between the spheres $x^2 + y^2 + z^2 = 4$ and $x^2 + y^2 + z^2 = 25$ in the first octant.

14. Use spherical coordinates to find the volume of the solid that lies within the sphere $x^2+y^2+z^2=16$ above the xy-plane and below the cone $z=\sqrt{x^2+y^2}$. Round the answer to two decimal places.

15. Use spherical coordinates.

Evaluate $\iiint_B (x^2+y^2+z^2)^2\,dV$, where B is the ball with center the origin and radius 2.

Select the correct answer.

a. $252\pi/7$ b. $128\pi/7$ c. $512/7$ d. $256\pi/7$ e. $512\pi/7$

16. Find the Jacobian of the transformation.

$x=2\alpha\sin\beta,\ \ y=2\alpha\cos\beta$

17. Use polar coordinates to evaluate.

$$\int_{-\sqrt{\pi}}^{\sqrt{\pi}}\int_{-\sqrt{\pi-y^2}}^{\sqrt{\pi-y^2}}\sin(x^2+y^2)\,dxdy$$

18. Use the given transformation to evaluate the integral.

$\iint_R xy\ dA$, where R is the region in the first quadrant bounded by the lines $y=x,\ \ y=3x$ and the hyperbolas $y=2,\ xy=4;\ x=\dfrac{u}{v},\ \ y=v$.

Select the correct answer.

a. 4.447 b. 5.088 c. 3.296 d. 8.841 e. 9.447

19. Use the given transformation to evaluate the integral.

$\iint_R (x+y)\,dA$, where R is the square with vertices (0, 0), (4, 6), (6, -4), (10, 2), and

$x=4u+6v,\ \ y=6u-4v$

Select the correct answer.

a. 208 b. 52 c. 312 d. 42 e. 343

20. Evaluate the integral by making an appropriate change of variables. Round your answer to two decimal places.

$\iint_R xy\ dA$

R is the parallelogram bounded by the lines $2x-3y=-5,\ 2x-3y=-2,\ 5x+2y=-5,\ 5x+2y=-3$.

ANSWER KEY

Stewart - Calculus ET 7e Chapter 15 Form G

1. c

2. $4+16y$

3. c

4. 468.6

5. b

6. 0.23

7. d

8. a

9. b

10. 2/3

11. 0

12. c

13. $\frac{\pi}{16}\left(e^{625}-e^{16}\right)$

14. 39.26

15. e

16. -4α

17. 2π

18. c

19. c

20. –0.16

1. Find the volume of the given solid that is under the paraboloid $z = x^2 + 4y^2$ and above the rectangle $R = [0,3] \times [1,5]$.

2. Use the Midpoint Rule with four squares of equal size to estimate the double integral.

$$\iint_R \cos(x^4 + y^4)\, dA,\ R = \{ (x,y) |\ 0 \le x \le 0.75, 0 \le y \le 0.75 \}$$

Select the correct answer.

a. 0.55824 b. 2.22545 c. 1.48865 d. 1.98487 e. 10.58602

3. Calculate the double integral. Round your answer to two decimal places.

$$\iint_R x\sin(x+y)\, dA,\ R = \left[0,\ \pi/6\right] \times \left[0,\ \pi/2\right]$$

4. Find the area of the part of the plane $36x + 9y + z = 27$ that lies in the first octant.

5. Find the area of the surface. The part of the surface $z = 9 - x^2 - y^2$ that lies above the *xy*-plane.

6. Find the area of the surface. The part of the surface $z = xy$ that lies within the cylinder $x^2 + y^2 = 64$.

7. Find the area of the part of the sphere $x^2 + y^2 + z^2 = 9z$ that lies inside the paraboloid $z = x^2 + y^2$.

Select the correct answer.

a. 81π b. 40.5π c. 4.5π d. 9π e. 7π

8. Use the Midpoint Rule for double integrals with $m = n = 2$ to estimate the area of the surface. Round your answer to three decimal places.

$$z = xy + x^2 + y^2,\ 0 \le x \le 5,\ 0 \le y \le 5$$

9. Use polar coordinates to evaluate.

$$\int_{-\sqrt{\pi}}^{\sqrt{\pi}} \int_{-\sqrt{\pi - y^2}}^{\sqrt{\pi - y^2}} \sin(x^2 + y^2)\, dx dy$$

10. Evaluate the triple integral.

$$\iiint_E 5x\, dV,\ E = \left\{ (x,y,z) \mid 0 \le y \le 3,\ 0 \le x \le \sqrt{9 - y^2},\ 0 \le z \le y \right\}$$

11. Express the integral as an iterated integral of the form $\int_a^b \int_{u(x)}^{v(x)} \int_{c(x,y)}^{d(x,y)} f\, dz\, dy\, dx$ where E is the solid bounded by the surfaces $x^2 = 1 - y$, $z = 0$, and $z = y$.

$$\iiint_E f(x, y, z)\ dV$$

12. Calculate the iterated integral.

$$\int_0^{\pi/4} \int_0^1 \int_0^{\sqrt{1-y^2}} y \sin x\, dz\, dy\, dx$$

13. Find the mass of the solid E, if E is the cube given by $0 \le x \le 4,\ 0 \le y \le 4,\ 0 \le z \le 4$ and the density function ρ is $\rho(x, y, z) = x^2 + y^2 + z^2$.

14. Find the region E for which the triple integral $\iiint_E (1 - 4x^2 - 6y^2 - 7z^2)\ dV$ is a maximum.

15. Use cylindrical coordinates to evaluate $\iiint_E \sqrt{x^2 + y^2}\ dV$, where E is the region that lies inside the cylinder $x^2 + y^2 = 25$ and between the planes $z = -6$ and $z = 5$. Round the answer to two decimal places.

Select the correct answer.

a. 2879.79 b. 2931.90 c. 2818.41 d. 2431.90 e. 2218.41

16. Use cylindrical coordinates to find the volume of the solid that the cylinder $r = 3\cos\theta$ cuts out of the sphere of radius 3 centered at the origin.

17. Find the mass of the solid S bounded by the paraboloid $z = 7x^2 + 7y^2$ and the plane $z = 3$ if S has constant density 5. Round your answer to two decimal places.

18. Use spherical coordinates to evaluate $\iiint_E xe^{(x^2+y^2+z^2)^2}\ dV$, where E is the solid that lies between the spheres $x^2 + y^2 + z^2 = 4$ and $x^2 + y^2 + z^2 = 25$ in the first octant.

19. Use spherical coordinates.

Evaluate $\iiint_B (x^2 + y^2 + z^2)^2\, dV$, where B is the ball with center the origin and radius 5.

20. Find an approximation to $\iint_R (4x - 3y^2)\ dA$.

Use a double Riemann sum with $m = n = 2$ and the sample point in the lower right corner to approximate the double integral, where $R = \left\{ (x, y)\ \middle|\ 0 \le x \le 6,\ 0 \le y \le 4 \right\}$.

ANSWER KEY

Stewart - Calculus ET 7e Chapter 15 Form H

1. 532

2. a

3. 0.17

4. $\dfrac{9\sqrt{1378}}{8}$

5. $\dfrac{\pi}{6}\left(37\sqrt{37}-1\right)$

6. $\dfrac{2\pi}{3}\left(65\sqrt{65}-1\right)$

7. d

8. 546.875

9. 2π

10. 50.625

11. $\int_{-1}^{1}\int_{0}^{1-x^2}\int_{0}^{y} f\,dz\,dy\,dx$

12. $\dfrac{2-\sqrt{2}}{6}$

13. 1024

14. $4x^2+6y^2+7z^2=1$

15. a

16. 32.55

17. 10.1

18. $\dfrac{\pi}{16}\left(e^{625}-e^{16}\right)$

19. $312500\pi/7$

20. 288

1. Find the gradient vector field of f.

   $f(x,y,z)=\sqrt{x^2+2y^2+3z^2}$

2. Evaluate $\int_C xy^4\,ds$, where C is the right half of the circle $x^2+y^2=9$. Round your answer to one decimal place.

3. Evaluate $\int_C yz\,dy+xy\,dz$, where C is given by $x=4\sqrt{t},\ y=5t,\ z=2t^2,\ 0\le t\le 1$. Round your answer to two decimal places.

4. Find the work done by the force field $\mathbf{F}(x,y)=6x\mathbf{i}+(6y+3)\mathbf{j}$ in moving an object along an arch of the cycloid $\mathbf{r}(t)=(t-\sin(t))\mathbf{i}+(1-\cos(t))\mathbf{j},\ 0\le t\le 2\pi$.

5. Find the work done by the force field $\mathbf{F}(x,y)=xz\mathbf{i}+yx\mathbf{j}+zy\mathbf{k}$ on a particle that moves along the curve $\mathbf{r}(t)=t^2\mathbf{i}-t^3\mathbf{j}+t^4\mathbf{k},\ 0\le t\le 1$.

6. Determine whether or not $\mathbf{F}$ is a conservative vector field. If it is, find a function f such that $\mathbf{F}=\nabla f$.

   $\mathbf{F}=(14x+8y)\mathbf{i}+(8x+18y)\mathbf{j}$

7. Determine whether or not $\boldsymbol{F}$ is a conservative vector field. If it is, find a function f such that $\mathbf{F}=\nabla f$.

   $\mathbf{F}=(8x\cos y-y\cos x)\mathbf{i}+(-4x^2\sin y-\sin x)\mathbf{j}$

8. Find a function f such that $\mathbf{F}=\nabla f$, and use it to evaluate $\int_C \mathbf{F}\cdot d\mathbf{r}$ along the given curve C.

   $\mathbf{F}(x,y)=x^5y^6\mathbf{i}+y^5x^6\mathbf{j}$

   $C:\mathbf{r}(t)=\sqrt{t}\mathbf{i}+(1+t^3)\mathbf{j},\ 0\le t\le 1$

9. Find a parametric representation for the part of the plane $z=8$ that lies inside the cylinder $x^2+y^2=9$.

10. Suppose that $\mathbf{F}$ is an inverse square force field, that is, $\mathbf{F}=\dfrac{5\mathbf{r}}{|\mathbf{r}|^3}$ where $\mathbf{r}=x\,\mathbf{i}+y\,\mathbf{j}+z\,\mathbf{k}$. Find the work done by $\mathbf{F}$ in moving an object from a point P_1 along a path to a point P_2 in terms of the distances d_1 and d_2 from these points to the origin.

11. Use Green's Theorem to evaluate $\int_C x^2y\,dx-xy^2\,dy$, where C is the circle $x^2+y^2=9$ with counterclockwise orientation.

12. Find the curl of the vector field.

    $\mathbf{F}(x,y,z)=10e^x\sin(y)\mathbf{i}+5e^x\cos(y)\mathbf{j}+4z\mathbf{k}$

13. Let $\mathbf{r} = x\mathbf{i} + y\mathbf{j} + z\mathbf{k}$ and $r = |\,\mathbf{r}\,|$.

Find $\nabla \cdot (2r\ \mathbf{r})$.

14. Evaluate the line integral.

$$\int_C yz \cos x \, ds$$

$C: x = t,\ y = \cos t,\ z = \sin t \qquad 0 \le t \le \pi$

15. Find a parametric representation for the part of the elliptic paraboloid $x + y^2 + 4z^2 = 16$ that lies in front of the plane $x = 0$.

16. Set up, but do not evaluate, a double integral for the area of the surface with parametric equations $x = 3u \cos v,\ \ y = 5u \sin v,\ \ z = u^2,\ \ 0 \le u \le 6,\ \ 0 \le v \le 2\pi$.

17. Find the curl of $x^2 z\mathbf{i} + 0\mathbf{j} + xz^2\mathbf{k}$.

18. Evaluate the surface integral $\iint_S \mathbf{F} \cdot d\mathbf{S}$ for the given vector field **F** and the oriented surface *S*. In other words, find the flux of *F* across *S*.

$\mathbf{F}(x, y, z) = 4\,x\mathbf{i} + 4\,y\mathbf{j} + 4\,z\mathbf{k}$, S is the sphere $x^2 + y^2 + z^2 = 3$.

19. Use Stoke's theorem to calculate the surface integral $\iint_S \mathbf{F} \cdot d\mathbf{S}$, where $\mathbf{F}(x, y, z) = (e^x \sin y)\mathbf{i} + (e^x \cos y - z)\mathbf{j} + y\mathbf{k}$, and S is the part of the cone $z^2 = x^2 + y^2$ for which $1 \le z \le 2$.

20. Calculate the work done by the force field $\mathbf{F}(x, y, z) = (x^2 + 10z^2)\ \mathbf{i} + (y^2 + 14x^2)\ \mathbf{j} + (z^2 + 12y^2)\ \mathbf{k}$ when a particle moves under its influence around the edge of the part of the sphere $x^2 + y^2 + z^2 = 16$ that lies in the first octant, in a counterclockwise direction as viewed from above.

ANSWER KEY

Stewart - Calculus ET 7e Chapter 16 Form A

1. $x/\sqrt{x^2+2y^2+3z^2}$ **i** + $2y/\sqrt{x^2+2y^2+3z^2}$ **j** + $3z/\sqrt{x^2+2y^2+3z^2}$ **k**

2. 291.6

3. 35.36

4. $12\pi^2$

5. $\dfrac{23}{88}$

6. $7x^2+8yx+9y^2+K$

7. $4x^2\cos(y)-y\sin(x)+K$

8. $\dfrac{32}{3}$

9. $x=r\cos(\phi),\ \ y=r\sin(\phi),\ \ z=8,\ \ 0\le r\le 3,\ \ 0\le\phi\le 2\pi$

10. $5\left(\dfrac{1}{d_1}-\dfrac{1}{d_2}\right)$

11. $-81\pi/2$

12. $-5e^x\cos(y)k$

13. $8r$

14. $2\sqrt{2}/3$

15. $x=16-y^2-4z^2,\ \ z=z,\ \ y=y,\ \ y^2+4z^2\le 16$

16. $\int_0^6\int_0^{2\pi}\sqrt{100u^4\cos^2(v)+36u^4\sin^2(v)+225u^2}\ dvdu$

17. (x^2-z^2)**j**

18. $48\sqrt{3}\pi$

19. 0

20. 1536

1. Find the gradient vector field of f.

$f(x,y,z)=\sqrt{2x^2+y^2+2z^2}$

2. Find the gradient vector field of $f(x,y,z)=x\cos\dfrac{2y}{9z}$.

3. The **flow lines** (or **streamlines**) of a vector field are the paths followed by a particle whose velocity field is the given vector field. Thus, the vectors in a vector field are tangent to the flow lines. The flow lines of the vector field $\mathbf{F}(x, y) = 8x\mathbf{i} - 24y\mathbf{j}$ satisfy the differential equations $\dfrac{dx}{dt}=8x$ and $\dfrac{dy}{dt}=-24y$.

Solve these differential equations to find the equations of the family of flow lines.

4. Evaluate the line integral.

$\int_C yz\cos x\,ds$

$C: x=t,\ y=2\cos t,\ z=2\sin t \qquad 0\le t\le \pi$

5. Find the curl of the vector field.

$\mathbf{F}(x,y,z)=(x-9z)\mathbf{i}+(x+y+6z)\mathbf{j}+(x-9y)\mathbf{k}$

6. Find the curl of the vector field.

$\mathbf{F}(x,y,z)=2e^x\sin(y)\mathbf{i}+4e^x\cos(y)\mathbf{j}+9z\mathbf{k}$

7. Find the divergence of the vector field.

$$\mathbf{F}(x,y,z)=\frac{x}{2x^2+9y^2+7z^2}\mathbf{i}+\frac{y}{2x^2+9y^2+7z^2}\mathbf{j}+\frac{z}{2x^2+9y^2+7z^2}\mathbf{k}$$

8. Determine whether or not the vector field is conservative. If it is conservative, find a function f such that $\mathbf{F}=\nabla f$.

$\mathbf{F}(x,y,z)=10x\mathbf{i}+4y\mathbf{j}+6z\mathbf{k}$

9. Find the div F if $\mathbf{F}(x,y,z)=e^{xz}(\cos yz\,\mathbf{i}+\sin yz\,\mathbf{j}-\mathbf{k})$.

10. Determine whether or not the vector field is conservative. If it is conservative, find a function f such that $\mathbf{F}=\nabla f$.

$\mathbf{F}(x,y,z)=35yze^{7xz}\mathbf{i}+5e^{7xz}\mathbf{j}+35xye^{7xz}\mathbf{k}$

11. Let $\mathbf{r}=x\mathbf{i}+y\mathbf{j}+z\mathbf{k}$ and $r=|\mathbf{r}|$.

Find $\nabla\times(10\mathbf{r})$.

12. Use Green's Theorem to evaluate $\int_C x^2 y\,dx - xy^2 dy$, where C is the circle $x^2 + y^2 = 1$ with counterclockwise orientation.

13. Use the divergence theorem to calculate the surface integral $\iint_S \mathbf{F} \cdot d\mathbf{S}$, where $\mathbf{F}(x, y, z) = x^3\mathbf{i} + y^3\mathbf{j} + z\mathbf{k}$, and S is the surface bounded by $x^2 + y^2 = 1$, $z = 0$, *and* $z = x + 2$.

14. Evaluate the surface integral $\iint_S \mathbf{F} \cdot d\mathbf{S}$, where $F(x, y, z) = x$, and S is the part of the plane $x + y + z = 1$ in the first octant.

15. A fluid with density 1,330 flows with velocity $\mathbf{v} = y\mathbf{i} + \mathbf{j} + z\mathbf{k}$. Find the rate of flow upward through the paraboloid $z = 9 - (x^2 + y^2)/3,\ x^2 + y^2 \le 36$.

16. Use Stokes' Theorem to evaluate $\iint_C \mathbf{F} \cdot d\mathbf{r}$.

$\mathbf{F}(x, y, z) = 0.81x\mathbf{i} + 9y\mathbf{j} + 3(y^2 + x^2)\mathbf{k}$

C is the boundary of the part of the paraboloid $z = 0.81 - x^2 - y^2$ in the first octant. C is oriented counterclockwise as viewed from above.

17. Let $\mathbf{F}(x, y, z) = \left\langle 5ax^3 - xz^2,\ x^2y + by^3,\ 2cz^3 \right\rangle$ and consider all surfaces S whose boundary is a fixed closed curve C.

Find the values of a, b, and c for which $\iint_S \mathbf{F} \cdot d\mathbf{S}$ is independent of the choice of S.

18. Use the Divergence Theorem to calculate the surface integral $\iint_S \mathbf{F} \cdot d\mathbf{S}$.

$\mathbf{F}(x, y, z) = xy\mathbf{i} + yz\mathbf{j} + zx\mathbf{k}$, S is the surface of the solid cylinder $x^2 + y^2 \le 9,\ 0 \le z \le 2$.

19. Use the Divergence Theorem to calculate the surface integral $\iint_S \mathbf{F} \cdot d\mathbf{S}$, that is, calculate the flux of **F** across S.

$\mathbf{F}(x, y, z) = (x^3 + y\sin z)\mathbf{i} + (y^3 + z\cos x)\mathbf{j} + 3z\mathbf{k}$

S is the surface of the solid bounded by the hemispheres $z = \sqrt{25 - x^2 - y^2}$, $z = \sqrt{1 - x^2 - y^2}$, and the plane $z = 0$.

20. Use a computer algebra system to compute the flux of **F** across S.

$\mathbf{F}(x, y, z) = \sin x \cos^2 y\mathbf{i} + \sin^3 z \cos^4 z\mathbf{j} + \sin^5 z \cos^6 x\mathbf{k}$

S is the surface of the cube cut from the first octant by the planes $x = \frac{\pi}{2},\ y = \frac{\pi}{2},\ z = \frac{\pi}{2}$.

ANSWER KEY

Stewart - Calculus ET 7e Chapter 16 Form B

1. $2x/\sqrt{2x^2+y^2+2z^2}\,\mathbf{i}+y/\sqrt{2x^2+y^2+2z^2}\,\mathbf{j}+2z/\sqrt{2x^2+y^2+2z^2}\,\mathbf{k}$

2. $\cos\left(\frac{2y}{9z}\right)\mathbf{i}-\frac{2x}{9z}\sin\left(\frac{2y}{9z}\right)\mathbf{j}+\frac{2xy}{9z^2}\sin\left(\frac{2y}{9z}\right)\mathbf{k}$

3. $y=\frac{C}{x^3}$

4. $8\sqrt{5}/3$

5. $-15\mathbf{i}-10\mathbf{j}+\mathbf{k}$

6. $2e^x\cos(y)\mathbf{k}$

7. $\frac{1}{2x^2+9y^2+7z^2}$

8. $5x^2+2y^2+3z^2+K$

9. $e^{xz}(2z\cos yz-x)$

10. $5ye^{7xz}+K$

11. 0

12. $-\pi/2$

13. 5π

14. $\frac{\sqrt{3}}{6}$

15. 143640π

16. 0

17. $a=\frac{-1}{15},\ b=0,\ c=\frac{1}{6}$

18. 18π

19. $13736\pi/5$

20. $\frac{13\pi^2}{64}\approx 2.0$

1. Which plot illustrates the vector field $\mathbf{F}(x, y, z) = \mathbf{j}$?

Select the correct answer.

a. 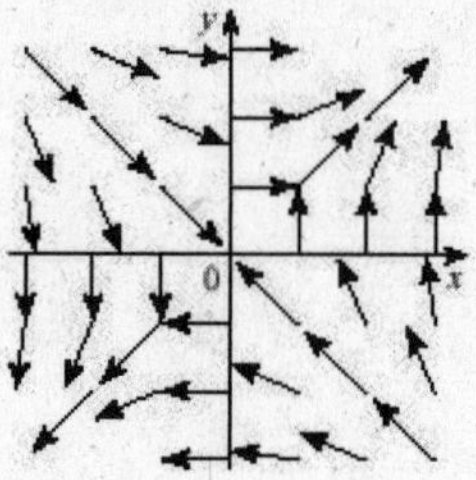

b. 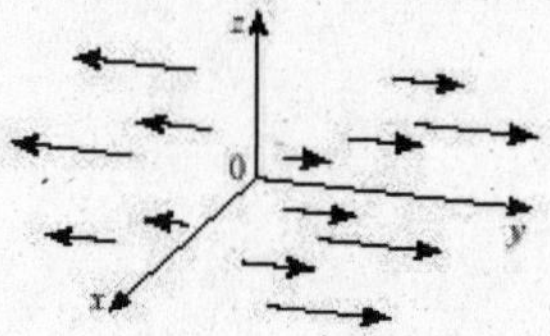

c. 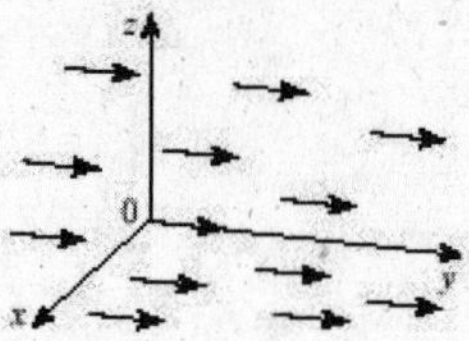

d. 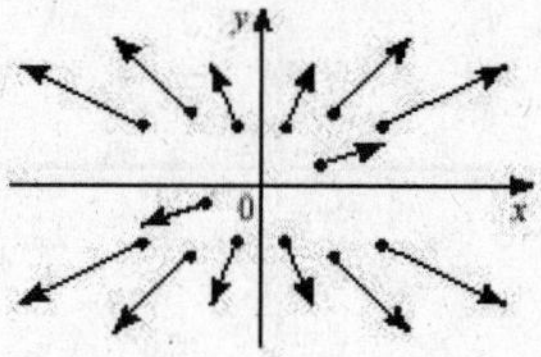

2. Which plot illustrates the vector field $\mathbf{F}(x, y, z) = y\mathbf{j}$?

Select the correct answer.

a. 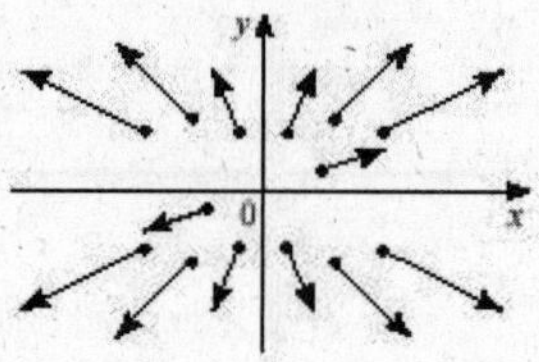

b. 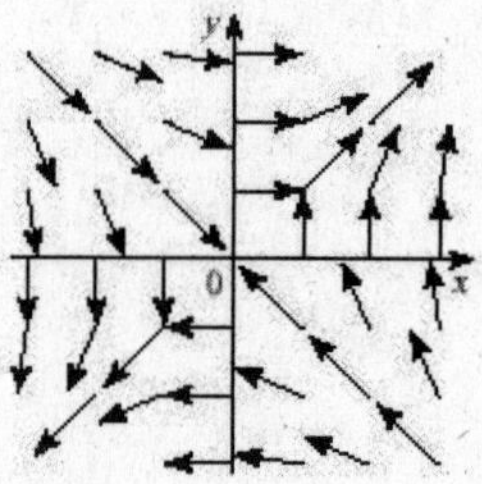

c. 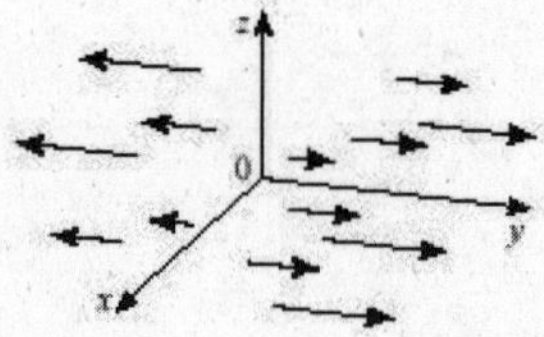

d. 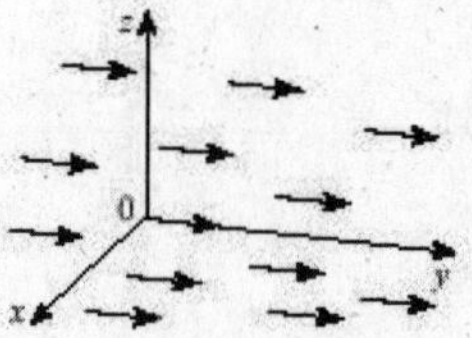

3. Evaluate the line integral $\int_C \mathbf{F} \cdot d\mathbf{r}$, where $\mathbf{F}(x, y) = (x - y)\mathbf{i} + (xy)\mathbf{j}$ and C is the arc of the circle $x^2 + y^2 = 9$ traversed counterclockwise from (3, 0) to (0, -3). Round your answer to two decimal places.

Select the correct answer.

a. 257.06   b. 28.85   c. 25.71   d. 5.14   e. 51.41

4. Find the exact mass of a thin wire in the shape of the helix $x = 2\sin(t),\ \ y = 2\cos(t),\ \ z = 3t,\ \ 0 \le t \le 2\pi$ if the density is 4.

Select the correct answer.

a. $8\sqrt{13}\pi$ b. $4\sqrt{13}\pi$ c. $8\sqrt{13}\pi^2$ d. $8\sqrt{13}$ e. $4\sqrt{13}$

5. Find the work done by the force field $\mathbf{F}(x, y) = x\sin(y)\mathbf{i} + y\mathbf{j}$ on a particle that moves along the parabola $y = x^2$ from (1, 1) to (2, 4).

Select the correct answer.

a. $(17 - \cos(1) + \cos(4)) / 2$
b. $(17 + \cos(1) - \cos(4)) / 2$
c. $(15 + \sin(1) - \sin(4)) / 2$
d. $(15 + \cos(1) - \cos(4)) / 2$
e. $(15 + \sin(1) - \cos(4)) / 2$

6. Use Green's Theorem and/or a computer algebra system to evaluate $\int_C P\ dx + Q\ dy$, where $P(x, y) = x^4 y^5,\ Q(x, y) = -x^7 y^6$, and C is the circle $x^2 + y^2 = 16$. C is positively oriented.

Select the correct answer.

a. $-2{,}703{,}361\pi$ b. $2{,}670{,}592$ c. $-1{,}335{,}296\pi$ d. $1{,}400{,}832\pi$ e. $8{,}011{,}776\pi^2$

7. Use Green's Theorem to evaluate $\int_C x^2 y\,dx - xy^2 dy$, where C is the circle $x^2 + y^2 = 4$ with counterclockwise orientation.

Select the correct answer.

a. -8π b. -4π c. 6π d. 2π e. none of these

8. Find the correct identity, if f is a scalar field, **F** and **G** are vector fields.

Select the correct answer.

a. $\text{div}(f\mathbf{F}) = f\,\text{curl}(\mathbf{F}) + (\nabla f) \times \mathbf{F}$
b. $\text{div}(f\mathbf{F}) = f\,\text{div}(\mathbf{F}) + \mathbf{F} \cdot \nabla f$
c. $\text{curl}(f\mathbf{F}) = f\,\text{div}(\mathbf{F}) + \mathbf{F} \cdot \nabla f$
d. None of these

9. Which of the equations below is an equation of a cone?

Select the correct answer.

a. $r(x,\theta) = \langle x, \cos 7\theta, \sin 7\theta \rangle$
b. $r(x,\theta) = \langle x, x\cos 10\theta, x\sin 10\theta \rangle$

10. Suppose that $f(x,y,z) = g\left(\sqrt{x^2+y^2+z^2}\right)$ where g is a function of one variable such that $g(5) = 6$.

Evaluate $\iint_S f(x,y,z)\; dS$ where S is the sphere $x^2+y^2+z^2 = 25$.

Select the correct answer.

a. 150π b. 300π c. 600π d. 250π e. none of these

11. Let $\mathbf{r} = x\mathbf{i} + y\mathbf{j} + z\mathbf{k}$ and $r = |\mathbf{r}|$.

Find $\nabla \cdot (6\mathbf{r})$.

Select the correct answer.

a. 24 b. 18 c. 30 d. 35 e. none of these

12. Evaluate the surface integral.

$$\iint_S 6yz\; dS$$

S is the part of the plane $x+y+z=6$ that lies in the first octant.

Select the correct answer.

a. $I = 648\sqrt{5}$ b. $I = 54\sqrt{7}$ c. $I = 324$ d. $I = 1{,}296$ e. $I = 324\sqrt{3}$

13. Evaluate the surface integral. Round your answer to four decimal places.

$$\iint_S 6x\; dS$$

S is the surface $y = x^2 + 6z,\; 0 \le x \le 5,\; 0 \le z \le 4$.

Select the correct answer.

a. 2,756.9733
b. 2,756.9633
c. 918.9878
d. 1,378.4817
e. 1,978.4817

14. The temperature at the point (*x*, *y*, *z*) in a substance with conductivity $K = 2.5$ is $u(x,y,z) = 5x^2 + 5y^2$.

Find the rate of heat flow inward across the cylindrical surface $y^2 + z^2 = 2,\ 0 \le x \le 7$.

Select the correct answer.

a. 700π b. 100π c. 175π d. 700 e. 720π

15. Let *D* be a region bounded by a simple closed path *C* in the *xy*. Then the coordinates of the centroid $(\bar{x},\ \bar{y})$ of *D* are $\bar{x} = \frac{1}{2A}\int_C x^2\,dy,\ \bar{y} = -\frac{1}{2A}\int_C y^2\,dx$ where *A* is the area of *D*.

Find the centroid of the triangle with vertices (0, 0), (8, 0) and (0, 8).

Select the correct answer.

a. $\left(\frac{8}{3}, -\frac{8}{3}\right)$ b. $\left(\frac{1}{24}, \frac{1}{8}\right)$ c. $\left(\frac{1}{8}, \frac{1}{64}\right)$ d. $\left(\frac{8}{3}, \frac{8}{3}\right)$ e. $\left(\frac{1}{8}, \frac{1}{8}\right)$

16. Let $\mathbf{F}(x,y,z) = \langle 5ax^3 - xz^2,\ x^2y + by^3,\ 2cz^3 \rangle$ and consider all surfaces *S* whose boundary is a fixed closed curve *C*. Find the values of *a*, *b*, and *c* for which $\iint_S \mathbf{F} \cdot d\mathbf{S}$ is independent of the choice of *S*.

Select the correct answer.

a. $a = 0,\ b = 0,\ c = 0$

b. $a = -\frac{1}{15},\ b = 7,\ c = -\frac{1}{6}$

c. $a = -\frac{1}{15},\ b = 0,\ c = \frac{1}{6}$

d. $a = \frac{1}{15},\ b = 0,\ c = -\frac{1}{6}$

e. $a = \frac{1}{6},\ b = 0,\ c = -\frac{1}{6}$

17. Find the gradient vector field of *f*.

$f(x,y,z) = \sqrt{x^2 + y^2 + z^2}$

Select the correct answer.

a. $x/\sqrt{x^2+y^2+z^2}\ \mathbf{i} + y/\sqrt{x^2+y^2+z^2}\ \mathbf{j} + z/\sqrt{x^2+y^2+z^2}\ \mathbf{k}$

b. $1/\sqrt{x^2+y^2+z^2}\ \mathbf{i} + 1/\sqrt{x^2+y^2+z^2}\ \mathbf{j} + z/\sqrt{x^2+y^2+z^2}\ \mathbf{k}$

c. $2x/\sqrt{x^2+y^2+z^2}\ \mathbf{i} + 2y/\sqrt{x^2+y^2+z^2}\ \mathbf{j} + 2z/\sqrt{x^2+y^2+z^2}\ \mathbf{k}$

d. $y/\sqrt{x^2+y^2+z^2}\ \mathbf{i} + x/\sqrt{x^2+y^2+z^2}\ \mathbf{j} + z/\sqrt{x^2+y^2+z^2}\ \mathbf{k}$

e. none of these

18. Use the Divergence Theorem to calculate the surface integral $\iint_S \mathbf{F} \cdot d\mathbf{S}$.

$\mathbf{F}(x, y, z) = xy\mathbf{i} + yz\mathbf{j} + zx\mathbf{k}$

S is the surface of the solid cylinder $x^2 + y^2 \leq 25,\ 0 \leq z \leq 5$.

Select the correct answer.

a. 625π b. 312.5π c. 125π d. 62.5π e. 125

19. Use the Divergence Theorem to calculate the surface integral $\iint_S \mathbf{F} \cdot d\mathbf{S}$.

$\mathbf{F}(x, y, z) = x\mathbf{i} + y\mathbf{j} + z\mathbf{k}$

S is the surface of the unit ball $x^2 + y^2 + z^2 \leq 9$.

Select the correct answer.

a. 108 b. 9π c. 3π d. 3 e. 108π

20. Use the Divergence Theorem to calculate the surface integral $\iint_S \mathbf{F} \cdot d\mathbf{S}$; that is, calculate the flux of $\mathbf{F}$ across S.

$\mathbf{F}(x, y, z) = 3xy^2\mathbf{i} + 2xe^z\mathbf{j} + z^3\mathbf{k}$

S is the surface of the solid bounded by the cylinder $y^2 + z^2 = 16$ and the planes $x = -1$ and $x = 4$.

Select the correct answer.

a. 640π
b. $1,152\pi$
c. $1,920\pi$
d. $1,280\pi$
e. $1,640\pi$

ANSWER KEY

Stewart - Calculus ET 7e Chapter 16 Form C

1. c

2. c

3. c

4. a

5. d

6. c

7. a

8. b

9. b

10. c

11. b

12. e

13. b

14. a

15. d

16. c

17. a

18. b

19. e

20. c

1. Use Green's Theorem and/or a computer algebra system to evaluate $\int_C P\,dx + Q\,dy$,

where $P(x, y) = x^4 y^5$, $Q(x, y) = -x^7 y^6$, and C is the circle $x^2 + y^2 = 4$. C is positively oriented.

Select the correct answer.

a. $624\pi^2$ b. $65{,}640\pi$ c. $-32{,}977\pi$ d. -104π e. 208

2. Use Green's Theorem to evaluate $\int_C x^2 y\,dx - xy^2\,dy$, where C is the circle $x^2 + y^2 = 16$ with counterclockwise orientation.

Select the correct answer.

a. -128π b. -64π c. 16π d. -16π e. 256π

3. Use Green's Theorem to evaluate to two decimal places the line integral along the given positively oriented curve.

$$\int_C \mathbf{F}\,d\mathbf{r},\quad \mathbf{F}(x, y) = (y^2 - x^2 y)\mathbf{i} + xy^2\mathbf{j}$$

C consists of the circle $x^2 + y^2 = 16$ from (4, 0) to $\left(2\sqrt{2}, 2\sqrt{2}\right)$ and the line segments from $\left(2\sqrt{2}, 2\sqrt{2}\right)$ to (0, 0) and from (0, 0) to (4, 0).

Select the correct answer.

a. $I \approx 37.77$ b. $I \approx 42.71$ c. $I \approx 41.39$ d. $I \approx 35.43$ e. $I \approx 32.43$

4. Use Green's Theorem to find the work done by the force $\mathbf{F}(x, y) = x(x + 5y)\mathbf{i} + 4xy^2\mathbf{j}$ in moving a particle from the origin along the x-axis to (4, 0) then along the line segment to (0, 4) and then back to the origin along the y-axis.

Select the correct answer.

a. -6 b. 32 c. -32 d. 192 e. -192

5. A particle starts at the point (-3, 0), moves along the x-axis to (3, 0) and then along the semicircle $y = \sqrt{9 - x^2}$ to the starting point. Use Green's Theorem to find the work done on this particle by the force field $\mathbf{F}(x, y) = \langle 24x,\ 8x^3 + 24xy^2 \rangle$.

Select the correct answer.

a. 486π b. 972π c. 486 d. 0 e. 48π

6. A plane lamina with constant density $\rho(x, y) = 12$ occupies a region in the *xy*-plane bounded by a simple closed path *C*. Its moments of inertia about the axes are $I_x = -\frac{\rho}{3}\int_C y^3\, dx$ and $I_y = \frac{\rho}{3}\int_C x^3\, dy$.

Find the moments of inertia about the axes, if *C* is a rectangle with vertices (0, 0), (4, 0), (4, 5) and (0, 5).

Select the correct answer.

a. (2,000, 1,280) b. (-1,280, 1,280) c. (2,000, -1,280) d. (-2,000, 1,280) e. (-2,880, 1,200)

7. Find the curl of the vector field.

$\mathbf{F}(x, y, z) = 2xy\mathbf{i} + 10yz\mathbf{j} + 5xz\mathbf{k}$

Select the correct answer.

a. $-10y\mathbf{i} - 5z\mathbf{j} - 2x\mathbf{k}$
b. $-5y\mathbf{i} - 10z\mathbf{j} - 2x\mathbf{k}$
c. $-2y\mathbf{i} - 5z\mathbf{j} - 10x\mathbf{k}$
d. $2y\mathbf{i} - 5z\mathbf{j} + 10x\mathbf{k}$
e. none of these

8. Find the gradient vector field of *f*.

$f(x, y, z) = \sqrt{x^2 + 2y^2 + 3z^2}$

Select the correct answer.

a. $x/\sqrt{x^2+2y^2+3z^2}\ \mathbf{i} + 2y/\sqrt{x^2+2y^2+3z^2}\ \mathbf{j} + 3z/\sqrt{x^2+2y^2+3z^2}\ \mathbf{k}$
b. $2x/\sqrt{x+2y+3z}\ \mathbf{i} + y/\sqrt{x+2y+3z}\ \mathbf{j} + z/\sqrt{x+2y+3z}\ \mathbf{k}$
c. $2x\sqrt{x^2+2y^2+3z^2}\ \mathbf{i} + 4y\sqrt{x^2+2y^2+3z^2}\ \mathbf{j} + 6z\sqrt{x^2+2y^2+3z^2}\ \mathbf{k}$
d. $2x/\sqrt{x^2+2y^2+3z^2}\ \mathbf{i} + 2y/\sqrt{x^2+2y^2+3z^2}\ \mathbf{j} + 3z/\sqrt{x^2+2y^2+3z^2}\ \mathbf{k}$
e. none of these

9. Find the correct identity, if *f* is a scalar field, **F** and **G** are vector fields.

Select the correct answer.

a. $\text{div}(f\mathbf{F}) = f\,\text{curl}(\mathbf{F}) + (\nabla f)\times\mathbf{F}$

b. $\text{div}(f\mathbf{F}) = f\,\text{div}(\mathbf{F}) + \mathbf{F}\cdot\nabla f$

c. $\text{curl}(f\mathbf{F}) = f\,\text{div}(\mathbf{F}) + \mathbf{F}\cdot\nabla f$

d. none of these

10. Use Stokes' Theorem to evaluate $\int_C \mathbf{F} \cdot d\mathbf{r}$, where $\mathbf{F}(x, y, z) = e^{-7x}\mathbf{i} + e^{4y}\mathbf{j} + e^{5z}\mathbf{k}$ and C is the boundary of the part of the plane $8x + y + 8z = 8$ in the first octant.

Select the correct answer.

a. 0 b. 23 c. 49 d. 16 e. 69

11. Find a parametric representation for the part of the elliptic paraboloid $x + y^2 + 6z^2 = 9$ that lies in front of the plane $x = 0$.

Select the correct answer.

a. $x = x,\ y = \pm\sqrt{9 - x + 6z^2},\ z = z$

b. $x = x,\ y = \sqrt{9 - x + 6z^2},\ z = z$

c. $x = 9 - y^2 - 6z^2,\ y = y,\ z = y,\ 0 \le y^2 + 6z^2 \le 3$

d. $x = 9 - y^2 - 6z^2,\ y = y,\ z = y,\ y^2 + 6z^2 \ge 9$

e. $x = 9 - y^2 - 6z^2,\ y = y,\ z = y,\ y^2 + 6z^2 \le 9$

12. Let S be the cube with vertices $(\pm1, \pm1, \pm1)$. Approximate $\iint_S \sqrt{x^2 + 2y^2 + 7z^2}$ by using a Riemann sum as in Definition 1, taking the patches S_{ij} to be the squares that are the faces of the cube and the points P_{ij} to be the centers of the squares.

Select the correct answer.

a. $4(1 + \sqrt{2} + \sqrt{7})$ b. $8(1 + \sqrt{2} + \sqrt{7})$ c. $8(3 + \sqrt{7})$ d. $8(3 + \sqrt{2})$ e. none of these

13. Suppose that $f(x, y, z) = g\left(\sqrt{x^2 + y^2 + z^2}\right)$ where g is a function of one variable such that $g(2) = 3$. Evaluate $\iint_S f(x, y, z)\ dS$ where S is the sphere $x^2 + y^2 + z^2 = 4$.

Select the correct answer.

a. 24π b. 48π c. 12π d. 18π e. none of these

14. Evaluate the surface integral where S is the surface with parametric equations $x = 7uv$, $y = 6(u + v)$, $z = 6(u - v)$, $u^2 + v^2 = 3$.

$$\iint_S 10yz\ dS$$

Select the correct answer.

a. $I = 10\pi$ b. $I = 3$ c. $I = 0$ d. $I = 10 + 7\pi$ e. $I = 10 + 3\pi$

15. The temperature at the point (*x*, *y*, *z*) in a substance with conductivity $K = 9$ is $u(x, y, z) = 6x^2 + 6y^2$. Find the rate of heat flow inward across the cylindrical surface $y^2 + z^2 = 3,\ 0 \le x \le 10$.

Select the correct answer.

a. 6,480 b. $6{,}480\pi$ c. 648π d. $1{,}620\pi$ e. 324π

16. Use Stokes' Theorem to evaluate $\iint_S \text{curl}\,\mathbf{F} \cdot d\mathbf{S}$.

$\mathbf{F}(x, y, z) = 7xy\mathbf{i} + 7e^z\mathbf{j} + 7xy^2\mathbf{k}$

S consists of the four sides of the pyramid with vertices (0, 0, 0), (3, 0, 0), (0, 0, 3), (3, 0, 3) and (0, 3, 0) that lie to the right of the *xz*-plane, oriented in the direction of the positive *y*-axis.

Select the correct answer.

a. 12 b. 16 c. 49 d. 0 e. 1

17. Use the Divergence Theorem to calculate the surface integral $\iint_S \mathbf{F} \cdot d\mathbf{S}$; that is, calculate the flux of **F** across *S*.

$\mathbf{F}(x, y, z) = x^3\mathbf{i} + y^3\mathbf{j} + y^3\mathbf{k}$, *S* is the sphere $x^2 + y^2 + z^2 = 25$

Select the correct answer.

a. 500π b. $2{,}500\pi$ c. 500 d. 7,500 e. $7{,}500\pi$

18. Use a computer algebra system to compute the flux of **F** across *S*. *S* is the surface of the cube cut from the first octant by the planes $x = \pi / 2,\ y = \pi / 2,\ z = \pi / 2$.

$\mathbf{F}(x, y, z) = \sin x \cos^2 y\mathbf{i} + \sin^3 z \cos^4 z\mathbf{j} + \sin^5 z \cos^6 x\mathbf{k}$

Select the correct answer.

a. 0.67 b. 2 c. 4.01 d. 1 e. 3

19. Which of the equations below is an equation of a cone?

a. $\mathbf{r}(x,\theta) = \langle x, \cos 7\theta, \sin 7\theta \rangle$
b. $\mathbf{r}(x,\theta) = \langle x, x\cos 5\theta, x\sin 5\theta \rangle$

20. Use the Divergence Theorem to calculate the surface integral. *S* is the surface of the box bounded by the planes $x = 0, x = 5, y = 0, y = 3, z = 0, z = 4$.

$\iint_S \mathbf{F} \cdot d\mathbf{S}$; $\mathbf{F}(x, y, z) = 4x\mathbf{i} + 5xy\mathbf{j} + 3xz\mathbf{k}$

Select the correct answer.

a. 2,640 b. 1,440 c. -960 d. 120 e. 140

ANSWER KEY

Stewart - Calculus ET 7e Chapter 16 Form D

1. d
2. a
3. a
4. b
5. a
6. a
7. a
8. a
9. b
10. a
11. a
12. b
13. b
14. c
15. b
16. d
17. e
18. b
19. b
20. b

1. Evaluate the line integral.

$$\int_C yz \cos x \, ds$$

$C: x = t,\ y = 4\cos t,\ z = 4\sin t \qquad 0 \le t \le \pi$

2. Consider the vector field $\mathbf{F}(x, y) = \mathbf{i} + x\mathbf{j}$. If a particle starts at the point (10, 4) in the velocity field given by **F**, find an equation of the path it follows.

3. If a wire with linear density 10 lies along a space curve *C*, its **moment of inertia** about the z-axis is given by $I_z = \int_C 10(x^2 + y^2)\ ds$. Find the moment of inertia for the wire in the shape of the helix

$x = 2\sin(t),\ y = 2\cos(t),\ z = 3t,\ 0 \le t \le 2\pi$

4. Find a function *f* such that $\mathbf{F} = \nabla f$, and use it to evaluate $\int_C \mathbf{F} \cdot d\mathbf{r}$ along the given curve *C*.

$\mathbf{F} = e^{2y}\mathbf{i} + (1 + 2xe^{2y})\mathbf{j}, \qquad C:\ \mathbf{r}(t) = te^t\mathbf{i} + (1+t)\mathbf{j},\ 0 \le t \le 1$

5. Suppose that **F** is an inverse square force field, that is, $\mathbf{F} = \dfrac{2\mathbf{r}}{|\mathbf{r}|^3}$ where $\mathbf{r} = x\,\mathbf{i} + y\,\mathbf{j} + z\,\mathbf{k}$. Find the work done by **F** in moving an object from a point P_1 along a path to a point P_2 in terms of the distances d_1 and d_2 from these points to the origin.

6. Use Green's Theorem to find the work done by the force $\mathbf{F}(x, y) = x(x + 5y)\mathbf{i} + (4xy^2)\mathbf{j}$ in moving a particle from the origin along the *x*-axis to (3, 0) then along the line segment to (0, 3) and then back to the origin along the *y*-axis.

Select the correct answer.

a. 49.5 b. -1.5 c. 4.5 d. -4.5 e. -49.5

7. Let $\mathbf{r} = x\mathbf{i} + y\mathbf{j} + z\mathbf{k}$ and $r = |\mathbf{r}|$.

Find $\nabla \cdot (9\ r\ \mathbf{r})$.

8. Which of the equations below is an equation of a plane?

Select the correct answer.

a. $\mathbf{r}(u, v) = (5 + 10u)\mathbf{i} + (-u + 9v)\mathbf{j} + (2 + 6u + 4v)\mathbf{k}$ b. $\mathbf{r}(u, v) = u\cos v\mathbf{i} + u\sin v\mathbf{j} + u^2\mathbf{k}$

9. Find a parametric representation for the part of the sphere $x^2 + y^2 + z^2 = 4$ that lies above the cone $z = \sqrt{x^2 + y^2}$.

10. Find the area of the part of paraboloid $x = y^2 + z^2$ that lies inside the cylinder $z^2 + y^2 = 25$.

11. Find the gradient vector field of $f(x,y,z)=\sqrt{x^2+2y^2+3z^2}$.

Select the correct answer.

a. $x/\sqrt{x^2+2y^2+3z^2}\,\mathbf{i} + 2y/\sqrt{x^2+2y^2+3z^2}\,\mathbf{j} + 3z/\sqrt{x^2+2y^2+3z^2}\,\mathbf{k}$
b. $2x/\sqrt{x+2y+3z}\,\mathbf{i} + y/\sqrt{x+2y+3z}\,\mathbf{j} + z/\sqrt{x+2y+3z}\,\mathbf{k}$
c. $2x\sqrt{x^2+2y^2+3z^2}\,\mathbf{i} + 4y\sqrt{x^2+2y^2+3z^2}\,\mathbf{j} + 6z\sqrt{x^2+2y^2+3z^2}\,\mathbf{k}$
d. $2x/\sqrt{x^2+2y^2+3z^2}\,\mathbf{i} + 2y/\sqrt{x^2+2y^2+3z^2}\,\mathbf{j} + 3z/\sqrt{x^2+2y^2+3z^2}\,\mathbf{k}$
e. none of these

12. Evaluate the surface integral. S is the part of the cylinder $x^2+y^2=9$ between the planes $z=0$ and $z=4$.

$$\iint_S 4(x^2y+z^2)\,dS$$

13. Evaluate the surface integral $\iint_S \mathbf{F}\cdot d\mathbf{S}$, where $\mathbf{F}(x,y,z)=x$, and S is the part of the plane $x+y+z=1$ in the first octant.

14. Find parametric equations for C, if C is the curve of intersection of the hyperbolic paraboloid $z=y^2-x^2$ and the cylinder $x^2+y^2=16$ oriented counterclockwise as viewed from above.

15. Find the moment of inertia about the z-axis of a thin funnel in the shape of a cone $z=5\sqrt{4x^2+4y^2}$, $1\le z\le 4$, if its density function is $\rho(x,y,z)=3-z$.

16. Use *Gauss's Law* to find the charge contained in the solid hemisphere $x^2+y^2+z^2\le 81,\ z\ge 0$, if the electric field is $\mathbf{E}(x,y,z)=x\mathbf{i}+y\mathbf{j}+2z\mathbf{k}$.

17. Use Stokes' Theorem to evaluate $\iint_S \text{curl}\,\mathbf{F}\cdot d\mathbf{S}$. S consists of the top and the four sides (but not the bottom) of the cube with vertices $(\pm 3, \pm 3, \pm 3)$ oriented outward.

$$\mathbf{F}(x,y,z)=2xyz\mathbf{i}+2xy\mathbf{j}+2x^2yz\mathbf{k}$$

18. Use Stoke's theorem to calculate the surface integral $\iint_S \mathbf{F}\cdot d\mathbf{S}$.

$\mathbf{F}(x,y,z)=(e^x\sin y)\mathbf{i}+(e^x\cos y-z)\mathbf{j}+y\mathbf{k}$, and S is the part of the cone $z^2=x^2+y^2$ for which $1\le z\le 2$.

19. Use Stokes' Theorem to evaluate $\iint_C \mathbf{F}\cdot d\mathbf{r}$. C is the boundary of the part of the paraboloid $z=0.16-x^2-y^2$ in the first octant. C is oriented counterclockwise as viewed from above.

$$\mathbf{F}(x,y,z)=0.16x\mathbf{i}+5y\mathbf{j}+6(y^2+x^2)\mathbf{k}$$

20. Find the div F if $\mathbf{F}(x,y,z)=e^{xz}(\cos yz\,\mathbf{i}+\sin yz\,\mathbf{j}-\mathbf{k})$.

ANSWER KEY

Stewart - Calculus ET 7e Chapter 16 Form E

1. $32\sqrt{17}/3$

2. $y=\dfrac{x^2}{2}-46$

3. $80\sqrt{13}\pi$

4. e^5+1

5. $2\left(\dfrac{1}{d_1}-\dfrac{1}{d_2}\right)$

6. c

7. $36r$

8. a

9. $x=x,\ z=\sqrt{4-x^2-y^2},\ y=y,\ 2\le y^2+x^2\le 4$

10. $\dfrac{\pi\left(101\sqrt{101}-1\right)}{6}$

11. a

12. $512\pi/3$

13. $\dfrac{\sqrt{3}}{6}$

14. $x=4\cos(t),\ y=4\sin(t),\ z=-16\cos(2t)$

15. -0.047

16. $1944\pi\varepsilon_0$

17. 0

18. 0

19. 0

20. $e^{xz}(2z\cos yz-x)$

1. Find the gradient vector field of $f(x, y) = \ln(x + 2y)$.

2. Find the gradient vector field of f.

$f(x, y, z) = \sqrt{3x^2 + 2y^2 + z^2}$

3. Consider the vector field $\mathbf{F}(x, y) = \mathbf{i} + x\mathbf{j}$. If a particle starts at the point (10, 4) in the velocity field given by **F**, find an equation of the path it follows.

4. Evaluate $\int_C xy^4 \, ds$, where C is the right half of the circle $x^2 + y^2 = 25$.

5. Evaluate $\int_C xy \, dx + (x - y) \, dy$, where C consists of line segments from (0, 0) to (3, 0) and from (3, 0) to (2, 5). Round your answer to two decimal places.

6. Evaluate $\int_C yz \, dy + xy \, dz$, where C is given by $x = 10\sqrt{t},\ y = 3t,\ z = 10t^2,\ 0 \le t \le 1$. Round your answer to two decimal places.

Select the correct answer.

a. 193.93 b. 20.82 c. 208.23 d. 1,939.29 e. 225.25

7. A thin wire is bent into the shape of a semicircle $x^2 + y^2 = 4,\ x > 0$. If the linear density is 7, find the exact mass of the wire.

8. Find the curl of the vector field.

$\mathbf{F}(x, y, z) = 5e^x \sin(y)\mathbf{i} + 3e^x \cos(y)\mathbf{j} + 8z\mathbf{k}$

9. If a wire with linear density 6 lies along a space curve C, its **moment of inertia** about the z-axis is given by $I_z = \int_C 6(x^2 + y^2) \, ds$. Find the moment of inertia for the wire in the shape of the helix $x = 2\sin(t),\ y = 2\cos(t),\ z = 3t,\ 0 \le t \le 2\pi$.

Select the correct answer.

a. $48\sqrt{13}\pi$ b. $48\sqrt{13}\pi^2$ c. $12\sqrt{13}$ d. $24\sqrt{11}\pi$ e. $12\sqrt{11}\pi$

10. Find the work done by the force field $\mathbf{F}(x, y) = 3x\mathbf{i} + (3y + 10)\mathbf{j}$ in moving an object along an arch of the cycloid $\mathbf{r}(t) = (t - \sin(t))\mathbf{i} + (1 - \cos(t))\mathbf{j}$, $0 \le t \le 2\pi$.

11. Find the work done by the force field $\mathbf{F}(x, y) = x\sin(y)\mathbf{i} + y\mathbf{j}$ on a particle that moves along the parabola $y = x^2$ from (-2, 4) to (1, 1). Round your answer to two decimal places.

12. Find the work done by the force field $\mathbf{F}(x, y, z) = xz\mathbf{i} + yx\mathbf{j} + zy\mathbf{k}$ on a particle that moves along the curve $\mathbf{r}(t) = t^2\mathbf{i} + t^3\mathbf{j} + t^4\mathbf{k},\ 0 \le t \le 1$.

13. Determine whether or not **F** is a conservative vector field. If it is, find a function f such that $\mathbf{F} = \nabla f$.

$$\mathbf{F} = (4 + 2xy + \ln x)\mathbf{i} + x^2\mathbf{j}$$

14. Determine whether or not F is a conservative vector field. If it is, find a function f such that $\mathbf{F} = \nabla f$.

$$\mathbf{F} = (9ye^{9x} + \sin y)\mathbf{i} + (e^{9x} + x\cos y)\mathbf{j}$$

15. Find a function f such that $\mathbf{F} = \nabla f$ and use it to evaluate $\int_C \mathbf{F} \cdot d\mathbf{r}$ along the given curve C.

$$\mathbf{F} = y\mathbf{i} + (x + 2y)\mathbf{j}$$

C is the upper semicircle that starts at (1, 2) and ends at (5, 2).

16. Determine whether or not the vector field is conservative. If it is conservative, find a function f such that $\mathbf{F} = \nabla f$.

$$\mathbf{F}(x, y, z) = 10x\mathbf{i} + 10y\mathbf{j} + 10z\mathbf{k}$$

17. Find the work done by the force field **F** in moving an object from P to Q.

$$\mathbf{F}(x, y) = x^3y^4\mathbf{i} + x^4y^3\mathbf{j};\ P(0, 0),\ Q(3, 2)$$

18. Let $\mathbf{F} = \nabla f$, where $f(x, y) = \sin(x - 8y)$.

Which of the following equations does the line segment from (0, 0) to $(0, \pi)$ satisfy?

Select the correct answer.

a. $\int_C \mathbf{F} \cdot d\mathbf{r} = 0$

b. $\int_C \mathbf{F} \cdot d\mathbf{r} = 1$

c. none of these

19. Suppose that $\mathbf{F} = \dfrac{9\mathbf{r}}{|\mathbf{r}|^3}$ is an inverse square force field, where $\mathbf{r} = x\,\mathbf{i} + y\,\mathbf{j} + z\,\mathbf{k}$.
Find the work done by **F** in moving an object from a point P_1 along a path to a point P_2 in terms of the distances d_1 and d_2 from these points to the origin.

20. Use Green's Theorem to find the work done by the force $\mathbf{F}(x, y) = x(x + 4y)\mathbf{i} + 4xy^2\mathbf{j}$ in moving a particle from the origin along the x-axis to (1, 0) then along the line segment to (0, 1) and then back to the origin along the y-axis.

ANSWER KEY

Stewart - Calculus ET 7e Chapter 16 Form F

1. $\dfrac{1}{x+2y}\mathbf{i}+\dfrac{2}{x+2y}\mathbf{j}$

2. $3x/\sqrt{3x^2+2y^2+z^2}\ \mathbf{i} + 2y/\sqrt{3x^2+2y^2+z^2}\ \mathbf{j} + z/\sqrt{3x^2+2y^2+z^2}\ \mathbf{k}$

3. $y=\dfrac{x^2}{2}-46$

4. 6250

5. -5.83

6. a

7. 28π

8. $-2e^x\cos(y)k$

9. a

10. $6\pi^2$

11. -8.1

12. $\dfrac{-87}{88}$

13. $4x+yx^2+x(\ln x-1)+K$

14. $ye^{9x}+x\sin(y)+K$

15. 8

16. $f=5x^2+5y^2+5z^2+K$

17. 324

18. a

19. $9\left(\dfrac{1}{d_1}-\dfrac{1}{d_2}\right)$

20. $-1/3$

1. Evaluate the line integral.

$\int_C yz \cos x \, ds$

$C: x = t,\ y = 3\cos t,\ z = 3\sin t \quad 0 \le t \le \pi$

2. Find the exact value of $\int_C xe^{yz}\, ds$, where C is the line segment from (0, 0, 0) to (1, 4, 3).

3. Find the exact value of the line integral $\int_C \mathbf{F} \cdot d\mathbf{r}$, where $\mathbf{F}(x, y, z) = \sin(x)\mathbf{i} + \cos(y)\mathbf{j} + xz\mathbf{k}$ and C is given by $\mathbf{r}(t) = t^3\mathbf{i} - t^2\mathbf{j} + t\mathbf{k},\ 0 \le t \le 1$.

4. Evaluate the line integral $\int_C \mathbf{F} \cdot d\mathbf{r}$, where $\mathbf{F}(x, y) = (x - y)\mathbf{i} + (xy)\mathbf{j}$ and C is the arc of the circle $x^2 + y^2 = 4$ traversed counterclockwise from (2, 0) to (0, -2). Round your answer to two decimal places.

5. Find the exact value of $\int_C \mathbf{F} \cdot d\mathbf{r}$, where $\mathbf{F}(x, y) = e^{x-1}\mathbf{i} + (xy)\mathbf{j}$ and C is given by $\mathbf{r}(t) = t^2\mathbf{i} + t^3\mathbf{j},\ 0 \le t \le 1$.

6. Find the area of the part of the surface $y = 4x + z^2$ that lies between the planes $x = 0,\ x = 4,\ z = 0$, and $z = 1$.

Select the correct answer.

a. 19.148 b. 17.118 c. 13.638 d. 27.218 e. 16.113

7. Evaluate the surface integral.

$\iint_S 10yz \, dS$

S is the surface with parametric equations $x = 5\,uv,\ y = 6\,(u + v),\ z = 6\,(u - v),\ u^2 + v^2 = 3$.

8. Evaluate the surface integral $\iint_S \mathbf{F} \cdot d\mathbf{S}$ for the given vector field $\mathbf{F}$ and the oriented surface S. In other words, find the flux of $\mathbf{F}$ across S.

$\mathbf{F}(x, y, z) = 4x\mathbf{i} + 4y\mathbf{j} + 4z\mathbf{k}$, S is the sphere $x^2 + y^2 + z^2 = 2$.

9. A fluid with density 1,230 flows with velocity $\mathbf{v} = y\mathbf{i} + \mathbf{j} + z\mathbf{k}$. Find the rate of flow upward through the paraboloid $z = 9 - \frac{1}{4}(x^2 + y^2),\ x^2 + y^2 \le 36$.

10. Find the curl of $x^2z\mathbf{i} + 0\mathbf{j} + xz^2\mathbf{k}$

11. Use Stokes' Theorem to evaluate $\iint_S \text{curl } \mathbf{F} \cdot d\mathbf{S}$

$\mathbf{F}(x, y, z) = 8xy\mathbf{i} + 8e^z\mathbf{j} + 8xy^2\mathbf{k}$

S consists of the four sides of the pyramid with vertices (0, 0, 0), (5, 0, 0), (0, 0, 5), (5, 0, 5), and (0, 5, 0) that lie to the right of the xz-plane, oriented in the direction of the positive y-axis.

12. Use Stokes' Theorem to evaluate $\int_C \mathbf{F} \cdot d\mathbf{r}$.

$\mathbf{F}(x, y, z) = 4z\mathbf{i} + 2x\mathbf{j} + 6y\mathbf{k}$

C is the curve of intersection of the plane $z = x + 9$ and the cylinder $x^2 + y^2 = 9$

13. Calculate the work done by the force field $\mathbf{F}(x, y, z) = (x^2 + 14z^2)\mathbf{i} + (y^2 + 6x^2)\mathbf{j} + (z^2 + 12y^2)\mathbf{k}$ when a particle moves under its influence around the edge of the part of the sphere $x^2 + y^2 + z^2 = 4$ that lies in the first octant, in a counterclockwise direction as viewed from above. Round the answer to two decimal places.

Select the correct answer.

a. 512 b. 85.33 c. 170.67 d. 539.07 e. 266.92

14. Use the Divergence Theorem to calculate the surface integral $\iint_S \mathbf{F} \cdot d\mathbf{S}$.

$\mathbf{F}(x, y, z) = xz\mathbf{i} + yz\mathbf{j} + 5z^2\mathbf{k}$

S is the surface of the solid bounded by the paraboloid $z = x^2 + y^2$ and the plane $z = 6$.

15. The temperature at the point (x, y, z) in a substance with conductivity K = 14 is $u(x, y, z) = 5x^2 + 5y^2$.

Find the rate of heat flow inward across the cylindrical surface $y^2 + z^2 = 4,\ 0 \le x \le 5$.

16. Use Green's Theorem to evaluate $\int_C x^2 y\,dx - xy^2 dy$, where C is the circle $x^2 + y^2 = 4$ with counterclockwise orientation.

17. Use the Divergence Theorem to calculate the surface integral $\iint_S \mathbf{F} \cdot d\mathbf{S}$, that is, calculate the flux of **F** across S.

$\mathbf{F}(x, y, z) = x^3\mathbf{i} + y^3\mathbf{j} + z^3\mathbf{k}$, S is the sphere $x^2 + y^2 + z^2 = 25$.

Select the correct answer.

a. $2{,}500\pi$ b. 500π c. 7,500 d. 500 e. $7{,}500\pi$

18. Use the Divergence Theorem to calculate the surface integral $\iint_S \mathbf{F} \cdot d\mathbf{S}$, that is, calculate the flux of **F** across *S*.

$\mathbf{F}(x, y, z) = e^y \cos z\mathbf{i} + y\sqrt{1 - x^2}\,\mathbf{j} + x\cos y\mathbf{k}$

S is the surface of the solid that lies above the *xy*-plane and below the surface

$z = 5 - x^4 - y^4, \ -1 \le x \le 1, \ -1 \le y \le 1$.

19. Evaluate the surface integral $\iint_S \mathbf{F} \cdot d\mathbf{S}$ for the given vector field **F** and the oriented surface *S*. In other words, find the flux of **F** across *S*.

$\mathbf{F}(x, y, z) = 9x\mathbf{i} + 2y\mathbf{j} + 6z\mathbf{k}$

S is the cube with vertices $(\pm1, \pm1, \pm1)$.

20. Assume that *S* and **F** satisfy the conditions of the Divergence Theorem and the scalar functions and components of the vector fields have continuous second-order partial derivatives. Which of the following expressions is equal to zero?

Select the correct answer.

a. $\iint_S (f \nabla g) \cdot \mathbf{n}\, dS$

b. $\iint_S \mathbf{a} \cdot \mathbf{n}\, dS$, **a** is a constant vector

c. $\iint_S (f \nabla g - g \nabla f) \cdot \mathbf{n}\, dS$

ANSWER KEY

Stewart - Calculus ET 7e Chapter 16 Form G

1. $6\sqrt{10}$

2. $\dfrac{\sqrt{26}(e^{12}-1)}{24}$

3. $\dfrac{6}{5}-\cos(1)-\sin(1)$

4. 10.09

5. $1+\dfrac{3}{8}-\dfrac{1}{e}$

6. b

7. 0

8. $32\sqrt{2}\pi$

9. $199260\,\pi$

10. $(x^2-z^2)\mathbf{j}$

11. 0

12. -36π

13. c

14. 864π

15. 5600π

16. -8π

17. e

18. $\dfrac{187\pi}{40}$

19. 136

20. b

1. Evaluate $\int_C y\ ds$, where C is given by $x = t^2,\ y = t,\ 2 \le t \le 9$. Round your answer to two decimal places.

2. Evaluate $\int_C xy^4\ ds$, where C is the right half of the circle $x^2 + y^2 = 4$.

   Select the correct answer.

   a. 0.8 b. 267.0 c. 25.6 d. 97.4 e. 90.4

3. Evaluate $\int_C xy\ dx + (x - y)\ dy$, where C consists of line segments from (0, 0) to (4, 0) and from (4, 0) to (4, 2).

4. Evaluate $\int_C xy^3\ ds$, where C is given by $x = 9\sin t,\ y = \cos t,\ z = 9t,\ 0 \le t \le \pi/2$. Round your answer to two decimal places.

5. Let $\mathbf{r} = x\mathbf{i} + y\mathbf{j} + z\mathbf{k}$ and $\mathrm{r} = |\,\mathbf{r}\,|$.

   Find $\nabla \cdot (4\mathbf{r})$.

6. Evaluate (to four places) $\int_C \mathbf{F} \cdot d\mathbf{r}$, where $\mathbf{F}(x, y) = \dfrac{x}{\sqrt{x^2 + y^2}}\mathbf{i} + \dfrac{y}{\sqrt{x^2 + y^2}}\mathbf{j}$ and C is the parabola $y = 1 + x^2$ from (-3, 10) to (-2, 5).

7. Find the exact value of $\int_C \mathbf{F} \cdot d\mathbf{r}$, where $\mathbf{F}(x, y) = e^{x-1}\mathbf{i} + xy\mathbf{j}$ and C is given by $\mathbf{r}(t) = t^2\mathbf{i} + t^3\mathbf{j},\ 0 \le t \le 1$.

8. Determine whether or not the vector field is conservative. If it is conservative, find a function f such that $\mathbf{F} = \nabla f$.

   $\mathbf{F}(x, y, z) = 5zy\mathbf{i} + 5xz\mathbf{j} + 5xy\mathbf{k}$

9. A thin wire is bent into the shape of a semicircle $x^2 + y^2 = 4,\ x > 0$. If the linear density is 3, find the mass of the wire.

   Select the correct answer.

   a. 18π b. $6\pi^2$ c. 3π d. 6π e. 2π

10. Find the exact mass of a thin wire in the shape of the helix $x = 2\sin t,\ y = 2\cos t,\ z = 3t,\ 0 \le t \le 2\pi$ if the density is 5.

11. Find the work done by the force field $\mathbf{F}(x, y) = 2x\mathbf{i} + (2y + 5)\mathbf{j}$ in moving an object along an arch of the cycloid $\mathbf{r}(t) = (t - \sin(t))\mathbf{i} + (1 - \cos(t))\mathbf{j},\ 0 \le t \le 2\pi$.

12. Determine whether or not **F** is a conservative vector field. If it is, find a function *f* such that $\mathbf{F} = \nabla f$.

$\mathbf{F} = (6ye^{6x} + \sin y)\mathbf{i} + (e^{6x} + x\cos y)\mathbf{j}$

13. Find a function *f* such that $\mathbf{F} = \nabla f$ and use it to evaluate $\int_C \mathbf{F}\cdot d\mathbf{r}$ along the given curve *C*.

$\mathbf{F} = y\mathbf{i} + (x + 2y)\mathbf{j}$; *C* is the upper semicircle that starts at (1, 4) and ends at (5, 4).

14. Find the work done by the force field **F** in moving an object from *P* to *Q*.

$\mathbf{F}(x, y) = x^2y^3\mathbf{i} + x^3y^2\mathbf{j}$; $P(0, 0)$, $Q(4, 1)$

15. Use Green's Theorem to evaluate the line integral along the given positively oriented curve.

$\int_C \sin y\, dx + x\cos y\, dy$

C is the ellipse $x^2 + xy + y^2 = 1$.

16. Use Green's Theorem to evaluate $\int_C x^2y\,dx - xy^2\,dy$, where *C* is the circle $x^2 + y^2 = 9$ with counterclockwise orientation.

17. Find the area of the region bounded by the hypocycloid with vector equation.

$\mathbf{r}(t) = 12\cos^3 t\mathbf{i} + 80\sin^3 t\mathbf{j},\ 0 \le t \le 2\pi$

Select the correct answer.

a. 360 b. $360\pi^2$ c. 360π d. 2.25π e. $2.25\pi^2$

18. Determine whether or not the vector field is conservative. If it is conservative, find a function *f* such that $\mathbf{F} = \nabla f$.

$\mathbf{F}(x, y, z) = 27yze^{9xz}\mathbf{i} + 3e^{9xz}\mathbf{j} + 27xye^{9xz}\mathbf{k}$

19. Use Stokes' Theorem to evaluate $\int_C \mathbf{F}\cdot d\mathbf{r}$, where $\mathbf{F}(x, y, z) = 6yx^2\mathbf{i} + 2x^3\mathbf{j} + 6xy\mathbf{k}$.

C is the curve of intersection of the hyperbolic paraboloid $z = y^2 - x^2$ and the cylinder $x^2 + y^2 = 25$ oriented counterclockwise as viewed from above.

20. Use the divergence theorem to calculate the surface integral $\iint_S \mathbf{F}\cdot d\mathbf{S}$, where $\mathbf{F}(x, y, z) = x^3\mathbf{i} + y^3\mathbf{j} + z\mathbf{k}$, and *S* is the surface bounded by $x^2 + y^2 = 1$, $z = 0$, *and* $z = x + 2$.

ANSWER KEY

Stewart - Calculus ET 7e Chapter 16 Form H

1. 482.41

2. c

3. 6

4. 20876.97

5. 12

6. −5.0551

7. $1+\frac{3}{8}-\frac{1}{e}$

8. $5xyz+K$

9. d

10. $10\sqrt{13}\pi$

11. $4\pi^2$

12. $ye^{6x}+x\sin(y)+K$

13. 16

14. $\frac{64}{3}$

15. 0

16. $-81\pi/2$

17. c

18. $f=3ye^{9xz}+K$

19. -3750π

20. 5π

1. Solve the differential equation.

   $y'' - 2y' - 15y = 0$

2. Solve the differential equation.

   $y'' + 10y' + 41y = 0$

3. Solve the differential equation.

   $y'' - y = \cos x$

4. Solve the differential equation.

   $13y'' = 5y'$

5. Solve the differential equation.

   $4y'' + y' = 0$

6. Solve the initial-value problem.

   $2y'' + 21y' + 54y = 0, \quad y(0) = 0, \quad y'(0) = 1$

7. Solve the initial value problem.

   $y'' - 2y' - 3y = 0 \qquad y(0) = 2, \;\; y'(0) = 1$

8. Solve the initial-value problem.

   $y'' + 49y = 0 \;,\;\; y\left(\frac{\pi}{7}\right) = 0 \;,\;\; y'\left(\frac{\pi}{7}\right) = 1$

9. Solve the boundary-value problem, if possible.

   $y'' - y' - 2y = 0 \;,\;\; y(-1) = 1 \;,\;\; y(1) = 0$

10. Solve the differential equation using the method of undetermined coefficients.

    $y'' + 6y' + 9y = 1 + x$

11. Solve the differential equation using the method of undetermined coefficients.

    $y'' - 4y' + 5y = e^{-x}$

12. Solve the initial-value problem using the method of undetermined coefficients.

    $y'' + y' - 2y = x + \sin x \;,\;\; y(0) = \frac{19}{20} \;,\;\; y'(0) = 0$

13. Solve the differential equation.

$$y'' - 2y' = e^x$$

14. Solve the differential equation using the method of variation of parameters.

$$y'' - 4y = \frac{1}{x}$$

15. A spring with a 7-kg mass is held stretched 1.4 m beyond its natural length by a force of 80 N. If the spring begins at its equilibrium position but a push gives it an initial velocity of 1.2 m/s, find the position $x\ (t)$ of the mass after t seconds.

16. A spring with a mass of 2 kg has damping constant 14, and a force of 3.6 N is required to keep the spring stretched 0.3 m beyond its natural length. Find the mass that would produce critical damping.

17. A series circuit consists of a resistor $R = 20\ \Omega$, an inductor with $L = 1$ H, a capacitor with $C = 0.002$ F, and a 12-V battery. If the initial charge and current are both 0, find the charge $Q(t)$ at time t.

18. A series circuit consists of a resistor $R = 24\ \Omega$, an inductor with $L = 2$ H, a capacitor with $C = 0.005$ F, and a generator producing a voltage of $E(t)$ = 12cos 10t. If the initial charge is $Q = 0.001$ C and the initial current is 0, find the charge $Q(t)$ at time t.

19. Use power series to solve:

$$y'' + xy' + 2y = 0$$

20. Use power series to solve.

$$y'' - y' = 0$$

ANSWER KEY

Stewart - Calculus ET 7e Chapter 17 Form A

1. $y = C_1 e^{5x} + C_2 e^{-3x}$

2. $y = e^{-5x}(C_1 \cos(4x) + C_2 \sin(4x))$

3. $y = -\frac{1}{2}\cos x + C_1 e^{x} + C_2 e^{-x}$

4. $y = C_1 + C_2 e^{\frac{5x}{13}}$

5. $y = C_1 + C_2 e^{\frac{-x}{4}}$

6. $y = \frac{2}{3} e^{\frac{-9x}{2}} - \frac{2}{3} e^{-6x}$

7. $y = \frac{5}{4} e^{-x} + \frac{3}{4} e^{3x}$

8. $y = -\frac{1}{7}\sin(7x)$

9. $y = \frac{1}{e^6 - 1}(e^{5-x} - e^{2(x+1)})$

10. $y(x) = C_1 e^{-3x} + C_2 x e^{-3x} + \frac{1}{9}x + \frac{1}{27}$

11. $y(x) = e^{2x}(C_1 \cos(x) + C_2 \sin(x)) + \frac{1}{10} e^{-x}$

12. $y(x) = \frac{17}{15} e^{x} + \frac{1}{6} e^{-2x} - \frac{1}{2}x - \frac{1}{4} - \frac{1}{10}\cos(x) - \frac{3}{10}\sin(x)$

13. $y = C_1 + C_2 e^{2x} - e^{x}$

14. $y(x) = \left(C_1 - \int \frac{e^{2x}}{4x}\, dx \right) e^{-2x} + \left(C_2 + \int \frac{e^{-2x}}{4x}\, dx \right) e^{2x}$

15. $x(t) = 0.42 \sin\left(\frac{20t}{7}\right)$

16. 49/12

17. $Q(t) = \frac{-e^{-10t}}{250}(6\cos(20t) + 3\sin(20t)) + \frac{3}{125}$

18. $Q(t) = e^{-6t}(0.001\cos(8t) - 0.06175\sin(8t)) + \frac{1}{20}\sin(10t)$

19. $a_0 \sum_{k=0}^{\infty} \frac{(-1)^k x^{2k}}{1\cdot 3\cdot 5 \cdot\ldots\cdot (2k-1)} + a_1 \sum_{k=0}^{\infty} \frac{(-1)^k x^{2k+1}}{2^k k!}$

20. $a_0 \sum_{k=0}^{\infty} \frac{x^{2k}}{(2k)!} + a_1 \sum_{k=0}^{\infty} \frac{x^{2k+1}}{(2k+1)!}$

1. Solve the differential equation.

$y'' - 2y' - 3y = 0$

2. Solve the differential equation.

$y'' - 12y' + 36y = 0$

3. Solve the differential equation.

$7y'' = 2y'$

4. Solve the differential equation.

$y'' - y = \cos x$

5. Solve the differential equation.

$\frac{d^2y}{dt^2} + \frac{dy}{dt} + 2y = 0$

6. Solve the initial-value problem.

$y'' + 36y = 0\ ,\ y\left(\frac{\pi}{6}\right) = 0\ ,\ y'\left(\frac{\pi}{6}\right) = 1$

7. Solve the initial value problem.

$y'' + 2y' - 3y = 0 \qquad y(0) = 2,\ \ y'(0) = 1$

8. Solve the boundary-value problem, if possible.

$y'' - y' - 30y = 0\ ,\ y(-1) = 1\ ,\ y(1) = 0$

9. Solve the boundary-value problem, if possible.

$y'' + 2y' + 37y = 0\ ,\ y(0) = 1\ ,\ y(\pi) = 2$

10. Solve the differential equation using the method of undetermined coefficients.

$y'' + 9y = e^{2x}$

11. Solve the differential equation using the method of undetermined coefficients.

$y'' - 8y' + 17y = e^{-x}$

12. Solve the initial - value problem using the method of undetermined coefficients.

$y'' - y = xe^{2x}\ ,\ y(0) = 0\ ,\ y'(0) = 1$

13. Solve the differential equation using the method of variation of parameters.

$y'' + 9y = x$

14. Solve the differential equation using the method of variation of parameters.

$y'' - 5y' + 4y = \sin x$

15. Solve the differential equation using the method of variation of parameters.

$y'' + 6y' + 9y = \dfrac{e^{-3x}}{x^3}$

16. A series circuit consists of a resistor $R = 24\ \Omega$, an inductor with $L = 2$ H, a capacitor with $C = 0.005$ F, and a generator producing a voltage of $E(t) = 12\cos 10t$. If the initial charge is $Q = 0.001$ C and the initial current is 0, find the charge $Q(t)$ at time t.

17. Use power series to solve.

$y'' - y' = 0$

18. Use power series to solve:

$y'' + xy' + 2y = 0$

19. The figure shows a pendulum with length L and the angle θ from the vertical to the pendulum. It can be shown that θ, as a function of time, satisfies the nonlinear differential equation $\dfrac{d^2\theta}{dt^2} + \dfrac{g}{L}\sin\theta = 0$ where g = 9.8 m/s ^{2} is the acceleration due to gravity. For small values of θ we can use the linear approximation $\sin\theta = \theta$ and then the differential equation becomes linear. Find the equation of motion of a pendulum with length 1 m if θ is initially 0.1 rad and the initial angular velocity is $\dfrac{d\theta}{dt} = 1$ rad/s.

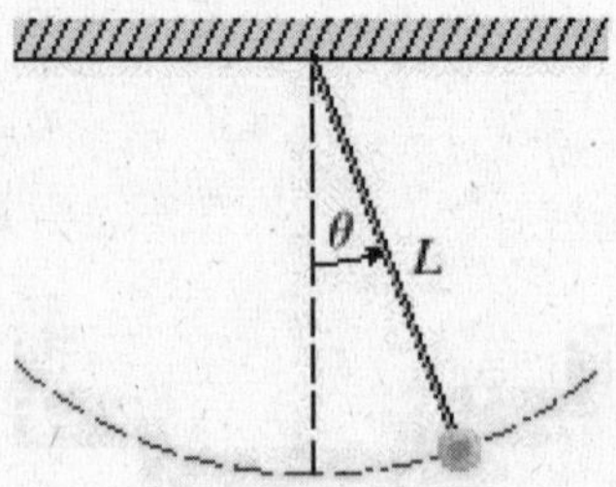

20. Use power series to solve the differential equation.

$y'' - xy' - y = 0\ ,\quad y(0) = 1\ ,\quad y'(0) = 0$

ANSWER KEY

Stewart - Calculus ET 7e Chapter 17 Form B

1. $y = C_1 e^{-x} + C_2 e^{3x}$

2. $y = e^{6x}(C_1 + C_2 x)$

3. $y = C_1 + C_2 e^{\frac{2x}{7}}$

4. $y = -\frac{1}{2}\cos x + C_1 e^{x} + C_2 e^{-x}$

5. $y = e^{\frac{-t}{2}}\left(C_1 \cos\left(\frac{\sqrt{7}t}{2}\right) + C_2 \sin\left(\frac{\sqrt{7}t}{2}\right)\right)$

6. $y = -\frac{1}{6}\sin(6x)$

7. $y = \frac{7}{4}e^{x} + \frac{1}{4}e^{-3x}$

8. $y = \frac{1}{e^{22}-1}\left(e^{17-5x} - e^{6(x+1)}\right)$

9. no solution

10. $y(x) = C_1 \cos(3x) + C_2 \sin(3x) + \frac{1}{13}e^{2x}$

11. $y(x) = e^{4x}(C_1 \cos(x) + C_2 \sin(x)) + \frac{1}{26}e^{-x}$

12. $y(x) = e^{x} - \frac{5}{9}e^{-x} + e^{2x}\left(\frac{1}{3}x - \frac{4}{9}\right)$

13. $y(x) = C_1 \cos(3x) + C_2 \sin(3x) + \frac{1}{9}x$

14. $y(x) = C_1 e^{4x} + C_2 e^{x} + \frac{5}{34}\cos(x) + \frac{3}{34}\sin(x)$

15. $y(x) = e^{-3x}\left(C_1 + C_2 x + \frac{1}{2x}\right)$

16. $Q(t) = e^{-6t}(0.001\cos(8t) - 0.06175\sin(8t)) + \frac{1}{20}\sin(10t)$

17. $a_0 \sum_{k=0}^{\infty} \frac{x^{2k}}{(2k)!} + a_1 \sum_{k=0}^{\infty} \frac{x^{2k+1}}{(2k+1)!}$

18. $a_0 \sum_{k=0}^{\infty} \frac{(-1)^k x^{2k}}{1 \cdot 3 \cdot 5 \cdot\cdots\cdot (2k-1)} + a_1 \sum_{k=0}^{\infty} \frac{(-1)^k x^{2k+1}}{2^k k!}$

19. $\theta(t) = 0.1\cos(\sqrt{9.8}t) + \frac{1}{\sqrt{9.8}}\sin(\sqrt{9.8}t)$

20. $y(x) = e^{\frac{x^2}{2}}$

1. Solve the differential equation.

$y'' + 2y' - 3y = 0$

Select the correct answer.

a. $y = C_1e^x + C_2e^{-3x}$
b. $y = C_1e^x + C_2e^{-4x}$
c. $y = C_1e^x / 3 + C_2e^{-3x} / 2$
d. $y = C_1e^{3x} + C_2e^{-3x}$
e. none of these

2. Solve the initial-value problem.

$y'' + 8y' + 41y = 0\ ,\ \ y(0) = 1,\ \ y'(0) = 2$

Select the correct answer.

a. $y(x) = e^{4x}\left(\cos(5x) - \frac{2}{5}\sin(5x)\right)$

b. $y(x) = e^{-4x}\left(\cos(5x) + \frac{6}{5}\sin(5x)\right)$

c. $y(x) = e^{5x}\left(\cos(5x) + \frac{6}{5}\sin(5x)\right)$

d. $y(x) = e^{5x}\left(\cos(4x) + \frac{6}{5}\sin(4x)\right)$

e. $y(x) = e^{-5x}\left(\cos(5x) + \frac{2}{5}\sin(5x)\right)$

3. Solve the initial value problem.

$y'' + 3y' - 4y = 0 \qquad y(0) = 2,\ \ y'(0) = 1$

Select the correct answer.

a. $y = \frac{9}{5}e^x + \frac{1}{5}e^{-4x}$

b. $y = \frac{1}{5}e^{2x} + \frac{9}{5}e^{-2x}$

c. $y = e^x + \frac{1}{5}e^{-3x}$

d. $y = e^{2x} + \frac{1}{5}e^{-2x}$

e. none of these

4. Solve the boundary-value problem, if possible.

$y'' + 5y' - 24y = 0\ ,\ \ y(0) = 0,\ \ y(2) = 1$

Select the correct answer.

a. $y(x) = \left(e^{6} - e^{-16} \right)\left(e^{6x} - e^{-8x} \right)$

b. $y(x) = \left(e^{6} - e^{-16} \right)^{-1}\left(e^{6x} - e^{-16x} \right)$

c. $y(x) = \left(e^{6} - e^{-16} \right)^{-1}\left(e^{3x} - e^{-8x} \right)$

d. $y(x) = \left(e^{8} - e^{-16} \right)^{-1}\left(e^{x} - e^{-8x} \right)$

e. no solution

5. Solve the differential equation using the method of undetermined coefficients.

$y'' + 5y' + 6y = x^2$

Select the correct answer.

a. $y(x) = c_1e^{-2x} + c_2e^{-3x} + \frac{19}{108}c_3$

b. $y(x) = \frac{1}{6}x^2 - \frac{5}{18}x + \frac{19}{108}$

c. $y(x) = c_1e^{-2x} + c_2e^{-3x}$

d. $y(x) = c_1e^{-2x} + c_2e^{-3x} + \frac{1}{6}x^2 - \frac{5}{18}x + \frac{19}{108}$

e. $y(x) = c_1e^{-2x} + c_2e^{-3x} + \frac{1}{6}x^2$

6. Solve the differential equation using the method of undetermined coefficients.

$y'' + 6y' + 9y = 1 + x$

Select the correct answer.

a. $y(x) = c_1e^{-3x} + c_2xe^{-3x}$

b. $y(x) = c_1e^{-3x} + c_2xe^{-3x} + \frac{1}{9}x + \frac{1}{27}$

c. $y(x) = c_1e^{-3x} + \frac{1}{9}x + \frac{1}{27}$

d. $y(x) = c_1e^{-3x} + c_2xe^{-3x} + \frac{2}{9}x$

e. $y(x) = c_1xe^{-3x} + c_2x^2e^{-3x} + \frac{1}{27}x$

7. Solve the differential equation using the method of variation of parameters.

$y'' - 4y' + 3y = \sin x$

Select the correct answer.

a. $y(x) = c_1 \sin 3x + \frac{c_2}{4} x + \cos 3x$

b. $y(x) = c_1 \sin x + \frac{c_2}{5} x + \frac{1}{10} \sin x$

c. $y(x) = c_1 e^{3x} + c_2 e^x + \frac{1}{5} \cos x + \frac{1}{10} \sin x$

d. $y(x) = c_1 e^{3x} + c_2 e^x + \frac{1}{10} \sin x$

e. $y(x) = c_1 e^{3x} + c_2 e^x + \frac{1}{5} \sin x$

8. Solve the differential equation using the method of variation of parameters.

$y'' - y' = e^x$

Select the correct answer.

a. $y(x) = c_1 + c_2 x e^x + e^x$

b. $y(x) = c_1 + c_2 e^x + x e^x$

c. $y(x) = c_1 + c_2 e^x$

d. $y(x) = c_1 + (1 + x) x e^x$

e. $y(x) = c_1 + x e^x$

9. Solve the differential equation using the method of variation of parameters.

$y'' + y = \sec x \ , \ \frac{\pi}{4} < x < \frac{\pi}{2}$

Select the correct answer.

a. $y(x) = (c_1 + x) \sin x + c_2 + \ln(\cos x)$

b. $y(x) = \frac{\pi}{2} \sin x + \left[\frac{\pi}{2} + \ln(\cos x) \right] \cos x$

c. $y(x) = \left[\frac{\pi}{4} + \ln(\cos x) \right] \cos x$

d. $y(x) = (c_1 + x) \sin x + [c_2 + \ln(\cos x)] \cos x$

e. $y(x) = c_1 + [c_2 + \ln(\sin x)] \sin x$

10. A spring with a 3-kg mass is held stretched 0.9 m beyond its natural length by a force of 30 N. If the spring begins at its equilibrium position but a push gives it an initial velocity of 1.2 m/s, find the position $x(t)$ of the mass after t seconds.

Select the correct answer.

a. $x(t) = 1.2\sin(7t)$

b. $x(t) = 0.36\sin\left(\frac{10}{3}t\right) + 0.48\cos\left(\frac{10}{3}t\right)$

c. $x(t) = 0.48\cos\left(\frac{10}{3}t\right)$

d. $x(t) = 0.36\sin\left(\frac{10}{3}t\right)$

e. $x(t) = \frac{10}{3}\sin(7t)$

11. A spring with a mass of 5 kg has damping constant 28 and spring constant 195. Find the damping constant that would produce critical damping.

Select the correct answer.

a. $c = 10\sqrt{77}$

b. $c = 10\sqrt{39}$

c. $c = 15\sqrt{39}$

d. $c = 15\sqrt{77}$

e. $c = 39\sqrt{10}$

12. A series circuit consists of a resistor $R = 16\ \Omega$, an inductor with $L = 2$ H, a capacitor with $C = 0.00625$ F, and a 12-V battery. If the initial charge is 0.0008 C and the initial current is 0, find the current $I(t)$ at time t.

Select the correct answer.

a. $I(t) = 0.742e^{-4t}\sin(8t)$

b. $I(t) = 0.742e^{-8t}$

c. $I(t) = \frac{e^{-160t}}{160}(0.00625\cos(4t) + 8\sin(4t)) - \frac{1}{2}$

d. $I(t) = \frac{e^{-4t}}{160}\cos(8t)$

e. $I(t) = \frac{e^{-4t}}{160}\cos(8t) - \frac{1}{2}$

13. The figure shows a pendulum with length L and the angle θ from the vertical to the pendulum. It can be shown that θ, as a function of time, satisfies the nonlinear differential equation $\dfrac{d^2\theta}{dt^2}+\dfrac{g}{L}\sin\theta=0$ where g = 9.8 m/s ^{2} is the acceleration due to gravity. For small values of θ we can use the linear approximation $\sin\theta=\theta$ and then the differential equation becomes linear. Find the equation of motion of a pendulum with length 1 m if θ is initially 0.1 rad and the initial angular velocity is $\dfrac{d\theta}{dt}=1$ rad/s.

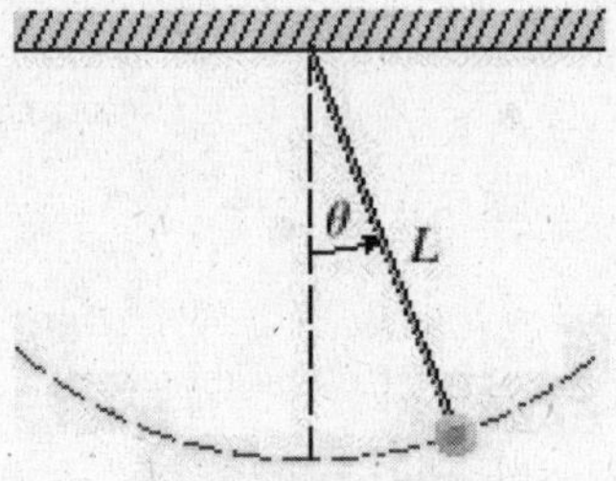

Select the correct answer.

a. $\theta(t)=0.1\cos(\sqrt{9.8}t)+\dfrac{1}{\sqrt{9.8}}\sin(\sqrt{9.8}t)$

b. $\theta(t)=0.1\sin(\sqrt{9.8}t)+\dfrac{1}{\sqrt{9.8}}\cos(\sqrt{9.8}t)$

c. $\theta(t)=2\cos(9.8t)+\dfrac{1}{9.8}\sin(9.8t)$

d. $\theta(t)=0.1\cos(\sqrt{9.8}t)+2\sin(\sqrt{9.8}t)$

e. $\theta(t)=\dfrac{1}{9.8}\cos(\sqrt{9.8}t)+0.1\sin(\sqrt{9.8}t)$

14. Use power series to solve the differential equation.

$y'=4x^2y$

Select the correct answer.

a. $y(x)=ce^{\frac{4x^3}{3}}$

b. $y(x)=ce^{4x}$

c. $y(x)=ce^{-\frac{4x^3}{3}}$

d. $y(x)=4e^{\frac{x^3}{3}}$

e. $y(x)=e^{-\frac{x^3}{3}}$

15. Use power series to solve the differential equation.

$(x-6)y' + 2y = 0$

Select the correct answer.

a. $y(x) = c_0 \sum_{n=0}^{\infty} \frac{n+1}{6^n} x^n$

b. $y(x) = c_0 \sum_{n=0}^{\infty} \frac{x^n}{6^n}$

c. $y(x) = c_0 \sum_{n=0}^{\infty} \frac{nx^n}{6^n}$

d. $y(x) = c_0 \sum_{n=0}^{\infty} (n+1)x^n$

e. $y(x) = c_0 \sum_{n=0}^{\infty} \frac{(n+1)}{x^n}$

16. Use power series to solve the differential equation.

$y'' - xy' - y = 0$, $y(0) = 5$, $y'(0) = 0$

Select the correct answer.

a. $y(x) = e^{5x}$ b. $y(x) = 5e^{\frac{x^2}{2}}$ c. $y(x) = 5e^x$ d. $y(x) = ce^{\frac{x^2}{2}}$ e. $y(x) = 5e^{-\frac{x^2}{2}}$

17. Use power series to solve the differential equation.

$y'' + x^2 y = 0$, $y(0) = 6$, $y'(0) = 0$

Select the correct answer.

a. $y(x) = 6 - \sum_{n=1}^{\infty} (-1)^n \frac{x^{4n}}{4n(4n-1)\cdot(4n-4)(4n-5)\cdots 4\cdot 3}$

b. $y(x) = \sum_{n=1}^{\infty} (-1)^n \frac{6x^{4n}}{4n(4n-1)\cdot(4n-4)(4n-5)\cdots 4\cdot 3}$

c. $y(x) = 6 + \sum_{n=1}^{\infty} (-1)^n \frac{6x^{4n}}{4n(4n-1)\cdot(4n-4)(4n-5)\cdots 4\cdot 3}$

d. $y(x) = -6 + \sum_{n=1}^{\infty} (-1)^n \frac{x^{4n}}{4n(4n-1)\cdot(4n-4)(4n-5)\cdots 4\cdot 3}$

e. $y(x) = \sum_{n=1}^{\infty} (-1)^n \frac{x^{4n}}{4n(4n-1)\cdot(4n-4)(4n-5)\cdots 4\cdot 3}$

18. The solution of the initial-value problem $x^2y'' + xy' + x^2y = 0$, $y(0) = 1$, $y'(0) = 0$ is called a Bessel function of order 0. Solve the initial - value problem to find a power series expansion for the Bessel function.

Select the correct answer.

a. $y(x) = x + \sum_{n=0}^{\infty} (-1)^n \frac{x^{2n}}{2^{2n}(n!)^2}$

b. $y(x) = \sum_{n=0}^{\infty} (-1)^{n+1} \frac{nx^{2n-1}}{2^{2n-1}(n!)^2}$

c. $y(x) = \sum_{n=0}^{\infty} (-1)^n \frac{x^{2n}}{2^{2n}(n!)^2}$

d. $y(x) = \sum_{n=0}^{\infty} (-1)^n \frac{x^n}{2^n(2n!)}$

e. $y(x) = 2^x + \sum_{n=0}^{\infty} (-1)^n \frac{x^{2n}}{(n!)^2}$

19. Solve the differential equation.

$y'' - 8y' + 25y = 0$

Select the correct answer.

a. $y(x) = e^{4x}(c_1 \cos(3x) + c_2 \sin(3x))$
b. $y(x) = e^{4x}(c_1 \cos(3x) + c_2 x \sin(3x))$
c. $y(x) = ce^{4x} \cos(3x)$
d. $y(x) = c_1 \cos(3x) + c_2 x \sin(3x)$
e. $y(x) = e^{4x}(c_1 \cos(4x) + c_2 x \sin(4x))$

20. A series circuit consists of a resistor $R = 24\ \Omega$, an inductor with $L = 2$ H, a capacitor with C = 0.005 F, and a generator producing a voltage of $E(t)$ = 12cos(10t). If the initial charge is $Q = 0.001\,\text{C}$ and the initial current is 0, find the charge $Q(t)$ at time t.

Select the correct answer.

a. $Q(t) = e^{-2t}(0.051\cos(2t) - 0.06175\sin(2t)) + \frac{1}{20}\sin(10t)$

b. $Q(t) = e^{-6t}(0.001\cos(8t) - 0.06175\sin(8t)) + \frac{1}{20}\sin(10t)$

c. $Q(t) = e^{-3t}(\cos(5t) - 0.06175\sin(5t))$

d. $Q(t) = e^{-6t}(\cos(6t) - 0.06175\sin(6t))$

e. $Q(t) = e^{-6t}(0.001\cos(8t) - 0.06175\sin(8t))$

ANSWER KEY

Stewart - Calculus ET 7e Chapter 17 Form C

1. a
2. b
3. a
4. c
5. d
6. b
7. c
8. b
9. d
10. d
11. b
12. a
13. a
14. a
15. a
16. b
17. c
18. c
19. a
20. b

1. Solve the initial value problem.

$y'' + 3y' - 4y = 0 \qquad y(0) = 2, \quad y'(0) = 1$

Select the correct answer.

a. $y = \frac{9}{5}e^{x} + \frac{1}{5}e^{-4x}$

b. $y = \frac{1}{5}e^{2x} + \frac{9}{5}e^{-2x}$

c. $y = e^{x} + \frac{1}{5}e^{-3x}$

d. $y = e^{2x} + \frac{1}{5}e^{-2x}$

e. none of these

2. A spring with a mass of 3 kg has damping constant 35 and spring constant 129. Find the damping constant that would produce critical damping.

Select the correct answer.

a. $c = 6\sqrt{43}$

b. $c = 6\sqrt{7}$

c. $c = 9\sqrt{7}$

d. $c = 9\sqrt{43}$

e. $c = 43\sqrt{7}$

3. Solve the differential equation.

$\frac{d^2y}{dt^2} + \frac{dy}{dt} + 3y = 0$

Select the correct answer.

a. $y(t) = ce^{-\frac{t}{2}}\cos\left(\sqrt{\frac{11t}{2}}\right)$

b. $y(t) = e^{-\frac{t}{2}}\left[c_1\cos\left(\frac{\sqrt{11}t}{2}\right) + c_2\sin\left(\frac{\sqrt{11}t}{2}\right)\right]$

c. $y(t) = t^2e^{-\frac{t}{2}}\left[c_1\cos\left(\sqrt{\frac{11t}{2}}\right) + c_2\sin\left(\sqrt{\frac{11t}{2}}\right)\right]$

d. $y(t) = te^{\frac{t}{2}}\left[c_1\cos\left(\frac{\sqrt{11}t}{2}\right) + c_2\sin\left(\frac{\sqrt{11}t}{2}\right)\right]$

e. $y(t) = e^{\frac{\sqrt{t}}{2}}\left[c_1\cos\left(\frac{\sqrt{t}}{2}\right) + c_2\sin\left(\frac{\sqrt{t}}{2}\right)\right]$

4. Solve the differential equation.

$36y'' + y = 0$

Select the correct answer.

a. $y(x) = c_1 \cos\left(-\frac{x}{36}\right) + c_2 \sin\left(-\frac{x}{6}\right)$
b. $y(x) = c_1 \cos(6x) + c_2 \sin(6x)$
c. $y(x) = c_1 \cos(-6x) + c_2 \sin(-6x)$
d. $y(x) = c_1 \cos\left(\frac{x}{6}\right) + c_2 \sin\left(\frac{x}{6}\right)$
e. $y(x) = c_1 \cos(36x) - c_2 \sin(36x)$

5. Solve the initial-value problem.

$y'' - 2y' - 24y = 0\ ,\ \ y(1) = 4,\ \ y'(1) = 1$

Select the correct answer.

a. $y(x) = \frac{1}{10}e^{4(x-1)} + \frac{1}{23}e^{-6(x-1)}$
b. $y(x) = e^{6x} - e^{-4x}$
c. $y(x) = \frac{17}{10}e^{6(x-1)} + \frac{23}{10}e^{-4(x-1)}$
d. $y(x) = \frac{1}{10}e^{4x} - \frac{1}{23}e^{-6x}$
e. $y(x) = \frac{1}{10}e^{x} - \frac{1}{23}e^{-x}$

6. Use power series to solve the differential equation.

$y'' - xy' - y = 0\ ,\ \ y(0) = 6,\ \ y'(0) = 0$

Select the correct answer.

a. $y(x) = 6e^{x}$ b. $y(x) = 6e^{x^2/2}$ c. $y(x) = e^{6x}$ d. $y(x) = 3e^{x^3/2}$ e. $y(x) = e^{-6x}$

7. Solve the boundary-value problem, if possible.

$y'' + 2y' - 63y = 0\ ,\ \ y(0) = 0,\ \ y(2) = 1$

Select the correct answer.

a. $y(x) = \left(e^{14} - e^{-18}\right)^{-1}\left(e^{14x} - e^{-18x}\right)$ b. $y(x) = \left(e^{14} - e^{-18}\right)^{-1}\left(e^{7x} - e^{-9x}\right)$
c. $y(x) = \left(e^{14} - e^{-18}\right)^{-1}\left(e^{14x} - e^{-9x}\right)$ d. $y(x) = \left(e^{14} - e^{-18}\right)^{-1}\left(e^{8x} - e^{-9x}\right)$
e. no solution

8. Solve the boundary-value problem, if possible.

$$y'' - y' - 6y = 0\ ,\quad y(-1) = 1,\quad y(1) = 0$$

Select the correct answer.

a. $y(x) = \dfrac{1}{e^{10}+1}\left(e^{8-2x} - e^{3(x+1)}\right)$

b. $y(x) = \dfrac{1}{e^{10}-1}\left(e^{8-2x} + e^{3(x+1)}\right)$

c. $y(x) = \dfrac{1}{e^{10}-1}\left(e^{8-2x} - e^{3(x+1)}\right)$

d. $y(x) = \dfrac{1}{e^{10}+1}\left(e^{8x} + e^{3(x+1)}\right)$

e. no solution

9. Graph the particular solution and several other solutions.

$$2y'' + 3y' + y = 2 + \cos 2x$$

Select the correct answer.

a.

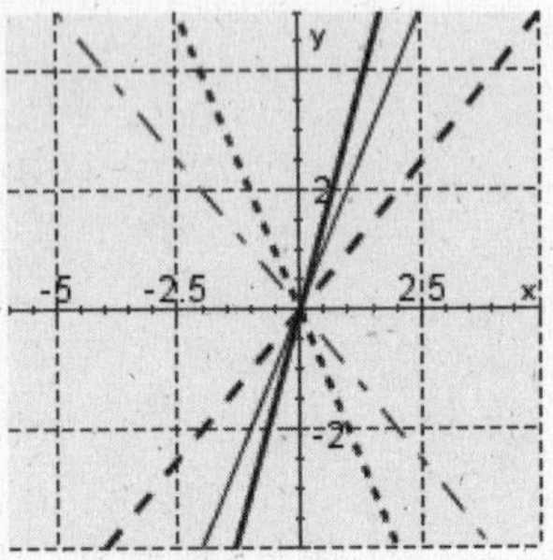

b.

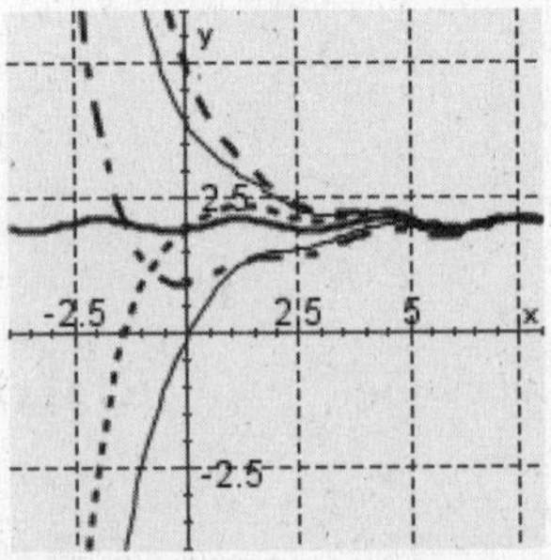

c.

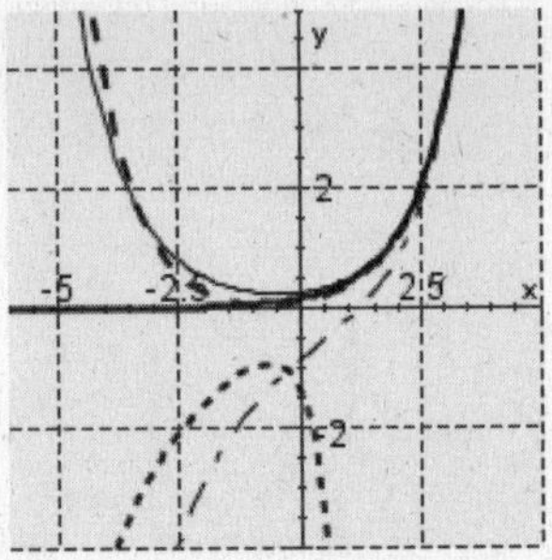

10. Solve the differential equation using the method of variation of parameters.

$$y'' + y = \sec x \ , \quad -\frac{\pi}{2} < x < \frac{\pi}{2}$$

Select the correct answer.

a. $y(x) = \left[-\frac{\pi}{2} + \ln(\cos x) \right] \cos x$

b. $y(x) = (c_1 + x)\sin x + c_2 + \ln(\cos x)$

c. $y(x) = (c_1 + x)\sin x + [c_2 + \ln(\cos x)]\cos(x)$

d. $y(x) = \frac{\pi}{2}\sin x + \left[\frac{\pi}{2} + \ln(\cos x) \right] \cos(x)$

e. $y(x) = \frac{\pi}{2}\sin x + \frac{\pi}{2}\cos(x)$

11. A spring with a 16-kg mass has natural length 0.8 m and is maintained stretched to a length of 1.2 m by a force of 19.6 N. If the spring is compressed to a length of 0.7 m and then released with zero velocity, find the position $x(t)$ of the mass at any time t.

Select the correct answer.

a. $x(t) = -0.1\cos(1.75t) + 0.8\sin(1.75t)$

b. $x(t) = -0.1\cos(1.75t)$

c. $x(t) = 0.8\sin(1.75t)$

d. $x(t) = -0.1e^{-4t}\cos(1.75t)$

e. $x(t) = -0.1e^{-4t}\cos(0.8t)$

12. A spring has a mass of 1 kg and its damping constant is $c = 10$. The spring starts from its equilibrium position with a velocity of 1 m/s. Graph the position function for the spring constant $k = 20$.

Select the correct answer.

a.
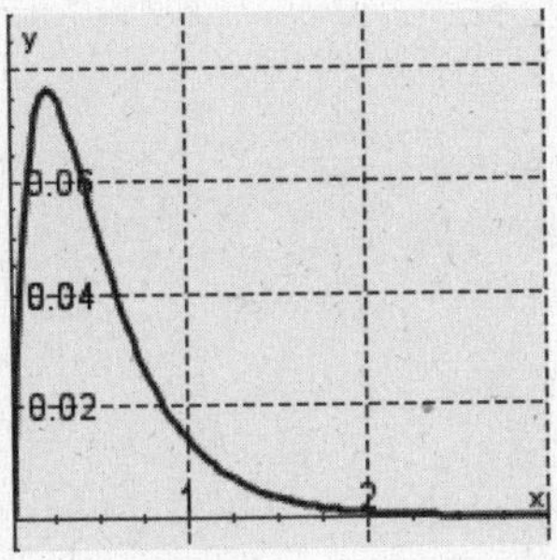

b.
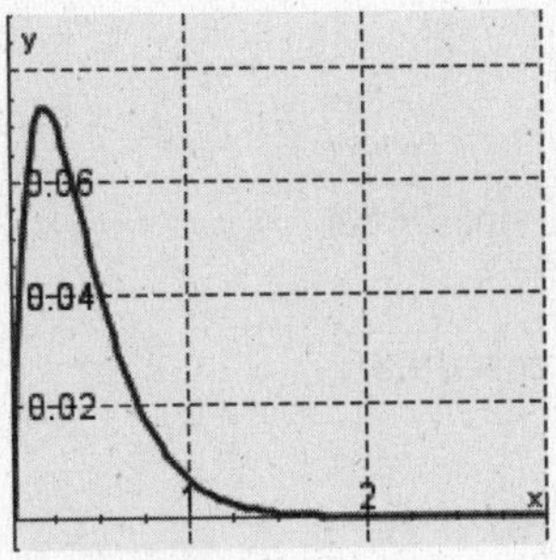

c.
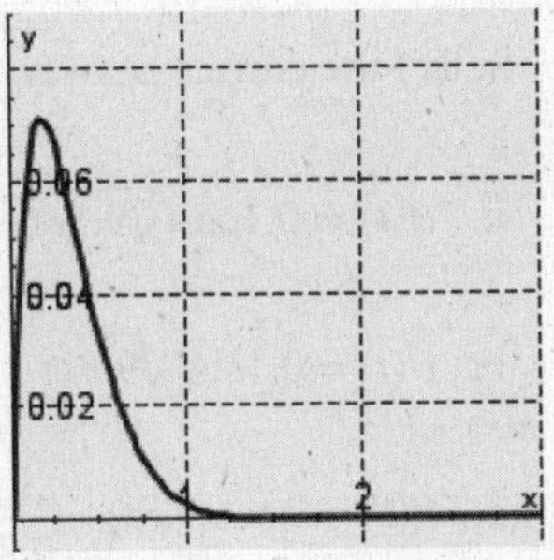

13. A series circuit consists of a resistor $R = 24\ \Omega$, an inductor with $L = 2$ H, a capacitor with $C = 0.005$ F, and a 12-V battery. If the initial charge is 0.0009 C and the initial current is 0, find the current $I(t)$ at time t.

Select the correct answer.

a. $I(t) = \dfrac{e^{-200t}}{200}(0.005\cos(6t) + 8\sin(6t)) - 1$

b. $I(t) = \dfrac{e^{-24t}}{200}$

c. $I(t) = 0.73875e^{-6t}\sin(8t)$

d. $I(t) = \dfrac{e^{-6t}}{200}\cos(8t)$

e. $I(t) = \dfrac{e^{-6t}}{20}\sin(8t)$

14. The figure shows a pendulum with length L and the angle θ from the vertical to the pendulum. It can be shown that θ, as a function of time, satisfies the nonlinear differential equation $\dfrac{d^2\theta}{dt^2} + \dfrac{g}{L}\sin\theta = 0$ where g = 9.8 m/s ^{2} is the acceleration due to gravity. For small values of θ we can use the linear approximation $\sin\theta = \theta$ and then the differential equation becomes linear. Find the equation of motion of a pendulum with length 1 m if θ is initially 0.1 rad and the initial angular velocity is $\dfrac{d\theta}{dt} = 1$ rad/s.

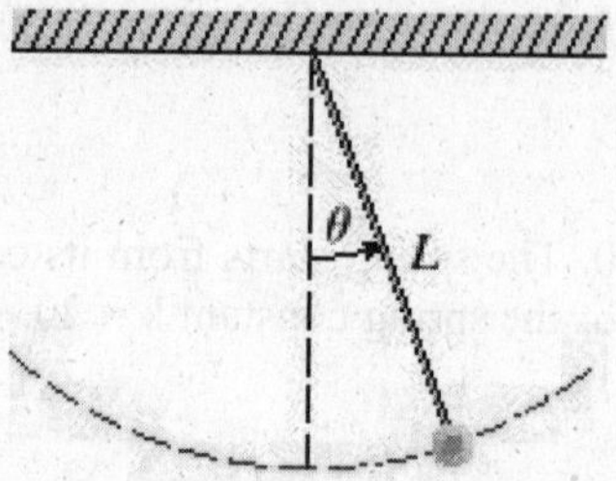

Select the correct answer.

a. $\theta(t) = 0.1\cos(\sqrt{9.8}t) + \dfrac{1}{\sqrt{9.8}}\sin(\sqrt{9.8}t)$

b. $\theta(t) = 0.1\sin(\sqrt{9.8}t) + \dfrac{1}{\sqrt{9.8}}\cos(\sqrt{9.8}t)$

c. $\theta(t) = 2\cos(9.8t) + \dfrac{1}{9.8}\sin(9.8t)$

d. $\theta(t) = 0.1\cos(\sqrt{9.8}t) + 2\sin(\sqrt{9.8}t)$

e. $\theta(t) = \dfrac{1}{9.8}\cos(\sqrt{9.8}t) + 0.1\sin(\sqrt{9.8}t)$

15. The solution of the initial-value problem $x^2y'' + xy' + x^2y = 0$, $y(0) = 1$, $y'(0) = 0$ is called a Bessel function of order 0. Solve the initial - value problem to find a power series expansion for the Bessel function.

Select the correct answer.

a. $y(x) = x + \sum_{n=0}^{\infty} (-1)^n \frac{x^{2n}}{2^{2n}(n!)^2}$

b. $y(x) = \sum_{n=0}^{\infty} (-1)^{n+1} \frac{nx^{2n-1}}{2^{2n-1}(n!)^2}$

c. $y(x) = \sum_{n=0}^{\infty} (-1)^n \frac{x^{2n}}{2^{2n}(n!)^2}$

d. $y(x) = \sum_{n=0}^{\infty} (-1)^n \frac{x^n}{2^n(2n!)}$

e. $y(x) = 2^x + \sum_{n=0}^{\infty} (-1)^n \frac{x^{2n}}{(n!)^2}$

16. Use power series to solve the differential equation.

$(x-6)y' + 2y = 0$

Select the correct answer.

a. $y(x) = c_0 \sum_{n=0}^{\infty} \frac{n+1}{6^n} x^n$

b. $y(x) = c_0 \sum_{n=0}^{\infty} \frac{x^n}{6^n}$

c. $y(x) = c_0 \sum_{n=0}^{\infty} \frac{nx^n}{6^n}$

d. $y(x) = c_0 \sum_{n=0}^{\infty} (n+1)x^n$

e. $y(x) = c_0 \sum_{n=0}^{\infty} \frac{(n+1)}{x^n}$

17. Solve the differential equation using the method of undetermined coefficients.

$y'' - 2y' = \sin 6x$

Select the correct answer.

a. $y(x) = c_1 + c_2e^{2x} + \frac{1}{120}\cos(6x) - \frac{1}{40}\sin(6x)$

b. $y(x) = c_1 + c_2e^{2x} - \frac{1}{40}\sin(6x)$

c. $y(x) = \frac{1}{120}\cos(6x) - \frac{1}{40}\sin(6x)$

d. $y(x) = c_1e^{2x} + \frac{1}{120}\cos(6x) - \frac{1}{40}\sin(6x)$

e. $y(x) = c_1e^{2x} + \frac{1}{40}\cos(6x) + \frac{1}{120}\sin(6x)$

18. Use power series to solve the differential equation.

$(x^2+1)y''+xy'-y=0$

Select the correct answer.

a. $y(x)=c_0+c_1x+c_0\dfrac{x^2}{2}+c_0\sum_{n=2}^{\infty}\dfrac{(-1)^{n-1}(2n-3)!}{2^{2n-2}n!(n-2)!}x^{2n+1}$

b. $y(x)=c_0\sum_{n=2}^{\infty}\dfrac{(-1)^{n-1}(2n-3)!}{2^{2n-2}n!(n-2)!}x^{2n}$

c. $y(x)=c_0+c_1x+c_0\dfrac{x^2}{2}+c_0\sum_{n=2}^{\infty}\dfrac{(-1)^{n-1}(2n-3)!}{2^{2n-2}(n-2)!}x^{2n}$

d. $y(x)=c_0+c_1x+c_0\dfrac{x^2}{2}+c_0\sum_{n=2}^{\infty}\dfrac{(-1)^{n-1}(2n-3)!}{2^{2n-2}n!(n-2)!}x^{2n}$

e. $y(x)=c_0+c_1x+c_0\dfrac{x^2}{2}+c_0\sum_{n=2}^{\infty}\dfrac{(-1)^{n+1}(2n)!}{2^{2n+2}n!(n-2)!}x^{2n+1}$

19. Use power series to solve the differential equation.

$y''+x^2y=0\ ,\quad y(0)=3,\ \ y'(0)=0$

Select the correct answer.

a. $y(x)=\sum_{n=1}^{\infty}\dfrac{(-1)^n3x^{4n}}{4n(4n-1)\cdot(4n-4)(4n-5)\cdots4\cdot3}$

b. $y(x)=3+\sum_{n=1}^{\infty}\dfrac{(-1)^n3x^{4n}}{4n(4n-1)\cdot(4n-4)(4n-5)\cdots4\cdot3}$

c. $y(x)=3-\sum_{n=1}^{\infty}\dfrac{(-1)^nx^{4n}}{4n(4n-1)\cdot(4n-4)(4n-5)\cdots4\cdot3}$

d. $y(x)=-3+\sum_{n=1}^{\infty}\dfrac{(-1)^n3x^{4n}}{4n(4n-1)\cdot(4n-4)(4n-5)\cdots4\cdot3}$

e. $y(x)=-1+\sum_{n=1}^{\infty}\dfrac{(-1)^nx^{4n}}{4n(4n-1)\cdot(4n-4)(4n-5)\cdots4\cdot3}$

20. Use power series to solve the differential equation.

$y''=16y$

Select the correct answer.

a. $y(x)=c_1\cosh 4x+c_2\sinh 4x+x^2$
b. $y(x)=c_1\cosh 4x+c_2\sinh 4x$
c. $y(x)=4\cosh x+4\sinh x$
d. $y(x)=c_1\cosh 4x+c_2\sinh 4x+e^x$
e. $y(x)=c_14\cosh x+c_24\sinh x+e^x$

ANSWER KEY

Stewart - Calculus ET 7e Chapter 17 Form D

1. a
2. a
3. b
4. d
5. c
6. b
7. b
8. c
9. b
10. c
11. b
12. a
13. c
14. a
15. c
16. a
17. a
18. d
19. b
20. b

1. Solve the initial-value problem.

$$y''+16y'+233y=0\ ,\quad y(0)=1,\ \ y'(0)=2$$

2. Solve the initial-value problem.

$$y''-16y'+64y=0\ ,\quad y(2)=0,\ \ y'(2)=1$$

3. Solve the initial-value problem.

$$y''+49y=0\ ,\quad y\left(\frac{\pi}{7}\right)=0,\ \ y'\left(\frac{\pi}{7}\right)=1$$

4. Solve the boundary-value problem, if possible.

$$y''+14y'+49y=0\ ,\quad y(0)=0,\ \ y(1)=6$$

Select the correct answer.

a. $y=7xe^{(-6x+6)}$ b. $y=6xe^{(-7x+7)}$ c. $y=6xe^{(-7x-7)}$ d. $y=6e^{(-7x-7)}$ e. no solution

5. Solve the differential equation using the method of undetermined coefficients.

$$y''+5y'+4y=x^2$$

Select the correct answer.

a. $y(x)=c_1e^{-4x}+c_2e^{-x}+\frac{21}{32}c_3$

b. $y(x)=c_1e^{-4x}+c_2e^{-x}+\frac{1}{4}x^2-\frac{5}{8}x+\frac{21}{32}$

c. $y(x)=\frac{1}{4}x^2-\frac{5}{8}x+\frac{21}{32}$

d. $y(x)=c_1e^{-4x}+c_2e^{-x}$

e. $y(x)=c_1e^{4x}+c_2e^{x}$

6. Use power series to solve the differential equation.

$$y'=7x^2y$$

7. Solve the differential equation.

$$y''-2y'-15y=0$$

8. Solve the differential equation.

$$y''-y=\cos x$$

9. Solve the differential equation using the method of variation of parameters.

$y'' - 2y' + y = e^{3x}$

Select the correct answer.

a. $y(x) = e^{x} + xe^{x}$

b. $y(x) = c_1e^{x} + c_2xe^{x} + \frac{1}{4}e^{3x}$

c. $y(x) = c_1e^{x} + c_2e^{x} + \frac{1}{4}e^{3x}$

d. $y(x) = c_1e^{x} + \frac{1}{4}e^{3x}$

e. $y(x) = c_1e^{x} + c_2e^{x} + \frac{x}{4}e^{3x}$

10. Solve the differential equation using the method of variation of parameters.

$y'' - 3y' = e^{3x}$

11. Solve the differential equation using the method of variation of parameters.

$y'' - 3y' + 2y = \dfrac{1}{1+e^{-x}}$

12. Solve the differential equation using the method of variation of parameters.

$y'' + 4y' + 4y = \dfrac{e^{-2x}}{x^3}$

Select the correct answer.

a. $y(x) = e^{-2x}\left(c_1 + c_2\frac{1}{2x}\right)$

b. $y(x) = e^{-2x}\left(c_1 + c_2x + c_3\frac{1}{2x}\right)$

c. $y(x) = e^{-2x}\left(c_1 + c_2x + \frac{1}{2x}\right)$

d. $y(x) = e^{-2x}(c_1 + c_2x) + \frac{1}{2x}$

e. $y(x) = e^{-2x}(c_1 + c_2)$

13. A spring with a 16-kg mass has natural length 0.8 m and is maintained stretched to a length of 1.2 m by a force of 19.6 N. If the spring is compressed to a length of 0.6 m and then released with zero velocity, find the position $x(t)$ of the mass at any time t.

14. A spring with a mass of 2 kg has damping constant 14, and a force of 6 N is required to keep the spring stretched 0.5 m beyond its natural length. The spring is stretched 1m beyond its natural length and then released with zero velocity. Find the position $x(t)$ of the mass at any time t.

15. A spring with a mass of 2 kg has damping constant 14, and a force of 4.8 N is required to keep the spring stretched 0.4 m beyond its natural length. Find the mass that would produce critical damping.

16. A spring with a mass of 3 kg has damping constant 35 and spring constant 129. Find the damping constant that would produce critical damping.

Select the correct answer.

a. $c = 6\sqrt{43}$ b. $c = 6\sqrt{7}$ c. $c = 9\sqrt{7}$ d. $c = 9\sqrt{43}$ e. $c = 43\sqrt{7}$

17. A series circuit consists of a resistor $R = 20\ \Omega$, an inductor with $L = 1$ H, a capacitor with $C = 0.002$F, and a generator producing a voltage of $E(t) = 12\cos 10t$. If the initial charge and current are both 0, find the charge $Q(t)$ at time t.

18. Use power series to solve the differential equation.

$$y'' - xy' - y = 0, \quad y(0) = 4, \quad y'(0) = 0$$

19. Use power series to solve the differential equation.

$$y'' + x^2 y = 0, \quad y(0) = 2, \quad y'(0) = 0$$

Select the correct answer.

a. $y(x) = \sum_{n=1}^{\infty} (-1)^n \dfrac{2x^{4n}}{4n(4n-1)...4\cdot 3}$

b. $y(x) = 2 - \sum_{n=1}^{\infty} (-1)^n \dfrac{x^{4n}}{4n(4n-1)...4\cdot 3}$

c. $y(x) = -2 + \sum_{n=1}^{\infty} (-1)^n \dfrac{2x^{4n}}{4n(4n-1)...4\cdot 3}$

d. $y(x) = 2 + \sum_{n=1}^{\infty} (-1)^n \dfrac{2x^{4n}}{4n(4n-1)...4\cdot 3}$

e. $y(x) = 2 - \sum_{n=1}^{\infty} (-1)^n \dfrac{x^{n}}{4n(4n-1)...4\cdot 3}$

20. Solve the differential equation.

$$y'' - 11y' + 24y = 0$$

Select the correct answer.

a. $y(x) = c_1 e^{8x} + c_2 x e^{8x}$
b. $y(x) = c_1 e^{3x} + c_2 e^{8x}$
c. $y(x) = ce^{3x}$
d. $y(x) = c_1 e^{3x} + c_2 x e^{3x}$
e. $y(x) = c_1 e^{-3x} + c_2 x e^{-x}$

ANSWER KEY

Stewart - Calculus ET 7e Chapter 17 Form E

1. $e^{-8x}\left(\cos(13x)+\frac{10}{13}\sin(13x)\right)$

2. $(x-2)e^{8(x-2)}$

3. $\frac{-1}{7}\sin(7x)$

4. b

5. b

6. $y(x)=ce^{\frac{7x^3}{3}}$

7. $y=C_1e^{5x}+C_2e^{-3x}$

8. $y=-\frac{1}{2}\cos x+c_1e^x+c_2e^{-x}$

9. b

10. $y(x)=c_1+c_2e^{3x}+\frac{1}{3}xe^{3x}$

11. $y(x)=[c_1+\ln(1+e^{-x})]e^x+[c_2-e^{-x}+\ln(1+e^{-x})]e^{2x}$

12. c

13. $x(t)=-0.2\cos\left(\frac{7}{4}t\right)$

14. $x(t)=-\frac{1}{5}e^{-6t}+\frac{6}{5}e^{-t}$

15. 49/12

16. a

17. $Q(t)=e^{-10t}\left(\frac{-3}{125}\cos(20t)-\frac{9}{500}\sin(20t)\right)+\frac{3}{250}\sin(10t)+\frac{3}{125}\cos(10t)$

18. $y(x)=4e^{\frac{x^2}{2}}$

19. d

20. b

1. Solve the differential equation.

$$y'' - 2y' = e^x$$

2. Solve the differential equation.

$$y'' - 8y' + 41y = 0$$

Select the correct answer.

a. $y(x) = e^{4x}(c_1 \cos(5x) + c_2 \sin(5x))$
b. $y(x) = ce^{4x} \cos(5x)$
c. $y(x) = e^{5x}(c_1 \cos(4x) + c_2 \sin(4x))$
d. $y(x) = e^{4x}(c_1 \cos(5x) + c_2 x \sin(5x))$
e. $y(x) = e^{4x}(c_1 \cos(4x) + c_2 x \sin(4x))$

3. Solve the differential equation.

$$y'' - 14y' + 49y = 0$$

4. Solve the differential equation.

$$11y'' = 2y'$$

5. Solve the differential equation.

$$9y'' + y = 0$$

6. Solve the differential equation.

$$7y'' + y' = 0$$

7. Solve the differential equation.

$$\frac{d^2y}{dt^2} + \frac{dy}{dt} + 10y = 0$$

8. Solve the initial-value problem.

$$2y'' + 19y' + 24y = 0, \quad y(0) = 0, \quad y'(0) = 1$$

9. Solve the initial-value problem.

$$y'' - 16y' + 64y = 0, \quad y(2) = 0, \quad y'(2) = 1$$

10. Solve the differential equation using the method of undetermined coefficients.

$$y'' + 4y = e^{2x}$$

11. Solve the differential equation using the method of variation of parameters.

$y'' - 5y' + 4y = \sin x$

12. Solve the initial-value problem.

$y'' + 81y = 0,\ y(\pi/9) = 0,\ y'(\pi/9) = 1$

Select the correct answer.

a. $y(x) = \frac{1}{9} x \sin(9x)$

b. $y(x) = -\frac{1}{9} \sin(9x)$

c. $y(x) = \frac{1}{9} \sin(9x)$

d. $y(x) = -\frac{1}{9} x \sin(9x)$

e. $y(x) = -x \sin(9x)$

13. Solve the boundary-value problem, if possible.

$y'' + 10y' + 25y = 0,\quad y(0) = 0,\quad y(1) = 8$

14. Solve the boundary-value problem, if possible.

$y'' + 3y' - 54y = 0,\quad y(0) = 0,\quad y(2) = 1$

15. Solve the boundary-value problem, if possible.

$y'' - y' - 2y = 0,\quad y(-1) = 1,\quad y(1) = 0$

16. Solve the differential equation using the method of undetermined coefficients.

$y'' - 3y' = \sin 9x$

17. Graph the particular solution and several other solutions.

$2y'' + 3y' + y = 2 + \cos 2x$

Select the correct answer.

a.

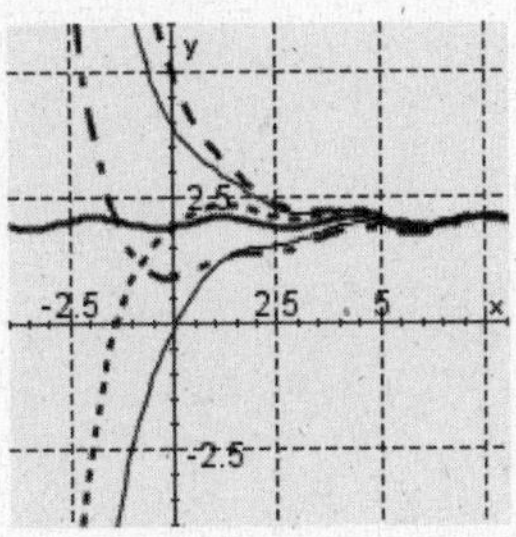

b.

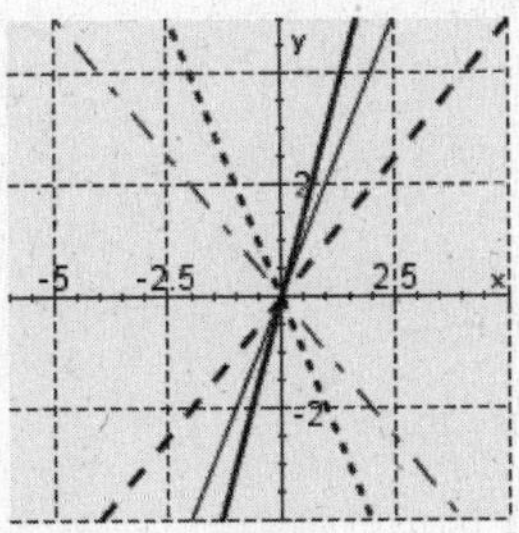

c.

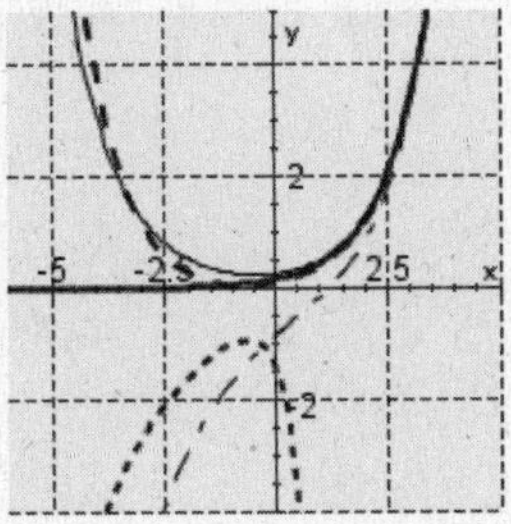

18. Solve the differential equation using the method of undetermined coefficients.

$y'' - 8y' + 17y = e^{-x}$

19. Find a trial solution for the method of undetermined coefficients. Do not determine the coefficients.

$y'' + 3y' + 5y = x^4 e^{2x}$

Select the correct answer.

a. $y_p(x) = \left(Ax^3 + Bx^2 + Cx + D\right) e^{2x}$

b. $y_p(x) = \left(Ax^4 + B\right) e^{2x}$

c. $y_p(x) = Ax^4$

d. $y_p(x) = \left(Ax^4 + Bx^3 + Cx^2 + Dx + E\right) e^{2x}$

e. $y_p(x) = \left(Ax^4 + Bx^2 + C\right) e^{-2x}$

20. Find a trial solution for the method of undetermined coefficients. Do not determine the coefficients.

$y'' + 2y' = 1 + xe^{-2x}$

Select the correct answer.

a. $y_{p1}(x) = A$
$y_{p2}(x) = x(A + B)e^{-2x}$

b. $y_{p1}(x) = Ax$
$y_{p2}(x) = x^2(Ax + B)e^{-2x}$

c. $y_{p1}(x) = Ax$
$y_{p2}(x) = x(Ax + B)e^{-2x}$

d. $y_{p1}(x) = A$
$y_{p2}(x) = x(A + Bx)e^{-2x}$

e. $y_{p1}(x) = A$
$y_{p2}(x) = Bxe^{2x}$

ANSWER KEY

Stewart - Calculus ET 7e Chapter 17 Form F

1. $y = c_1 + c_2 e^{2x} - e^x$

2. a

3. $e^{7x}(c_1 + c_2 x)$

4. $c_1 + c_2 e^{\frac{2x}{11}}$

5. $c_1 \cos\left(\frac{x}{3}\right) + c_2 \sin\left(\frac{x}{3}\right)$

6. $c_1 + c_2 e^{\frac{-x}{7}}$

7. $e^{\frac{-t}{2}}\left(c_1 \cos\left(\frac{\sqrt{39}t}{2}\right) + c_2 \sin\left(\frac{\sqrt{39}t}{2}\right)\right)$

8. $\frac{2}{13} e^{\frac{-3x}{2}} - \frac{2}{13} e^{-8x}$

9. $y = e^{8x-16}(x-2)$

10. $y(x) = c_1 \cos(2x) + c_2 \sin(2x) + \frac{1}{8} e^{2x}$

11. $y(x) = c_1 e^{4x} + c_2 e^x + \frac{5}{34} \cos(x) + \frac{3}{34} \sin(x)$

12. b

13. $8xe^{-5x+5}$

14. $\left(e^{12} - e^{-18}\right)^{-1}\left(e^{6x} - e^{-9x}\right)$

15. $\frac{1}{e^6 - 1}\left(e^{5-x} - e^{2(x+1)}\right)$

16. $y(x) = c_1 + c_2 e^{3x} + \frac{1}{270} \cos(9x) - \frac{1}{90} \sin(9x)$

17. a

18. $y(x) = e^{4x}\left(c_1 \cos(x) + c_2 \sin(x)\right) + \frac{1}{26} e^{-x}$

19. d

20. c

1. Solve the differential equation.

$y'' + 2y' - 3y = 0$

2. Solve the differential equation.

$y'' - 10y' + 25y = 0$

Select the correct answer.

a. $y(x) = cxe^{5x}$
b. $y(x) = ce^{5x}$
c. $y(x) = e^{5x}(c_1 + c_2 x)$
d. $y(x) = e^{-5x}(c_1 + c_2 x)$
e. $y(x) = xe^{-5x}(c_1 + c_2 x)$

3. Solve the initial-value problem.

$2y'' + 21y' + 27y = 0, \quad y(0) = 0, \quad y'(0) = 1$

4. Solve the initial value problem.

$y'' + 2y' - 3y = 0 \qquad y(0) = 2, \quad y'(0) = 1$

5. Solve the boundary-value problem, if possible.

$y'' - y' - 42y = 0, \quad y(-1) = 1, \quad y(1) = 0$

6. Solve the boundary-value problem, if possible.

$y'' + 2y' + 65y = 0, \quad y(0) = 1, \quad y(\pi) = 2$

7. Solve the differential equation using the method of undetermined coefficients.

$y'' - 6y' + 10y = e^{-x}$

8. Use power series to solve the differential equation.

$y' = 9xy$

9. Solve the differential equation.

$y'' - y = \cos x$

10. Solve the differential equation using the method of variation of parameters.

$y'' + 4y = x$

Select the correct answer.

a. $y(x) = c_1 \cos 2x + c_2 \sin 2x + \frac{1}{4}x$

b. $y(x) = c_1 \cos 2x + c_2 \sin 2x + \frac{c_3}{4}x$

c. $y(x) = c_1 \sin 2x + \frac{c_2}{4}x + \cos 2x$

d. $y(x) = Ax$

e. $y(x) = c_1 \sin 2x + \frac{c_2}{4}x$

11. Solve the differential equation using the method of variation of parameters.

$y'' - 2y' + y = e^{3x}$

Select the correct answer.

a. $y(x) = c_1 e^x + c_2 e^x + \frac{1}{4}e^{3x}$

b. $y(x) = c_1 e^x + \frac{1}{4}e^{3x}$

c. $y(x) = e^x + xe^x$

d. $y(x) = c_1 e^x + c_2 xe^x + \frac{1}{4}e^{3x}$

e. $y(x) = c_1 e^x + c_2 xe^x + e^{3x}$

12. Solve the differential equation using the method of variation of parameters.

$y'' - 2y' = e^{2x}$

13. Solve the differential equation using the method of variation of parameters.

$y'' + 4y' + 4y = \frac{e^{-2x}}{x^3}$

14. A spring with a mass of 2 kg has damping constant 10, and a force of 3.2 N is required to keep the spring stretched 0.4 m beyond its natural length. Find the mass that would produce critical damping.

15. A spring with a mass of 4 kg has damping constant 30 and spring constant 184. Find the damping constant that would produce critical damping.

16. Use power series to solve the differential equation.

$y'' - xy' - y = 0, \quad y(0) = 8, \quad y'(0) = 0$

17. A series circuit consists of a resistor $R = 8\ \Omega$, an inductor with $L = 1$ H, a capacitor with $C = 0.0125$ F, and a 28-V battery. If the initial charge and current are both 0, find the charge $Q(t)$ at time t.

18. The figure shows a pendulum with length L and the angle θ from the vertical to the pendulum. It can be shown that θ, as a function of time, satisfies the nonlinear differential equation $\frac{d^2\theta}{dt^2} + \frac{g}{L}\sin\theta = 0$ where g = 9.8 m/s ^{2} is the acceleration due to gravity. For small values of θ we can use the linear approximation $\sin\theta = \theta$ and then the differential equation becomes linear. Find the equation of motion of a pendulum with length 1 m if θ is initially 0.2 rad and the initial angular velocity is $\frac{d\theta}{dt} = 2$ rad/s.

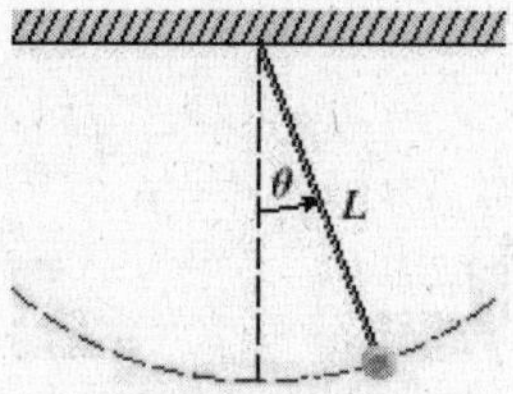

19. Suppose a spring has mass M and spring constant k and let $\omega = \sqrt{k/M}$. Suppose that the damping constant is so small that the damping force is negligible. If an external force $F(t) = F_0\cos(\omega t)$ is applied (the applied frequency equals the natural frequency), use the method of undetermined coefficients to find the equation that describes the motion of the mass.

Select the correct answer.

a. $x(t) = \frac{F_0 t}{2M\omega}(c_1\cos(\omega t) + c_2\sin(\omega t))$

b. $x(t) = \frac{F_0 t^2}{2M\omega}\cos(\omega t)$

c. $x(t) = c_1\cos(\omega t) + c_2\sin(\omega t) + \frac{F_0 e^{-\omega t}}{2M\omega}$

d. $x(t) = c_1\cos(\omega t) + c_2\sin(\omega t) + \frac{F_0 t}{2M\omega}\sin(\omega t)$

e. $x(t) = c_1\cos(\omega t) + c_2\sin(\omega t) + \frac{F_0 t^{-2}}{2M\omega}\sin(\omega t)$

20. Use power series to solve the differential equation.

$y' = 4x^2 y$

Select the correct answer.

a. $y(x) = ce^{\frac{-4x^3}{3}}$ b. $y(x) = ce^{\frac{4x^3}{3}}$ c. $y(x) = 4e^{\frac{x^3}{3}}$ d. $y(x) = ce^{4x}$ e. $y(x) = 3e^{-4x}$

ANSWER KEY

Stewart - Calculus ET 7e Chapter 17 Form G

1. $y = C_1 e^x + C_2 e^{-3x}$

2. c

3. $y = \frac{2}{15} e^{-\frac{3x}{2}} - \frac{2}{15} e^{-9x}$

4. $y = \frac{7}{4} e^x + \frac{1}{4} e^{-3x}$

5. $y = \frac{1}{e^{26} - 1}\left(e^{20-6x} - e^{7(x+1)}\right)$

6. no solution

7. $y(x) = e^{3x}(c_1 \cos(x) + c_2 \sin(x)) + \frac{1}{17} e^{-x}$

8. $y(x) = ce^{\frac{9x^2}{2}}$

9. $y = -\frac{1}{2} \cos x + c_1 e^x + c_2 e^{-x}$

10. a

11. d

12. $y(x) = c_1 + c_2 e^{2x} + \frac{1}{2} x e^{2x}$

13. $y(x) = e^{-2x}\left(c_1 + c_2 x + \frac{1}{2x}\right)$

14. 25/8

15. $c = 8\sqrt{46}$

16. $y(x) = 8e^{\frac{x^2}{2}}$

17. $Q(t) = -\frac{e^{-4t}}{40}(14\cos(8t) + 7\sin(8t)) + \frac{7}{20}$

18. $\theta(t) = 0.2\cos(\sqrt{9.8}t) + \frac{2}{\sqrt{9.8}} \sin(\sqrt{9.8}t)$

19. d

20. b

1. Solve the differential equation.

$y'' - y = \cos x$

2. Solve the differential equation.

$19y'' = 3y'$

3. Solve the differential equation.

$81y'' + y = 0$

4. Solve the differential equation.

$y'' - 2y' - 15y = 0$

5. Solve the initial value problem.

$y'' + 2y' - 3y = 0 \qquad y(0) = 2, \;\; y'(0) = 1$

6. Solve the initial-value problem.

$y'' - 64y = 0, \;\; y(0) = 6, \;\; y'(0) = 0$

7. Use power series to solve the differential equation.

$y'' - xy' - y = 0, \;\; y(0) = 2, \;\; y'(0) = 0$

8. Solve the boundary-value problem, if possible.

$y'' - y' - 90y = 0, \;\; y(-1) = 1, \;\; y(1) = 0$

Select the correct answer.

a. $y(x) = \dfrac{1}{e^{38} - 1}\left(e^{29-9x} - e^{10(x+1)}\right)$

b. $y(x) = \dfrac{1}{e^{38} - 1}\left(e^{29-9x} + e^{10(x+1)}\right)$

c. $y(x) = \dfrac{1}{e^{38} + 1}\left(e^{29-9x} - e^{10(x+1)}\right)$

d. $y(x) = \dfrac{e^{10(x+1)}}{e^{38} + 1}$

e. no solution

9. Solve the differential equation using the method of undetermined coefficients.

$y'' + 4y = e^{2x}$

10. Solve the differential equation using the method of undetermined coefficients.

$y'' - 2y' = \sin 6x$

11. Solve the differential equation using the method of variation of parameters.

$$y'' - 3y' + 2y = \frac{1}{1+e^{-x}}$$

Select the correct answer.

a. $y(x) = \left(c_1 + \ln(1+e^{-x})\right) e^{-x}$
b. $y(x) = (c_1 + \ln(1+e^{-x}))e^{x} + (c_2 - e^{-x} + \ln(1+e^{-x}))e^{2x}$
c. $y(x) = \left(\ln(1+e^{-x})\right) e^{-x} + \left(c_2 + e^{x} + \ln(1+e^{x})\right) e^{x}$
d. $y(x) = \left(c_1 - e^{-x} + \ln(1+e^{-x})\right) e^{2x}$
e. $y(x) = \left(c_1 + \ln(1+e^{-2x})\right) e^{-2x} + \left(c_2 - e^{-2x} + \ln(1+e^{-2x})\right) e^{-x}$

12. A spring with a mass of 2 kg has damping constant 18, and a force of 8 N is required to keep the spring stretched 0.5 m beyond its natural length. Find the mass that would produce critical damping.

13. A spring with a mass of 2 kg has damping constant 8 and spring constant 80. Graph the position function of the mass at time t if it starts at the equilibrium position with a velocity of 2 m / s.

Select the correct answer.

a.
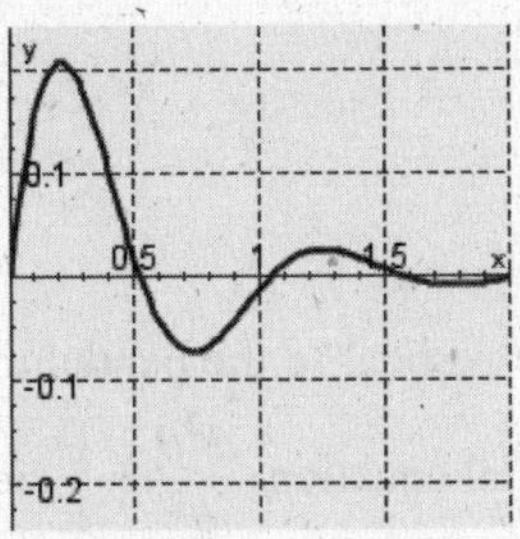

b.
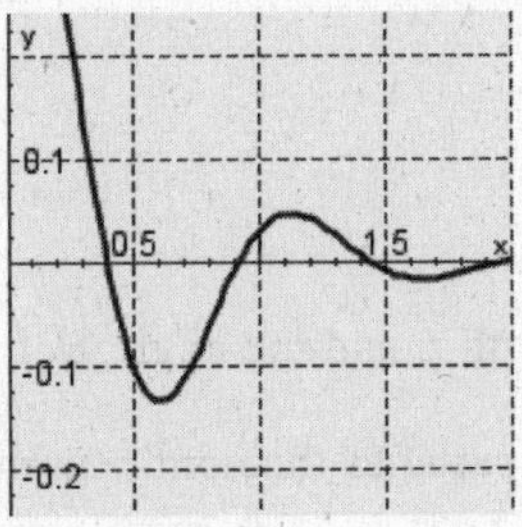

c.
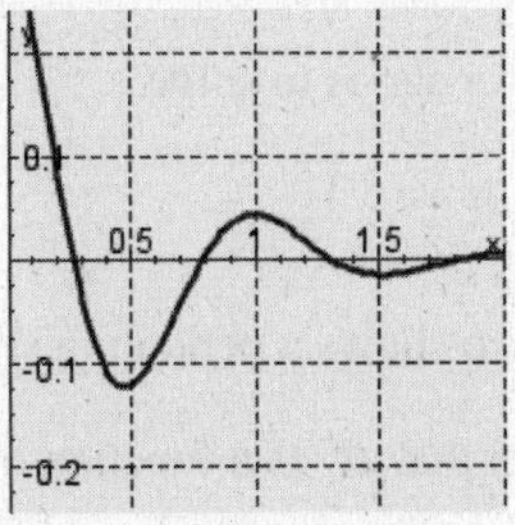

14. A spring with a mass of 5 kg has damping constant 31 and spring constant 205. Find the damping constant that would produce critical damping.

Select the correct answer.

a. $c = 5\sqrt{7}$
b. $c = 10\sqrt{7}$
c. $c = 10\sqrt{41}$
d. $c = 5\sqrt{41}$
e. $c = 7\sqrt{41}$

15. A series circuit consists of a resistor $R = 16\ \Omega$, an inductor with $L = 2$ H, a capacitor with $C = 0.00625$F, and a 12-V battery. If the initial charge is 0.001 C and the initial current is 0, find the current $I(t)$ at time t.

Select the correct answer.

a. $I(t) = \dfrac{e^{-160t}}{160}(0.00625\cos(4t) + 8\sin(4t)) - \dfrac{1}{2}$

b. $I(t) = 0.74e^{-4t}\sin(8t)$

c. $I(t) = \dfrac{e^{-160t}}{160}\cos(8t)$

d. $I(t) = \dfrac{e^{-16t}}{160}$

e. $I(t) = \dfrac{e^{-16t}}{160}(\cos(8t) + \sin(8t))$

16. Use power series to solve.

$y'' + xy' + 2y = 0$

17. Use power series to solve the differential equation.

$y' = 7xy$

18. Use power series to solve the differential equation.

$y' = 7x^2 y$

19. Use power series to solve.

$y'' - y' = 0$

20. The figure shows a pendulum with length L and the angle θ from the vertical to the pendulum. It can be shown that θ, as a function of time, satisfies the nonlinear differential equation $\dfrac{d^2\theta}{dt^2} + \dfrac{g}{L}\sin\theta = 0$ where g = 9.8 m/s ^{2} is the acceleration due to gravity. For small values of θ we can use the linear approximation $\sin\theta = \theta$ and then the differential equation becomes linear. Find the equation of motion of a pendulum with length 1 m if θ is initially 0.3 rad and the initial angular velocity is $\dfrac{d\theta}{dt} = 2$ rad/s.

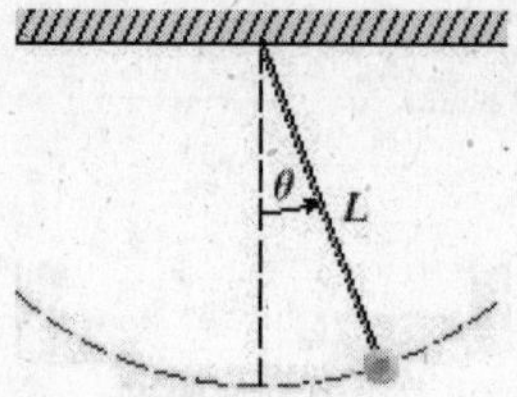

ANSWER KEY

Stewart - Calculus ET 7e Chapter 17 Form H

1. $y = -\frac{1}{2}\cos x + C_1 e^x + C_2 e^{-x}$

2. $y = C_1 + C_2 e^{\frac{3x}{19}}$

3. $y = C_1 \cos\left(\frac{x}{9}\right) + C_2 \sin\left(\frac{x}{9}\right)$

4. $y = C_1 e^{5x} + C_2 e^{-3x}$

5. $y = \frac{7}{4}e^x + \frac{1}{4}e^{-3x}$

6. $y = 3\left(e^{8x} + e^{-8x}\right)$

7. $y(x) = 2e^{\frac{x^2}{2}}$

8. a

9. $y(x) = C_1 \cos(2x) + C_2 \sin(2x) + \frac{1}{8}e^{2x}$

10. $y(x) = C_1 + C_2 e^{2x} + \frac{1}{120}\cos(6x) - \frac{1}{40}\sin(6x)$

11. b

12. 81/16

13. a

14. c

15. b

16. $a_0 \sum_{k=0}^{\infty} \frac{(-1)^k x^{2k}}{1 \cdot 3 \cdot 5 \cdots \cdot (2k-1)} + a_1 \sum_{k=0}^{\infty} \frac{(-1)^k x^{2k+1}}{2^k k!}$

17. $y(x) = Ce^{\frac{7x^2}{2}}$

18. $y(x) = Ce^{\frac{7x^3}{3}}$

19. $a_0 \sum_{k=0}^{\infty} \frac{x^{2k}}{(2k)!} + a_1 \sum_{k=0}^{\infty} \frac{x^{2k+1}}{(2k+1)!}$

20. $\theta(t) = 0.3\cos(\sqrt{9.8}t) + \frac{2}{\sqrt{9.8}}\sin(\sqrt{9.8}t)$

1. The graphs of $f(x)$ and $g(x)$ are given.
   a) For what values of x is $f(x) = g(x)$?
   b) Find the values of $f(-4)$ and $g(3)$.

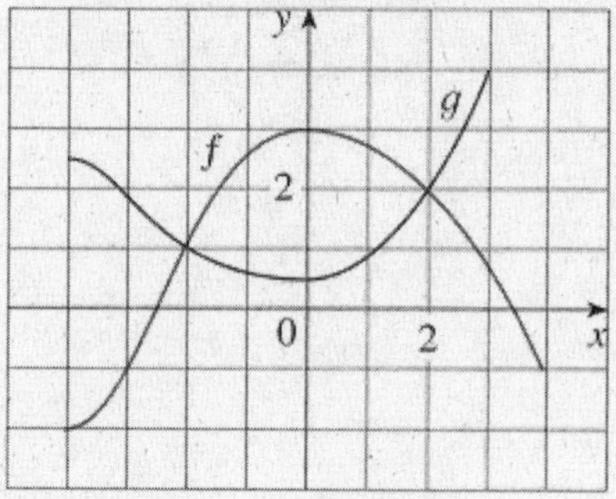

2. If $f(x) = x^2 - x + 2$, evaluate the difference quotient $\frac{f(a+h) - f(a)}{h}$.

3. If an equation of the tangent line to the curve $y = f(x)$ at the point where $a = 2$ is $y = 4x - 5$, find $f(2)$ and $f'(2)$.

4. How would you define $f(3)$ in order to make f continuous at 3?

$$f(x) = \frac{x^2 - 2x - 3}{x - 3}$$

5. The height (in meters) of a projectile shot vertically upward from a point 2 m above ground level with an initial velocity of 24.5 m/s is $h = 2 + 24.5t - 4.9t^2$ after t seconds.

   a) When does the projectile reach its maximum height?
   b) What is the maximum height?

6. Use implicit differentiation to find an equation of the tangent line to the curve at the given point.

$$y \sin 2x = x \cos 2y, \quad (\pi/2, \pi/4)$$

7. The top of a ladder slides down a vertical wall at a rate of 0.15 m/s. At the moment when the bottom of the ladder is 3 m from the wall, it slides away from the wall at a rate of 0.2 m/s. How long is the ladder?

8. Find the local and absolute extreme values of the function on the given interval.

$$f(x) = x^3 - 6x^2 + 9x + 1, \quad [2,4]$$

9. Find the number c that satisfies the conclusion of the Mean Value Theorem on the given interval.

$$f(x) = 2\sqrt{x}, \quad [0,4]$$

10. If $f(x) = \sqrt{x} - 2$, $1 \le x \le 6$, find the Riemann sum with $n = 5$ correct to 3 decimal places, taking the sample points to be midpoints.

11. Find the volume of the solid obtained by rotating the region bounded by the given curves about the specified axis.

$y = x^2 + 4, \quad y = 12 - x^2; \;$ about $y = -1$

12. Find the average value of the function $f(t) = t\sin(t^2)$ on the interval $[0, 20]$. Round your answer to 3 decimal places.

13. Evaluate the integral using the indicated trigonometric substitution.

$$\int \frac{dx}{x^2\sqrt{x^2 - 16}}; \quad x = 4\sec\theta$$

14. Find the volume of the resulting solid if the region under the curve $y = 1/\left(x^2 + 3x + 2\right)$ from $x = 0$ to $x = 1$ is rotated about the x-axis. Round your answer to six decimal places.

15. Find the length of the curve.

$$y = 2\ln\left(\sin\frac{x}{2}\right), \quad \pi/3 \le x \le \pi$$

16. The masses m_i are located at the points P_i. Find the moments M_x and M_y and the center of mass of the system.

$m_1 = 2,\ m_2 = 4,\ m_3 = 8;$
$P_1(1,5),\ P_2(3,-2),\ P_3(-2,-1)$

17. Use Euler's method with step size 0.1 to estimate $y(0.5)$, where $y(x)$ is the solution of the initial-value problem. Round your answer to four decimal places.

$y' = y(x+1), \quad y(0) = 1$

18. Solve the initial-value problem.

$$\frac{dr}{dt} + 2tr - r = 0, \quad r(0) = 4$$

19. Find the area of the region that is bounded by the given curve and lies in the specified sector.

$r = \sqrt{\sin\theta}, \quad 0 \le \theta \le 2\pi/3$

20. Determine whether the series is convergent or divergent by expressing s_n as a telescoping sum. If it is convergent, find its sum.

$$\sum_{n=1}^{\infty} 3/(n^2 + 3n)$$

21. Calculate the given quantities if $\mathbf{a} = \mathbf{i} - \mathbf{j}$ and $\mathbf{b} = -\mathbf{j} + 2\mathbf{k}$.

I. $\mathbf{a} \cdot \mathbf{b}$

II. $\mathbf{a} \times \mathbf{b}$

III. The angle between **a** and **b** (correct to the nearest degree)

22. Find the unit tangent vector for the curve given by $\mathbf{r}(t) = \left\langle \frac{1}{4}t^4, \frac{1}{3}t^3, t \right\rangle$.

23. Find the curvature of the curve $y = x^3$ at the point $(-1, -1)$.

24. Find all the second partial derivatives of

$$f(x, y) = 4x^3 y - 7xy^2$$

25. Find the directional derivative of $f(x, y) = 2\sqrt{x} - y^2$ at the point (1, 3) in the direction toward the point (3, 1).

26. Use Lagrange multipliers to find the maximum and the minimum of f subject to the given constraint(s).

$$f(x, y) = xyz; \qquad x^2 + y^2 + z^2 = 27$$

27. Find the volume of the given solid.

Under the paraboloid $z = x^2 + 3y^2$ and above the rectangle $R = [0,3] \times [1,5]$

28. Use spherical coordinates.

Evaluate $\iiint_B (x^2 + y^2 + z^2)^2 \, dV$, where B is the ball with center the origin and radius 4.

29. Find the gradient vector field of f.

$$f(x, y, z) = \sqrt{2x^2 + y^2 + 2z^2}$$

30. Evaluate the line integral.

$$\int_C yz \cos x \, ds$$

$$C: x = t,\ y = 2\cos t,\ z = 2\sin t \qquad 0 \le t \le \pi$$

ANSWER KEY

Stewart - Calculus ET 7e Final Exam Form A

1. a) $x = -2, 2$
b) $f(-4) = -2, \; g(3) = 4$

2. $2a + h - 1$

3. $f(2) = 3$
$f'(2) = 4$

4. $f(3) = 4$

5. 2.5 s
32.625 m

6. $y = \frac{1}{2}x$

7. 5 m

8. Max $(4,5)$, Min $(3,1)$

9. $c = 1$

10. –0.857

11. 384π

12. 0.038

13. $\frac{\sqrt{x^2 - 16}}{16x} + C$

14. 0.286835

15. $2\ln(2 + \sqrt{3})$

16. $M_x = -6, \; M_y = -2, \; (-1/7, -3/7)$

17. $y(0.5) \approx 1.7616$

18. $r(t) = 4e^{t - t^2}$

19. 3/4

20. Converges; 11/6

21. $\mathbf{a} \cdot \mathbf{b} = 1$
$\mathbf{a} \times \mathbf{b} = -2\mathbf{i} - 2\mathbf{j} - \mathbf{k}$
72°

22. $\dfrac{\langle t^3, t^2, 1\rangle}{\sqrt{t^6+t^4+1}}$

23. $\dfrac{3\sqrt{10}}{50}$

24. $f_{xy} = 12x^2 - 14y$ $\quad f_{yx} = 12x^2 - 14y$
$f_{xx} = 24xy$ $\quad f_{yy} = -14x$

25. $7\sqrt{2}/2$

26. maximum = 27, minimum = –27

27. 408

28. $65536\pi/7$

29. $2x/\sqrt{2x^2+y^2+2z^2}\,\mathbf{i} + y/\sqrt{2x^2+y^2+2z^2}\,\mathbf{j} + 2z/\sqrt{2x^2+y^2+2z^2}\,\mathbf{k}$

30. $8\sqrt{5}/3$

1. The graphs of $f(x)$ and $g(x)$ are given. For what values of x is $f(x) = g(x)$?

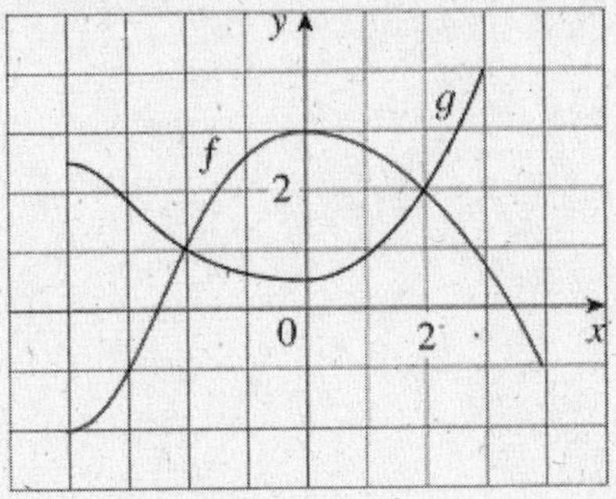

Select the correct answer.

a. 2 b. −2, 2 c. −1, 2 d. 0 e. 1, 2

2. If $f(x) = x^2 - x + 4$, evaluate the difference quotient $\dfrac{f(a+h) - f(a)}{h}$.

Select the correct answer.

a. h b. $2a - 2$ c. $2a - h - 2$ d. $2a + h - 2$ e. none of these

3. How would you define $f(3)$ in order to make f continuous at 3?

$$f(x) = \frac{x^2 - x - 6}{x - 3}$$

Select the correct answer.

a. $f(3) = 5$ b. $f(3) = 0$ c. $f(3) = 1$ d. $f(3) = -5$ e. none of these

4. If an equation of the tangent line to the curve $y = f(x)$ at the point where $a = 2$ is $y = 4x - 11$, find $f(2)$ and $f'(2)$.

Select the correct answer.

a. $f(2) = -4$, $f'(2) = 4$ b. $f(2) = 3$, $f'(2) = 4$ c. $f(2) = -4$, $f'(2) = 3$ d. $f(2) = -3$, $f'(2) = 4$ e. none of these

5. The height (in meters) of a projectile shot vertically upward from a point 1.5 m above ground level with an initial velocity of 25.48 m/s is $h = 1.5 + 25.48t - 4.9t^2$ after t seconds.

a) When does the projectile reach its maximum height?
b) What is the maximum height?

Select the correct answer.

a. 2.8 s, 34.428 m b. 2.6 s, 34.624 m c. 2 s, 32.86 m d. 2.4 s, 34.428 m e. 2.3 s, 34.183 m

6. Use implicit differentiation to find an equation of the tangent line to the curve at the given point.

$y \sin 2x = x \cos 2y, \quad (\pi/2, \pi/4)$

Select the correct answer.

a. $y = x/4 + \pi/8$
b. $y = x/4$
c. $y = x/2$
d. $y = 2x - 3\pi/4$
e. $y = -x/2 + \pi/2$

7. Find f.

$f''(x) = 12x + 24x^2$

Select the correct answer.

a. $f(x) = 6x^3 + 4x^4 + Cx + D$
b. $f(x) = 2x^3 + 2x^4 + Cx + D$
c. $f(x) = 4x^3 + 8x^4 + Cx + D$
d. $f(x) = 2x^3 + x^4 + Cx + D$
e. $f(x) = x^3 + 4x^4 + Cx + D$

8. Find the number c that satisfies the conclusion of the Mean Value Theorem on the given interval.

$f(x) = 2\sqrt{x}, \ [0, 9]$

Select the correct answer.

a. $c = 9/4$
b. $c = 0$
c. $c = 1/4$
d. $c = 5$
e. none of these

9. A piece of wire 10 m long is cut into two pieces. One piece is bent into a square and the other is bent into an equilateral triangle. How should the wire be cut for the square so that the total area enclosed is a minimum? Round the result to the nearest hundredth.

Select the correct answer.

a. 5.35 m
b. 4.4 m
c. 4.35 m
d. 1 m
e. 3.25 m

10. Find the area of the region that lies under the given curve. Round the answer to three decimal places.

$y = \sqrt{2x+2},\ 0 \le x \le 1$

Select the correct answer.

a. 1.834 b. 1.727 c. 1.704 d. 1.724 e. 1.824

11. The acceleration function (in m / s^2) and the initial velocity are given for a particle moving along a line. Find the velocity at time t and the distance traveled during the given time interval.

$a(t) = t + 4,\ v(0) = 3,\ 0 \le t \le 10$

Select the correct answer.

a. $v(t) = \dfrac{t^2}{2} + 4t + 3$ m/s, $396\frac{2}{3}$ m

b. $v(t) = \dfrac{t^2}{2} + 4t + 3$ m/s, $391\frac{2}{3}$ m

c. $v(t) = \dfrac{t^2}{2} + 3$ m/s, $411\frac{2}{3}$ m

d. $v(t) = \dfrac{t^2}{2} + 4t$ m/s, $406\frac{2}{3}$ m

e. $v(t) = \dfrac{t^2}{2} + 4t$ m/s, $415\frac{2}{3}$ m

12. Find the average value of the function $f(t) = t\sin(t^2)$ on the interval $[0, 20]$. Round your answer to 3 decimal places.

Select the correct answer.

a. 0.381 b. 0.008 c. 0.028 d. 0.038 e. none of these

13. Find the volume of the solid obtained by rotating the region bounded by the given curves about the specified axis.

$y = x^2 + 4,\ \ y = 12 - x^2;$ about $y = -1$

Select the correct answer.

a. 384π b. 128π c. 128 d. 96π e. none of these

14. Evaluate the integral.

$$\int_1^{\infty} \frac{dx}{x \ln x}$$

Select the correct answer.

a. 1/2 b. 0 c. −1/4 d. 1/4 e. divergent

15. Evaluate the integral.

$$\int x \sin x \cos x dx$$

Select the correct answer.

a. $-(x\cos^2 x)/2+(\cos x \sin x)/4+x/4+c$
b. $-(x\cos^2 x)/2+\cos x+x/4+c$
c. $-(\cos x \sin x)/4+x/4+c$
d. $-(x\sin^2 x)/2+(\cos x)/4+c$
e. none of these

16. The masses m_i are located at the points P_i. Find the moments M_x and M_y and the center of mass of the system.

$m_1 = 6,\ m_2 = 5,\ m_3 = 10;$
$P_1(1,5),\ P_2(3,-2),\ P_3(-2,-1)$

Select the correct answer.

a. $M_x = 10$, $M_y = 1$, $(1/21, 10/21)$
b. $M_x = -10$, $M_y = 1$, $(1/21, -10/21)$
c. $M_x = 10$, $M_y = -1$, $(-1/21, 10/21)$
d. $M_x = 1$, $M_y = 10$, $(1/21, 10/21)$
e. $M_x = 10$, $M_y = 1$, $(10/21, 1/21)$

17. Find the length of the curve.

$$x = \frac{y^4}{8} + \frac{1}{4y^2},\quad 1 \le y \le 2$$

Select the correct answer.

a. $33/16$ b. 2 c. 3 d. $2/3$ e. none of these

18. Which equation does the function $y = e^{-3t}$ satisfy?

Select the correct answer.

a. $y'' + y' + 12y = 0$
b. $y'' + y' - 12y = 0$
c. $y'' - y' - 12y = 0$
d. $y'' - y' + 12y = 0$
e. $y'' - 3y' + 12y = 0$

19. Solve the initial-value problem.

$xy' = y + x^2 \sin x, \quad y(\pi) = 0$

Select the correct answer.

a. $y = x\sin x$
b. $y = x\sin x - x$
c. $y = -x\cos x - x$
d. $y = -x\sin x + x$
e. $y = x\cos x - \sin x$

20. Set up an integral that represents the length of the curve. Then use your calculator to find the length correct to four decimal places.

$x = t - 2\sin t, \qquad y = t - 2\cos t \qquad 0 \le t \le 2\pi$

Select the correct answer.

a. 14.675
b. 7.0974
c. 7.0970
d. 21.2921
e. none of these

21. Determine whether the series is convergent or divergent by expressing s_n as a telescoping sum. If it is convergent, find its sum.

$$\sum_{n=1}^{\infty} \frac{2}{n^2 + 2n}$$

Select the correct answer.

a. $2/3$ b. $3/2$ c. $1/3$ d. 2 e. diverges

22. Find the sum of the series.

$$\frac{3}{1\cdot 5} - \frac{3^2}{2\cdot 5^2} + \frac{3^3}{3\cdot 5^3} - \frac{3^4}{4\cdot 5^4} + \ldots$$

Select the correct answer.

a. $\ln(8/5)$ b. $\ln(5/3)$ c. $\ln(7/4)$ d. $e^{8/5}$ e. $8e/5$

23. Find a nonzero vector orthogonal to the plane through the points *P*, *Q*, and *R*.

$P(1,0,0),\ Q(3,2,0),\ R(0,2,1)$

Select the correct answer.

a. $2\mathbf{i} - 2\mathbf{j} + 6\mathbf{k}$ b. $5\mathbf{i} - 2\mathbf{j} + \mathbf{k}$ c. $-2\mathbf{i} + \mathbf{j} + 6\mathbf{k}$ d. $\mathbf{i} - 7\mathbf{j} + 4\mathbf{k}$ e. none of these

24. Find the curvature of $y = x^7$.

Select the correct answer.

a. $\dfrac{7x^6}{(1+49x^{12})^{3/2}}$ b. $\dfrac{42\,|\,x\,|^5}{(1+7x^6)^{3/2}}$ c. $\dfrac{42\,|\,x\,|^5}{(1+49x^{12})^{3/2}}$ d. $\dfrac{49\,|\,x\,|^5}{(1+7x^{12})^{3/2}}$ e. $\dfrac{|\,x\,|^5}{(1+x^6)^{3/2}}$

25. If $\mathbf{r}(t) = \mathbf{i} + t\cos \pi t\,\mathbf{j} + \sin \pi t\,\mathbf{k}$, evaluate $\int_0^1 \mathbf{r}(t)\,dt$.

Select the correct answer.

a. $\mathbf{i} - \dfrac{2}{\pi^2}\mathbf{j} + \dfrac{2}{\pi}\mathbf{k}$

b. $\dfrac{2}{\pi^2}\mathbf{j} + \dfrac{2}{\pi}\mathbf{k}$

c. $\dfrac{2}{\pi^2}\mathbf{i} - \mathbf{j} + \dfrac{\pi}{2}\mathbf{k}$

d. $\mathbf{i} - \dfrac{1}{\pi}\mathbf{j} + \dfrac{1}{\pi}\mathbf{k}$

e. $2\mathbf{i} - \dfrac{1}{\pi^2}\mathbf{j} + \dfrac{\pi}{2}\mathbf{k}$

26. Find f_{xy} for the function $f(x, y) = 4x^3y - 7xy^2$.

Select the correct answer.

a. $f_{xy} = 24x^2 - 14y$
b. $f_{xy} = 12x^2 + 14y$
c. $f_{xy} = 14x^2 - 12y$
d. $f_{xy} = 12x^2 - 14y$
e. $f_{xy} = 14x^2 + 12y$

27. Find the directional derivative of $f(x, y) = 2\sqrt{x} - y^3$ at the point (1, 3) in the direction toward the point (3, 1).

Select the correct answer.

a. $14\sqrt{2}$ b. $\sqrt{2}$ c. $7\sqrt{2}$ d. 28 e. none of these

28. Use spherical coordinates.

Evaluate $\iiint_B (x^2 + y^2 + z^2)^2\,dV$, where B is the ball with center the origin and radius 2.

Select the correct answer.

a. $252\pi/7$ b. $128\pi/7$ c. $512/7$ d. $256\pi/7$ e. $512\pi/7$

29. Find the gradient vector field of *f*.

$f(x, y, z) = \sqrt{x^2 + y^2 + z^2}$

Select the correct answer.

a. $x / \sqrt{x^2 + y^2 + z^2}\ \mathbf{i} + y / \sqrt{x^2 + y^2 + z^2}\ \mathbf{j} + z / \sqrt{x^2 + y^2 + z^2}\ \mathbf{k}$
b. $1 / \sqrt{x^2 + y^2 + z^2}\ \mathbf{i} + 1 / \sqrt{x^2 + y^2 + z^2}\ \mathbf{j} + z / \sqrt{x^2 + y^2 + z^2}\ \mathbf{k}$
c. $2x / \sqrt{x^2 + y^2 + z^2}\ \mathbf{i} + 2y / \sqrt{x^2 + y^2 + z^2}\ \mathbf{j} + 2z / \sqrt{x^2 + y^2 + z^2}\ \mathbf{k}$
d. $y / \sqrt{x^2 + y^2 + z^2}\ \mathbf{i} + x / \sqrt{x^2 + y^2 + z^2}\ \mathbf{j} + z / \sqrt{x^2 + y^2 + z^2}\ \mathbf{k}$
e. none of these

30. Evaluate the line integral.

$\int_C yz \cos x \, ds$

$C: x = t,\ y = 2\cos t,\ z = 2\sin t \qquad 0 \le t \le \pi$

Select the correct answer.

a. $\sqrt{5}/3$ b. $2\sqrt{2}/3$ c. $4\sqrt{5}/3$ d. $8\sqrt{5}/3$ e. $8\sqrt{5}/5$

ANSWER KEY

Stewart - Calculus ET 7e Final Exam Form B

1. b
2. e
3. a
4. d
5. b
6. c
7. b
8. a
9. c
10. d
11. a
12. d
13. a
14. e
15. a
16. a
17. a
18. c
19. c
20. e
21. b
22. a
23. a
24. c
25. a
26. d
27. a
28. e
29. a
30. d

1. The graphs of $f(x)$ and $g(x)$ are given. For what values of x is $f(x) = g(x)$?

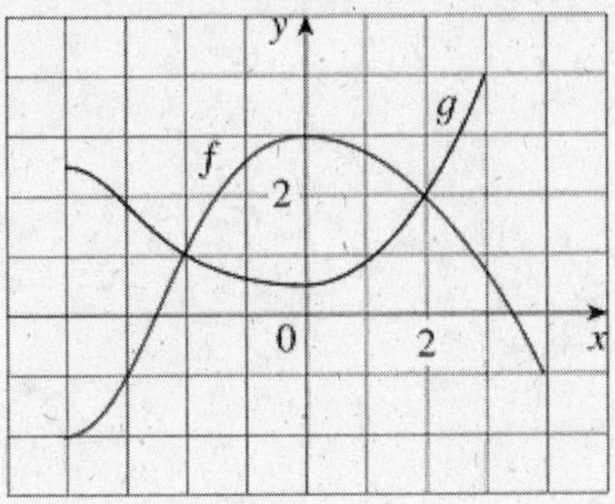

Select the correct answer.

a. 2 b. –2, 2 c. –1, 2 d. 0 e. 1, 2

2. If $f(x) = x^2 - x + 2$, evaluate the difference quotient $\dfrac{f(a+h) - f(a)}{h}$.

3. How would you define $f(3)$ in order to make f continuous at 3?

$$f(x) = \frac{x^2 - x - 6}{x - 3}$$

Select the correct answer.

a. $f(3) = 5$
b. $f(3) = 0$
c. $f(3) = 1$
d. $f(3) = -5$
e. none of these

4. If an equation of the tangent line to the curve $y = f(x)$ at the point where $a = 2$ is $y = 4x - 5$, find $f(2)$ and $f'(2)$.

5. The height (in meters) of a projectile shot vertically upward from a point 1.5 m above ground level with an initial velocity of 25.48 m/s is $h = 1.5 + 25.48t - 4.9t^2$ after t seconds.

a) When does the projectile reach its maximum height?
b) What is the maximum height?

Select the correct answer.

a. 2.8 s, 34.428 m
b. 2.6 s, 34.624 m
c. 2 s, 32.86 m
d. 2.4 s, 34.428 m
e. 2.3 s, 34.183 m

6. Use implicit differentiation to find an equation of the tangent line to the curve at the given point.

$y \sin 2x = x \cos 2y, \quad (\pi/2, \pi/4)$

7. Find f.

$f''(x) = 12x + 24x^2$

Select the correct answer.

a. $f(x) = 6x^3 + 4x^4 + Cx + D$
b. $f(x) = 2x^3 + 2x^4 + Cx + D$
c. $f(x) = 4x^3 + 8x^4 + Cx + D$
d. $f(x) = 2x^3 + x^4 + Cx + D$
e. $f(x) = x^3 + 4x^4 + Cx + D$

8. Find the number c that satisfies the conclusion of the Mean Value Theorem on the given interval.

$f(x) = 2\sqrt{x}, \quad [0,4]$

9. A piece of wire 10 m long is cut into two pieces. One piece is bent into a square and the other is bent into an equilateral triangle. How should the wire be cut for the square so that the total area enclosed is a minimum? Round the result to the nearest hundredth.

Select the correct answer.

a. 5.35 m
b. 4.4 m
c. 4.35 m
d. 1 m
e. 3.25 m

10. Find the area of the region that lies under the given curve. Round the answer to three decimal places.

$y = \sqrt{2x + 2}, \quad 0 \le x \le 1$

Select the correct answer.

a. 1.834 b. 1.727 c. 1.704 d. 1.724 e. 1.824

11. The top of a ladder slides down a vertical wall at a rate of 0.15 m/s. At the moment when the bottom of the ladder is 3 m from the wall, it slides away from the wall at a rate of 0.2 m/s. How long is the ladder?

12. Find the average value of the function $f(t) = t\sin(t^2)$ on the interval $[0, 20]$. Round your answer to 3 decimal places.

Select the correct answer.

a. 0.381 b. 0.008 c. 0.028 d. 0.038 e. none of these

13. Find the volume of the solid obtained by rotating the region bounded by the given curves about the specified axis.

$y = x^2 + 4, \quad y = 12 - x^2; \quad \text{about } y = -1$

14. Evaluate the integral.

$$\int_1^\infty \frac{dx}{x \ln x}$$

Select the correct answer.

a. 1/2   b. 0   c. −1/4   d. 1/4   e. divergent

15. Evaluate the integral using the indicated trigonometric substitution.

$$\int \frac{dx}{x^2\sqrt{x^2-16}}; \quad x = 4\sec\theta$$

16. The masses m_i are located at the points P_i. Find the moments M_x and M_y and the center of mass of the system.

$m_1 = 6,\ m_2 = 5,\ m_3 = 10;$
$P_1(1,5),\ P_2(3,-2),\ P_3(-2,-1)$

Select the correct answer.

a. $M_x = 10$, $M_y = 1$, $(1/21, 10/21)$
b. $M_x = -10$, $M_y = 1$, $(1/21, -10/21)$
c. $M_x = 10$, $M_y = -1$, $(-1/21, 10/21)$
d. $M_x = 1$, $M_y = 10$, $(1/21, 10/21)$
e. $M_x = 10$, $M_y = 1$, $(10/21, 1/21)$

17. Find the length of the curve.

$$x = \frac{y^4}{8} + \frac{1}{4y^2}, \quad 1 \le y \le 2$$

Select the correct answer.

a. 33/16
b. 2
c. 3
d. 2/3
e. none of these

18. Use Euler's method with step size 0.1 to estimate $y(0.5)$, where $y(x)$ is the solution of the initial-value problem. Round your answer to four decimal places.

$$y' = y(x+1), \quad y(0) = 1$$

19. Solve the initial-value problem.

$xy' = y + x^2 \sin x, \quad y(\pi) = 0$

Select the correct answer.

a. $y = x \sin x$
b. $y = x \sin x - x$
c. $y = -x \cos x - x$
d. $y = -x \sin x + x$
e. $y = x \cos x - \sin x$

20. Set up an integral that represents the length of the curve. Then use your calculator to find the length correct to four decimal places.

$x = t - 2\sin t, \quad y = t - 2\cos t \quad 0 \le t \le 2\pi$

Select the correct answer.

a. 14.675
b. 7.0974
c. 7.0970
d. 21.2921
e. none of these

21. Determine whether the series is convergent or divergent by expressing s_n as a telescoping sum. If it is convergent, find its sum.

$$\sum_{n=1}^{\infty} 3/(n^2 + 3n)$$

22. Find the sum of the series.

$$\frac{3}{1\cdot 5} - \frac{3^2}{2\cdot 5^2} + \frac{3^3}{3\cdot 5^3} - \frac{3^4}{4\cdot 5^4} + \ldots$$

Select the correct answer.

a. $\ln(8/5)$ b. $\ln(5/3)$ c. $\ln(7/4)$ d. $e^{8/5}$ e. $8e/5$

23. Calculate the given quantities if $\mathbf{a} = \mathbf{i} - \mathbf{j}$ and $\mathbf{b} = -\mathbf{j} + 2\mathbf{k}$.

I. $\mathbf{a} \cdot \mathbf{b}$
II. $\mathbf{a} \times \mathbf{b}$
III. The angle between **a** and **b** (correct to the nearest degree)

24. Find the curvature of the curve $y = x^3$ at the point $(-1, -1)$.

25. If $\mathbf{r}(t) = \mathbf{i} + t\cos \pi t\,\mathbf{j} + \sin \pi t\,\mathbf{k}$, evaluate $\int_0^1 \mathbf{r}(t)\,dt$.

Select the correct answer.

a. $\mathbf{i} - \frac{2}{\pi^2}\mathbf{j} + \frac{2}{\pi}\mathbf{k}$

b. $\frac{2}{\pi^2}\mathbf{j} + \frac{2}{\pi}\mathbf{k}$

c. $\frac{2}{\pi^2}\mathbf{i} - \mathbf{j} + \frac{\pi}{2}\mathbf{k}$

d. $\mathbf{i} - \frac{1}{\pi}\mathbf{j} + \frac{1}{\pi}\mathbf{k}$

e. $2\mathbf{i} - \frac{1}{\pi^2}\mathbf{j} + \frac{\pi}{2}\mathbf{k}$

26. Find f_{xy} for the function $f(x, y) = 4x^3y - 7xy^2$.

Select the correct answer.

a. $f_{xy} = 24x^2 - 14y$ b. $f_{xy} = 12x^2 + 14y$ c. $f_{xy} = 14x^2 - 12y$ d. $f_{xy} = 12x^2 - 14y$ e. $f_{xy} = 14x^2 + 12y$

27. Find the directional derivative of $f(x, y) = 2\sqrt{x} - y^2$ at the point (1, 3) in the direction toward the point (3, 1).

28. Use spherical coordinates.

Evaluate $\iiint_B (x^2 + y^2 + z^2)^2\,dV$, where B is the ball with center the origin and radius 2.

Select the correct answer.

a. $252\pi/7$ b. $128\pi/7$ c. $512/7$ d. $256\pi/7$ e. $512\pi/7$

29. Find the gradient vector field of f.

$$f(x, y, z) = \sqrt{2x^2 + y^2 + 2z^2}$$

30. Evaluate the line integral.

$$\int_C yz\cos x\,ds$$

$$C: x = t,\ y = 2\cos t,\ z = 2\sin t \qquad 0 \le t \le \pi$$

ANSWER KEY

Stewart - Calculus ET 7e Final Exam Form C

1. b

2. $2a+h-1$

3. a

4. $f(2)=3$
$f'(2)=4$

5. b

6. $y=\frac{1}{2}x$

7. b

8. $c=1$

9. c

10. d

11. 5 m

12. d

13. 384π

14. e

15. $\frac{\sqrt{x^2-16}}{16x}+C$

16. a

17. a

18. $y(0.5)\approx 1.7616$

19. c

20. e

21. Converges; 11/6

22. a

$\mathbf{a} \cdot \mathbf{b} = 1$

23. $\mathbf{a} \times \mathbf{b} = -2\mathbf{i} - 2\mathbf{j} - \mathbf{k}$

72°

24. $\dfrac{3\sqrt{10}}{50}$

25. a

26. d

27. $7\sqrt{2}/2$

28. e

29. $2x/\sqrt{2x^2+y^2+2z^2}\,\mathbf{i} + y/\sqrt{2x^2+y^2+2z^2}\,\mathbf{j} + 2z/\sqrt{2x^2+y^2+2z^2}\,\mathbf{k}$

30. $8\sqrt{5}/3$